Instructor's Resource Manual
to accompany

Electronics Fundamentals
and
Electric Circuits Fundamentals

Seventh Edition

Thomas L. Floyd

PEARSON
Prentice
Hall

Upper Saddle River, New Jersey
Columbus, Ohio

10 9 8 7 6 5 4 3 2 1

ISBN 0-13-219712-X

CONTENTS

The Test Item File included in this Instructor's Resource Manual is just one part of Prentice Hall's comprehensive testing support service, which includes TestGen for Windows and Macintosh.

TestGen: What is it?

TestGen is a test generator program that lets you view and edit testbank questions, transfer them to tests, and then administer those tests on paper, on a local area network, or over the Web. The program provides many options for organizing and displaying testbanks and tests. A built-in random number and text generator makes it ideal for creating multiple versions of questions and tests. Powerful search and sort functions let you easily locate questions and arrange them in the order you prefer.

TestGen makes test creation easy and convenient with uncluttered side-by-side testbank and test windows, symbol palettes, expression templates, keyboard shortcuts, a graphing tool, variable text and numbers, and graphics. In addition, you can assign multiple descriptors to any question, including page references, topic, skill, objective, difficulty level, and answer explanations.

TestGen provides several options for online testing—a simple export to WebCT and Blackboard formats, a conversion to HTML files, as well as a TestGen plug-in that displays the test in a Web browser and reports student results to the gradebook of Pearson's CourseCompass course management system.

TestGen: How do I get it?

The TestGen software is free. To order a testbank for a specific TestGen title, you may contact your local rep or call our Faculty Support Services Department at 1-800-526-0485. Please identify the main text author and title.

Toll-free **technical support** is offered to users of TestGen at 1-800-677-6337, or via e-mail at media.suppport@pearsoned.com.

NOTICE TO INSTRUCTORS

To access supplementary materials online, instructors need to request an instructor access code. Go to **www.prenhall.com**, click the **Instructor Resource Center** link, and then click **Register Today** for an instructor access code. Within 48 hours after registering you will receive a confirming e-mail including an instructor access code. Once you have received your code, go to the site and log on for full instructions on downloading the materials you wish to use.

The password to unlock PowerPoint® slides is **eclipse**.

PART ONE

Solutions to End-of-Chapter Problems

CHAPTER 1
QUANTITIES AND UNITS

SECTION 1-1 Scientific and Engineering Notation

1.   (a) $3000 = \mathbf{3 \times 10^3}$ (b) $75{,}000 = \mathbf{7.5 \times 10^4}$ (c) $2{,}000{,}000 = \mathbf{2 \times 10^6}$

2.   (a) $\dfrac{1}{500} = 0.002 = \mathbf{2 \times 10^{-3}}$

      (b) $\dfrac{1}{2000} = 0.0005 = \mathbf{5 \times 10^{-4}}$

      (c) $\dfrac{1}{5{,}000{,}000} = 0.0000002 = \mathbf{2 \times 10^{-7}}$

3.   (a) $8400 = \mathbf{8.4 \times 10^3}$ (b) $99{,}000 = \mathbf{9.9 \times 10^4}$ (c) $0.2 \times 10^6 = \mathbf{2 \times 10^5}$

4.   (a) $0.0002 = \mathbf{2 \times 10^{-4}}$ (b) $0.6 = \mathbf{6 \times 10^{-1}}$

      (c) $\mathbf{7.8 \times 10^{-2}}$ (already in scientific notation)

5.   (a) $2.5 \times 10^{-6} = \mathbf{0.0000025}$ (b) $5.0 \times 10^2 = \mathbf{500}$ (c) $3.9 \times 10^{-1} = \mathbf{0.39}$

6.   (a) $4.5 \times 10^{-6} = \mathbf{0.0000045}$

      (b) $8 \times 10^{-9} = \mathbf{0.000000008}$

      (c) $4.0 \times 10^{-12} = \mathbf{0.0000000000040}$

7.   (a) $9.2 \times 10^6 + 3.4 \times 10^7 = 9.2 \times 10^6 + 34 \times 10^6 = \mathbf{4.32 \times 10^7}$

      (b) $5 \times 10^3 + 8.5 \times 10^{-1} = 5 \times 10^3 + 0.00085 \times 10^3 = \mathbf{5.00085 \times 10^3}$

      (c) $5.6 \times 10^{-8} + 4.6 \times 10^{-9} = 56 \times 10^{-9} + 4.6 \times 10^{-9} = \mathbf{6.06 \times 10^{-8}}$

8.   (a) $3.2 \times 10^{12} - 1.1 \times 10^{12} = \mathbf{2.1 \times 10^{12}}$

      (b) $2.6 \times 10^8 - 1.3 \times 10^7 = 26 \times 10^7 - 1.3 \times 10^7 = \mathbf{24.7 \times 10^7}$

      (c) $1.5 \times 10^{-12} - 8 \times 10^{-13} = 15 \times 10^{-13} - 8 \times 10^{-13} = \mathbf{7 \times 10^{-13}}$

9.   (a) $(5 \times 10^3)(4 \times 10^5) = 5 \times 4 \times 10^{3+5} = 20 \times 10^8 = \mathbf{2 \times 10^9}$

     (b) $(1.2 \times 10^{12})(3 \times 10^2) = 1.2 \times 3 \times 10^{12+2} = \mathbf{3.6 \times 10^{14}}$

     (c) $(2.2 \times 10^{-9})(7 \times 10^{-6}) = 2.2 \times 7 \times 10^{-9-6} = 15.4 \times 10^{-15} = \mathbf{1.54 \times 10^{-14}}$

10.   (a) $\dfrac{1.0 \times 10^3}{2.5 \times 10^2} = 0.4 \times 10^{3-2} = 0.4 \times 10^1 = \mathbf{4}$

     (b) $\dfrac{2.5 \times 10^{-6}}{5.0 \times 10^{-8}} = 0.5 \times 10^{-6-(-8)} = 0.5 \times 10^2 = \mathbf{50}$

     (c) $\dfrac{4.2 \times 10^8}{2 \times 10^{-5}} = 2.1 \times 10^{8-(-5)} = \mathbf{2.1 \times 10^{13}}$

11.   (a) $89{,}000 = \mathbf{89 \times 10^3}$

     (b) $450{,}000 = \mathbf{450 \times 10^3}$

     (c) $12{,}040{,}000{,}000{,}000 = \mathbf{12.04 \times 10^{12}}$

12.   (a) $2.35 \times 10^5 = \mathbf{235 \times 10^3}$

     (b) $7.32 \times 10^7 = \mathbf{73.2 \times 10^6}$

     (c) $\mathbf{1.333 \times 10^9}$ (already in engineering notation)

13.   (a) $0.000345 = \mathbf{345 \times 10^{-6}}$

     (b) $0.025 = \mathbf{25 \times 10^{-3}}$

     (c) $0.00000000129 = \mathbf{1.29 \times 10^{-9}}$

14.   (a) $9.81 \times 10^{-3} = \mathbf{9.81 \times 10^{-3}}$

     (b) $4.82 \times 10^{-4} = \mathbf{482 \times 10^{-6}}$

     (c) $4.38 \times 10^{-7} = \mathbf{438 \times 10^{-9}}$

15.   (a) $2.5 \times 10^{-3} + 4.6 \times 10^{-3} = (2.5 + 4.6) \times 10^{-3} = \mathbf{7.1 \times 10^{-3}}$

     (b) $68 \times 10^6 + 33 \times 10^6 = (68 + 33) \times 10^6 = \mathbf{101 \times 10^6}$

     (c) $1.25 \times 10^6 + 250 \times 10^3 = 1.25 \times 10^6 + 0.25 \times 10^6 = (1.25 + 0.25) \times 10^6 = \mathbf{1.50 \times 10^6}$

16.   (a) $(32 \times 10^{-3})(56 \times 10^3) = 1792 \times 10^{(-3+3)} = 1792 \times 10^0 = \mathbf{1.792 \times 10^3}$

     (b) $(1.2 \times 10^{-6})(1.2 \times 10^{-6}) = 1.44 \times 10^{(-6-6)} = \mathbf{1.44 \times 10^{-12}}$

(c) $(100)(55 \times 10^{-3}) = 5500 \times 10^{-3} = \textbf{5.5}$

17. (a) $\dfrac{50}{2.2 \times 10^3} = \textbf{22.7} \times \textbf{10}^{-3}$

   (b) $\dfrac{5 \times 10^3}{25 \times 10^{-6}} = 0.2 \times 10^{(3-(-6))} = 0.2 \times 10^9 = \textbf{200} \times \textbf{10}^6$

   (c) $\dfrac{560 \times 10^3}{660 \times 10^3} = 0.848 \times 10^{(3-3)} = 0.848 \times 10^0 = \textbf{848} \times \textbf{10}^{-3}$

SECTION 1-2 Units and Metric Prefixes

18. (a) $89{,}000 \ \Omega = 89 \times 10^3 = \textbf{89 k}\boldsymbol{\Omega}$

   (b) $450{,}000 \ \Omega = 450 \times 10^3 = \textbf{450 k}\boldsymbol{\Omega}$

   (c) $12{,}040{,}000{,}000{,}000 \ \Omega = 12.04 \times 10^{12} = \textbf{12.04 T}\boldsymbol{\Omega}$

19. (a) $0.000345 \ \text{A} = 345 \times 10^{-6} \ \text{A} = \textbf{345} \ \boldsymbol{\mu}\textbf{A}$

   (b) $0.025 \ \text{A} = 25 \times 10^{-3} \ \text{A} = \textbf{25 mA}$

   (c) $0.00000000129 \ \text{A} = 1.29 \times 10^{-9} \ \text{A} = \textbf{1.29 nA}$

20. (a) $31 \times 10^{-3} \ \text{A} = \textbf{31 mA}$ (b) $5.5 \times 10^3 \ \text{V} = \textbf{5.5 kV}$ (c) $20 \times 10^{-12} \ \text{F} = \textbf{20 pF}$

21. (a) $3 \times 10^{-6} \ \text{F} = \textbf{3} \ \boldsymbol{\mu}\textbf{F}$ (b) $3.3 \times 10^6 \ \Omega = \textbf{3.3 M}\boldsymbol{\Omega}$ (c) $350 \times 10^{-9} \ \text{A} = \textbf{350 nA}$

22. (a) $5 \ \mu\text{A} = \textbf{5} \times \textbf{10}^{-6} \ \textbf{A}$ (b) $43 \ \text{mV} = \textbf{43} \times \textbf{10}^{-3} \ \textbf{V}$

   (c) $275 \ \text{k}\Omega = \textbf{275} \times \textbf{10}^3 \ \boldsymbol{\Omega}$ (d) $10 \ \text{MW} = \textbf{10} \times \textbf{10}^6 \ \textbf{W}$

SECTION 1-3 Metric Unit Conversions

23. (a) $(5 \ \text{mA}) (1 \times 10^3 \ \mu\text{A/mA}) = 5 \times 10^3 \ \mu\text{A} = \textbf{5000} \ \boldsymbol{\mu}\textbf{A}$

   (b) $(3200 \ \mu\text{W})(1 \times 10^{-3} \ \text{W/}\mu\text{W}) = \textbf{3.2 mW}$

   (c) $(5000 \ \text{kV})(1 \times 10^{-3}) \ \text{MV/kV} = \textbf{5 MV}$

   (d) $(10 \ \text{MW})(1 \times 10^3 \ \text{kW/MW}) = 10 \times 10^3 \ \text{kW} = \textbf{10,000 kW}$

24. (a) $\dfrac{1\text{ mA}}{1\text{ }\mu\text{A}} = \dfrac{1\times10^{-3}\text{ A}}{1\times10^{-6}\text{ A}} = 1\times10^{3} = \textbf{1000}$

(b) $\dfrac{0.05\text{ kV}}{1\text{ mV}} = \dfrac{0.05\times10^{3}\text{ V}}{1\times10^{-3}\text{ V}} = 0.05\times10^{6} = \textbf{50,000}$

(c) $\dfrac{0.02\text{ k}\Omega}{1\text{ M}\Omega} = \dfrac{0.02\times10^{3}\text{ }\Omega}{1\times10^{6}\text{ }\Omega} = 0.02\times10^{-3} = \mathbf{2\times10^{-5}}$

(d) $\dfrac{155\text{ mW}}{1\text{ kW}} = \dfrac{155\times10^{-3}\text{ W}}{1\times10^{3}\text{ W}} = 155\times10^{-6} = \mathbf{1.55\times10^{-4}}$

25. (a) $50\text{ mA} + 680\text{ }\mu\text{A} = 50\text{ mA} + 0.68\text{ mA} = \textbf{50.68 mA}$

(b) $120\text{ k}\Omega + 2.2\text{ M}\Omega = 0.12\text{ M}\Omega + 2.2\text{ M}\Omega = \textbf{2.32 M}\Omega$

(c) $0.02\text{ }\mu\text{F} + 3300\text{ pF} = 0.02\text{ }\mu\text{F} + 0.0033\text{ }\mu\text{F} = \textbf{0.0233 }\mu\textbf{F}$

26. (a) $\dfrac{10\text{ k}\Omega}{2.2\text{ k}\Omega + 10\text{ k}\Omega} = \dfrac{10\text{ k}\Omega}{12.2\text{ k}\Omega} = \textbf{0.8197}$

(b) $\dfrac{250\text{ mV}}{50\text{ }\mu\text{V}} = \dfrac{250\times10^{-3}}{50\times10^{-6}} = \textbf{5000}$

(c) $\dfrac{1\text{ MW}}{2\text{ kW}} = \dfrac{1\times10^{6}}{2\times10^{3}} = \textbf{500}$

SECTION 1-4 Measured Numbers

27. (a) 1.00×10^{3} has 3 significant digits. (b) 0.0057 has 4 significant digits.

(c) 1502.0 has 5 significant digits. (d) 0.000036 has 6 significant digits.

(e) 0.105 has 3 significant digits. (f) 2.6×10^{2} has 2 significant digits.

28. (a) $50,505 \cong \mathbf{50.5\times10^{3}}$ (b) $220.45 \cong \textbf{220}$

(c) $4646 \cong \mathbf{4.65\times10^{3}}$ d) $10.99 \cong \textbf{11.0}$

(e) $1.005 \cong \textbf{1.00}$

CHAPTER 2
VOLTAGE, CURRENT, AND RESISTANCE

BASIC PROBLEMS

SECTION 2-2 Electrical Charge

1. $Q = $ (charge per electron)(number of electrons) $= (1.6 \times 10^{-19} \text{ C/e})(50 \times 10^{31}\text{e}) = \mathbf{80 \times 10^{12} \text{ C}}$

2. $(6.25 \times 10^{18} \text{ e/C})(80 \times 10^{-6} \text{ C}) = \mathbf{5 \times 10^{14} \text{ e}}$

3. $(1.6 \times 10^{-19} \text{ C/e})(29 \text{ e}) = \mathbf{4.64 \times 10^{-18} \text{ C}}$

4. $(1.6 \times 10^{-19} \text{ C/e})(17 \text{ e}) = \mathbf{2.72 \times 10^{-18} \text{ C}}$

SECTION 2-3 Voltage

5. (a) $V = \dfrac{W}{Q} = \dfrac{10 \text{ J}}{1 \text{ C}} = \mathbf{10 \text{ V}}$ (b) $V = \dfrac{W}{Q} = \dfrac{5 \text{ J}}{2 \text{ C}} = \mathbf{2.5 \text{ V}}$

    (c) $V = \dfrac{W}{Q} = \dfrac{100 \text{ J}}{25 \text{ C}} = \mathbf{4 \text{ V}}$

6. $V = \dfrac{W}{Q} = \dfrac{500 \text{ J}}{100 \text{ C}} = \mathbf{5 \text{ V}}$

7. $V = \dfrac{W}{Q} = \dfrac{800 \text{ J}}{40 \text{ C}} = \mathbf{20 \text{ V}}$

8. $W = VQ = (12 \text{ V})(2.5 \text{ C}) = \mathbf{30 \text{ J}}$

SECTION 2-4 Current

9. (a) $I = \dfrac{Q}{t} = \dfrac{75 \text{ C}}{1 \text{ s}} = \mathbf{75 \text{ A}}$ (b) $I = \dfrac{Q}{t} = \dfrac{10 \text{ C}}{0.5 \text{ s}} = \mathbf{20 \text{ A}}$

(c) $I = \dfrac{Q}{t} = \dfrac{5\,\text{C}}{2\,\text{s}} = \textbf{2.5 A}$

10. $I = \dfrac{Q}{t} = \dfrac{0.6\,\text{C}}{3\,\text{s}} = \textbf{0.2 A}$

11. $I = \dfrac{Q}{t};$ $\qquad\qquad t = \dfrac{Q}{I} = \dfrac{10\,\text{C}}{5\,\text{A}} = \textbf{2 s}$

12. $Q = I \times t = (1.5\,\text{A})(0.1\,\text{s}) = \textbf{0.15 C}$

SECTION 2-5 Resistance

13. A: Blue, gray, red, silver: **6800 Ω ± 10%**
     B: Orange, orange, black, silver: **33 Ω ± 10%**
     C: Yellow, violet, orange, gold: **47,000 Ω ± 5%**

14. A: $R_{min} = 6800\,\Omega - 0.1(6800\,\Omega) = 6800\,\Omega - 680\,\Omega = \textbf{6120 }\boldsymbol{\Omega}$
        $R_{max} = 6800\,\Omega + 680\,\Omega = \textbf{7480 }\boldsymbol{\Omega}$
     B: $R_{min} = 33\,\Omega - 0.1(33\,\Omega) = 33\,\Omega - 3.3\,\Omega = \textbf{29.7 }\boldsymbol{\Omega}$
        $R_{max} = 33\,\Omega + 3.3\,\Omega = \textbf{36.3 }\boldsymbol{\Omega}$
     C: $R_{min} = 47,000\,\Omega - (0.05)(47,000\,\Omega) = 47,000\,\Omega - 2350\,\Omega = \textbf{44,650 }\boldsymbol{\Omega}$
        $R_{max} = 47,000\,\Omega + 2350\,\Omega = \textbf{49,350 }\boldsymbol{\Omega}$

15. (a) 1st band = **red**, 2nd band = **violet**, 3rd band = **brown**, 4th band = **gold**

     (b) 330 Ω; **orange, orange, brown, (B)**
          2.2 kΩ: **red, red, red (D)**
          39 kΩ: **orange, white, orange (A)**
          56 kΩ: **green, blue, orange (L)**
          100 kΩ: **brown, black, yellow (F)**

16. (a) **36.5 Ω ± 2%**

     (b) **2.74 kΩ ± 0.25%**

     (c) **82.5 kΩ ± 1%**

17. (a) Brown, black, black, gold: **10 Ω ± 5%**

     (b) Green, brown, green, silver: 5,100,000 Ω ± 10% = **5.1 MΩ ± 10%**

     (c) Blue, gray, black, gold: **68 Ω ± 5%**

18. (a) 0.47 Ω ± 5%: **yellow, violet, silver, gold**

(b)   270 kΩ ± 5%: **red, violet, yellow, gold**

(c)   5.1 MΩ ± 5%: **green, brown, green, gold**

19.   (a)   Red, gray, violet, red, brown: 28,700 Ω ± 1% = **28.7 kΩ ± 1%**

(b)   Blue, black, yellow, gold, brown: **60.4 Ω ± 1%**

(c)   White, orange, brown, brown, brown: 9310 ± 1% = **9.31 kΩ ± 1%**

20.   (a)   14.7 kΩ ± 1%: **brown, yellow, violet, red, brown**

(b)   39.2 Ω ± 1%: **orange, white, red, gold, brown**

(c)   9.76 kΩ ± 1%: **white, violet, blue, brown, brown**

21.   (a)   220 = **22 Ω**   (b)   472 = **4.7 kΩ**

(c)   823 = **82 kΩ**   (d)   3K3 = **3.3 kΩ**

(e)   560 = **56 Ω**   (f)   10M = **10 MΩ**

22.   **500 Ω**, equal resistance on each side of the contact.

SECTION 2-6 The Electric Circuit

23.   There is current through **Lamp 2.**

24.   See Figure 2-1.

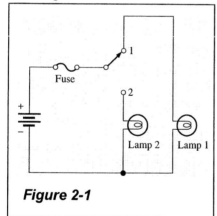

Figure 2-1

SECTION 2-7 Basic Circuit Measurements

25.   See Figure 2-2(a).

9

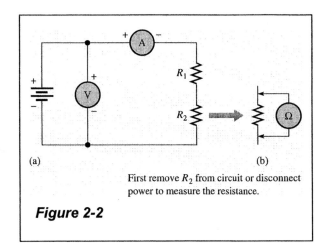

(a)

(b)

First remove R_2 from circuit or disconnect power to measure the resistance.

Figure 2-2

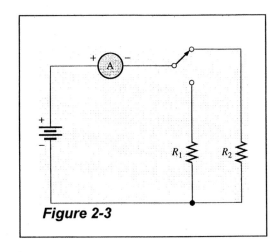

Figure 2-3

26. See Figure 2-2(b).

27. Position 1: V1 = **0 V**, V2 = V_S
    Position 2: V1 = V_S, V2 = **0 V**

28. See Figure 2-3.

29. On the 600 V DC scale: **250 V**

30. $R = (10)(10\ \Omega) = \mathbf{100\ \Omega}$

31. (a) $2(100\ \Omega) = \mathbf{200\ \Omega}$ (b) $15(10\ M\Omega) = \mathbf{150\ M\Omega}$

    (c) $45(100\ \Omega) = \mathbf{4500\ \Omega}$

32. See Figure 2-4.

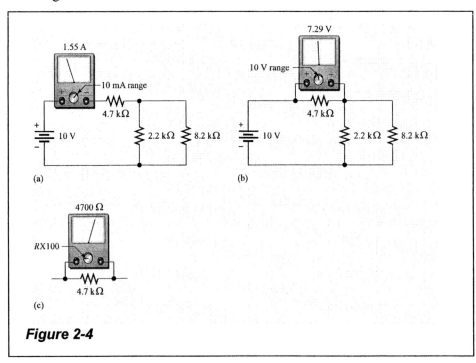

(a)

(b)

(c)

Figure 2-4

ADVANCED PROBLEMS

33. $I = \dfrac{Q}{t}$

$Q = I \times t = (2 \text{ A})(15 \text{ s}) = 30 \text{ C}$

$V = \dfrac{W}{Q} = \dfrac{1000 \text{ J}}{30 \text{ C}} = \textbf{33.3 V}$

34. $I = \dfrac{Q}{t}$

$Q = (\text{number of electrons}) / (\text{number of electrons/coulomb})$

$Q = \dfrac{574 \times 10^{15} \text{ e}}{6.25 \times 10^{18} \text{ e/C}} = 9.184 \times 10^{-2} \text{ C}$

$I = \dfrac{Q}{t} = \dfrac{9.184 \times 10^{-2} \text{ C}}{250 \times 10^{-3} \text{ s}} = \textbf{0.367 A}$

35. Total wire length = 100 ft
Resistance per 1000 ft = (1000 ft)(6 Ω/100 ft) = 60 Ω
Smallest wire size is **AWG 27** which has 51.47 Ω/1000 ft

36. (a) 4R7J = **4.7 Ω ± 5%**

    (b) 560KF = **560 kΩ ± 1%**

    (c) 1M5G = **1.5 MΩ ± 2%**

37. The circuit in (b) can have both lamps on at the same time.

38. There is always current through R_5.

39. See Figure 2-5.

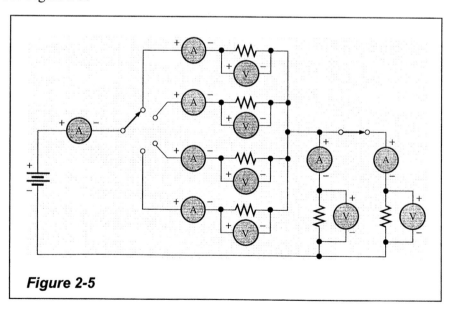

Figure 2-5

40.　See Figure 2-5.

41.　See Figure 2-6.

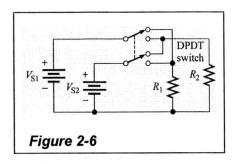

Figure 2-6

42.　See Figure 2-7.

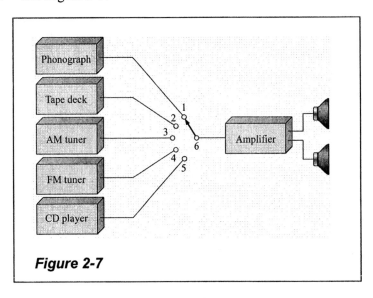

Figure 2-7

CHAPTER 3
OHM'S LAW, ENERGY, AND POWER

BASIC PROBLEMS

SECTION 3-1 Ohm's Law

1. I is directly proportional to V and will change the same percentage as V.
   - (a) $I = 3(1 \text{ A}) = \textbf{3 A}$
   - (b) $I = 1 \text{ A} - (0.8)(1 \text{ A}) = 1 \text{ A} - 0.8 \text{ A} = \textbf{0.2 A}$
   - (c) $I = 1 \text{ A} + (0.5)(1 \text{ A}) = 1 \text{ A} + 0.5 \text{ A} = \textbf{1.5 A}$

2.
   - (a) When the resistance doubles, the current is halved from 100 mA to **50 mA.**
   - (b) When the resistance is reduced by 30%, the current increases from 100 mA to
     $I = V/0.7R = 1.429(V/R) = (1.429)(100 \text{ mA}) \cong \textbf{143 mA}$
   - (c) When the resistance is quadrupled, the current decreases from 100 mA to **25 mA.**

3. Tripling the voltage triples the current from 10 mA to 30 mA, but doubling the resistance halves the current to **15 mA.**

SECTION 3-2 Application of Ohm's Law

4.
   - (a) $I = \dfrac{V}{R} = \dfrac{5 \text{ V}}{1 \, \Omega} = \textbf{5 A}$
   - (b) $I = \dfrac{V}{R} = \dfrac{15 \text{ V}}{10 \, \Omega} = \textbf{1.5 A}$
   - (c) $I = \dfrac{V}{R} = \dfrac{50 \text{ V}}{100 \, \Omega} = \textbf{0.5 A}$
   - (d) $I = \dfrac{V}{R} = \dfrac{30 \text{ V}}{15 \text{ k}\Omega} = \textbf{2 mA}$
   - (e) $I = \dfrac{V}{R} = \dfrac{250 \text{ V}}{4.7 \text{ M}\Omega} = \textbf{53.2 } \boldsymbol{\mu}\textbf{A}$

5.
   - (a) $I = \dfrac{V}{R} = \dfrac{9 \text{ V}}{2.7 \text{ k}\Omega} = \textbf{3.33 mA}$
   - (b) $I = \dfrac{V}{R} = \dfrac{5.5 \text{ V}}{10 \text{ k}\Omega} = \textbf{550 } \boldsymbol{\mu}\textbf{A}$
   - (c) $I = \dfrac{V}{R} = \dfrac{40 \text{ V}}{68 \text{ k}\Omega} = \textbf{588 } \boldsymbol{\mu}\textbf{A}$
   - (d) $I = \dfrac{V}{R} = \dfrac{1 \text{ kV}}{2 \text{ k}\Omega} = \textbf{500 mA}$
   - (e) $I = \dfrac{V}{R} = \dfrac{66 \text{ kV}}{10 \text{ M}\Omega} = \textbf{6.60 mA}$

6. $I = \dfrac{V}{R} = \dfrac{12\ \text{V}}{10\ \Omega} = \mathbf{1.2\ A}$

7. (a) $I = \dfrac{V}{R} = \dfrac{25\ \text{V}}{10\ \text{k}\Omega} = \mathbf{2.50\ mA}$ (b) $I = \dfrac{V}{R} = \dfrac{5\ \text{V}}{2.2\ \text{M}\Omega} = \mathbf{2.27\ \mu A}$

   (c) $I = \dfrac{V}{R} = \dfrac{15\ \text{V}}{1.8\ \text{k}\Omega} = \mathbf{8.33\ mA}$

8. Orange, violet, yellow, gold, brown $\equiv 37.4\ \Omega \pm 1\%$

   $I = \dfrac{V_S}{R} = \dfrac{12\ \text{V}}{37.4\ \Omega} = \mathbf{0.321\ A}$

9. $I = \dfrac{24\ \text{V}}{37.4\ \Omega} = 0.642\ \text{A}$

   0.642 A is greater than 0.5 A, so **the fuse will blow.**

10. (a) $V = IR = (2\ \text{A})(18\ \Omega) = \mathbf{36\ V}$ (b) $V = IR = (5\ \text{A})(47\ \Omega) = \mathbf{235\ V}$
    (c) $V = IR = (2.5\ \text{A})(620\ \Omega) = \mathbf{1550\ V}$ (d) $V = IR = (0.6\ \text{A})(47\ \Omega) = \mathbf{28.2\ V}$
    (e) $V = IR = (0.1\ \text{A})(470\ \Omega) = \mathbf{47\ V}$

11. (a) $V = IR = (1\ \text{mA})(10\ \Omega) = \mathbf{10\ mV}$ (b) $V = IR = (50\ \text{mA})(33\ \Omega) = \mathbf{1.65\ V}$
    (c) $V = IR = (3\ \text{A})(4.7\ \text{k}\Omega) = \mathbf{14.1\ kV}$ (d) $V = IR = (1.6\ \text{mA})(2.2\ \text{k}\Omega) = \mathbf{3.52\ V}$
    (e) $V = IR = (250\ \mu\text{A})(1\ \text{k}\Omega) = \mathbf{250\ mV}$ (f) $V = IR = (500\ \text{mA})(1.5\ \text{M}\Omega) = \mathbf{750\ kV}$
    (g) $V = IR = (850\ \mu\text{A})(10\ \text{M}\Omega) = \mathbf{8.5\ kV}$ (h) $V = IR = (75\ \mu\text{A})(47\ \Omega) = \mathbf{3.53\ mV}$

12. $V_S = IR = (3\ \text{A})(27\ \Omega) = \mathbf{81\ V}$

13. (a) $V = IR = (3\ \text{mA})(27\ \text{k}\Omega) = \mathbf{81\ V}$ (b) $V = IR = (5\ \mu\text{A})(100\ \text{M}\Omega) = \mathbf{500\ V}$
    (c) $V = IR = (2.5\ \text{A})(47\ \Omega) = \mathbf{117.5\ V}$

14. (a) $R = \dfrac{V}{I} = \dfrac{10\ \text{V}}{2\ \text{A}} = \mathbf{5\ \Omega}$ (b) $R = \dfrac{V}{I} = \dfrac{90\ \text{V}}{45\ \text{A}} = \mathbf{2\ \Omega}$

    (c) $R = \dfrac{V}{I} = \dfrac{50\ \text{V}}{5\ \text{A}} = \mathbf{10\ \Omega}$ (d) $R = \dfrac{V}{I} = \dfrac{5.5\ \text{V}}{10\ \text{A}} = \mathbf{0.55\ \Omega}$

    (e) $R = \dfrac{V}{I} = \dfrac{150\ \text{V}}{0.5\ \text{A}} = \mathbf{300\ \Omega}$

15. (a) $R = \dfrac{V}{I} = \dfrac{10\ \text{kV}}{5\ \text{A}} = \mathbf{2\ k\Omega}$ (b) $R = \dfrac{V}{I} = \dfrac{7\ \text{V}}{2\ \text{mA}} = \mathbf{3.5\ k\Omega}$

    (c) $R = \dfrac{V}{I} = \dfrac{500\ \text{V}}{250\ \text{mA}} = \mathbf{2\ k\Omega}$ (d) $R = \dfrac{V}{I} = \dfrac{50\ \text{V}}{500\ \mu\text{A}} = \mathbf{100\ k\Omega}$

(e) $\quad R = \dfrac{V}{I} = \dfrac{1\,\text{kV}}{1\,\text{mA}} = 1\,\textbf{M}\boldsymbol{\Omega}$

16. $\quad R = \dfrac{V}{I} = \dfrac{6\,\text{V}}{2\,\text{mA}} = \textbf{3 k}\boldsymbol{\Omega}$

17. (a) $\quad R = \dfrac{V}{I} = \dfrac{8\,\text{V}}{2\,\text{A}} = \textbf{4 }\boldsymbol{\Omega}$ \qquad (b) $\quad R = \dfrac{V}{I} = \dfrac{12\,\text{V}}{4\,\text{mA}} = \textbf{3 k}\boldsymbol{\Omega}$

(c) $\quad R = \dfrac{V}{I} = \dfrac{30\,\text{V}}{150\,\mu\text{A}} = 0.2\,\text{M}\Omega = \textbf{200 k}\boldsymbol{\Omega}$

SECTION 3-3 Energy and Power

18. Since 1 watt = 1 joule, $P = 350\,\text{J/s} = \textbf{350 W}$

19. $\quad P = \dfrac{W}{t} = \dfrac{7500\,\text{J}}{5\,\text{h}}$

$\left(\dfrac{7500\,\text{J}}{5\,\text{h}}\right)\left(\dfrac{1\,\text{h}}{3600\,\text{s}}\right) = \dfrac{7500\,\text{J}}{18{,}000\,\text{s}} = 0.417\,\text{J/s} = \textbf{417 mW}$

20. (a) $1000\,\text{W} = 1 \times 10^3\,\text{W} = \textbf{1 kW}$ \qquad (b) $3750\,\text{W} = 3.750 \times 10^3\,\text{W} = \textbf{3.75 kW}$

(c) $160\,\text{W} = 0.160 \times 10^3\,\text{W} = \textbf{0.160 kW}$ \qquad (d) $50{,}000\,\text{W} = 50 \times 10^3\,\text{W} = \textbf{50 kW}$

21. (a) $1{,}000{,}000\,\text{W} = 1 \times 10^6\,\text{W} = \textbf{1 MW}$ \qquad (b) $3 \times 10^6\,\text{W} = \textbf{3 MW}$

(c) $15 \times 10^7\,\text{W} = 150 \times 10^6\,\text{W} = \textbf{150 MW}$ \qquad (d) $8700\,\text{kW} = 8.7 \times 10^6\,\text{W} = \textbf{8.7 MW}$

22. (a) $1\,\text{W} = 1000 \times 10^{-3}\,\text{W} = \textbf{1000 mW}$ \qquad (b) $0.4\,\text{W} = 400 \times 10^{-3}\,\text{W} = \textbf{400 mW}$

(c) $0.002\,\text{W} = 2 \times 10^{-3}\,\text{W} = \textbf{2 mW}$ \qquad (d) $0.0125\,\text{W} = 12.5 \times 10^{-3}\,\text{W} = \textbf{12.5 mW}$

23. (a) $2\,\text{W} = \textbf{2{,}000{,}000 }\boldsymbol{\mu}\textbf{W}$ \qquad (b) $0.0005\,\text{W} = \textbf{500 }\boldsymbol{\mu}\textbf{W}$

(c) $0.25\,\text{mW} = \textbf{250 }\boldsymbol{\mu}\textbf{W}$ \qquad (d) $0.00667\,\text{mW} = \textbf{6.67 }\boldsymbol{\mu}\textbf{W}$

24. (a) $1.5\,\text{kW} = 1.5 \times 10^3\,\text{W} = \textbf{1500 W}$ \qquad (b) $0.5\,\text{MW} = 0.5 \times 10^6\,\text{W} = \textbf{500{,}000 W}$

(c) $350\,\text{mW} = 350 \times 10^{-3}\,\text{W} = \textbf{0.350 W}$ \qquad (d) $9000\,\mu\text{W} = 9000 \times 10^{-6}\,\text{W} = \textbf{0.009 W}$

25. $P = \dfrac{W}{t}$ in watts

$V = \dfrac{W}{Q}$

$I = \dfrac{Q}{t}$

$P = VI = \dfrac{W}{t}$

So, (1 V)(1 A) = 1 W

26. $P = \dfrac{W}{t} = \dfrac{1 \text{ J}}{1 \text{ s}} = 1$ W

$1 \text{ kW} = 1000 \text{ W} = \dfrac{1000 \text{ J}}{1 \text{ s}}$

1 kW-second = 1000 J

1 kWh = 3600 × 1000 J

1 kWh = 3.6 × 10^6 J

SECTION 3-4 Power in an Electric Circuit

27. $P = VI = (5.5 \text{ V})(3 \text{ mA}) = \mathbf{16.5 \text{ mW}}$

28. $P = VI = (115 \text{ V})(3 \text{ A}) = \mathbf{345 \text{ W}}$

29. $P = I^2 R = (500 \text{ mA})^2 (4.7 \text{ k}\Omega) = \mathbf{1.18 \text{ kW}}$

30. $P = I^2 R = (100 \times 10^{-6} \text{ A})^2 (10 \times 10^3 \ \Omega) = 1 \times 10^{-4} \text{ W} = \mathbf{100 \ \mu W}$

31. $P = \dfrac{V^2}{R} = \dfrac{(60 \text{ V})^2}{620 \ \Omega} = \mathbf{5.81 \text{ W}}$

32. $P = \dfrac{V^2}{R} = \dfrac{(1.5 \text{ V})^2}{56 \ \Omega} = 0.0402 \text{ W} = \mathbf{40.2 \text{ mW}}$

33. $P = I^2 R$

$R = \dfrac{P}{I^2} = \dfrac{100 \text{ W}}{(2 \text{ A})^2} = \mathbf{25 \ \Omega}$

34. 5×10^6 watts for 1 minute $= 5 \times 10^3$ kWmin

$$\frac{5 \times 10^3 \text{ kWmin}}{60 \text{ min}/1 \text{ hr}} = \textbf{83.3 kWh}$$

35. $$\frac{6700 \text{ W/s}}{(1000 \text{ W/kW})(3600 \text{ s/h})} = \textbf{0.00186 kWh}$$

36. $(50 \text{ W})(12 \text{ h}) = \textbf{600 Wh}$
$50 \text{ W} = 0.05 \text{ kW}$
$(0.05 \text{ kW})(12 \text{ h}) = \textbf{0.6 kWh}$

37. $I = \dfrac{V}{R_L} = \dfrac{1.25 \text{ V}}{10 \text{ }\Omega} = 0.125 \text{ A}$

$P = VI = (1.25 \text{ V})(0.125 \text{ A}) = 0.156 \text{ W} = \textbf{156 mW}$

38. $P = \dfrac{W}{t}$

$156 \text{ mW} = \dfrac{156 \text{ mJ}}{1 \text{ s}}$

$W_{\text{tot}} = (156 \text{ mJ/s})(90 \text{ h})(3600 \text{ s/h}) = \textbf{50,544 J}$

SECTION 3-5 The Power Rating of Resistors

39. $P = I^2 R = (10 \text{ mA})^2 (6.8 \text{ k}\Omega) = 0.68 \text{ W}$
Use the next highest standard power rating of **1 W**.

40. If the 8 W resistor is used, it will be operating in a marginal condition.
To allow for a **safety margin of 20%**, use a **12 W** resistor.

SECTION 3-6 Energy Conversion and Voltage Drop in a Resistance

41. (a)   + at top, − at bottom of resistor   (b)   + at bottom, − at top of resistor

(c)   + on right, − on left of resistor

SECTION 3-7 Power Supplies

42. $V_{\text{OUT}} = \sqrt{P_L R_L} = \sqrt{(1 \text{ W})(50 \text{ }\Omega)} = \textbf{7.07 V}$

43. Ampere-hour rating $= (1.5 \text{ A})(24 \text{ h}) = \textbf{36 Ah}$

44. $I = \dfrac{80 \, \text{Ah}}{10 \, \text{h}} = \textbf{8 A}$

45. $I = \dfrac{650 \, \text{mAh}}{48 \, \text{h}} = \textbf{13.5 mA}$

46. $P_{\text{LOST}} = P_{\text{IN}} - P_{\text{OUT}} = 500 \, \text{mW} - 400 \, \text{mW} = \textbf{100 mW}$

    % efficiency $= \left(\dfrac{P_{\text{OUT}}}{P_{\text{IN}}} \right) 100\% = \left(\dfrac{400 \, \text{mW}}{500 \, \text{mW}} \right) 100\% = \textbf{80\%}$

47. $P_{\text{OUT}} = (\text{efficiency}) P_{\text{IN}} = (0.85)(5 \, \text{W}) = \textbf{4.25 W}$

SECTION 3-8 Introduction to Troubleshooting

48. The 4th bulb from the left is open.

49. If should take **five** (maximum) resistance measurements.

ADVANCED PROBLEMS

50. Assume that the total consumption of the power supply is the input power plus the power lost.
    $P_{\text{OUT}} = 2 \, \text{W}$

    % efficiency $= \left(\dfrac{P_{\text{OUT}}}{P_{\text{IN}}} \right) 100\%$

    $P_{\text{IN}} = \left(\dfrac{P_{\text{OUT}}}{\% \text{ efficiency}} \right) 100\% = \left(\dfrac{2 \, \text{W}}{60\%} \right) 100\% = 3.33 \, \text{W}$

    The power supply itself uses
    $P_{\text{IN}} - P_{\text{OUT}} = 3.33 \, \text{W} - 2 \, \text{W} = 1.33 \, \text{W}$
    Energy $= W = Pt = (1.33 \, \text{W})(24 \, \text{h}) = 31.9 \, \text{Wh} \cong \textbf{0.032 kWh}$

51. $R_f = \dfrac{V}{I} = \dfrac{120 \, \text{V}}{0.8 \, \text{A}} = \textbf{150 } \boldsymbol{\Omega}$

52. Measure the current with an ammeter connected as shown in Figure 3-1. Then calculate the unknown resistance with the formula, $R = 12\text{ V}/I$.

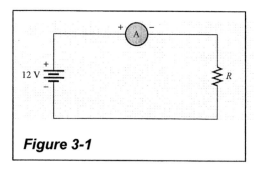

Figure 3-1

53. Calculate I for each value of V:

$I_1 = \dfrac{0\text{ V}}{100\ \Omega} = \textbf{0 A}$ $\qquad$ $I_2 = \dfrac{10\text{ V}}{100\ \Omega} = \textbf{100 mA}$

$I_3 = \dfrac{20\text{ V}}{100\ \Omega} = \textbf{200 mA}$ $\qquad$ $I_4 = \dfrac{30\text{ V}}{100\ \Omega} = \textbf{300 mA}$

$I_5 = \dfrac{40\text{ V}}{100\ \Omega} = \textbf{400 mA}$ $\qquad$ $I_6 = \dfrac{50\text{ V}}{100\ \Omega} = \textbf{500 mA}$

$I_7 = \dfrac{60\text{ V}}{100\ \Omega} = \textbf{600 mA}$ $\qquad$ $I_8 = \dfrac{70\text{ V}}{100\ \Omega} = \textbf{700 mA}$

$I_9 = \dfrac{80\text{ V}}{100\ \Omega} = \textbf{800 mA}$ $\qquad$ $I_{10} = \dfrac{90\text{ V}}{100\ \Omega} = \textbf{900 mA}$

$I_{11} = \dfrac{100\text{ V}}{100\ \Omega} = \textbf{1 A}$

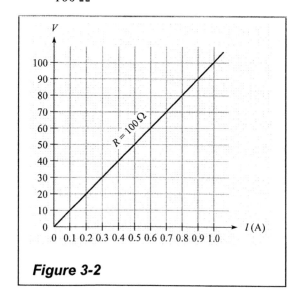

Figure 3-2

The graph is a straight line as shown in Figure 3-2. This indicates a *linear* relationship between I and V.

54. $R = \dfrac{V_S}{I} = \dfrac{1\,\text{V}}{5\,\text{mA}} = \mathbf{200\ \Omega}$

(a) $I = \dfrac{V_S}{R} = \dfrac{1.5\,\text{V}}{200\,\Omega} = \mathbf{7.5\ mA}$

(b) $I = \dfrac{V_S}{R} = \dfrac{2\,\text{V}}{200\,\Omega} = \mathbf{10\ mA}$

(c) $I = \dfrac{V_S}{R} = \dfrac{3\,\text{V}}{200\,\Omega} = \mathbf{15\ mA}$

(d) $I = \dfrac{V_S}{R} = \dfrac{4\,\text{V}}{200\,\Omega} = \mathbf{20\ mA}$

(e) $I = \dfrac{V_S}{R} = \dfrac{10\,\text{V}}{200\,\Omega} = \mathbf{50\ mA}$

55. $R_1 = \dfrac{V}{I} = \dfrac{1\,\text{V}}{2\,\text{A}} = \mathbf{0.5\ \Omega}$ $\qquad R_2 = \dfrac{V}{I} = \dfrac{1\,\text{V}}{1\,\text{A}} = \mathbf{1\ \Omega}$ $\qquad R_3 = \dfrac{V}{I} = \dfrac{1\,\text{V}}{0.5\,\text{A}} = \mathbf{2\ \Omega}$

56. $\dfrac{V_2}{30\,\text{mA}} = \dfrac{10\,\text{V}}{50\,\text{mA}}$

$V_2 = \dfrac{(10\,\text{V})(30\,\text{mA})}{50\,\text{mA}} = 6\,\text{V}$ **new value**

The voltage decreased by 4 V, from 10 V to 6 V.

57. The current increase is 50%, so the voltage increase must be the same; that is, the voltage must be increased by $(0.5)(20\,\text{V}) = \mathbf{10\ V}$.

The new value of voltage is $V_2 = 20\,\text{V} + (0.5)(20\,\text{V}) = 20\,\text{V} + 10\,\text{V} = \mathbf{30\ V}$

58. $R = \dfrac{100\,\text{V}}{750\,\text{mA}}\ 0.133\,\text{k}\Omega = \mathbf{133\ \Omega};$ $\qquad R = \dfrac{100\,\text{V}}{1\,\text{A}} = \mathbf{100\ \Omega}$

If $R = 0\,\Omega$, the voltage source will be shorted causing possible damage.

59. Resistance value $= 3300\,\Omega \pm 5\%$
$R_{\text{max}} = 3300\,\Omega + (0.05)(3300\,\Omega) = 3465\,\Omega$
$R_{\text{min}} = 3300\,\Omega - (0.05)(3300\,\Omega) = 3135\,\Omega$
$I_{\text{max}} = \dfrac{V_S}{R_{\text{min}}} = \dfrac{12\,\text{V}}{3135\,\Omega} = \mathbf{3.83\ mA}$
$I_{\text{min}} = \dfrac{V_S}{R_{\text{max}}} = \dfrac{12\,\text{V}}{3465\,\Omega} = \mathbf{3.46\ mA}$

60. Wire resistance: $R_W = \dfrac{(10.4\,\text{CM}\cdot\Omega/\text{ft})(24\,\text{ft})}{1624.3\,\text{CM}} = 0.154\,\Omega$

(a) $I = \dfrac{V}{R+R_W} = \dfrac{6\,\text{V}}{100.154\,\Omega} = \textbf{59.9 mA}$

(b) $V_R = (59.9\,\text{mA})(100\,\Omega) = \textbf{5.99 V}$

(c) $V_{R_W} = 6\,\text{V} - 5.99\,\text{V} = 0.01\,\text{V}$

   For one length of wire, $V = \dfrac{0.01\,\text{V}}{2} = \textbf{0.005 V}$

61. $300\,\text{W} = 0.3\,\text{kW}$
   $30\,\text{days} = (30\,\text{days})(24\,\text{h/day}) = 720\,\text{h}$
   Energy $= (0.3\,\text{kW})(720\,\text{h}) = \textbf{216 kWh}$

62. $\dfrac{1500\,\text{kWh}}{31\,\text{days}} = 48.39\,\text{kWh/day}$

   $P = \dfrac{48.39\,\text{kWh/day}}{24\,\text{h/day}} = \textbf{2.02 kW}$

63. The minimum power rating you should use is **12 W** so that the power dissipation does not exceed the rating.

64. (a) $P = \dfrac{V^2}{R} = \dfrac{(12\,\text{V})^2}{10\,\Omega} = \textbf{14.4 W}$

(b) $W = Pt = (14.4\,\text{W})(2\,\text{min})(1/60\,\text{h/min}) = \textbf{0.48 Wh}$

(c) Neither, the power is the same because it is not time dependent.

65. $V_{R(\text{max})} = 120\,\text{V} - 100\,\text{V} = 20\,\text{V}$

   $I_{\text{max}} = \dfrac{V_{R(\text{max})}}{R_{\text{min}}} = \dfrac{20\,\text{V}}{8\,\Omega} = 2.5\,\text{A}$

   A fuse with a rating of less than 2.5 A must be used. **A 2 A fuse is recommended.**

Multisim Troubleshooting Problems

66. R is open.

67. No fault

68. R_1 is shorted.

69. Lamp 4 is shorted.

70. Lamp 6 is open.

CHAPTER 4
SERIES CIRCUITS

BASIC PROBLEMS

SECTION 4-1 Resistors in Series

1. See Figure 4-1.

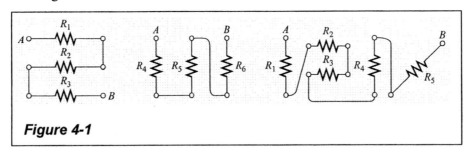

Figure 4-1

2. The groups of series resistors are

$R_1, R_2, R_3, R_9 R_4;$ $R_{13}, R_7, R_{14}, R_{16};$ $R_6, R_8, R_{12};$ $R_{10}, R_{11}, R_{15}, R_5$

See Figure 4-2.

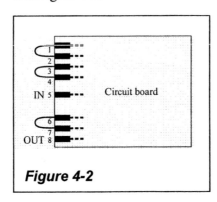

Figure 4-2

3. $R_{1-8} = R_{13} + R_7 + R_{14} + R_{16}$

$= 68 \text{ k}\Omega + 33 \text{ k}\Omega + 47 \text{ k}\Omega + 22 \text{ k}\Omega$

$= \textbf{170 k}\boldsymbol{\Omega}$

4. $R_{2-3} = R_{12} + R_8 + R_6 = 10 \text{ }\Omega + 18 \text{ }\Omega + 22 \text{ }\Omega = \textbf{50 }\boldsymbol{\Omega}$

5. $R_T = 82\ \Omega + 56\ \Omega = \mathbf{138\ \Omega}$

6.   (a) $R_T = 560\ \Omega + 1.0\ k\Omega = \mathbf{1560\ \Omega}$
         (b) $R_T = 47\ \Omega + 33\ \Omega = \mathbf{80\ \Omega}$
         (c) $R_T = 1.5\ k\Omega + 2.2\ k\Omega + 10\ k\Omega = \mathbf{13.7\ k\Omega}$
         (d) $R_T = 1.0\ k\Omega + 1.8\ k\Omega + 100\ k\Omega + 1.0\ M\Omega = \mathbf{1,102,800\ \Omega}$

7.   (a) $R_T = 1.0\ k\Omega + 4.7\ k\Omega + 2.2\ k\Omega = \mathbf{7.9\ k\Omega}$
         (b) $R_T = 10\ \Omega + 10\ \Omega + 12\ \Omega + 1.0\ \Omega = \mathbf{33\ \Omega}$
         (c) $R_T = 1.0\ M\Omega + 560\ k\Omega + 1.0\ M\Omega + 680\ k\Omega + 10\ M\Omega = \mathbf{13.24\ M\Omega}$

     See Figure 4-3.

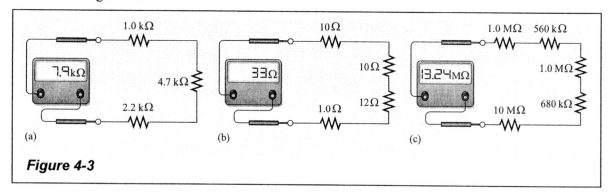

Figure 4-3

8. $R_T = 12(5.6\ k\Omega) = \mathbf{67.2\ k\Omega}$

9. $R_T = 6(47\ \Omega) + 8(100\ \Omega) + 2(22\ \Omega) = 282\ \Omega + 800\ \Omega + 44\ \Omega = \mathbf{1126\ \Omega}$

10. $R_T = R_1 + R_2 + R_3 + R_4 + R_5$
       $R_5 = R_T - (R_1 + R_2 + R_3 + R_4)$
           $= 20\ k\Omega - (4.7\ k\Omega + 1.0\ k\Omega + 2.2\ k\Omega + 3.9\ k\Omega)$
           $= 20\ k\Omega - 11.8\ k\Omega$
           $= \mathbf{8.2\ k\Omega}$

11.   (a) $R_{1-8} = R_{13} + R_7 + R_{14} + R_{16}$
               $= 68\ k\Omega + 33\ k\Omega + 47\ k\Omega + 22\ k\Omega = \mathbf{170\ k\Omega}$

        (b) $R_{2-3} = R_{12} + R_8 + R_6$
               $= 10\ \Omega + 18\ \Omega + 22\ \Omega = \mathbf{50\ \Omega}$

        (c) $R_{4-7} = R_{10} + R_{11} + R_{15} + R_5$
               $= 2.2\ k\Omega + 8.2\ k\Omega + 1.0\ k\Omega + 1.0\ k\Omega = \mathbf{12.4\ k\Omega}$

        (d) $R_{5-6} = R_1 + R_2 + R_3 + R_9 + R_4$
               $= 220\ \Omega + 330\ \Omega + 390\ \Omega + 470\ \Omega + 560\ \Omega = \mathbf{1.97\ k\Omega}$

12. $R_T = R_{1-8} + R_{2-3} + R_{4-7} + R_{5-6}$

   $= 170 \text{ k}\Omega + 50 \Omega + 12.4 \text{ k}\Omega + 1.97 \text{ k}\Omega = \mathbf{184.42 \text{ k}\Omega}$

SECTION 4-3 Current in a Series Circuit

13. $I = \dfrac{V_S}{R_T} = \dfrac{12 \text{ V}}{120 \Omega} = \mathbf{0.1 \text{ A}}$

14. $I = \mathbf{5 \text{ mA}}$ at all points in the circuit.

SECTION 4-4 Application of Ohm's Law

15. (a) $R_T = 2.2 \text{ k}\Omega + 5.6 \text{ k}\Omega + 1.0 \text{ k}\Omega = 8.8 \text{ k}\Omega$

   $I = \dfrac{V}{R_T} = \dfrac{5.5 \text{ V}}{8.8 \text{ k}\Omega} = \mathbf{625 \text{ }\mu\text{A}}$

   (b) $R_T = 1.0 \text{ M}\Omega + 2.2 \text{ M}\Omega + 560 \text{ k}\Omega = 3.76 \text{ M}\Omega$

   $I = \dfrac{16 \text{ V}}{3.76 \text{ M}\Omega} = \mathbf{4.26 \text{ }\mu\text{A}}$

   The ammeters are connected in series. See Figure 4-4.

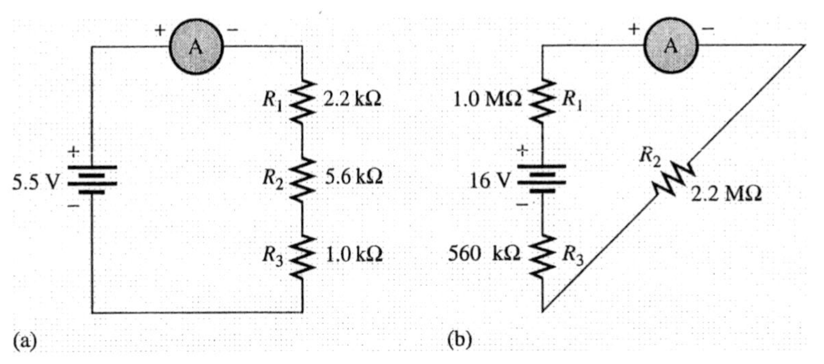

(a)   (b)

Figure 4-4

16. (a) $V_1 = \left(\dfrac{R_1}{R_T}\right)V_S = \left(\dfrac{2.2 \text{ k}\Omega}{8.8 \text{ k}\Omega}\right)5.5 \text{ V} = \mathbf{1.375 \text{ V}}$

   $V_2 = \left(\dfrac{R_2}{R_T}\right)V_S = \left(\dfrac{5.6 \text{ k}\Omega}{8.8 \text{ k}\Omega}\right)5.5 \text{ V} = \mathbf{3.5 \text{ V}}$

   $V_3 = \left(\dfrac{R_3}{R_T}\right)V_S = \left(\dfrac{1.0 \text{ k}\Omega}{8.8 \text{ k}\Omega}\right)5.5 \text{ V} = \mathbf{625 \text{ mV}}$

(b) $V_1 = \left(\dfrac{R_1}{R_T}\right)V_S = \left(\dfrac{1.0\ \text{M}\Omega}{3.76\ \text{M}\Omega}\right)16\ \text{V} = \textbf{4.26 V}$

$V_2 = \left(\dfrac{R_2}{R_T}\right)V_S = \left(\dfrac{2.2\ \text{M}\Omega}{3.76\ \text{M}\Omega}\right)16\ \text{V} = \textbf{9.36 V}$

$V_3 = \left(\dfrac{R_3}{R_T}\right)V_S = \left(\dfrac{560\ \text{k}\Omega}{3.76\ \text{M}\Omega}\right)16\ \text{V} = \textbf{2.38 V}$

17. (a) $R_T = 3(470\ \Omega) = 1410\ \Omega$

$I = \dfrac{48\ \text{V}}{1410\ \Omega} = \textbf{34.0 mA}$

(b) $V_R = IR = (34.0\ \text{mA})(470\ \Omega) = \textbf{16 V}$

(c) $P_{\min} = I^2 R = (34.0\ \text{mA})^2\, 470\ \Omega = \textbf{0.543 W}$

18. $R_T = \dfrac{V_S}{I_T} = \dfrac{5\ \text{V}}{1\ \text{mA}} = 5\ \text{k}\Omega$

$R_{each} = \dfrac{5\ \text{k}\Omega}{4} = \textbf{1.25 k}\Omega$

SECTION 4-5 Voltage Sources in Series

19. $V_T = 5\ \text{V} + 9\ \text{V} = \textbf{14 V}$

20. (a) $V_{S(tot)} = 10\ \text{V} + 5\ \text{V} + 8\ \text{V} = \textbf{23 V}$ (b) $V_{S(tot)} = 10\ \text{V} + 50\ \text{V} - 25\ \text{V} = \textbf{35 V}$

(c) $V_{S(tot)} = 8\ \text{V} - 8\ \text{V} = \textbf{0 V}$

SECTION 4-6 Kirchhoff's Voltage Law

21. $V_S = 5.5\ \text{V} + 8.2\ \text{V} + 12.3\ \text{V} = \textbf{26 V}$

22. $V_S = V_1 + V_2 + V_3 + V_4 + V_5$
$V_5 = V_S - (V_1 + V_2 + V_3 + V_4) = 20\ \text{V} - (1.5\ \text{V} + 5.5\ \text{V} + 3\ \text{V} + 6\ \text{V}) = 20\ \text{V} - 16\ \text{V} = \textbf{4 V}$

23. (a) By Kirchhoff's voltage law:

$15\ \text{V} = 2\ \text{V} + V_2 + 3.2\ \text{V} + 1\ \text{V} + 1.5\ \text{V} + 0.5\ \text{V}$
$V_2 = 15\ \text{V} - (2\ \text{V} + 3.2\ \text{V} + 1\ \text{V} + 1.5\ \text{V} + 0.5\ \text{V}) = 15\ \text{V} - 8.2\ \text{V} = \textbf{6.8 V}$

See Figure 4-5(a).

(b) $V_R = \textbf{8 V}$; $V_{2R} = \textbf{16 V}$; $V_{3R} = \textbf{24 V}$; $V_{4R} = \textbf{32 V}$

See Figure 4-5(b).

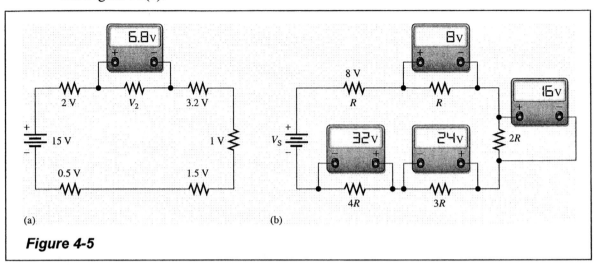

(a)   (b)

Figure 4-5

SECTION 4-7 Voltage Dividers

24. $\left(\dfrac{22\ \Omega}{500\ \Omega}\right)100 = \textbf{4.4\%}$

25.   (a) $V_{AB} = \left(\dfrac{47\ \Omega}{147\ \Omega}\right)12\ \text{V} = \textbf{3.84 V}$

(b) $V_{AB} = \left(\dfrac{2.2\ \text{k}\Omega + 3.3\ \text{k}\Omega}{1.0\ \text{k}\Omega + 2.2\ \text{k}\Omega + 3.3\ \text{k}\Omega}\right)8\ \text{V} = \left(\dfrac{5.5\ \text{k}\Omega}{6.5\ \text{k}\Omega}\right)8\ \text{V} = \textbf{6.77 V}$

26. $V_A = V_S = \textbf{15 V}$

$V_B = \left(\dfrac{R_2 + R_3}{R_1 + R_2 + R_3}\right)V_S = \left(\dfrac{13.3\ \text{k}\Omega}{18.9\ \text{k}\Omega}\right)15\ \text{V} = \textbf{10.6 V}$

$V_C = \left(\dfrac{R_3}{R_1 + R_2 + R_3}\right)V_S = \left(\dfrac{3.3\ \text{k}\Omega}{18.9\ \text{k}\Omega}\right)15\ \text{V} = \textbf{2.62 V}$

27. $V_{\min} = \left(\dfrac{R_3}{R_1 + R_2 + R_3}\right)V_S = \left(\dfrac{680\ \Omega}{2150\ \Omega}\right)12\ \text{V} = \textbf{3.80 V}$

$V_{\max} = \left(\dfrac{R_2 + R_3}{R_1 + R_2 + R_3}\right)V_S = \left(\dfrac{1680\ \Omega}{2150\ \Omega}\right)12\ \text{V} = \textbf{9.38 V}$

28. $R_T = R + 2R + 3R + 4R + 5R = 15R$

$$V_R = \left(\frac{R}{15R}\right)9\ \text{V} = \textbf{0.6 V} \qquad V_R = \left(\frac{2R}{15R}\right)9\ \text{V} = \textbf{1.2 V} \qquad V_R = \left(\frac{3R}{15R}\right)9\ \text{V} = \textbf{1.8 V}$$

$$V_R = \left(\frac{4R}{15R}\right)9\ \text{V} = \textbf{2.4 V} \qquad V_R = \left(\frac{5R}{15R}\right)9\ \text{V} = \textbf{3.0 V}$$

29. $V_{5.6k} = \textbf{10 V}$ (by measurement); $\qquad I = \dfrac{10\ \text{V}}{5.6\ \text{k}\Omega} = 1.79\ \text{mA};$

$V_{1k} = (1.79\ \text{mA})(1\ \text{k}\Omega) = \textbf{1.79 V}; \qquad V_{560}\ (1.79\ \text{mA})(560\ \Omega) = \textbf{1 V};$

$V_{10k} = (1.79\ \text{mA})(10\ \text{k}\Omega) = \textbf{17.9 V}$

SECTION 4-8 Power in a Series Circuit

30. $P_T = 5(50\ \text{mW}) = \textbf{250 mW}$

31. $R_T = 5.6\ \text{k}\Omega + 1\ \text{k}\Omega + 560\ \Omega + 10\ \text{k}\Omega = 17.16\ \text{k}\Omega$
$P = I^2 R_T = (1.79\ \text{mA})^2(17.16\ \text{k}\Omega) = 0.055\ \text{W} = \textbf{55 mW}$

SECTION 4-9 Voltage Measurement

32. Voltage from point A to ground (G): $\ V_{AG} = \textbf{10 V}$

Resistance between A and G: $\ R_{AG} = 5.6\ \text{k}\Omega + 5.6\ \text{k}\Omega + 1.0\ \text{k}\Omega + 1.0\ \text{k}\Omega = 13.2\ \text{k}\Omega$

Resistance between B and G: $\ R_{BG} = 5.6\ \text{k}\Omega + 1.0\ \text{k}\Omega + 1.0\ \text{k}\Omega = 7.6\ \text{k}\Omega$

Resistance between C and G: $\ R_{CG} = 1.0\ \text{k}\Omega + 1.0\ \text{k}\Omega = 2\ \text{k}\Omega$

$$V_{BG} = \left(\frac{R_{BG}}{R_{AG}}\right)10\ \text{V} = \left(\frac{7.6\ \text{k}\Omega}{13.2\ \text{k}\Omega}\right)10\ \text{V} = \textbf{5.76 V}$$

$$V_{CG} = \left(\frac{R_{CG}}{R_{AG}}\right)10\ \text{V} = \left(\frac{2\ \text{k}\Omega}{13.2\ \text{k}\Omega}\right)10\ \text{V} = \textbf{1.52 V}$$

$$V_{DG} = \left(\frac{R_{DG}}{R_{AG}}\right)10\ \text{V} = \left(\frac{1.0\ \text{k}\Omega}{13.2\ \text{k}\Omega}\right)10\ \text{V} = \textbf{0.758 V}$$

33. Measure the voltage at point A with respect to ground and the voltage at point B with respect to ground. The difference of these two voltages is V_{R2}.

$$V_{R2} = V_A - V_B$$

34. $R_T = R_1 + R_2 + R_3 + R_4 + R_5$
    $= 560 \text{ k}\Omega + 560 \text{ k}\Omega + 100 \text{ k}\Omega + 1.0 \text{ M}\Omega + 100 \text{ k}\Omega = 2.32 \text{ M}\Omega$

$V_T = 15 \text{ V}$

$V_A = \left(\dfrac{R_{AG}}{R_T}\right)V_T = \left(\dfrac{1.76 \text{ M}\Omega}{2.32 \text{ M}\Omega}\right)15 \text{ V} = \mathbf{11.4 \text{ V}}$

$V_B = \left(\dfrac{R_{BG}}{R_T}\right)V_T = \left(\dfrac{1.2 \text{ M}\Omega}{2.32 \text{ M}\Omega}\right)15 \text{ V} = \mathbf{7.76 \text{ V}}$

$V_C = \left(\dfrac{R_{CG}}{R_T}\right)V_T = \left(\dfrac{1.1 \text{ M}\Omega}{2.32 \text{ M}\Omega}\right)15 \text{ V} = \mathbf{7.11 \text{ V}}$

$V_D = \left(\dfrac{R_{DG}}{R_T}\right)V_T = \left(\dfrac{100 \text{ k}\Omega}{2.32 \text{ M}\Omega}\right)15 \text{ V} = \mathbf{647 \text{ mV}}$

SECTION 4-10 Troubleshooting

35. (a) Zero current indicates an open. **R_4 is open** since all the voltage is dropped across it.

    (b) $\dfrac{V_S}{R_1 + R_2 + R_3} = \dfrac{10 \text{ V}}{300 \ \Omega} = 33.3 \text{ mA}$

    R_4 and R_5 have no effect on the current. There is a **short from A to B.**

36. $R_T = 10 \text{ k}\Omega + 8.2 \text{ k}\Omega + 12 \text{ k}\Omega + 2.2 \text{ k}\Omega + 5.6 \text{ k}\Omega = 38 \text{ k}\Omega$
    The meter reads about 28 kΩ. It should read 38 kΩ. **The 10 kΩ resistor is shorted.**

ADVANCED PROBLEMS

37. $V_1 = IR_1 = (10 \text{ mA})(680 \ \Omega) = 6.8 \text{ V}$
    $V_2 = IR_2 = (10 \text{ mA})(1.0 \text{ k}\Omega) = 10 \text{ V}$
    $V_4 = IR_4 = (10 \text{ mA})(270 \ \Omega) = 2.7 \text{ V}$
    $V_5 = IR_5 = (10 \text{ mA})(270 \ \Omega) = 2.7 \text{ V}$
    $V_3 = V_S - (V_1 + V_2 + V_4 + V_5)$
    $V_3 = 30 \text{ V} - (6.8 \text{ V} + 10 \text{ V} + 2.7 \text{ V} + 2.7 \text{ V}) = 30 \text{ V} - 22.2 \text{ V} = 7.8 \text{ V}$
    $R_3 = \dfrac{V_3}{I} = \dfrac{7.8 \text{ V}}{10 \text{ mA}} = 0.78 \text{ k}\Omega = \mathbf{780 \ \Omega}$

38. $R_T = 3(5.6 \text{ k}\Omega) + 1.0 \text{ k}\Omega + 2(100 \ \Omega) = 18 \text{ k}\Omega$
    Three 5.6 kΩ resistors, one 1 kΩ resistor, and two 100 Ω resistors

39. $V_A = \mathbf{10 \text{ V}}, \quad R_T = 22 \text{ k}\Omega + 10 \text{ k}\Omega + 47 \text{ k}\Omega + 12 \text{ k}\Omega + 5.6 \text{ k}\Omega = 96.6 \text{ k}\Omega$
    $V_B = V_A - V_{22k} = 10 \text{ V} - \left(\dfrac{22 \text{ k}\Omega}{96.6 \text{ k}\Omega}\right)10 \text{ V} = 10 \text{ V} - 2.28 \text{ V} = \mathbf{7.72 \text{ V}}$

$$V_C = V_B - V_{10k} = 7.72 \text{ V} - \left(\frac{10 \text{ k}\Omega}{96.6 \text{ k}\Omega}\right)10 \text{ V} = 7.72 \text{ V} - 1.04 \text{ V} = \mathbf{6.68 \text{ V}}$$

$$V_D = V_C - V_{47k} = 6.68 \text{ V} - \left(\frac{47 \text{ k}\Omega}{96.6 \text{ k}\Omega}\right)10 \text{ V} = 6.68 \text{ V} - 4.87 \text{ V} = \mathbf{1.81 \text{ V}}$$

$$V_E = V_D - V_{12k} = 1.81 \text{ V} - \left(\frac{12 \text{ k}\Omega}{96.6 \text{ k}\Omega}\right)10 \text{ V} = 1.81 \text{ V} - 1.24 \text{ V} = \mathbf{0.57 \text{ V}}$$

$$V_F = \mathbf{0 \text{ V}}$$

40. $V_2 = IR_2 = (20 \text{ mA})(100 \text{ }\Omega) = \mathbf{2 \text{ V}}$

   $R_5 = \dfrac{V_S}{I} = \dfrac{6.6 \text{ V}}{20 \text{ mA}} = \mathbf{330 \text{ }\Omega}$

   $R_6 = \dfrac{P_6}{I^2} = \dfrac{112 \text{ mW}}{(20 \text{ mA})^2} = \mathbf{280 \text{ }\Omega}$

   $V_6 = IR_6 = (20 \text{ mA})(280 \text{ }\Omega) = \mathbf{5.6 \text{ V}}$

   $V_1 = V_S - (20 \text{ V} + V_6) = 30 \text{ V} - (20 \text{ V} + 5.6 \text{ V}) = \mathbf{4.4 \text{ V}}$

   $R_1 = \dfrac{V_1}{I} = \dfrac{4.4 \text{ V}}{20 \text{ mA}} = \mathbf{220 \text{ }\Omega}$

   $V_3 + V_4 = 20 \text{ V} - V_2 - V_5 = 20 \text{ V} - 2 \text{ V} - 6.6 \text{ V} = 11.4 \text{ V}$

   $V_3 = V_4 = \dfrac{11.4 \text{ V}}{2} = \mathbf{5.7 \text{ V}} \qquad R_3 = R_4 = \dfrac{V_3}{I} = \dfrac{5.7 \text{ V}}{20 \text{ mA}} = \mathbf{285 \text{ }\Omega}$

41. $V_S = IR_T = (250 \text{ mA})(1.5 \text{ k}\Omega) = 375 \text{ V}$

   $I_{new} = 250 \text{ mA} - 0.25(250 \text{ mA}) = 250 \text{ mA} - 62.5 \text{ mA} = 188 \text{ mA}$

   $R_{new} = \dfrac{V_S}{I_{new}} = \dfrac{375 \text{ V}}{188 \text{ mA}} \cong 2000 \text{ }\Omega$

   500 Ω must be added to the existing 1500 Ω to reduce I by 25%.

42. $P = I^2R$

   $I_{max} = \sqrt{\dfrac{P}{R}} = \sqrt{\dfrac{0.5 \text{ W}}{120 \text{ }\Omega}} = 0.0645 \text{ A} = 64.5 \text{ mA}$

   Since all resistors in series have the same current, use the largest R to determine the maximum current allowable because the largest R has the greatest power.
   Thus, the **120 Ω resistor burns out first.**

43. (a) $P_T = \dfrac{1}{8}\text{W} + \dfrac{1}{4}\text{W} + \dfrac{1}{2}\text{W} = 0.125 \text{ W} + 0.25 \text{ W} + 0.5 \text{ W} = 0.875 \text{ W}$

   $I = \sqrt{\dfrac{P_T}{R_T}} = \sqrt{\dfrac{0.875 \text{ W}}{2400 \text{ }\Omega}} = \mathbf{19.1 \text{ mA}}$

   (b) $V_S = I_T R_T = (19.1 \text{ mA})(2400 \text{ }\Omega) = \mathbf{45.8 \text{ V}}$

   (c) $R = \dfrac{P}{I^2}$

   $R_{1/8} = \dfrac{P}{I^2} = \dfrac{0.125 \text{ W}}{(19.1 \text{ mA})^2} = \mathbf{343 \text{ }\Omega}$

$$R_{1/4} = \frac{0.25 \text{ W}}{(19.1 \text{ mA})^2} = \mathbf{686 \ \Omega}$$

$$R_{1/2} = \frac{0.5 \text{ W}}{(19.1 \text{ mA})^2} = \mathbf{1371 \ \Omega}$$

44. See Figure 4-6.

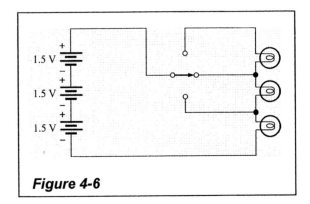

Figure 4-6

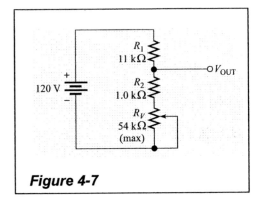

Figure 4-7

45. See Figure 4-7.

When the potentiometer is at minimum setting (0 Ω), $V_{OUT} = 10$ V:

$$R_1 + R_2 = \frac{120 \text{ V}}{10 \text{ mA}} = 12 \text{ k}\Omega$$

$$\left(\frac{R_2}{R_1 + R_2}\right)120 \text{ V} = 10 \text{ V}$$

$$R_2 = \frac{10 \text{ V}(12 \text{ k}\Omega)}{120 \text{ V}} = \mathbf{1.0 \ k\Omega}$$

$$R_1 = 12 \text{ k}\Omega - 1.0 \text{ k}\Omega = \mathbf{11 \ k\Omega}$$

When the potentiometer is at maximum setting, $V_{OUT} = 100$ V:

$$\left(\frac{R_2 + R_V}{R_1 + R_2 + R_V}\right)120 \text{ V} = 100 \text{ V}$$

$$\left(\frac{1.0 \text{ k}\Omega + R_V}{12 \text{ k}\Omega + R_V}\right)120 \text{ V} = 100 \text{ V}$$

$$(1.0 \text{ k}\Omega + R_V)120 \text{ V} = (12 \text{ k}\Omega + R_V)100 \text{ V}$$

$$120 \text{ k}\Omega + 120R_V = 1200 \text{ k}\Omega + 100R_V$$

$$20R_V = 1080 \text{ k}\Omega$$

$$R_V = \mathbf{54 \ k\Omega}$$

46. See Figure 4-8.

$$R_1 = \frac{(30 \text{ V} - 24.6 \text{ V})}{1 \text{ mA}} = 5.4 \text{ k}\Omega$$

$$R_2 = \frac{(24.6 \text{ V} - 14.7 \text{ V})}{1 \text{ mA}} = 9.9 \text{ k}\Omega$$

$$R_3 = \frac{(14.7\text{ V} - 8.18\text{ V})}{1\text{ mA}} = 6.52\text{ k}\Omega$$

$$R_4 = \frac{8.18\text{ V}}{1\text{ mA}} = 8.18\text{ k}\Omega$$

A series of standard value resistors must be used to approximately achieve each resistance as follows:

$R_1 = 4700\ \Omega + 680\ \Omega + 22\ \Omega = \textbf{5.4 k}\boldsymbol{\Omega}$
$R_2 = 8200\ \Omega + 1500\ \Omega + 220\ \Omega = \textbf{9.92 k}\boldsymbol{\Omega}$
$R_3 = 5600\ \Omega + 820\ \Omega + 100\ \Omega = \textbf{6.52 k}\boldsymbol{\Omega}$
$R_4 = 6800\ \Omega + 1000\ \Omega + 180\ \Omega + 100\ \Omega + 100\ \Omega = \textbf{8.18 k}\boldsymbol{\Omega}$

The highest power dissipation is in the 8200 Ω resistor.
$P = (1\text{ mA})^2 8200\ \Omega = 8.2\text{ mW}$

All resistors must be at least 1/8 W.

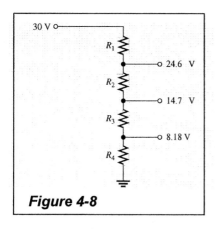

Figure 4-8

47. The groups are:

R_1, R_7, R_8, and R_{10}; R_2, R_4, R_6, and R_{11}; R_3, R_5, R_9, and R_{12}

See Figure 4-9.

$R_1 + R_7 + R_8 + R_{10} = 2.2\text{ k}\Omega + 560\ \Omega + 470\ \Omega + 1.0\text{ k}\Omega = \textbf{4.23 k}\boldsymbol{\Omega}$
$R_2 + R_4 + R_6 + R_{11} = 4.7\text{ k}\Omega + 5.6\text{ k}\Omega + 3.3\text{ k}\Omega + 10\text{ k}\Omega = \textbf{23.6 k}\boldsymbol{\Omega}$
$R_3 + R_5 + R_9 + R_{12} = 1.0\text{ k}\Omega + 3.9\text{ k}\Omega + 8.2\text{ k}\Omega + 6.8\text{ k}\Omega = \textbf{19.9 k}\boldsymbol{\Omega}$

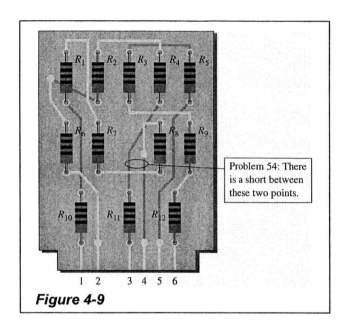

Problem 54: There is a short between these two points.

Figure 4-9

48. *Position 1:*
$R_T = R_1 + R_3 + R_5 = 510\ \Omega + 820\ \Omega + 680\ \Omega = \mathbf{2.01\ k\Omega}$

Position 2:
$R_T = R_1 + R_2 + R_3 + R_4 + R_5$
$\quad = 510\ \Omega + 910\ \Omega + 820\ \Omega + 750\ \Omega + 680\ \Omega = \mathbf{3.67\ k\Omega}$

49. *Position A:*
$R_T = R_1 + R_2 + R_3 + R_4 = 220\ \Omega + 470\ \Omega + 510\ \Omega + 1.0\ k\Omega = 2.2\ k\Omega$
$I = \dfrac{V}{R_T} = \dfrac{12\ V}{2.2\ k\Omega} = \mathbf{5.45\ mA}$

Position B:
$R_T = R_2 + R_3 + R_4 = 470\ \Omega + 510\ \Omega + 1.0\ k\Omega = 1.98\ k\Omega$
$I = \dfrac{V}{R_T} = \dfrac{12\ V}{1.98\ k\Omega} = \mathbf{6.06\ mA}$

Position C:
$R_T = R_3 + R_4 = 510\ \Omega + 1.0\ k\Omega = 1.51\ k\Omega$
$I = \dfrac{V}{R_T} = \dfrac{12\ V}{1.51\ k\Omega} = \mathbf{7.95\ mA}$

Position D:
$R_T = R_4 = 1.0\ k\Omega$
$I = \dfrac{V}{R_T} = \dfrac{12\ V}{1.0\ k\Omega} = \mathbf{12\ mA}$

50. *Position A:*
$R_T = R_1 = 1.0\ k\Omega$
$I = \dfrac{V}{R_T} = \dfrac{9\ V}{1.0\ k\Omega} = \mathbf{9\ mA}$

Position B:

$R_T = R_1 + R_2 + R_5 = 1.0\ k\Omega + 33\ k\Omega + 22\ k\Omega = 56\ k\Omega$

$I = \dfrac{V}{R_T} = \dfrac{9\ V}{56\ k\Omega} = \textbf{161 μA}$

Position C:

$R_T = R_1 + R_2 + R_3 + R_4 + R_5 = 1.0\ k\Omega + 33\ k\Omega + 68\ k\Omega + 27\ k\Omega + 22\ k\Omega = 151\ k\Omega$

$I = \dfrac{V}{R_T} = \dfrac{9\ V}{151\ k\Omega} = \textbf{59.6 μA}$

51. First, find the value of R_5 with the switch in Position *D*.

$6\ mA = \dfrac{18\ V}{R_5 + 1.8\ k\Omega}$

$R_5 = \dfrac{18\ V}{6\ mA} - 1.8\ k\Omega = 1.2\ k\Omega$

Position A:

$R_T = 5.38\ k\Omega$　　$I = 18\ V/5.38\ k\Omega = 3.35\ mA$
$V_1 = (3.35\ mA)(1.8\ k\Omega) = \textbf{6.03 V}$
$V_2 = (3.35\ mA)(1.0\ k\Omega) = \textbf{3.35 V}$
$V_3 = (3.35\ mA)(820\ \Omega) = \textbf{2.75 V}$
$V_4 = (3.35\ mA)(560\ \Omega) = \textbf{1.88 V}$
$V_5 = \textbf{4 V}$

Position B:

$R_T = 4.82\ k\Omega$　　$I = 18\ V/4.82\ k\Omega = 3.73\ mA$
$V_1 = (3.73\ mA)(1.8\ k\Omega) = \textbf{6.71 V}$
$V_2 = (3.73\ mA)(1.0\ k\Omega) = \textbf{3.73 V}$
$V_3 = (3.73\ mA)(820\ \Omega) = \textbf{3.06 V}$
$V_5 = \textbf{4.5 V}$

Position C:

$R_T = 4\ k\Omega$　　$I = 18\ V/4\ k\Omega = 4.5\ mA$
$V_1 = (4.5\ mA)(1.8\ k\Omega) = \textbf{8.1 V}$
$V_2 = (4.5\ mA)(1.0\ k\Omega) = \textbf{4.5 V}$
$V_5 = \textbf{5.4 V}$

Position D:

$R_T = 3\ k\Omega$　　$I = 18\ V/3\ k\Omega = 6\ mA$
$V_1 = (6\ mA)(1.8\ k\Omega) = \textbf{10.8 V}$
$V_5 = \textbf{7.2 V}$

Note: The voltage approach can also be used.

52. See Figure 4-9. The results in the table are correct.

53. Yes, R_3 and R_5 are each shorted. Refer to Figure 4-9.

54. Yes, there is a short between the points indicated in Figure 4-9.

55. (a) R_{11} burned open due to excessive power because it had the largest value in ohms.
    (b) Replace R_{11} (10 kΩ).
    (c) $R_T = 47.7$ kΩ

$$I_{max} = \sqrt{\frac{P_{11}}{R_{11}}} = \sqrt{\frac{0.5 \text{ W}}{10 \text{ k}\Omega}} = 7.07 \text{ mA}$$

$$V_{TOTAL} = I_{max}R_T = (7.07 \text{ mA})(47.7 \text{ k}\Omega) = \textbf{338 V}$$

Multisim Troubleshooting Problems

56. R_1 is open.

57. R_6 is shorted.

58. R_2 is open.

59. Lamp 4 is open.

60. No fault

61. The 82 Ω resistor is shorted.

CHAPTER 5
PARALLEL CIRCUITS

BASIC PROBLEMS

SECTION 5-1 Resistors in Parallel

1. See Figure 5-1.

2. See Figure 5-2.

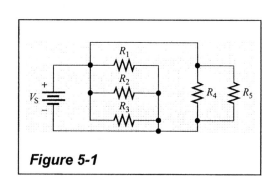

Figure 5-1

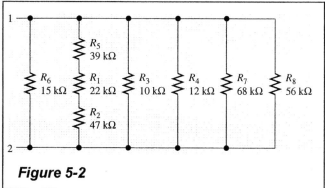

Figure 5-2

SECTION 5-2 Total Parallel Resistance

3. From Problem 2: $R_T = R_6 \parallel R_3 \parallel R_4 \parallel R_7 \parallel R_8 \parallel (R_1 + R_2 + R_5)$

$= 15\ k\Omega \parallel 10\ k\Omega \parallel 12\ k\Omega \parallel 68\ k\Omega \parallel 56\ k\Omega \parallel 108\ k\Omega = \textbf{3.43 k}\boldsymbol{\Omega}$

4. $R_T = \dfrac{1}{\dfrac{1}{1.0\ M\Omega} + \dfrac{1}{2.2\ M\Omega} + \dfrac{1}{4.7\ M\Omega} + \dfrac{1}{12\ M\Omega} + \dfrac{1}{22\ M\Omega}} = \textbf{557 k}\boldsymbol{\Omega}$

5. (a) $R = 47\ \Omega \parallel 6\ k\Omega = \textbf{25.6}\ \boldsymbol{\Omega}$
   (b) $R = 560\ \Omega \parallel 1.0\ k\Omega = \textbf{359}\ \boldsymbol{\Omega}$
   (c) $R = 1.5\ k\Omega \parallel 2.2\ k\Omega \parallel 10\ k\Omega = \textbf{819}\ \boldsymbol{\Omega}$
   (d) $R = 1.0\ k\Omega \parallel 2.2\ M\Omega \parallel 1.0\ M\Omega \parallel 470\ k\Omega = \textbf{996}\ \boldsymbol{\Omega}$

6. (a) $R_T = \dfrac{R_1 R_2}{R_1 + R_2} = \dfrac{(4.7\ \text{k}\Omega)(2.2\ \text{k}\Omega)}{4.7\ \text{k}\Omega + 2.2\ \text{k}\Omega} = \mathbf{1.5\ k\Omega}$

    (b) $R_T = \dfrac{R_1 R_2}{R_1 + R_2} = \dfrac{(27\ \Omega)(56\ \Omega)}{27\ \Omega + 56\ \Omega} = \mathbf{18.2\ \Omega}$

    (c) $R_T = \dfrac{R_1 R_2}{R_1 + R_2} = \dfrac{(1.5\ \text{k}\Omega)(2.2\ \text{k}\Omega)}{1.5\ \text{k}\Omega + 2.2\ \text{k}\Omega} = \mathbf{892\ \Omega}$

7. $R_T = \dfrac{22\ \text{k}\Omega}{11} = \mathbf{2\ k\Omega}$

8. $R_{T1} = \dfrac{15\ \Omega}{5} = 3\ \Omega$

    $R_{T2} = \dfrac{100\ \Omega}{10} = 10\ \Omega$

    $R_{T3} = \dfrac{10\ \Omega}{2} = 5\ \Omega$

    $R_T = \dfrac{1}{\dfrac{1}{3\ \Omega} + \dfrac{1}{10\ \Omega} + \dfrac{1}{5\ \Omega}} = \mathbf{1.58\ \Omega}$

SECTION 5-3 Voltage in a Parallel Circuit

9. $V_1 = V_2 = V_3 = V_4 = \mathbf{12\ V}$

    $I_T = \dfrac{V_T}{R_T} = \dfrac{12\ \text{V}}{600\ \Omega} = 20\ \text{mA}$

    The total current divides equally among the four equal resistors.

    $I_1 = I_2 = I_3 = I_4 = \dfrac{20\ \text{mA}}{4} = \mathbf{5\ mA}$

10. The resistors are all in parallel across the source. The voltmeters are each measuring the voltage across a resistor, so each meter indicates **100 V**.

SECTION 5-4 Application of Ohm's Law

11. (a) $R_T = 33\ \text{k}\Omega \parallel 33\ \text{k}\Omega \parallel 33\ \text{k}\Omega = 11\ \text{k}\Omega$

    $I_T = \dfrac{10\ \text{V}}{11\ \text{k}\Omega} = \mathbf{909\ \mu A}$

(b) $R_T = 1.0\ k\Omega\ \|\ 3.9\ k\Omega\ \|\ 560\ \Omega = 329\ \Omega$

$$I_T = \frac{25\ V}{329\ \Omega} = \textbf{76 mA}$$

12. $R_T = \dfrac{33\ \Omega}{3} = 11\ \Omega$

$$I_T = \frac{110\ V}{11\ \Omega} = \textbf{10 A}$$

13.   (a) $R_T = 56\ k\Omega\ \|\ 22\ k\Omega = 15.8\ k\Omega$

$$I_T = \frac{10\ V}{15.8\ k\Omega} = 633\ \mu A$$

      (b) $R_T = 18\ k\Omega\ \|\ 100\ k\Omega = 15.3\ k\Omega$

$$I_T = \frac{8\ V}{15.3\ k\Omega} = 523\ \mu A$$

Circuit (a) has more current than circuit (b).

14. $R_T = \dfrac{V_S}{I_T} = \dfrac{5\ V}{2.5\ mA} = 2\ k\Omega$

      $R_{each} = 4(2\ k\Omega) = \textbf{8 k}\boldsymbol{\Omega}$

SECTION 5-5   Kirchhoff's Current Law

15. $I_T = 250\ mA + 300\ mA + 800\ mA = \textbf{1350 mA}$

16. $I_T = I_1 + I_2 + I_3 + I_4 + I_5$
      $I_5 = I_T - (I_1 + I_2 + I_3 + I_4)$
      $I_5 = 500\ mA - (50\ mA + 150\ mA + 25\ mA + 100\ mA) = 500\ mA - 325\ mA = \textbf{175 mA}$

17. $I_{2-3} = I_T - (I_1 + I_4) = 50\ mA - 35\ mA = 15\ mA$
      $I_2 = I_3 = \textbf{7.5 mA}$
      See Figure 5-3.

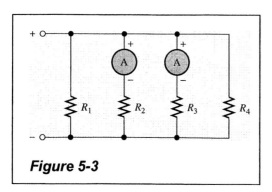

Figure 5-3

SECTION 5-6 Current Dividers

18. The 10 kΩ resistor has the highest current.

19. $I_1 = \left(\dfrac{R_2}{R_1 + R_2}\right)I_T = \left(\dfrac{2.7 \text{ k}\Omega}{3.7 \text{ k}\Omega}\right)3 \text{ A} = \textbf{2.19 A}$

    $I_2 = \left(\dfrac{R_1}{R_1 + R_2}\right)I_T = \left(\dfrac{1.0 \text{ k}\Omega}{3.7 \text{ k}\Omega}\right)3 \text{ A} = \textbf{811 mA}$

20. (a) $I_1 = \left(\dfrac{R_2}{R_1 + R_2}\right)I_T = \left(\dfrac{2.2 \text{ M}\Omega}{3.2 \text{ M}\Omega}\right)10 \text{ }\mu\text{A} = \textbf{6.88 }\boldsymbol{\mu}\textbf{A}$

    $I_2 = \left(\dfrac{R_1}{R_1 + R_2}\right)I_T = \left(\dfrac{1.0 \text{ M}\Omega}{3.2 \text{ M}\Omega}\right)10 \text{ }\mu\text{A} = \textbf{3.13 }\boldsymbol{\mu}\textbf{A}$

    (b) $R_T = \dfrac{1}{\dfrac{1}{1.0 \text{ k}\Omega} + \dfrac{1}{2.2 \text{ k}\Omega} + \dfrac{1}{3.3 \text{ k}\Omega} + \dfrac{1}{5.6 \text{ k}\Omega}} = 516 \text{ }\Omega$

    $I_1 = \left(\dfrac{R_T}{R_1}\right)I_T = \left(\dfrac{516 \text{ }\Omega}{1.0 \text{ k}\Omega}\right)10 \text{ mA} = \textbf{5.16 mA}$

    $I_2 = \left(\dfrac{R_T}{R_2}\right)I_T = \left(\dfrac{516 \text{ }\Omega}{2.2 \text{ k}\Omega}\right)10 \text{ mA} = \textbf{2.35 mA}$

    $I_3 = \left(\dfrac{R_T}{R_3}\right)I_T = \left(\dfrac{516 \text{ }\Omega}{3.3 \text{ k}\Omega}\right)10 \text{ mA} = \textbf{1.56 mA}$

    $I_4 = \left(\dfrac{R_T}{R_4}\right)I_T = \left(\dfrac{516 \text{ }\Omega}{5.6 \text{ k}\Omega}\right)10 \text{ mA} = \textbf{921 }\boldsymbol{\mu}\textbf{A}$

SECTION 5-7 Power in Parallel Circuits

21. $P_T = 5(40 \text{ mW}) = \textbf{200 mW}$

22. (a) $R_T = 1.0 \text{ M}\Omega \parallel 2.2 \text{ M}\Omega = 688 \text{ k}\Omega$

    $P_T = I_T^2 R_T = (10 \text{ }\mu\text{A})^2(688 \text{ k}\Omega) = \textbf{68.8 }\boldsymbol{\mu}\textbf{W}$

    (b) $R_T = 1.0 \text{ k}\Omega \parallel 2.2 \text{ k}\Omega \parallel 3.3 \text{ k}\Omega \parallel 5.6 \text{ k}\Omega = 516 \text{ }\Omega$

    $P_T = I_T^2 R_T = (10 \text{ mA})^2(516 \text{ }\Omega) = \textbf{51.6 mW}$

23. $P = VI$

    $I_{each} = \dfrac{P}{V} = \dfrac{75 \text{ V}}{110 \text{ V}} = \textbf{682 mA}$

    $I_T = 6(682 \text{ mA}) = \textbf{4.09 A}$

24. $I_{each} = \dfrac{P}{V} = \dfrac{75\ W}{110\ V} = \textbf{682 mA}$

    The current in each bulb is independent of the number of parallel bulbs.
    $I_T = 4.09\ A - 682\ mA = \textbf{3.41 A}$

25. First determine what the total current should be:

    $R_T = 220\ \Omega \parallel 100\ \Omega \parallel 1.0\ k\Omega \parallel 560\ \Omega \parallel 270\ \Omega = 47.54\ \Omega$

    $I_T = \dfrac{10\ V}{47.54\ \Omega} = 210.4\ mA$

    The measured current is 200.4 mA which is 10 mA less than it should be.
    Therefore, **one of the resistors must be open.**

    $R_{open} = \dfrac{V}{I} = \dfrac{10\ V}{10\ mA} = 1.0\ k\Omega$

    The 1.0 kΩ resistor is open.

26. $R_T = \dfrac{1}{\dfrac{1}{4.7\ k\Omega} + \dfrac{1}{10\ k\Omega} + \dfrac{1}{8.2\ k\Omega}} = 2.3\ k\Omega$

    $I_T = \dfrac{25\ V}{R_T} = \dfrac{25\ V}{2.3\ k\Omega} = 10.87\ mA$

    The meter indicates 7.82 mA. Therefore, a resistor must be open.

    $I_3 = \dfrac{25\ V}{8.2\ k\Omega} = 3.05\ mA$

    $I = I_T - I_M = 10.87\ mA - 7.82\ mA = 3.05\ mA$

    This shows that I_3 is missing from the total current as read on the meter.
    Therefore, R_3 **is open.**

27. $G_T = \dfrac{1}{560\ \Omega} + \dfrac{1}{270\ \Omega} + \dfrac{1}{330\ \Omega} = 8.52\ mS$

    $G_{meas} = \dfrac{1}{207.6\ \Omega} = 4.82\ mS$

    $G_{open} = G_T - G_{meas} = 8.52\ mS - 4.82\ mS = 3.70\ mS$

    So, $R_{open} = \dfrac{1}{G_{open}} = \dfrac{1}{3.70\ mS} = 270\ \Omega$

    R_2 **is open.**

28. $G_T = \dfrac{1}{100\ \Omega} + \dfrac{1}{100\ \Omega} + \dfrac{1}{220\ \Omega} + \dfrac{1}{220\ \Omega} = 29.1\ \text{mS}$

$G_{\text{meas}} = \dfrac{1}{40.7\ \Omega} = 24.6\ \text{mS}$

There is a resistor open.

$G_{\text{open}} = G_T - G_{\text{meas}} = 29.1\ \text{mS} - 24.6\ \text{mS} = 4.5\ \text{mS}$

So, $R_{\text{open}} = \dfrac{1}{4.5\ \text{mS}} = 221\ \Omega$

One of the 220 Ω resistors is open, but identification requires more information.

ADVANCED PROBLEMS

29. $V_S = I_1 R_1 = (1\ \text{mA})(50\ \Omega) = 50\ \text{mV}$

$R_2 = \dfrac{V_S}{I_2} = \dfrac{50\ \text{mV}}{2\ \text{mA}} = \mathbf{25\ \Omega}$

$R_3 = \dfrac{V_S}{I_3} = \dfrac{50\ \text{mV}}{0.5\ \text{mA}} = \mathbf{100\ \Omega}$

$I_4 = I_T - (I_1 + I_2 + I_3) = 7.5\ \text{mA} - 3.5\ \text{mA} = 4\ \text{mA}$

$R_4 = \dfrac{V_S}{I_4} = \dfrac{50\ \text{mV}}{4\ \text{mA}} = \mathbf{12.5\ \Omega}$

30. $V_T = I_T R_T = (100\ \text{mA})(25\ \Omega) = 2500\ \text{mV} = 2.5\ \text{V}$

$I_{220} = \dfrac{V_T}{R} = \dfrac{2.5\ \text{V}}{220\ \Omega} = \mathbf{11.4\ \text{mA}}$

31. $R_T = \dfrac{1}{\dfrac{1}{R} + \dfrac{1}{2R} + \dfrac{1}{3R} + \dfrac{1}{4R}} = \dfrac{R}{1 + \dfrac{1}{2} + \dfrac{1}{3} + \dfrac{1}{4}} = 0.48R$

$I_R = \left(\dfrac{R_T}{R}\right)10\ \text{A} = \left(\dfrac{0.48R}{R}\right)10\ \text{A} = \mathbf{4.8\ \text{A}}$

$I_{2R} = \left(\dfrac{R_T}{2R}\right)10\ \text{A} = \left(\dfrac{0.48R}{2R}\right)10\ \text{A} = \mathbf{2.4\ \text{A}}$

$I_{3R} = \left(\dfrac{R_T}{3R}\right)10\ \text{A} = \left(\dfrac{0.48R}{3R}\right)10\ \text{A} = \mathbf{1.6\ \text{A}}$

$I_{4R} = \left(\dfrac{R_T}{4R}\right)10\ \text{A} = \left(\dfrac{0.48R}{4R}\right)10\ \text{A} = \mathbf{1.2\ \text{A}}$

32. (a) $P_T = I_T^2 R_T = (50\ \text{mA})^2 (1.0\ \text{k}\Omega) = 2.5\ \text{W}$

Number of resistors $= n = \dfrac{P_T}{P_{\text{each}}} = \dfrac{2.5\ \text{W}}{0.25\ \text{W}} = \mathbf{10}$

All resistors are equal because each has the same power.

(b) $\quad R_T = \dfrac{R}{n}$

$R = nR_T = 10(1.0 \text{ k}\Omega) = \textbf{10 k}\boldsymbol{\Omega}$

(c) $\quad I = \dfrac{I_T}{n} = \dfrac{50 \text{ mA}}{10} = \textbf{5 mA}$

(d) $\quad V_S = I_T R_T = (50 \text{ mA})(1.0 \text{ k}\Omega) = \textbf{50 V}$

33. (a) $\quad I_2 = I_T - I_1 = 150 \text{ mA} - 100 \text{ mA} = \textbf{50 mA}$

$R_1 = \dfrac{10 \text{ V}}{100 \text{ mA}} = \textbf{100 }\boldsymbol{\Omega}$

$R_2 = \dfrac{10 \text{ V}}{50 \text{ mA}} = \textbf{200 }\boldsymbol{\Omega}$

(b) $\quad P_1 = P_T - P_2 = 2 \text{ W} - 0.75 \text{ W} = 1.25 \text{ W}$

$V_S I_1 = 1.25 \text{ W}$

$V_S = \dfrac{1.25 \text{ W}}{I_1}$

$V_S I_2 = 0.75 \text{ W}$

$V_S = \dfrac{0.75 \text{ W}}{I_2}$

Thus,

$\dfrac{1.25 \text{ W}}{I_1} = \dfrac{0.75 \text{ W}}{I_2}$

$1.25 I_2 = 0.75 I_1$

$I_1 = \left(\dfrac{1.25}{0.75}\right) I_2 = 1.67 I_2$

$I_1 + I_2 = 200 \text{ mA}$

$2.67 I_2 = 200 \text{ mA}$

$I_2 = \dfrac{200 \text{ mA}}{2.67} = \textbf{74.9 mA}$

$I_1 = 1.67(74.9 \text{ mA}) = \textbf{125 mA}$

$V_S = \dfrac{0.75 \text{ W}}{74.9 \text{ mA}} = \textbf{10 V}$

$R_1 = \dfrac{V_S}{I_1} = \dfrac{10 \text{ V}}{125 \text{ mA}} = \textbf{80 }\boldsymbol{\Omega}$

$R_2 = \dfrac{V_S}{I_2} = \dfrac{10 \text{ V}}{74.9 \text{ mA}} = \textbf{134 }\boldsymbol{\Omega}$

(c) $\quad I_3 = \dfrac{100 \text{ V}}{1.0 \text{ k}\Omega} = \textbf{100 mA}$

$I_2 = \dfrac{100 \text{ V}}{680 \text{ }\Omega} = \textbf{147 mA}$

$I_1 = I_T - I_1 - I_2 = 0.5 \text{ A} - 147 \text{ mA} - 100 \text{ mA} = \textbf{253 mA}$

$R_1 = \dfrac{100 \text{ V}}{253 \text{ mA}} = \textbf{395 }\boldsymbol{\Omega}$

34. (a) $R_T = R_1 = \mathbf{510\ k\Omega}$

(b) $R_T = R_1 \| R_2 = \dfrac{1}{\dfrac{1}{510\ k\Omega} + \dfrac{1}{470\ k\Omega}} = \mathbf{245\ k\Omega}$

(c) $R_T = R_1 = \mathbf{510\ k\Omega}$

(d) $R_T = R_1 \| R_2 \| R_3 = \dfrac{1}{\dfrac{1}{510\ k\Omega} + \dfrac{1}{470\ k\Omega} + \dfrac{1}{910\ k\Omega}} = \mathbf{193\ k\Omega}$

35. $I_{max} = 0.5\ A$

$R_{T(min)} = \dfrac{15\ V}{I_{max}} = \dfrac{15\ V}{0.5\ A} = 30\ \Omega$

$\dfrac{(68\ \Omega)R_2}{68\ \Omega + R_2} = R_{T(min)}$

$(68\ \Omega)R_2 = (30\ \Omega)(68\ \Omega + R_2)$

$68R_2 = 2040 + 30R_2$

$68R_2 - 30R_2 = 2040$

$38R_2 = 2040$

$R_2 = \mathbf{53.7\ \Omega}$

36. *Position A:*

$R_T = R_1 \| R_2 \| R_3 = 560\ k\Omega \| 220\ k\Omega \| 270\ k\Omega = 99.7\ k\Omega$

$I_T = \dfrac{24\ V}{R_T} = \dfrac{24\ V}{99.7\ k\Omega} = \mathbf{241\ \mu A}$

$I_1 = \dfrac{24\ V}{560\ k\Omega} = \mathbf{42.9\ \mu A}$

$I_2 = \dfrac{24\ V}{220\ k\Omega} = \mathbf{109\ \mu A}$

$I_3 = \dfrac{24\ V}{270\ k\Omega} = \mathbf{89.0\ \mu A}$

Position B:

$R_T = R_1 \| R_2 \| R_3 \| R_4 \| R_5 \| R_6$
$\quad = 560\ k\Omega \| 220\ k\Omega \| 270\ k\Omega \| 1.0\ M\Omega \| 820\ k\Omega \| 2.2\ M\Omega = 78.7\ k\Omega$

$I_T = \dfrac{24\ V}{R_T} = \dfrac{24\ V}{78.7\ k\Omega} = \mathbf{305\ \mu A}$

$I_1 = \mathbf{42.9\ \mu A}$

$I_2 = \mathbf{109\ \mu A}$

$I_3 = \mathbf{89.0\ \mu A}$

$I_4 = \dfrac{24\ V}{1.0\ M\Omega} = \mathbf{24.0\ \mu A}$

$I_5 = \dfrac{24\ V}{820\ k\Omega} = \mathbf{29.3\ \mu A}$

$$I_6 = \frac{24 \text{ V}}{2.2 \text{ M}\Omega} = \mathbf{10.9 \ \mu A}$$

Position C:

$R_T = R_4 \parallel R_5 \parallel R_6 = 1.0 \text{ M}\Omega \parallel 820 \text{ k}\Omega \parallel 2.2 \text{ M}\Omega = 374 \text{ k}\Omega$

$$I_T = \frac{24 \text{ V}}{R_T} = \frac{24 \text{ V}}{374 \text{ k}\Omega} = \mathbf{64.2 \ \mu A}$$

$I_4 = \mathbf{24.0 \ \mu A}$

$I_5 = \mathbf{29.3 \ \mu A}$

$I_6 = \mathbf{10.9 \ \mu A}$

37. $I_T = 1.25 \text{ A} + 0.833 \text{ A} + 0.833 \text{ A} + 1 \text{ A} = \mathbf{3.92 \ A}$

$I_4 = 5 \text{ A} - 3.92 \text{ A} = \mathbf{1.08 \ A}$

See Figure 5-4.

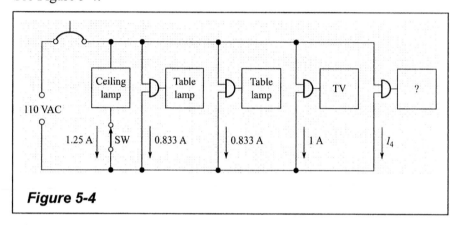

Figure 5-4

38. $V_T = I_4 R_4 = (100 \text{ mA})(25 \ \Omega) = 2500 \text{ mV} = 2.5 \text{ V}$

$$I_{220 \ \Omega} = \frac{V_T}{R} = \frac{2.5 \text{ V}}{220 \ \Omega} = \mathbf{11.4 \ mA}$$

39. $R_1 \parallel R_2 \parallel R_5 \parallel R_9 \parallel R_{10} \parallel R_{12}$

$= 100 \text{ k}\Omega \parallel 220 \text{ k}\Omega \parallel 560 \text{ k}\Omega \parallel 390 \text{ k}\Omega \parallel 1.2 \text{ M}\Omega \parallel 100 \text{ k}\Omega = \mathbf{33.6 \ k\Omega}$

$R_4 \parallel R_6 \parallel R_7 \parallel R_8$

$= 270 \text{ k}\Omega \parallel 1.0 \text{ M}\Omega \parallel 820 \text{ k}\Omega \parallel 680 \text{ k}\Omega = \mathbf{135.2 \ k\Omega}$

$R_3 \parallel R_{11} = 330 \text{ k}\Omega \parallel 1.8 \text{ M}\Omega = \mathbf{278.9 \ k\Omega}$

40. $R_T = \dfrac{R_1 R_2}{R_1 + R_2}$ $\qquad\qquad$ $R_2 = \dfrac{R_T R_1}{(R_1 - R_T)}$

$R_T(R_1 + R_2) = R_1 R_2$ $\qquad$ $R_2 = \dfrac{(680 \ \Omega)(200 \ \Omega)}{680 \ \Omega - 200 \ \Omega} = \mathbf{283 \ \Omega}$

$R_T R_1 + R_T R_2 = R_1 R_2$

$R_T R_1 = R_1 R_2 - R_T R_2$

$R_T R_1 = R_2(R_1 - R_T)$

41. $I_1 = 1.5 \text{ mA} - 1.2 \text{ mA} = 0.3 \text{ mA}$

$V_S = V_1 = V_2 = V_3 = V_4 = I_1 R_1 = (0.3 \text{ mA})(1.0 \text{ k}\Omega) = 0.3 \text{ V}$

$I_2 = 1.2 \text{ mA} - 0.8 \text{ mA} = 0.4 \text{ mA}$

$R_2 = \dfrac{V_2}{I_2} = \dfrac{0.3 \text{ V}}{0.4 \text{ mA}} = 0.75 \text{ k}\Omega = \mathbf{750 \ \Omega}$

$I_3 = \dfrac{V_3}{R_3} = \dfrac{0.3 \text{ V}}{3.3 \text{ k}\Omega} = 910 \ \mu\text{A}$

$I_4 = 0.8 \text{ mA} - 910 \ \mu\text{A} = 709 \ \mu\text{A}$

$R_4 = \dfrac{V_4}{I_4} = \dfrac{0.3 \text{ V}}{709 \ \mu\text{A}} = \mathbf{423 \ \Omega}$

42. $V_S = I_T R_T = (250 \text{ mA})(1.5 \text{ k}\Omega) = 375 \text{ V}$

$I_{new} = 250 \text{ mA} + (0.25)(250 \text{ mA}) = 250 \text{ mA} + 62.5 \text{ mA} = 313 \text{ mA}$

$R_{T(new)} = \dfrac{V_S}{I_{new}} = \dfrac{375 \text{ V}}{313 \text{ mA}} = 1.20 \text{ k}\Omega$

$R_{T(new)} = R_T \parallel R_{new}$

$\dfrac{1}{R_{T(new)}} = \dfrac{1}{R_T} + \dfrac{1}{R_{new}}$

$\dfrac{1}{R_{new}} = \dfrac{1}{R_{T(new)}} - \dfrac{1}{R_T} = \dfrac{R_T - R_{T(new)}}{R_T R_{T(new)}}$

$R_{new} = \dfrac{R_T R_{T(new)}}{R_T - R_{T(new)}} = \dfrac{(1.20 \text{ k}\Omega)(1.50 \text{ k}\Omega)}{1.50 \text{ k}\Omega - 1.20 \text{ k}\Omega} = \mathbf{6 \text{ k}\Omega}$

43. $R_T = 4.7 \text{ k}\Omega \parallel 10 \text{ k}\Omega \parallel 10 \text{ k}\Omega = 2.42 \text{ k}\Omega$

$I_T = \dfrac{24 \text{ V}}{2.42 \text{ k}\Omega} = 10.3 \text{ mA}$

With the 4.7 kΩ resistor open,

$I = \dfrac{25 \text{ V}}{5 \text{ k}\Omega} = 5 \text{ mA}$

Therefore, the 4.7 kΩ resistor is open.

44. **Pins 1-2**

$R_T = 1.0 \text{ k}\Omega \parallel 3.3 \text{ k}\Omega = 767 \ \Omega$ (correct reading)

When one resistor is open, the reading is either 1.0 kΩ or 3.3 kΩ.

Pins 3-4

$R_T = 270 \ \Omega \parallel 390 \ \Omega = 160 \ \Omega$ (correct reading)

When one resistor is open, the reading is either 270 Ω or 390 Ω.

Pins 5-6

$R_T = 1.0 \text{ M}\Omega \parallel 1.8 \text{ M}\Omega \parallel 680 \text{ k}\Omega \parallel 510 \text{ k}\Omega = 201 \text{ k}\Omega$ (correct reading)

R_5 open: $R_T = 1.8 \text{ M}\Omega \parallel 680 \text{ k}\Omega \parallel 510 \text{ k}\Omega = 251 \text{ k}\Omega$

R_6 open: $R_T = 1.0 \text{ M}\Omega \parallel 680 \text{ k}\Omega \parallel 510 \text{ k}\Omega = 226 \text{ k}\Omega$

R_7 open: $R_T = 1.0 \text{ M}\Omega \parallel 1.8 \text{ M}\Omega \parallel 510 \text{ k}\Omega = 284 \text{ k}\Omega$

R_8 open: $R_T = 1.0 \text{ M}\Omega \parallel 1.8 \text{ M}\Omega \parallel 680 \text{ k}\Omega = 330 \text{ k}\Omega$

45. (a) **One of the resistors has burned open** because the power exceeded 0.5 W. Since each resistor has the same voltage, the smallest value will reach the maximum power dissipation first, as per the formula $P = V^2/R$.

    (b) $P = \dfrac{V^2}{R}$, $V = \sqrt{PR} = \sqrt{(0.5 \text{ W})(1.8 \text{ k}\Omega)} = \textbf{30 V}$

    (c) **Replace the 1.8 kΩ resistor** and operate the circuit at less than 30 V or use a higher wattage resistor to replace the existing 1.8 kΩ.

46. (a) $R_{1-2} = R_1 \| R_2 \| R_3 \| R_4 \| R_{11} \| R_{12}$
    $= 10 \text{ k}\Omega \| 2.2 \text{ k}\Omega \| 2.2 \text{ k}\Omega \| 3.3 \text{ k}\Omega \| 18 \text{ k}\Omega \| 1.0 \text{ k}\Omega = \textbf{422 }\Omega$

    (b) $R_{2-3} = R_5 \| R_6 \| R_7 \| R_8 \| R_9 \| R_{10}$
    $= 4.7 \text{ k}\Omega \| 4.7 \text{ k}\Omega \| 6.8 \text{ k}\Omega \| 5.6 \text{ k}\Omega \| 5.6 \text{ k}\Omega \| 1.0 \text{ k}\Omega = \textbf{518 }\Omega$

    (c) $R_{3-4} = R_5 \| R_6 \| R_7 \| R_8 \| R_9 \| R_{10} = \textbf{518 }\Omega$

    (d) $R_{1-4} = R_1 \| R_2 \| R_3 \| R_4 \| R_{11} \| R_{12} = \textbf{422 }\Omega$

47. (a) $R_{1-2} = (R_1 \| R_2 \| R_3 \| R_4 \| R_{11} \| R_{12}) + (R_5 \| R_6 \| R_7 \| R_8 \| R_9 \| R_{10})$
    $= 422 \ \Omega + 518 \ \Omega = \textbf{940 }\Omega$

    (b) $R_{2-3} = R_5 \| R_6 \| R_7 \| R_8 \| R_9 \| R_{10} = \textbf{518 }\Omega$

    (c) $R_{2-4} = R_5 \| R_6 \| R_7 \| R_8 \| R_9 \| R_{10} = \textbf{518 }\Omega$

    (d) $R_{1-4} = R_1 \| R_2 \| R_3 \| R_4 \| R_{11} \| R_{12} = \textbf{422 }\Omega$

Multisim Troubleshooting Problems

48. R_1 is open.

49. R_3 is open.

50. No fault

51. (a) The measured resistance between pin 1 and pin 4 agrees with the calculated value.

    (b) The measured resistance between pin 2 and pin 3 agrees with the calculated value.

CHAPTER 6
SERIES-PARALLEL CIRCUITS

BASIC PROBLEMS

SECTION 6-1 Identifying Series-Parallel Relationships

1. R_2, R_3, and R_4 are in parallel and this parallel combination is in series with both R_1 and R_5.
     $R_T = (R_2 \parallel R_3 \parallel R_4) + R_1 + R_5$

2.   (a) R_1 in series with the parallel combination of R_2 and R_3. See Figure 6-1(a).
     (b) R_1 in parallel with the series combination of R_2 and R_3. See Figure 6-1(b).
     (c) R_1 in parallel with a branch containing R_2 in series with a parallel combination of four other resistors. See Figure 6-1(c).

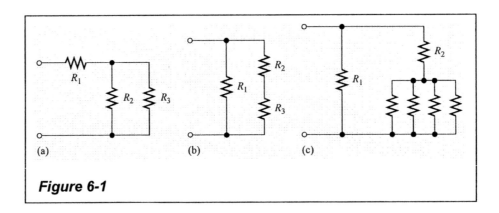

Figure 6-1

3.   See Figure 6-2.

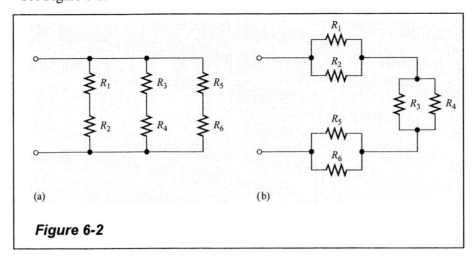

Figure 6-2

46

4.   (a) R_1 and R_4 are in series with the parallel combination of R_2 and R_3.

$$R_T = (R_2 \,||\, R_3) + R_1 + R_4$$

     (b) R_1 is in series with the parallel combination of R_2, R_3, and R_4.

$$R_T = R_1 + (R_2 \,||\, R_3 \,||\, R_4)$$

SECTION 6-2 Analysis of Series-Parallel Resistive Circuits

5. $R_T = \dfrac{R_1 R_2}{R_1 + R_2}$

$$R_2 = \dfrac{R_1 R_T}{R_1 - R_T} = \dfrac{(1.0\ \text{k}\Omega)(667\ \Omega)}{1.0\ \text{k}\Omega - 667\ \Omega} = \textbf{2003}\ \boldsymbol{\Omega}$$

6.   Brown, black, black, gold = $10\ \Omega \pm 5\%$

Orange, orange, black, gold = $33\ \Omega \pm 5\%$

Two $10\ \Omega$ resistors are in series with three $33\ \Omega$ resistors that are in parallel.

$$R_{AB} = 10\ \Omega + 10\ \Omega + \dfrac{33\ \Omega}{3} = 20\ \Omega + 11\ \Omega = \textbf{31}\ \boldsymbol{\Omega}$$

7.   (a) $R_T = 56\ \Omega + 22\ \Omega + 100\ \Omega \,||\, 100\ \Omega = 56\ \Omega + 22\ \Omega + 50\ \Omega = \textbf{128}\ \boldsymbol{\Omega}$

     (b) $R_T = 680\ \Omega \,||\, 330\ \Omega \,||\, 220\ \Omega + 680\ \Omega = 111\ \Omega + 680\ \Omega = \textbf{791}\ \boldsymbol{\Omega}$

8. $R_T = R_1 + R_5 + R_2 \,||\, R_3 \,||\, R_4 = 10\ \Omega + 10\ \Omega + 11\ \Omega = 31\ \Omega$

$$I_T = I_1 = I_5 = \dfrac{3\ \text{V}}{31\ \Omega} = \textbf{96.8 mA}$$

$$I_2 = I_3 = I_4 = \dfrac{96.8\ \text{mA}}{3} = \textbf{32.3 mA}$$

$$V_1 = V_5 = (96.8\ \text{mA})(10\ \Omega) = \textbf{968 mV}$$

$$V_2 = V_3 = V_4 = (32.3\ \text{mA})(33\ \Omega) = \textbf{1.07 V}$$

9.   (a) $R_T = 128\ \Omega$

$$I_T = \dfrac{1.5\ \text{V}}{128\ \Omega} = 11.7\ \text{mA}$$

$$I_1 = I_4 = I_T = \textbf{11.7 mA}$$

$$I_2 = I_3 = \dfrac{11.7\ \text{mA}}{2} = \textbf{5.85 mA}$$

$$V_1 = I_1 R_1 = (11.7\ \text{mA})(56\ \Omega) = \textbf{655 mV}$$

$$V_2 = V_3 = I_T(R_T \,||\, R_3) = (11.7\ \text{mA})(50\ \Omega) = \textbf{585 mV}$$

$$V_4 = I_4 R_4 = (11.7\ \text{mA})(22\ \Omega) = \textbf{257 mV}$$

     (b) $R_{T(p)} = R_2 \,||\, R_3 \,||\, R_4 = 680\ \Omega \,||\, 330\ \Omega \,||\, 220\ \Omega = 111\ \Omega$

$$R_T = R_{T(p)} + R_1 = 791\ \Omega$$

$$I_T = \dfrac{3\ \text{V}}{791\ \Omega} = 3.8\ \text{mA}$$

$$I_1 = I_T = \textbf{3.8 mA}$$

$$I_2 = \left(\frac{R_{T(p)}}{R_2} \right) I_T = \left(\frac{110.5\ \Omega}{680\ \Omega} \right) 3.8\ \text{mA} = \textbf{618}\ \boldsymbol{\mu}\textbf{A}$$

$$I_3 = \left(\frac{R_{T(p)}}{R_3} \right) I_T = \left(\frac{110.5\ \Omega}{330\ \Omega} \right) 3.8\ \text{mA} = \textbf{1.27 mA}$$

$$I_4 = \left(\frac{R_{T(p)}}{R_4} \right) I_T = \left(\frac{110.5\ \Omega}{220\ \Omega} \right) 3.8\ \text{mA} = \textbf{1.91 mA}$$

$V_1 = I_1 R_1 = (3.8\ \text{mA})(680\ \Omega) = \textbf{2.58 V}$
$V_2 = V_3 = V_4 = (3.8\ \text{mA})(111\ \Omega) = \textbf{420 mV}$

10.   (a) $R_4 \parallel R_5 = \dfrac{4.7\ \text{k}\Omega}{2} = 2.35\ \text{k}\Omega$

           $R_4 \parallel R_5 + R_3 = 2.35\ \text{k}\Omega + 3.3\ \text{k}\Omega + 5.65\ \text{k}\Omega$
           $5.65\ \text{k}\Omega \parallel R_2 = 5.65\ \text{k}\Omega \parallel 2.7\ \text{k}\Omega = 1.83\ \text{k}\Omega$
           $R_{AB} = 1.83\ \text{k}\Omega \parallel 10\ \text{k}\Omega = \textbf{1.55 k}\boldsymbol{\Omega}$

   (b) $I_T = \dfrac{V_S}{R_T} = \dfrac{6\ \text{V}}{1.55\ \text{k}\Omega} = \textbf{3.87 mA}$

   (c)   The resistance to the right of AB is 1.83 kΩ. The current through this part of the circuit is $I = 6\ \text{V}/1.83\ \text{k}\Omega = 3.28\ \text{mA}$.

$$I_3 = \left(\frac{R_2}{R_2 + 5.65\ \text{k}\Omega} \right) 3.28\ \text{mA} = \left(\frac{2.7\ \text{k}\Omega}{8.35\ \text{k}\Omega} \right) 3.28\ \text{mA} = 1.06\ \text{mA}$$

$$I_5 = \frac{I_3}{2} = \frac{1.06\ \text{mA}}{2} = \textbf{530}\ \boldsymbol{\mu}\textbf{A}$$

   (d) $V_2 = V_S = \textbf{6 V}$

11.   From Problem 10, $V_2 = 6$ V.

      $I_2 = \dfrac{V_2}{R_2} = \dfrac{6\ \text{V}}{2.7\ \text{k}\Omega} = \textbf{2.22 mA}$

12.   From Problem 10,

      $I_3 = 1.06$ mA
      $I_5 = 530\ \mu$A
      $I_4 = I_3 - I_5 = 1.06\ \text{mA} - 530\ \mu\text{A} = \textbf{530}\ \boldsymbol{\mu}\textbf{A}$

13. $V_{OUT} = \left(\dfrac{56 \text{ k}\Omega}{112 \text{ k}\Omega} \right) 15 \text{ V} = \textbf{7.5 V}$ **unloaded**

$R_L = 1.0 \text{ M}\Omega \parallel 56 \text{ k}\Omega = 53 \text{ k}\Omega$

$V_{OUT} = \left(\dfrac{56 \text{ k}\Omega}{109 \text{ k}\Omega} \right) 15 \text{ V} = \textbf{7.29 V}$ **loaded**

14. *With no load:*

$V_A = \left(\dfrac{6.6 \text{ k}\Omega}{9.9 \text{ k}\Omega} \right) 12 \text{ V} = 8 \text{ V}$

$V_B = \left(\dfrac{3.3 \text{ k}\Omega}{9.9 \text{ k}\Omega} \right) 12 \text{ V} = 4 \text{ V}$

With a 10 kΩ resistor connected from output A to ground:

$R_{AG} = \dfrac{(6.6 \text{ k}\Omega)(10 \text{ k}\Omega)}{6.6 \text{ k}\Omega + 10 \text{ k}\Omega} = 3.98 \text{ k}\Omega$

$V_{A(\text{loaded})} = \left(\dfrac{3.98 \text{ k}\Omega}{7.28 \text{ k}\Omega} \right) 12 \text{ V} = \textbf{6.56 V}$

With a 10 kΩ resistor connected from output B to ground:

$R_{BG} = \dfrac{(3.3 \text{ k}\Omega)(10 \text{ k}\Omega)}{13.3 \text{ k}\Omega} = 2.48 \text{ k}\Omega$

$V_{B(\text{loaded})} = \left(\dfrac{2.48 \text{ k}\Omega}{9.08 \text{ k}\Omega} \right) 12 \text{ V} = \textbf{3.28 V}$

Refer to Figure 6-3.

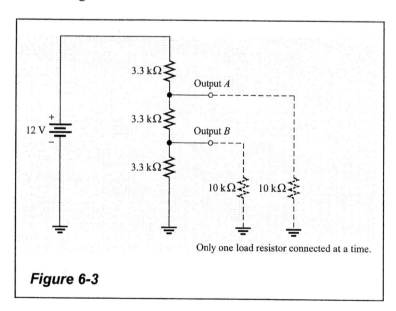

Figure 6-3

15. The **56 kΩ load** will cause a smaller decrease in output voltage for a given voltage divider because it has less effect on the circuit resistance than the 10 kΩ load does.

16. *With no load:*

$R_T = 10 \text{ k}\Omega + 5.6 \text{ k}\Omega + 2.7 \text{ k}\Omega = 18.3 \text{ k}\Omega$

$I = \dfrac{22 \text{ V}}{18.3 \text{ k}\Omega} = \textbf{1.2 mA}$

With a 10 kΩ load:

$R_T = 10 \text{ k}\Omega + \dfrac{(8.3 \text{ k}\Omega)(10 \text{ k}\Omega)}{8.3 \text{ k}\Omega + 10 \text{ k}\Omega} = 14.54 \text{ k}\Omega$

$I = \dfrac{22 \text{ V}}{14.54 \text{ k}\Omega} = \textbf{1.51 mA}$

SECTION 6-4 Loading Effect of a Voltmeter

17. The voltmeter presents the least loading across the 22 kΩ load.

18. $10 \text{ M}\Omega \parallel 1.0 \text{ M}\Omega = 909 \text{ k}\Omega$

$V_M = \left(\dfrac{909 \text{ k}\Omega}{1.0 \text{ M}\Omega + 909 \text{ k}\Omega + 1.0 \text{ M}\Omega} \right) 100 \text{ V} = \left(\dfrac{909 \text{ k}\Omega}{2.909 \text{ M}\Omega} \right) 10 \text{ V} = \textbf{31.3 V}$

19. $V_{ACT} = \left(\dfrac{1 \text{ M}\Omega}{3 \text{ M}\Omega} \right) 100 \text{ V} = 33.3 \text{ V}$

$V_M = 31.3 \text{ V}$

$\Delta V = V_{ACT} - V_M = 33.3 \text{ V} - 31.3 \text{ V} = \textbf{2 V}$

20. $\% V = \left(\dfrac{V_{ACT} - V_M}{V_M} \right) 100\% = \left(\dfrac{33.3 \text{ V} - 31.3 \text{ V}}{33.3 \text{ V}} \right) 100\% = \textbf{6\%}$

SECTION 6-5 The Wheatstone Bridge

21. $R_{UNK} = R_V \left(\dfrac{R_2}{R_4} \right) = (18 \text{ k}\Omega)(0.02) = \textbf{360 } \boldsymbol{\Omega}$

22. $R_{UNK} = R_V \left(\dfrac{R_1}{R_2} \right);$ $R_V = R_{UNK} \left(\dfrac{R_2}{R_1} \right) = 390 \ \Omega \left(\dfrac{560 \ \Omega}{1.0 \text{ k}\Omega} \right) = \textbf{218.4 } \boldsymbol{\Omega}$

23. $R_X = R_V \left(\dfrac{R_2}{R_4} \right) = 5 \text{ k}\Omega \left(\dfrac{2.2 \text{ k}\Omega}{1.5 \text{ k}\Omega} \right) = \textbf{7.33 k}\boldsymbol{\Omega}$

24. Change in thermistor resistance from 25°C to 65°C.

$$\Delta R_{therm} = 5\ \Omega(65°C - 25°C) = 5\ \Omega(40°C) = 200\ \Omega$$

At 65°C:

$$R_1 = R_{therm} = 1\ k\Omega + 200\ \Omega = 1.2\ k\Omega$$

$$V_A = \left(\frac{R_3}{R_1 + R_3}\right)V_S = \left(\frac{1.0\ k\Omega}{2.2\ k\Omega}\right)9\ V = 4.09\ V$$

$$V_B = \left(\frac{R_4}{R_3 + R_4}\right)V_S = \left(\frac{1.0\ k\Omega}{2.0\ k\Omega}\right)9\ V = 4.5\ V$$

$$V_{OUT} = V_B - V_A = 4.5\ V - 4.09\ V = \mathbf{0.41\ V}$$

SECTION 6-6 Thevenin's Theorem

25. $R_{TH} = 100\ k\Omega\ \|\ 22\ k\Omega = \mathbf{18\ k\Omega}$ $V_{TH} = \left(\frac{22\ k\Omega}{122\ k\Omega}\right)15\ V = \mathbf{2.7\ V}$

26. (a) $R_{TH} = 22\ \Omega + 78\ \Omega\ \|\ 147\ \Omega = 22\ \Omega + 51\ \Omega = \mathbf{73\ \Omega}$

$$V_{TH} = \left(\frac{78\ \Omega}{78\ \Omega + 100\ \Omega + 47\ \Omega}\right)2.5\ V = \mathbf{867\ mV}$$

  (b) $R_{TH} = 100\ \Omega\ \|\ 270\ \Omega = \mathbf{73\ \Omega}$

$$V_{TH} = \left(\frac{100\ \Omega}{370\ \Omega}\right)3\ V = \mathbf{811\ mV}$$

  (c) $R_{TH} = 100\ k\Omega\ \|\ 56\ k\Omega = \mathbf{35.9\ k\Omega}$

$$V_{TH} = \left(\frac{56\ k\Omega}{156\ k\Omega}\right)0.5\ V = \mathbf{179\ mV}$$

27. $R_{TH} = R_1\ \|\ R_3 + R_2\ \|\ R_4 = 1.0\ k\Omega\ \|\ 2.2\ k\Omega + 2.2\ k\Omega\ \|\ 1.5\ k\Omega = \mathbf{1.58\ k\Omega}$

$$V_{TH} = V_A - V_B = \left(\frac{R_3}{R_1 + R_3}\right)V_S - \left(\frac{R_4}{R_2 + R_4}\right)V_S = \left(\frac{2.2\ k\Omega}{3.2\ k\Omega}\right)5\ V - \left(\frac{1.5\ k\Omega}{3.7\ k\Omega}\right)5\ V$$

$$= 3.44\ V - 2.03\ V = 1.41\ V$$

$$V_{R_L} = \left(\frac{R_L}{R_{TH} + R_L}\right)V_{TH} = \left(\frac{4.7\ k\Omega}{6.28\ k\Omega}\right)1.41\ V = \mathbf{1.06\ V}$$

$$I_{R_L} = \frac{V_{R_L}}{R_L} = \frac{1.06\ V}{4.7\ k\Omega} = \mathbf{226\ \mu A}$$

28. $R_{TH} = R_1 \parallel R_2 = 100 \text{ k}\Omega \parallel 22 \text{ k}\Omega = 18 \text{ k}\Omega$
    $R_L = R_{TH} = \mathbf{18 \text{ k}\Omega}$

29. $R_L = R_{TH} = \mathbf{75 \ \Omega}$

30. $R_{TH} = 73 \ \Omega$
    Therefore, $R_L = R_{TH} = \mathbf{73 \ \Omega}$ for maximum power transfer.

SECTION 6-8 The Superposition Theorem

31. *For the 1 V source:*
    $R_T = R_1 + R_2 \parallel R_3 = 100 \ \Omega + 56 \ \Omega \parallel 27 \ \Omega = 118.2 \ \Omega$

    $I_T = \dfrac{1 \text{ V}}{118.2 \ \Omega} = 8.46 \text{ mA}$

    $I_3 = \left(\dfrac{R_2}{R_2 + R_3} \right) I_T = \left(\dfrac{56 \ \Omega}{83 \ \Omega} \right) 8.46 \text{ mA} = 5.71 \text{ mA} \ (\text{up})$

    For the 1.5 V source:
    $R_T = R_2 + R_1 \parallel R_3 = 56 \ \Omega + 100 \ \Omega \parallel 27 \ \Omega = 77.3 \ \Omega$

    $I_T = \dfrac{1.5 \text{ V}}{77.3 \ \Omega} = 19.4 \text{ mA}$

    $I_3 = \left(\dfrac{R_1}{R_1 + R_3} \right) I_T = \left(\dfrac{100 \ \Omega}{127 \ \Omega} \right) 19.4 \text{ mA} = 15.3 \text{ mA} \ (\text{up})$

    $I_{3(\text{total})} = 5.71 \text{ mA} + 15.3 \text{ mA} = \mathbf{21.0 \text{ mA}} \ (\mathbf{up})$

32. *For the 1 V source:*
    $I_2 = \left(\dfrac{R_3}{R_2 + R_3} \right) I_T = \left(\dfrac{27 \ \Omega}{83 \ \Omega} \right) 8.46 \text{ mA} = 2.75 \text{ mA} \ (\text{up})$

    For the 1.5 V source:
    $I_2 = I_T = 19.4 \text{ mA} \ (\text{down})$
    $I_{2(\text{total})} = 19.4 \text{ mA} - 2.75 \text{ mA} = \mathbf{16.7 \text{ mA} \ (down)}$

33. $R_{eq} = \dfrac{(680\ \Omega)(4.7\ k\Omega)}{680\ \Omega + 4.7\ k\Omega} = 594\ \Omega$

$R_T = 560\ \Omega + 470\ \Omega + 594\ \Omega = 1624\ \Omega$
The voltmeter indicates 9.84 V.

The voltmeter should read: $V = \left(\dfrac{594\ \Omega}{1624\ \Omega}\right) 12\ V = \textbf{4.39 V}$

The meter reading is incorrect, indicating that the 680 Ω resistor is open.

34. If R_2 opens: $V_A = \textbf{15 V}$, $V_B = \textbf{0 V}$, and $V_C = \textbf{0 V}$

35. $V_{3.3k\Omega} = \left(\dfrac{R_4 \parallel (R_3 + R_2)}{R_4 \parallel (R_3 + R_2) + R_1}\right) 10\ V = \left(\dfrac{1.62\ k\Omega}{2.62\ k\Omega}\right) 10\ V = 6.18\ V$

The 7.62 V reading is incorrect.

$V_{2.2k\Omega} = \left(\dfrac{2.2\ k\Omega}{3.2\ k\Omega}\right) 6.18\ V = 4.25\ V$

The 5.24 V reading is incorrect.
The 3.3 kΩ resistor is open.

36. (a) R_1 *open:*
  $V_{R1} = \textbf{15 V}$; $V_{R2} = V_{R3} = V_{R4} = V_{R5} = \textbf{0 V}$

  (b) R_3 *open:*
  $V_{R3} = \textbf{15 V}$; $V_{R12} = V_{R2} = V_{R4} = V_{R5} = \textbf{0 V}$

  (c) R_4 *open:*
  $R_T = R_1 + R_2 + R_3 + R_5 = 1.0\ k\Omega + 560\ \Omega + 470\ \Omega + 2.2\ k\Omega = 4.23\ k\Omega$

  $V_{R1} = \left(\dfrac{R_1}{R_T}\right) 15\ V = \left(\dfrac{1.0\ k\Omega}{4.23\ k\Omega}\right) 15\ V\ 15\ V = \textbf{3.55 V}$

  $V_{R2} = \left(\dfrac{R_2}{R_T}\right) 15\ V = \left(\dfrac{560\ \Omega}{4.23\ k\Omega}\right) 15\ V = \textbf{1.99 V}$

  $V_{R3} = \left(\dfrac{R_3}{R_T}\right) 15\ V = \left(\dfrac{470\ \Omega}{4.23\ k\Omega}\right) 15\ V = \textbf{1.67 V}$

  $V_{R4} = V_{R5} = \left(\dfrac{R_5}{R_T}\right) 15\ V = \left(\dfrac{2.2\ k\Omega}{4.23\ k\Omega}\right) 15\ V = \textbf{7.80 V}$

  (d) R_5 *open:*
  $R_T = R_1 + R_2 + R_3 + R_4 = 1.0\ k\Omega + 560\ \Omega + 470\ \Omega + 3.3\ k\Omega = 5.33\ k\Omega$

  $V_{R1} = \left(\dfrac{R_1}{R_T}\right) 15\ V = \left(\dfrac{1.0\ k\Omega}{5.33\ k\Omega}\right) 15\ V = \textbf{2.81 V}$

$$V_{R2} = \left(\frac{R_2}{R_T}\right)15 \text{ V} = \left(\frac{560 \text{ }\Omega}{5.33 \text{ k}\Omega}\right)15 \text{ V} = \mathbf{1.58 \text{ V}}$$

$$V_{R3} = \left(\frac{R_3}{R_T}\right)15 \text{ V} = \left(\frac{470 \text{ }\Omega}{5.33 \text{ k}\Omega}\right)15 \text{ V} = \mathbf{1.32 \text{ V}}$$

$$V_{R4} = V_{R5} = \left(\frac{R_5}{R_T}\right)15 \text{ V} = \left(\frac{3.3 \text{ k}\Omega}{5.33 \text{ k}\Omega}\right)15 \text{ V} = \mathbf{9.29 \text{ V}}$$

(e) *Point C shorted to ground:*
$R_T = R_1 + R_2 + R_3 = 1.0 \text{ k}\Omega + 560 \text{ }\Omega + 470 \text{ }\Omega = 2.03 \text{ k}\Omega$
$V_{R4} = V_{R5} = \mathbf{0 \text{ V}}$

$$V_{R1} = \left(\frac{R_1}{R_T}\right)15 \text{ V} = \left(\frac{1.0 \text{ k}\Omega}{2.03 \text{ k}\Omega}\right)15 \text{ V} = \mathbf{7.39 \text{ V}}$$

$$V_{R2} = \left(\frac{R_2}{R_T}\right)15 \text{ V} = \left(\frac{560 \text{ }\Omega}{2.03 \text{ k}\Omega}\right)15 \text{ V} = \mathbf{4.14 \text{ V}}$$

$$V_{R3} = \left(\frac{R_3}{R_T}\right)15 \text{ V} = \left(\frac{470 \text{ }\Omega}{2.03 \text{ k}\Omega}\right)15 \text{ V} = \mathbf{3.47 \text{ V}}$$

37. (a) R_1 *open:*
$V_{R1} = \mathbf{-10 \text{ V}}$, $V_{R2} = V_{R3} = V_{R4} = \mathbf{0 \text{ V}}$

(b) R_2 *open:*
$R_T = R_1 + R_4 = 1.0 \text{ k}\Omega + 3.3 \text{ k}\Omega = 4.3 \text{ k}\Omega$

$$V_{R1} = -\left(\frac{R_1}{R_T}\right)10 \text{ V} = -\left(\frac{1.0 \text{ k}\Omega}{4.3 \text{ k}\Omega}\right)10 \text{ V} = \mathbf{-2.33 \text{ V}}$$

$V_{R2} = \mathbf{-7.67 \text{ V}}$
$V_{R3} = \mathbf{0 \text{ V}}$

$$V_{R4} = -\left(\frac{R_4}{R_T}\right)10 \text{ V} = -\left(\frac{3.3 \text{ k}\Omega}{4.3 \text{ k}\Omega}\right)10 \text{ V} = \mathbf{-7.67 \text{ V}}$$

(c) R_3 *open:*
$R_T = R_1 + R_4 = 1.0 \text{ k}\Omega + 3.3 \text{ k}\Omega = 4.3 \text{ k}\Omega$

$$V_{R1} = -\left(\frac{R_1}{R_T}\right)10 \text{ V} = -\left(\frac{1.0 \text{ k}\Omega}{4.3 \text{ k}\Omega}\right)10 \text{ V} = \mathbf{-2.33 \text{ V}}$$

$V_{R2} = \mathbf{0 \text{ V}}$
$V_{R3} = \mathbf{-7.67 \text{ V}}$

$$V_{R4} = -\left(\frac{R_4}{R_T}\right)10 \text{ V} = -\left(\frac{3.3 \text{ k}\Omega}{4.3 \text{ k}\Omega}\right)10 \text{ V} = \mathbf{-7.67 \text{ V}}$$

(d) R_4 *shorted:*
$R_T = R_1 + R_2 + R_3 + R_4 = 1.0 \text{ k}\Omega + 560 \text{ }\Omega + 470 \text{ }\Omega + 3.3 \text{ k}\Omega = 5.33 \text{ k}\Omega$
$V_{R1} = \mathbf{-10 \text{ V}}$
$V_{R2} = V_{R3} = V_{R4} = \mathbf{0 \text{ V}}$

ADVANCED PROBLEMS

38. **(a)** The parallel combination of R_2 and R_3 is in series with the parallel combination of R_4 and R_5. This is all in parallel with R_1.

(b) R_1 and R_2 are in series with the parallel combination of R_3 and R_4. Also, R_5 and R_8 are in series with the parallel combination of R_6 and R_7. These two series-parallel combinations are in parallel with each other.

39. Resistors R_8, R_9, and R_{11} can be removed with no effect on the circuit because they are shorted by the pc connection. See Figure 6-4.

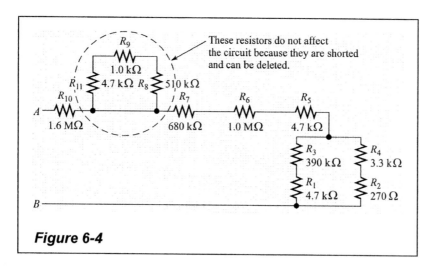

Figure 6-4

40. The circuit is redrawn and simplified as shown in Figure 6-5.

(a) $R_T = \left(\left(\left(\left((560\ \Omega + 560\ \Omega)\ \|\ 1.0\ \text{k}\Omega\right) + (1.0\ \text{k}\Omega + 1.0\ \text{k}\Omega)\ \|\ 560\ \Omega\right)\ \|\ 910\ \Omega\right)\ \|\ 56\ \Omega\right)\ \|\ 560\ \Omega$

$= \left(\left((528.3\ \Omega + 437.5\ \Omega)\ \|\ 910\ \Omega\right) + 56\ \Omega\right)\ \|\ 560\ \Omega = \mathbf{271\ \Omega}$

(b) $I_T = \dfrac{60\ \text{V}}{271\ \Omega} = \mathbf{221\ mA}$

(c) $I_{56\ \Omega} = \left(\dfrac{560\ \Omega}{560\ \Omega + 525\ \Omega}\right)I_T = (0.516)221\ \text{mA} = 114\ \text{mA}$

$I_{910\ \Omega} = \left(\dfrac{966\ \Omega}{910\ \Omega + 966\ \Omega}\right)I_{56\ \Omega} = (0.515)114\ \text{mA} = \mathbf{58.7\ mA}$

(d) $V_{910\ \Omega} = I_{910\ \Omega}(910\ \Omega) = (58.7\ \text{mA})\ 910\ \Omega = 53.4\ \text{V}$

The voltage from point B to the negative side of the battery is

$V_{B-} = \left(\dfrac{437.5\ \Omega}{437.5\ \Omega + 528.3\ \Omega}\right)V_{910\ \Omega} = \left(\dfrac{437.5\ \Omega}{966\ \Omega}\right)53.4\ \text{V} = \mathbf{24.2\ V}$

$V_{AB} = \dfrac{24.2\ \text{V}}{2} = \mathbf{12.1\ V}$

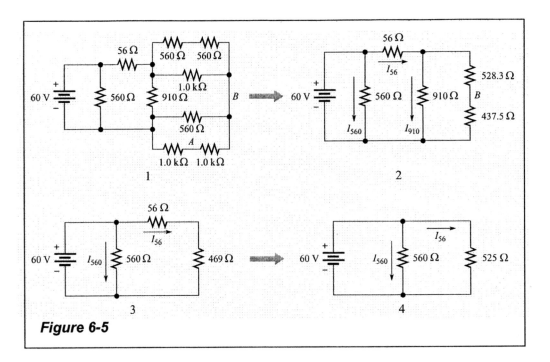

Figure 6-5

41. $R_B = 2.2 \text{ k}\Omega \parallel 2 \text{ k}\Omega = 1.05 \text{ k}\Omega$ $R_A = 2.2 \text{ k}\Omega \parallel 2.05 \text{ k}\Omega = 1.06 \text{ k}\Omega$
    $R_T = 4.7 \text{ k}\Omega + 1.06 \text{ k}\Omega = \textbf{5.76 k}\boldsymbol{\Omega}$

$$V_A = \left(\frac{1.06 \text{ k}\Omega}{5.76 \text{ k}\Omega}\right) 18 \text{ V} = \textbf{3.3 V}$$

$$V_B = \left(\frac{1.05 \text{ k}\Omega}{2.05 \text{ k}\Omega}\right) V_A = \left(\frac{1.05 \text{ k}\Omega}{2.05 \text{ k}\Omega}\right) 3.3 \text{ V} = \textbf{1.7 V}$$

$$V_C = \left(\frac{1.0 \text{ k}\Omega}{2 \text{ k}\Omega}\right) V_B = (0.5)(1.7 \text{ V}) = \textbf{850 mV}$$

42. The circuit is simplified in Figure 6-6 step-by-step to determine R_T.
    $R_T = \textbf{621 }\boldsymbol{\Omega}$

$$I_T = \frac{10 \text{ V}}{621 \text{ }\Omega} = \textbf{16.1 mA}$$

$$I_2 = \left(\frac{864 \text{ }\Omega}{1684 \text{ }\Omega}\right) 16.1 \text{ mA} = \textbf{8.26 mA}$$

$$I_3 = I_8 = \left(\frac{820 \text{ }\Omega}{1684 \text{ }\Omega}\right) 16.1 \text{ mA} = \textbf{7.84 mA}$$

$$I_4 = \left(\frac{880 \text{ }\Omega}{1700 \text{ }\Omega}\right) 7.84 \text{ mA} = \textbf{4.06 mA}$$

$$I_5 = \left(\frac{820 \text{ }\Omega}{1700 \text{ }\Omega}\right) 7.84 \text{ mA} = \textbf{3.78 mA}$$

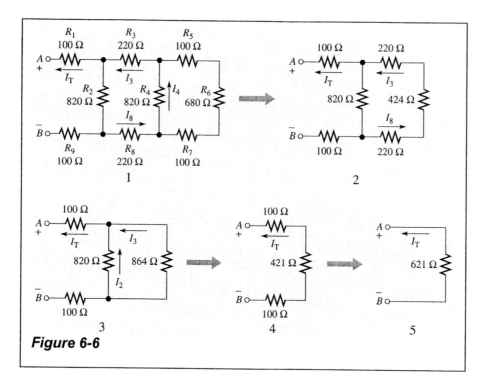

Figure 6-6

43. Using the currents found in Problem 42:

$V_1 = I_T R_1 = (16.1 \text{ mA})(100 \ \Omega) = \textbf{1.61 V}$
$V_2 = I_2 R_2 = (8.26 \text{ mA})(820 \ \Omega) = \textbf{6.77 V}$
$V_3 = I_3 R_3 = (7.84 \text{ mA})(220 \ \Omega) = \textbf{1.72 V}$
$V_4 = I_4 R_4 = (4.06 \text{ mA})(820 \ \Omega) = \textbf{3.33 V}$
$V_5 = I_5 R_5 = (3.78 \text{ mA})(100 \ \Omega) = \textbf{378 mV}$
$V_6 = I_5 R_6 = (3.78 \text{ mA})(680 \ \Omega) = \textbf{2.57 V}$
$V_7 = V_5 = \textbf{378 mV}$
$V_8 = I_8 R_8 = (7.84 \text{ mA})(220 \ \Omega) = \textbf{1.72 V}$
$V_9 = I_T R_9 = (16.1 \text{ mA})(100 \ \Omega) = \textbf{1.61 V}$

44. *Resistance of the right branch:*
$R_R = R_2 + R_5 \parallel R_6 + R_7 + R_8 = 330 \ \Omega + 600 \ \Omega + 680 \ \Omega + 100 \ \Omega = 1710 \ \Omega$
Resistance of the left branch:
$R_L = R_3 + R_4 = 470 \ \Omega + 560 \ \Omega = 1030 \ \Omega$
Total resistance:
$R_T = R_1 + R_L \parallel R_R = 1.0 \text{ k}\Omega + 642.8 \ \Omega = 1643 \ \Omega$
$I_T = \dfrac{100 \text{ V}}{1643 \ \Omega} = 60.9 \text{ mA}$

Current in right branch:
$I_R = \left(\dfrac{R_L}{R_L + R_R} \right) I_T = \left(\dfrac{1030 \ \Omega}{2740 \ \Omega} \right) 60.9 \text{ mA} = 22.9 \text{ mA}$

Current in left branch:
$I_L = \left(\dfrac{R_R}{R_L + R_R} \right) I_T = \left(\dfrac{1710 \ \Omega}{2740 \ \Omega} \right) 60.9 \text{ mA} = 38.0 \text{ mA}$

Voltages with respect to the negative terminal of the source:

$V_A = I_1 R_4 = (38.0 \text{ mA})(560 \text{ }\Omega) = 21.3 \text{ V}$

$V_B = I_R(R_7 + R_8) = (22.9 \text{ mA})(780 \text{ }\Omega) = 17.9 \text{ V}$

$V_{AB} = V_A - V_B = 21.3 \text{ V} - 17.9 \text{ V} = \textbf{3.40 V}$

45. $I_2 = \left(\dfrac{R_1}{R_1 + R_2} \right) I_T$

$1 \text{ A} = \left(\dfrac{47 \text{ }\Omega}{R_2 + 47 \text{ }\Omega} \right) I_T$

$R_2 + 47 = 47 I_T$

Also, $I_T = \dfrac{V}{R_T} = \dfrac{220}{33 + \left(\dfrac{47 R_2}{47 + R_2} \right)}$

Substituting, $R_2 + 47 = 47 \left(\dfrac{220}{33 + \dfrac{47 R_2}{47 + R_2}} \right)$

$(R_2 + 47) \left(33 + \dfrac{47 R_2}{47 + R_2} \right) = 47(220)$

$33 R_2 + (47)(33) + 47 R_2 = 47(220)$

$80 R_2 = 47(220) - 47(33)$

$R_2 = \dfrac{47(220 - 33)}{80} = \textbf{110 }\boldsymbol{\Omega}$

46. $R_{C-GND} = R_6 = 1.0 \text{ k}\Omega$

$R_{B-GND} = (R_5 + R_6) \| R_4 = 2 \text{ k}\Omega \| 2.2 \text{ k}\Omega = 1.05 \text{ k}\Omega$

$R_{A-GND} = (R_3 + R_{B-GND}) \| R_2 = 2.05 \text{ k}\Omega \| 2.2 \text{ k}\Omega = 1.06 \text{ k}\Omega$

$R_T = R_1 + R_{A-GND} = 5.6 \text{ k}\Omega + 1.06 \text{ k}\Omega = 6.66 \text{ k}\Omega$

$V_A = \left(\dfrac{1.06 \text{ k}\Omega}{6.66 \text{ k}\Omega} \right) 18 \text{ V} = \textbf{2.86 V}$

$V_B = \left(\dfrac{1.05 \text{ k}\Omega}{2.05 \text{ k}\Omega} \right) 2.86 \text{ V} = \textbf{1.47 V}$

$V_C = \left(\dfrac{1.0 \text{ k}\Omega}{2 \text{ k}\Omega} \right) 1.47 \text{ V} = \textbf{735 mV}$

47. $I_{max} = 100 \text{ mA}$

$R_T = \dfrac{24 \text{ V}}{100 \text{ mA}} = 240 \text{ }\Omega$

$\left(\dfrac{R_2}{R_T} \right) 24 \text{ V} = 6 \text{ V}$

$24 R_2 = 6 R_T$

$$R_2 = \frac{6(240\ \Omega)}{24} = \mathbf{60\ \Omega}$$

$R_1 = 140\ \Omega - 60\ \Omega = \mathbf{180\ \Omega}$

With load:

$R_2 \parallel R_L = 60\ \Omega \parallel 1000\ \Omega = 56.6\ \Omega$

$$V_{\text{OUT}} = \left(\frac{56.6\ \Omega}{180\ \Omega + 56.6\ \Omega}\right)24\ \text{V} = 5.74\ \text{V}$$

48. Refer to Figure 6-7.

$$R_T = \frac{10\ \text{V}}{5\ \text{mA}} = 2\ \text{k}\Omega$$

$R_1 = R_2 + R_3$

$R_2 = R_3$

$R_1 = 2R_2$

$R_1 + 2R_2 = 2\ \text{k}\Omega$

$2R_2 + 2R_2 = 2\ \text{k}\Omega$

$4R_2 = 2\ \text{k}\Omega$

$R_2 = R_3 = \mathbf{500\ \Omega}$

$R_1 = R_2 + R_3 = \mathbf{1000\ \Omega}$

With 1 kΩ loads across the 2.5 V and the 5 V outputs:

$$V_A = \left(\frac{(R_3 \parallel R_L + R_2)\parallel R_L}{(R_3 \parallel R_L + R_2)\parallel R_L + R_1}\right)V_S$$

$$= \left(\frac{(500\ \Omega \parallel 1\ \text{k}\Omega + 500\ \Omega)\parallel 1\ \text{k}\Omega}{(500\ \Omega \parallel 1\ \text{k}\Omega + 500\ \Omega)\parallel 1\ \text{k}\Omega + 1\ \text{k}\Omega}\right)10\ \text{V}$$

$$= \left(\frac{455\ \Omega}{455\ \Omega + 1\ \text{k}\Omega}\right)10\ \text{V} = \mathbf{3.13\ V}$$

$$V_B = \left(\frac{R_3 \parallel 1\ \text{k}\Omega}{R_3 \parallel 1\ \text{k}\Omega + R_2}\right)V_A = \left(\frac{333\ \Omega}{333\ \Omega + 500\ \Omega}\right)3.13\ \text{V} = \mathbf{1.25\ V}$$

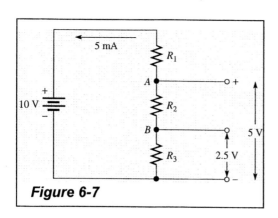

Figure 6-7

49. Refer to Figure 6-8(a).

With the 2 V source acting alone:

$R_T = 1.96 \text{ k}\Omega$

$I_T = \dfrac{2 \text{ V}}{1.96 \text{ k}\Omega} = 1.02 \text{ mA}$

$I_1 = \left(\dfrac{2.2 \text{ k}\Omega}{2.2 \text{ k}\Omega + 1.69 \text{ k}\Omega} \right) 1.02 \text{ mA} = 577 \text{ μA}$

$I_5 = \left(\dfrac{1.0 \text{ k}\Omega}{1.0 \text{ k}\Omega + 2.2 \text{ k}\Omega} \right) 577 \text{ μA} = 180 \text{ μA} \quad \text{up}$

Refer to Figure 6-8(b).

With the 3 V source acting alone:

$R_T = 1.96 \text{ k}\Omega$

$I_T = \dfrac{3 \text{ V}}{1.96 \text{ k}\Omega} = 1.53 \text{ mA}$

$I_5 = \left(\dfrac{1.69 \text{ k}\Omega}{2.2 \text{ k}\Omega + 1.69 \text{ k}\Omega} \right) 1.53 \text{ mA} = 665 \text{ μA} \quad \text{up}$

$I_{5(\text{total})} = 665 \text{ μA} + 180 \text{ μA} = \textbf{845 μA}$

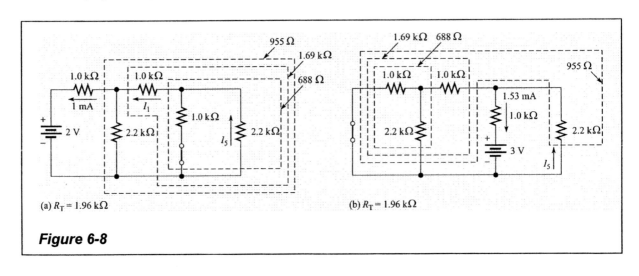

(a) $R_T = 1.96 \text{ k}\Omega$　　　　(b) $R_T = 1.96 \text{ k}\Omega$

Figure 6-8

50. *Using Superposition:*

Current from the 12 V source:
$R_T = 22 \text{ }\Omega + 10 \text{ }\Omega \parallel 56 \text{ }\Omega \parallel 10 \text{ }\Omega \parallel 82 \text{ }\Omega = 22 \text{ }\Omega + 4.35 \text{ }\Omega = 26.4 \text{ }\Omega$

$I_T = \dfrac{12 \text{ V}}{26.4 \text{ }\Omega} = 455 \text{ mA}$

$I_{R_L} = \left(\dfrac{4.35 \text{ }\Omega}{82 \text{ }\Omega} \right) 455 \text{ mA} = 24.1 \text{ mA} \quad \text{up}$

Current from the 6 V source:

$R_T = 10\ \Omega + 22\ \Omega \parallel 56\ \Omega \parallel 10\ \Omega \parallel 82\ \Omega = 10\ \Omega + 5.7\ \Omega = 15.7\ \Omega$

$I_T = \dfrac{6\ \text{V}}{15.7\ \Omega} = 382\ \text{mA}$

$I_{R_L} = \left(\dfrac{5.7\ \Omega}{82\ \Omega}\right)382\ \text{mA} = 26.6\ \text{mA}\quad\text{up}$

Current from the 10 V source:

$R_T = 56\ \Omega + 22\ \Omega \parallel 10\ \Omega \parallel 10\ \Omega \parallel 82\ \Omega = 56\ \Omega + 3.88\ \Omega = 59.9\ \Omega$

$I_T = \dfrac{10\ \text{V}}{59.9\ \Omega} = 167\ \text{mA}$

$I_{R_L} = \left(\dfrac{3.88\ \Omega}{82\ \Omega}\right)167\ \text{mA} = 7.9\ \text{mA}\quad\text{down}$

Current from the 5 V source:

$R_T = 10\ \Omega + 22\ \Omega \parallel 10\ \Omega \parallel 56\ \Omega \parallel 82\ \Omega = 10\ \Omega + 5.7\ \Omega = 15.7\ \Omega$

$I_T = \dfrac{5\ \text{V}}{15.7\ \Omega} = 318\ \text{mA}$

$I_{R_L} = \left(\dfrac{5.7\ \Omega}{82\ \Omega}\right)318\ \text{mA} = 22.1\ \text{mA}\quad\text{down}$

$I_{R_{L(total)}} = 24.1\ \text{mA} + 26.6\ \text{mA} - 7.9\ \text{mA} - 22.1\ \text{mA} = \mathbf{20.8\ mA}\quad\text{up}$

51. Refer to Figure 6-9(a).

$R_{TH} = 2.65\ \text{k}\Omega \parallel 2.35\ \text{k}\Omega = 1.25\ \text{k}\Omega$
Refer to Figure 6-9(b).

$V_{TH} = \left(\dfrac{1.69\ \text{k}\Omega}{6.39\ \text{k}\Omega}\right)50\ \text{V} = 13.2\ \text{V}$

Refer to Figure 6-9(c).

$V_4 = \left(\dfrac{10\ \text{k}\Omega}{11.3\ \text{k}\Omega}\right)13.2\ \text{V} = \mathbf{11.7\ V}$

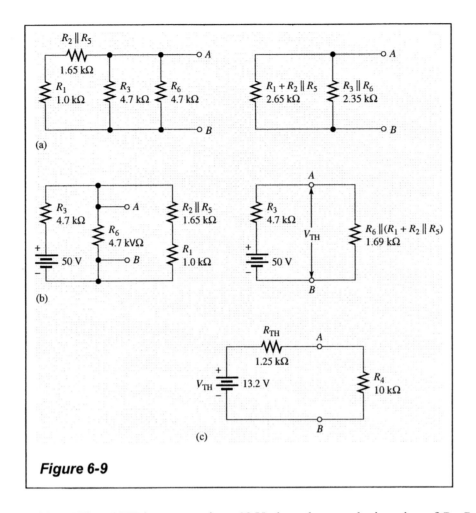

Figure 6-9

52. (a)   When SW2 is connected to +12 V, the voltage at the junction of R_3, R_4, and R_5 is

$$V_2 = \left(\frac{24 \text{ k}\Omega \parallel 26.4 \text{ k}\Omega}{24 \text{ k}\Omega + \left(24 \text{ k}\Omega \parallel 26.4 \text{ k}\Omega\right)} \right) 12 \text{ V} = \left(\frac{12.6 \text{ k}\Omega}{36.6 \text{ k}\Omega} \right) 12 \text{ V} = 4.13 \text{ V}$$

The voltage at the junction of R_5, R_6, and R_7 is

$$V_3 = \left(\frac{24 \text{ k}\Omega \parallel 36 \text{ k}\Omega}{12 \text{ k}\Omega + \left(24 \text{ k}\Omega \parallel 36 \text{ k}\Omega\right)} \right) V_2 = \left(\frac{14.4 \text{ k}\Omega}{36.4 \text{ k}\Omega} \right) 4.13 \text{ V} = 2.25 \text{ V}$$

$$V_{OUT} = \left(\frac{24 \text{ k}\Omega}{36 \text{ k}\Omega} \right) V_3 = \left(\frac{24 \text{ k}\Omega}{36 \text{ k}\Omega} \right) 2.25 \text{ V} = \mathbf{1.5 \text{ V}}$$

(b) When SW1 is connected to +12 V, the voltage at the junction of R_1, R_2, and R_3 is

$$V_1 = \left(\frac{24 \text{ k}\Omega \parallel 24.6 \text{ k}\Omega}{24 \text{ k}\Omega + \left(24 \text{ k}\Omega \parallel 24.6 \text{ k}\Omega\right)} \right) 12 \text{ V} = \left(\frac{12.1 \text{ k}\Omega}{36.1 \text{ k}\Omega} \right) 12 \text{ V} = 4.02 \text{ V}$$

The voltage at the junction of R_3, R_4, and R_5 is

$$V_2 = \left(\frac{24 \text{ k}\Omega \parallel 24.4 \text{ k}\Omega}{12 \text{ k}\Omega + \left(24 \text{ k}\Omega \parallel 24.4 \text{ k}\Omega\right)} \right) V_1 = \left(\frac{12.6 \text{ k}\Omega}{24.4 \text{ k}\Omega} \right) 4.02 \text{ V} = 2.08 \text{ V}$$

$$V_3 = \left(\frac{24 \text{ k}\Omega \parallel 14.4 \text{ k}\Omega}{12 \text{ k}\Omega + \left(24 \text{ k}\Omega \parallel 14.4 \text{ k}\Omega\right)} \right) V_2 = \left(\frac{14.4 \text{ k}\Omega}{26.4 \text{ k}\Omega} \right) 2.08 \text{ V} = 1.13 \text{ V}$$

$$V_{OUT} = \left(\frac{24 \text{ k}\Omega}{36 \text{ k}\Omega} \right) V_3 = \left(\frac{24 \text{ k}\Omega}{36 \text{ k}\Omega} \right) 1.13 \text{ V} = \mathbf{0.75 \text{ V}}$$

53. See Figure 6-10.

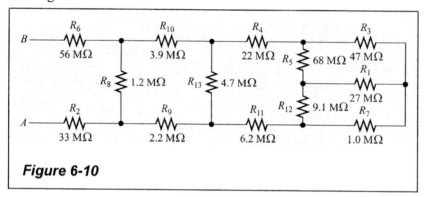

Figure 6-10

54. See Figure 6-11.

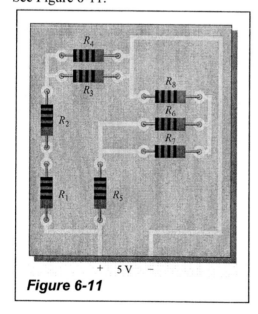

Figure 6-11

55. *Position 1:*

$R_T = 10\ \text{k}\Omega + 30\ \text{k}\Omega\ \|\ 330\ \text{k}\Omega = 10\ \text{k}\Omega + 27.5\ \text{k}\Omega = 37.5\ \text{k}\Omega$

$V_1 = \left(\dfrac{27.5\ \text{k}\Omega}{37.5\ \text{k}\Omega}\right)120\ \text{V} = \textbf{88.0 V}$

$V_2 = \left(\dfrac{20\ \text{k}\Omega}{30\ \text{k}\Omega}\right)88.0\ \text{V} = \textbf{58.7 V}$

$V_3 = \left(\dfrac{10\ \text{k}\Omega}{30\ \text{k}\Omega}\right)88.0\ \text{V} = \textbf{29.3 V}$

Position 2:

$R_T = 20\ \text{k}\Omega + 20\ \text{k}\Omega\ \|\ 330\ \text{k}\Omega = 20\ \text{k}\Omega + 18.9\ \text{k}\Omega = 38.9\ \text{k}\Omega$

$V_1 = \left(\dfrac{10\ \text{k}\Omega + 18.9\ \text{k}\Omega}{35.5\ \text{k}\Omega}\right)120\ \text{V} = \textbf{89.1 V}$

$V_2 = \left(\dfrac{18.9\ \text{k}\Omega}{38.9\ \text{k}\Omega}\right)120\ \text{V} = \textbf{58.2 V}$

$V_3 = \left(\dfrac{10\ \text{k}\Omega}{20\ \text{k}\Omega}\right)58.2\ \text{V} = \textbf{29.1 V}$

Position 3:

$R_T = 30\ \text{k}\Omega + 10\ \text{k}\Omega\ \|\ 330\ \text{k}\Omega = 30\ \text{k}\Omega + 9.71\ \text{k}\Omega = 39.7\ \text{k}\Omega$

$V_1 = \left(\dfrac{20\ \text{k}\Omega + 9.71\ \text{k}\Omega}{39.7\ \text{k}\Omega}\right)120\ \text{V} = \textbf{89.8 V}$

$V_2 = \left(\dfrac{10\ \text{k}\Omega + 9.71\ \text{k}\Omega}{39.7\ \text{k}\Omega}\right)120\ \text{V} = \textbf{59.6 V}$

$V_3 = \left(\dfrac{9.71\ \text{k}\Omega}{39.7\ \text{k}\Omega}\right)120\ \text{V} = \textbf{29.3 V}$

56. (a) $\quad V_G = \left(\dfrac{R_2}{R_1 + R_2}\right)V_{DD} = \left(\dfrac{270\ \text{k}\Omega}{2.47\ \text{M}\Omega}\right)16\ \text{V} = \textbf{1.75 V}$

$\quad V_S = V_G - 1.5\ \text{V} = 1.75 - 1.5\ \text{V} = \textbf{0.25 V}$

(b) $\quad I_1 = \dfrac{V_{DD} - V_G}{R_1} = \dfrac{16\ \text{V} - 1.75\ \text{V}}{2.2\ \text{M}\Omega} = \textbf{6.48 μA}$

$\quad I_2 = I_1 = \dfrac{V_G}{R_2} = \dfrac{1.75\ \text{V}}{270\ \text{k}\Omega} = \textbf{6.48 μA}$

$\quad I_S = \dfrac{V_S}{R_S} = \dfrac{0.25\ \text{V}}{1.5\ \text{k}\Omega} = \textbf{167 μA}$

$\quad I_D = I_S = \textbf{167 μA}$

(c) $\quad V_D = V_{DD} - I_D R_D = 16\ \text{V} - (167\ \text{μA})(4.7\ \text{k}\Omega) = 16\ \text{V} - 0.783\ \text{V} = 15.2\ \text{V}$

$\quad V_{DS} - V_D - V_S = 15.2\ \text{V} - 0.25\ \text{V} = 14.97\ \text{V} \cong \textbf{15.0 V}$

$\quad V_{DG} - V_D - V_G = 15.2\ \text{V} - 1.75\ \text{V} = 13.47\ \text{V} \cong \textbf{13.5 V}$

57. The circuit is redrawn in Figure 6-12.
The meter reading at point A should be:

$$V_A = \left(\frac{6\ k\Omega}{16\ k\Omega}\right)150\ V = 56.3\ V$$

The meter reading of 81.8 V is incorrect. The most likely failure is an open 12 kΩ resistor. This will cause the voltage at point A to be higher than it should be. To verify, let's calculate the voltage assuming that one of the 12 kΩ resistors is open.

$$V_A = \left(\frac{12\ k\Omega}{22\ k\Omega}\right)150\ V = 81.8\ V \quad \text{This verifies an \textbf{open 12 kΩ}.}$$

Now check V_B:

$$V_B = \left(\frac{2.2\ k\Omega}{7.8\ k\Omega}\right)150\ V = 42.3\ V$$

This meter reading is correct.

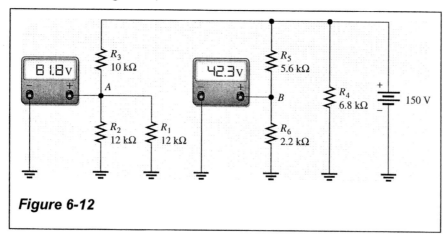

Figure 6-12

58. The circuit is redrawn in Figure 6-13.

$$R_{BG} = \frac{(10\ k\Omega + 47\ k\Omega)(100\ k\Omega)}{10\ k\Omega + 47\ k\Omega + 100\ k\Omega} = 36.3\ k\Omega$$

$R_{AG} = 33\ k\Omega + R_{BG} = 33\ k\Omega + 36.3\ k\Omega = 69.3\ k\Omega$
$R_T = R_{AG} = 27\ k\Omega = 69.3\ k\Omega + 27\ k\Omega = 96.3\ k\Omega$

$$V_{AG} = \left(\frac{R_{AG}}{R_T}\right)18\ V = \left(\frac{69.3\ k\Omega}{96.3\ k\Omega}\right)18\ V = 12.95\ V$$

$$V_{BG} = \left(\frac{R_{BG}}{R_T}\right)18\ V = \left(\frac{36.3\ k\Omega}{96.3\ k\Omega}\right)18\ V = 6.79\ V$$

$$V_{CG} = \left(\frac{47\ k\Omega}{57\ k\Omega}\right)V_{BG} = \left(\frac{47\ k\Omega}{57\ k\Omega}\right)6.79\ V = \textbf{5.60 V}\quad \textbf{correct}$$

$$V_{AC} = V_{AG} - V_{CG} = 12.95\ V - 5.60\ V = \textbf{7.35 V}\quad \textbf{correct}$$

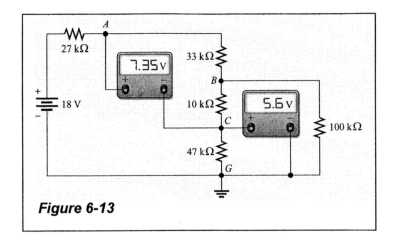

Figure 6-13

59. The 2.5 V reading indicated on one of the meters shows that the series-parallel branch containing the other meter is open. The 0 V reading on the other meter shows that there is no current in that branch. **Therefore, if only one resistor is open, it must be the 2.2 kΩ.**

60. The circuit is redrawn in Figure 6-14.
    The resistance from point A to ground is
    $R_A = 12 \text{ k}\Omega \parallel 8.2 \text{ k}\Omega = 4.87 \text{ k}\Omega$

    $$V_A = \left(\frac{4.87 \text{ k}\Omega}{4.7 \text{ k}\Omega + 4.87 \text{ k}\Omega} \right) 30 \text{ V} = \left(\frac{4.87 \text{ k}\Omega}{9.57 \text{ k}\Omega} \right) 30 \text{ V} = 15.3 \text{ V}$$

    The meter reading of 15.3 V at point A is correct.

    $$V_B = \left(\frac{3.3 \text{ k}\Omega}{8.9 \text{ k}\Omega} \right) 30 \text{ V} = 11.1 \text{ V}$$

    The meter reading of 30 V at point B is incorrect. Either the 5.6 kΩ resistor is shorted or the 3.3 kΩ resistor is open. Since resistors tend to fail open, **the 3.3 kΩ is most likely open.**

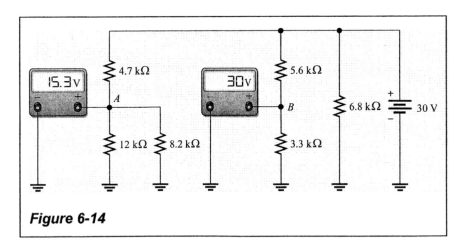

Figure 6-14

61. $V_A = \mathbf{0 \text{ V}}$

    $$V_B = \left(\frac{R_6}{R_5 + R_6} \right) 30 \text{ V} = \left(\frac{3.3 \text{ k}\Omega}{8.9 \text{ k}\Omega} \right) 30 \text{ V} = \mathbf{11.1 \text{ V}}$$

62. R_3 is open.

63. R_2 is open.

64. R_1 is open.

65. No fault

66. R_6 is open.

67. R_4 is shorted.

68. R_3 is open.

69. In fact, R_5 is shorted, but it must be removed from the bridge before that can be determined.

CHAPTER 7
MAGNETISM AND ELECTROMAGNETISM

BASIC PROBLEMS

SECTION 7-1 The Magnetic Field

1. Since $B = \dfrac{\phi}{A}$, when A increases, B (flux density) **decreases.**

2. $B = \dfrac{\phi}{A} = \dfrac{1500 \ \mu\text{Wb}}{0.5 \ \text{m}^2} = 3000 \ \mu\text{Wb/m}^2 = \textbf{3000} \ \boldsymbol{\mu}\textbf{T}$

3. $B = \dfrac{\phi}{A}$

   There are 100 centimeters per meter. $(1 \ \text{m}/100 \ \text{cm} = 1 \ \text{m}^2/10{,}000 \ \text{cm}^2$

   $A = 150 \ \text{cm}^2 \left(\dfrac{1 \ \text{m}^2}{10{,}000 \ \text{cm}^2} \right) = 0.015 \ \text{m}^2$

   $\phi = BA = (2500 \times 10^{-6} \ \text{T})(0.015 \ \text{m}^2) = \textbf{37.5} \ \boldsymbol{\mu}\textbf{Wb}$

4. $10^4 \ \text{G} = 1 \ \text{T}$

   $(0.6 \ \text{G})(1 \ \text{T}/10^4 \ \text{G}) = \textbf{60} \ \boldsymbol{\mu}\textbf{T}$

5. $1 \ \text{T} = 10^4 \ \text{G}$

   $(100{,}000 \ \mu\text{T})(10^4 \ \text{G/T}) = \textbf{1000 G}$

SECTION 7-2 Electromagnetism

6. The compass needle turns 180°.

7. $\mu_r = \dfrac{\mu}{\mu_0}$

   $\mu_0 = 4\pi \times 10^{-7} \ \text{Wb/At·m}$

   $\mu_r = \dfrac{750 \times 10^{-6} \ \text{Wb/At·m}}{4\pi \times 10^{-7} \ \text{Wb/At·m}} = \textbf{597}$

8. $\mathcal{R} = \dfrac{l}{\mu A} = \dfrac{0.28 \text{ m}}{(150 \times 10^{-7} \text{ Wb/At·m })(0.08 \text{ m}^2)} = \mathbf{233 \times 10^3 \text{ At/Wb}}$

9. $F_m = NI = (500 \text{ t})(3 \text{ A}) = \mathbf{1500 \text{ At}}$

SECTION 7-3 Electromagnetic Devices

10. When a solenoid is activated, its plunger is **retracted**.

11. (a) An **electromagnetic force** moves the plunger when the solenoid is activated.
    (b) A **spring force** returns the plunger to its at-rest position.

12. The relay connects +9 V to pin 2 turning *on* lamp 2 and turning *off* lamp 1.

13. The pointer in a d'Arsonval movement is deflected by the **electromagnetic force** when there is current through the coil.

SECTION 7-4 Magnetic Hysteresis

14. $F_m = 1500 \text{ At}$

    $H = \dfrac{F_m}{l} = \dfrac{1500 \text{ At}}{0.2 \text{ m}} = \mathbf{7500 \text{ At/m}}$

15. The flux density can be changed by **changing the current**.

16. (a) $H = \dfrac{F_m}{l} = \dfrac{NI}{l} = \dfrac{500(0.25 \text{ A})}{0.3 \text{ m}} = \mathbf{417 \text{ At/m}}$

    (b) $\phi = \dfrac{F_m}{\mathcal{R}} = \dfrac{NI}{\left(\dfrac{l}{\mu A}\right)}$

    $\mu_r = \dfrac{\mu}{\mu_0}$

    $\mu = \mu_r \mu_0 = (250)(4\pi \times 10^{-7}) = 3142 \times 10^{-7} \text{ Wb/At·m}$
    $A = (2 \text{ cm})(2 \text{ cm}) = (0.02 \text{ m})(0.02 \text{ m}) = 0.0004 \text{ m}^2$

    $\phi = \dfrac{(500 \text{ t})(0.25 \text{ A})}{\left(\dfrac{0.3 \text{ m}}{(3142 \times 10^{-7})(0.0004 \text{ m}^2)}\right)} = \dfrac{125 \text{ At}}{2.39 \times 10^6 \text{ At/Wb}} = \mathbf{52.3 \text{ } \mu Wb}$

    (c) $B = \dfrac{\phi}{A} = \dfrac{52.3 \text{ } \mu Wb}{0.0004 \text{ m}^2} = \mathbf{130{,}750 \text{ } \mu Wb/m^2}$

17. **Material A** has the most retentivity.

SECTION 7-5 Electromagnetic Induction

18. The **induced voltage doubles** when the rate of change of the magnetic flux doubles.

19. $I_{induced} = \dfrac{V_{induced}}{R} = \dfrac{100\,\text{mV}}{100\,\Omega} = \textbf{1 mA}$

SECTION 7-6 Applications of Electromagnetic Induction

20. **The magnetic field is not changing**; therefore, there is no induced voltage.

21. The commutator and brush arrangement **electrically connects the loop to the external circuit.**

ADVANCED PROBLEMS

22. 60 rev/s × 2 peaks/rev = **120 peaks/s**

23. See Figure 7-1.

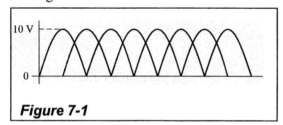

Figure 7-1

Multisim Troubleshooting Problems

24. Upper lamp is open.

25. The design is flawed. 12 V is too little voltage to operate two 12 V relays in series but 24 V is too much to operate a 12 V lamp. Install a separate 12 V power supply for the lamps and change the 12 V to 24 V for the relays.

CHAPTER 8
INTRODUCTION TO ALTERNATING CURRENT AND VOLTAGE

BASIC PROBLEMS

SECTION 8-1 The Sinusoidal Waveform

1. (a) $f = \dfrac{1}{T} = \dfrac{1}{1\,\text{s}} = \mathbf{1\ Hz}$

   (b) $f = \dfrac{1}{T} = \dfrac{1}{0.2\,\text{ms}} = \mathbf{5\ Hz}$

   (c) $f = \dfrac{1}{T} = \dfrac{1}{50\,\text{ms}} = \mathbf{20\ Hz}$

   (d) $f = \dfrac{1}{T} = \dfrac{1}{1\,\text{ms}} = \mathbf{1\ kHz}$

   (e) $f = \dfrac{1}{T} = \dfrac{1}{500\,\mu\text{s}} = \mathbf{2\ kHz}$

   (f) $f = \dfrac{1}{T} = \dfrac{1}{10\,\mu\text{s}} = \mathbf{100\ kHz}$

2. (a) $T = \dfrac{1}{f} = \dfrac{1}{1\,\text{Hz}} = \mathbf{1\ s}$

   (b) $T = \dfrac{1}{f} = \dfrac{1}{60\,\text{Hz}} = \mathbf{16.7\ ms}$

   (c)) $T = \dfrac{1}{f} = \dfrac{1}{500\,\text{Hz}} = \mathbf{2\ ms}$

   (d) $T = \dfrac{1}{f} = \dfrac{1}{1\,\text{kHz}} = \mathbf{1\ ms}$

   (e) $T = \dfrac{1}{f} = \dfrac{1}{200\,\text{kHz}} = \mathbf{5\ \mu s}$

   (f) $T = \dfrac{1}{f} = \dfrac{1}{5\,\text{MHz}} = \mathbf{200\ ns}$

3. $T = \dfrac{10\,\mu\text{s}}{5\,\text{cycles}} = \mathbf{2\ \mu s}$

4. $T = \dfrac{1}{f} = \dfrac{1}{50\,\text{kHz}} = 20\,\mu s = 0.02\,\text{ms}$

$\dfrac{10\,\text{ms}}{0.02\,\text{ms}} = \textbf{500 cycles in 10 ms}$

SECTION 8-2 Sinusoidal Voltage Sources

5. f = number of pole pairs × rev/s = 1 × 250 rev/s = **250 Hz**

6. f = number of pole pairs × rev/s

   rev/s $= \dfrac{3600\,\text{rev/min}}{60\,\text{s/min}} = 60\,\text{rev/s}$

   f = 2 pole pairs × 60 rev/s = **120 Hz**

7. rev/s $= \dfrac{f}{\text{pole pairs}} = \dfrac{400\,\text{Hz}}{2} = \textbf{200 rps}$

SECTION 8-3 Voltage and Current Values of Sine Waves

8. (a) $V_{rms} = 0.707 V_p = 0.707(12\,\text{V}) = \textbf{8.48 V}$
   (b) $V_{pp} = 2V_p = 2(12\,\text{V}) = \textbf{24 V}$
   (c) $V_{AVG} = \left(\dfrac{2}{\pi}\right)V_p = \left(\dfrac{2}{\pi}\right)12\,\text{V} = \textbf{7.64 V}$

9. (a) $I_p = 1.414 I_{rms} = 1.414(5\,\text{mA}) = \textbf{7.07 mA}$
   (b) $I_{AVG} = 0.6371 I_p = 0.637(7.07\,\text{mA}) = \textbf{4.5 mA}$
   (c) $I_{pp} = 2I_p = 2(7.07\,\text{mA}) = \textbf{14.14 mA}$

10. $V_p = \textbf{25 V}$
    $V_{pp} = 2V_p = \textbf{50 V}$
    $V_{rms} = 0.707 V_p = \textbf{17.7 V}$
    $V_{AVG} = 0.637 V_p = \textbf{15.9 V}$

11. (a) 17.5 V   (b) 25 V   (c) 0 V   (d) −19 V

SECTION 8-4 Angular Measurement of a Sine Wave

12. (a) 17.5 V   (b) 25 V   (c) 0 V

13. $\theta = 45° - 30° = \textbf{15° waveform } A \textbf{ leading}$

14. With respect to 0°: Sine wave with peak at 75° is shifted **15° leading**. Sine wave with peak at 100° is shifted **10° lagging**.
    Phase difference: $\theta = 100° - 75° = \textbf{25°}$

15. See Figure 8-1.

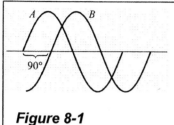

Figure 8-1

16. (a) $\dfrac{\pi \text{ rad}}{180°} \times 30° = \textbf{0.524 rad}$

    (b) $\dfrac{\pi \text{ rad}}{180°} \times 45° = \textbf{0.785 rad}$

    (c) $\dfrac{\pi \text{ rad}}{180°} \times 78° = \textbf{1.36 rad}$

    (d) $\dfrac{\pi \text{ rad}}{180°} \times 135° = \textbf{2.36 rad}$

    (e) $\dfrac{\pi \text{ rad}}{180°} \times 200° = \textbf{3.49 rad}$

    (f) $\dfrac{\pi \text{ rad}}{180°} \times 300° = \textbf{5.24 rad}$

17. (a) $\dfrac{\pi}{8 \text{ rad}} \times 57.3°/\text{rad} = \textbf{22.5°}$

    (b) $\dfrac{\pi}{3 \text{ rad}} \times 57.3°/\text{rad} = \textbf{60°}$

    (c) $\dfrac{\pi}{2 \text{ rad}} \times 57.3°/\text{rad} = \textbf{90°}$

    (d) $\dfrac{3\pi}{5 \text{ rad}} \times 57.3°/\text{rad} = \textbf{108°}$

    (e) $\dfrac{6\pi}{5 \text{ rad}} \times 57.3°/\text{rad} = \textbf{216°}$

    (f) $\dfrac{1.8\pi}{\text{rad}} \times 57.3°/\text{rad} = \textbf{324°}$

18. $V_p = 1.414(20 \text{ V}) = 28.28 \text{ V}$

    (a) $v = V_p \sin \theta = (28.28 \text{ V}) \sin 15° = \textbf{7.32 V}$
    (b) $v = (28.28 \text{ V}) \sin 33° = \textbf{15.4 V}$
    (c) $v = (28.28 \text{ V}) \sin 50° = \textbf{21.7 V}$
    (d) $v = (28.28 \text{ V}) \sin 110° = \textbf{26.6 V}$
    (e) $v = (28.28 \text{ V}) \sin 70° = \textbf{26.6 V}$
    (f) $v = (28.28 \text{ V}) \sin 145° = \textbf{16.2 V}$
    (g) $v = (28.28 \text{ V}) \sin 250° = \textbf{–26.6 V}$
    (h) $v = (28.28 \text{ V}) \sin 325° = \textbf{–16.2 V}$

19.   (a) $i = I_p \sin \theta = (100 \text{ mA}) \sin 35° = \textbf{57.4 mA}$
    (b) $i = (100 \text{ mA}) \sin 95° = \textbf{99.6 mA}$
    (c) $i = (100 \text{ mA}) \sin 190° = \textbf{–17.4 mA}$
    (d) $i = (100 \text{ mA}) \sin 215° = \textbf{–57.4 mA}$
    (e) $i = (100 \text{ mA}) \sin 275° = \textbf{–99.6 mA}$
    (f) $i = (100 \text{ mA}) \sin 360° = \textbf{0 mA}$

20. $V_p = 1.414 V_{\text{rms}} = 1.414(6.37 \text{ V}) = 9 \text{ V}$

    (a) $\dfrac{\pi}{8} = 22.5°$
         $v = (9 \text{ V}) \sin 22.5° = \textbf{3.44 V}$

    (b) $\dfrac{\pi}{4} = 45°$
         $v = (9 \text{ V}) \sin 45° = \textbf{6.36 V}$

    (c) $\dfrac{\pi}{2} = 90°$
         $v = (9 \text{ V}) \sin 90° = \textbf{9 V}$

    (d) $\dfrac{3\pi}{4} = 135°$
         $v = (9 \text{ V}) \sin 135° = \textbf{6.36 V}$

    (e) $\pi = 180°$
         $v = (9 \text{ V}) \sin 180° = \textbf{0 V}$

    (f) $\dfrac{3\pi}{2} = 270°$
         $v = (9 \text{ V}) \sin 270° = \textbf{–9 V}$

    (g) $2\pi = 360°$
         $v = (9 \text{ V}) \sin 360° = \textbf{0 V}$

21. $v = (15 \text{ V}) \sin (30° + 30°) = \textbf{13.0 V}$
      $v = (15 \text{ V}) \sin (30° + 45°) = \textbf{14.5 V}$
      $v = (15 \text{ V}) \sin (30° + 90°) = \textbf{13.0 V}$
      $v = (15 \text{ V}) \sin (30° + 180°) = \textbf{–7.5 V}$

$v = (15 \text{ V})\sin (30° + 200°) = \mathbf{-11.5 \text{ V}}$
$v = (15 \text{ V})\sin (30° + 300°) = \mathbf{-7.5 \text{ V}}$

22. $v = (15 \text{ V})\sin (30° - 30°) = \mathbf{0 \text{ V}}$
      $v = (15 \text{ V})\sin (45° - 30°) = \mathbf{3.88 \text{ V}}$
      $v = (15 \text{ V})\sin (90° - 30°) = \mathbf{13.0 \text{ V}}$
      $v = (15 \text{ V})\sin (180° - 30°) = \mathbf{7.5 \text{ V}}$
      $v = (15 \text{ V})\sin (200° - 30°) = \mathbf{2.60 \text{ V}}$
      $v = (15 \text{ V})\sin (300° - 30°) = \mathbf{-15 \text{ V}}$

SECTION 8-6   Analysis of AC Circuits

23.   (a) $I_{\text{rms}} = 0.707\left(\dfrac{V_p}{R}\right) = 0.707\left(\dfrac{10 \text{ V}}{1.0 \text{ k}\Omega}\right) = \mathbf{7.07 \text{ mA}}$

      (b) $I_{\text{AVG}} = \mathbf{0 \text{ A}}$ over a full cycle.

      (c) $I_p = \dfrac{10 \text{ V}}{1.0 \text{ k}\Omega} = \mathbf{10 \text{ mA}}$

      (d) $I_{pp} = 2(10 \text{ mA}) = \mathbf{20 \text{ mA}}$
      (e) $i = I_p = \mathbf{10 \text{ mA}}$

24. $V_{2(\text{rms})} = V_4 - V_3 = 65 \text{ V} - 30 \text{ V} = 35 \text{ V}$
      $V_{2(p)} = 1.414(35 \text{ V}) = 49.5 \text{ V}$
      $V_{2(\text{AVG})} = 0.637(49.5 \text{ V}) = \mathbf{31.5 \text{ V}}$
      $V_{1(\text{rms})} = V_s - V_4 = 110 \text{ V} - 65 \text{ V} = 45 \text{ V}$
      $V_{1(p)} = 1.414(45 \text{ V}) = 63.6 \text{ V}$
      $V_{1(\text{AVG})} = 0.637(63.6 \text{ V}) = \mathbf{40.5 \text{ V}}$

25. $I_{pp} = \dfrac{16 \text{ V}}{R_1} = \dfrac{16 \text{ V}}{1.0 \text{ k}\Omega} = 16 \text{ mA}$

      $I_{\text{rms}} = 0.707\left(\dfrac{I_{pp}}{2}\right) = 0.707\left(\dfrac{16 \text{ mA}}{2}\right) = 5.66 \text{ mA}$

      $V_{R4} = I_{\text{rms}}R_4 = (5.66 \text{ mA})(560 \text{ }\Omega) = 3.17 \text{ V rms}$
      Applying Kirchhoff's voltage law:
      $V_{R1} + V_{R2} + V_{R3} + V_{R4} = V_s$
      $0.707(8 \text{ V}) + 5 \text{ V} + V_{R3} + 3.17 \text{ V} = 0.707(30 \text{ V})$
      $V_{R3} = 21.21 \text{ V} - 5.66 \text{ V} - 5 \text{ V} - 3.17 \text{ V} = \mathbf{7.38 \text{ V}}$

SECTION 8-7   Superimposed DC and AC Voltages

26. $V_p = (1.414)(10.6 \text{ V}) = 15 \text{ V}$
      $V_{max} = 24 \text{ V} + V_p = \mathbf{39 \text{ V}}$
      $V_{min} = 24 \text{ V} - V_p = \mathbf{9 \text{ V}}$

27. $V_p = (1.414)(3 \text{ V}) = 4.242 \text{ V}$
    $V_{DC} = V_p = \textbf{4.24 V}$

28. $V_{min} = V_{DC} - V_p = 5 \text{ V} - 6 \text{ V} = \textbf{-1 V}$

SECTION 8-8 Nonsinusoidal Waveforms

29. $t_r \cong 3.5 \text{ ms} - 0.5 \text{ ms} = \textbf{3.0 ms}$
    $t_f \cong 16.0 \text{ ms} - 13 \text{ ms} = \textbf{3.0 ms}$
    $t_W \cong 14.5 \text{ ms} - 2.5 \text{ ms} = \textbf{12.0 ms}$
    Amplitude = **5 V**

30. (a) % duty cycle $= \left(\dfrac{t_W}{T}\right)100\% = \left(\dfrac{1 \, \mu s}{4 \, \mu s}\right)100\% = \textbf{25\%}$

    (b) % duty cycle $= \left(\dfrac{t_W}{T}\right)100\% = \left(\dfrac{20 \text{ ms}}{30 \text{ ms}}\right)100\% = \textbf{66.7\%}$

31. (a) $V_{AVG} = \text{baseline} + (\text{duty cycle})(\text{amplitude}) = -1 \text{ V} + (0.25)(2.5 \text{ V}) = \textbf{-0.375 V}$
    (b) $V_{AVG} = 1 \text{ V} + (0.67)(3 \text{ V}) = \textbf{3.01 V}$

32. (a) $f = \dfrac{1}{4 \, \mu s} = \textbf{250 kHz}$

    (b) $f = \dfrac{1}{30 \text{ ms}} = \textbf{33.3 Hz}$

33. (a) $f = \dfrac{1}{20 \, \mu s} = \textbf{50 kHz}$

    (b) $f = \dfrac{1}{100 \, \mu s} = \textbf{10 Hz}$

34. $f = \dfrac{1}{T} = \dfrac{1}{40 \, \mu s} = 25 \text{ kHz}$
    3rd harmonic = **75 kHz**
    5th harmonic = **125 kHz**
    7th harmonic = **175 kHz**
    9th harmonic = **225 kHz**
    11th harmonic = **275 kHz**
    13th harmonic = **325 kHz**

35. fundamental frequency = **25 kHz**

36. Volts/div = 0.2 mV; Time/div = 50 ms
    V_p = Volts/div × Number of divisions = 0.2 V/div × 3 divisions = **0.6 V**
    T = Time/div × Number of divisions = 50 ms/div × 10 divisions = **500 ms**

37. V_p = 0.6 V
    V_{rms} = 0.707V_p = 0.707(0.6 V) = **0.424 V**
    T = 500 ms
    $$f = \frac{1}{T} = \frac{1}{500 \text{ ms}} = \textbf{2 Hz}$$

38. V_p = Volts/div × Number of divisions = 1 V/div 2.2 divisions = 2.2 V
    V_{rms} = 0.707V_p = 0.707(2.2 V) = **1.56 V**
    T = Time/div × Number of divisions = 0.1 μs/div × 6.8 divisions = 0.68 μs
    $$f = \frac{1}{T} = \frac{1}{0.68 \text{ μs}} = \textbf{1.47 MHz}$$

39. Amplitude = Volts/div × Number of divisions = 0.5 V/div × 2.8 div = **1.4 V**
    t_W = Time/div × Number of divisions = 0.1 s × 1.2 div = 0.12 s = **120 ms**
    T = Time/div × Number of divisions = 0.1 s × 4 div = 0.4 s = 400 ms
    $$\% \text{ duty cycle} = \left(\frac{t_W}{T}\right)100\% = \left(\frac{120 \text{ ms}}{400 \text{ ms}}\right)100\% = (0.3)100\% = \textbf{30\%}$$

ADVANCED PROBLEMS

40. $$t = \frac{1}{f} = \frac{1}{2.2 \text{ kHz}} = 0.455 \text{ ms}$$
    At t = 0.12 ms:
    $$\theta = \left(\frac{0.12 \text{ ms}}{0.455 \text{ ms}}\right)360° = 94.9°$$
    $v = \sqrt{2}$ (25 V)sin 94.9° = (35.36)sin 94.9° = 35.2 V

    At t = 0.2 ms:
    $$\theta = \left(\frac{0.2 \text{ ms}}{0.455 \text{ ms}}\right)360° = 158.2°$$
    $v = \sqrt{2}$ (25 V)sin 158.2° = (35.36)sin 158.2° = 13.1 V
    Δv = 35.2 V − 13.1 V = **22.1 V**

41. $I_{max} = \dfrac{V_{max}}{R_T} = \dfrac{200\text{ V} + 150\text{ V}}{100\ \Omega + 47\ \Omega} = \dfrac{350\text{ V}}{147\ \Omega} = \textbf{2.38 A}$

$V_{AVG} = V_{DC} = \left(\dfrac{R_L}{R_T}\right)V_{DC} = \left(\dfrac{100\ \Omega}{147\ \Omega}\right)200\text{ V} = \textbf{136 V}$

See Figure 8-2.

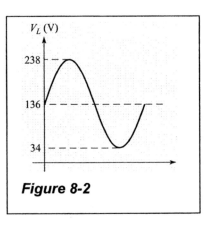

Figure 8-2

42. Average value = area under curve/period

$V_{AVG} = \dfrac{(0\text{ V} + 1\text{ V} + 2\text{ V} + 3\text{ V} + 4\text{ V} + 5\text{ V} + 6\text{ V})(1\text{ ms})}{7\text{ ms}} = \dfrac{21\text{ V}\cdot\text{ms}}{7\text{ ms}} = \textbf{3 V}$

43. (a) **2.5 cycles** are displayed.

(b) $V_p = 2$ V/div $\times$ 2.8 div = 5.6 V, $V_{rms} = 0.707(5.6\text{ V}) = \textbf{3.96 V}$

(c) $T = 4$ div $\times$ 20 μs/div = 80 μs, $f = \dfrac{1}{T} = \dfrac{1}{80\ \mu s} = \textbf{12.5 kHz}$

44. See Figure 8-3.

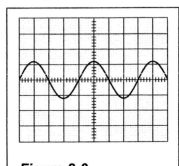

Figure 8-3

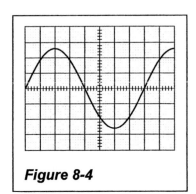

Figure 8-4

45. See Figure 8-4.

46. $V_{p(in)} = (1\text{ div})(5\text{ V/div}) = \textbf{5 V}$

$T_{in} = (2\text{ div})(0.1\text{ ms/div}) = 200\ \mu s$

$f_{in} = \dfrac{1}{200\ \mu s} = \textbf{5 kHz}$

$R_{tot} = 560\ \Omega + (470\ \Omega \parallel (560\ \Omega + 470\ \Omega)) = 560\ \Omega + 323\ \Omega = 883\ \Omega$

$V_{p(out)} = \left(\dfrac{470\ \Omega}{470\ \Omega + 560\ \Omega}\right)\left(\dfrac{323\ \Omega}{883\ \Omega}\right)V_{p(in)} = \left(\dfrac{470\ \Omega}{1030\ \Omega}\right)\left(\dfrac{323\ \Omega}{883\ \Omega}\right)5\text{ V} = \textbf{835 mV}$

$f_{out} = f_{in} = \textbf{5 kHz}$

The scope display for channel 1 shows five cycles of the output waveform with the peak being 0.835 division high relative to the zero crossing of the sine wave.

47. $V_{p(out)} = (0.2 \text{ V/div})(3 \text{ div}) = 0.6 \text{ V}$
$T_{out} = (10 \text{ div})(50 \text{ ms/div}) = 500 \text{ ms}$

$f_{out} = \dfrac{1}{500 \text{ ms}} = 2 \text{ Hz}$

$V_{p(out)} = \left(\dfrac{1.0 \text{ k}\Omega}{1.0 \text{ k}\Omega + 2.2 \text{ k}\Omega} \right) \left(\dfrac{1.0 \text{ k}\Omega \parallel (2.2 \text{ k}\Omega + 1.0 \text{ k}\Omega)}{1.0 \text{ k}\Omega + 1.0 \text{ k}\Omega \parallel (2.2 \text{ k}\Omega + 1.0 \text{ k}\Omega)} \right) V_{p(in)}$

$= (0.313) \left(\dfrac{762 \; \Omega}{1.762 \text{ k}\Omega} \right) V_{p(in)} = 0.135 V_{p(in)}$

$V_{p(in)} = \dfrac{V_{p(out)}}{0.135} = \dfrac{0.6 \text{ V}}{0.135} = \mathbf{4.44 \text{ V}}$

$f_{in} = f_{out} = \mathbf{2 \text{ Hz}}$

Multisim Troubleshooting Problems

48. $V_p = 35.3 \text{ V}; \quad T = 1 \text{ ms}$

49. R_3 is open.

50. R_1 is open.

51. Amplitude $= 5 \text{ V}; \quad T = 1 \text{ ms}$

52. No fault

CHAPTER 9
CAPACITORS

BASIC PROBLEMS

SECTION 9-1 The Basic Capacitor

1.   (a) $C = \dfrac{Q}{V} = \dfrac{50\,\mu\text{C}}{10\,\text{V}} = \mathbf{5\,\mu F}$

    (b) $Q = CV = (0.001\,\mu\text{F})(1\ \text{kV}) = \mathbf{1\,\mu C}$

    (c) $V = \dfrac{Q}{C} = \dfrac{2\,\text{mC}}{200\,\mu\text{F}} = \mathbf{10\ V}$

2.   (a) $(0.1\,\mu\text{F})(10^6\ \text{pF/}\mu\text{F}) = \mathbf{100{,}000\ pF}$

    (b) $(0.0025\,\mu\text{F})(10^6\ \text{pF/}\mu\text{F}) = \mathbf{2500\ pF}$

    (c) $(5\,\mu\text{F})(10^6\ \text{pF/}\mu\text{F}) = \mathbf{5{,}000{,}000\ pF}$

3.   (a) $(1000\ \text{pF})(10^{-6}\ \mu\text{F/pF}) = \mathbf{0.001\,\mu F}$

    (b) $(3500\ \text{pF})(10^{-6}\ \mu\text{F/pF}) = \mathbf{0.0035\,\mu F}$

    (c) $(250\ \text{pF})(10^{-6}\ \mu\text{F/pF}) = \mathbf{0.00025\,\mu F}$

4.   (a) $(0.0000001\ \text{F})(10^6\ \mu\text{F/F}) = \mathbf{0.1\,\mu F}$

    (b) $(0.0022\ \text{F})(10^6\ \mu\text{F/F}) = \mathbf{2200\,\mu F}$

    (c) $(0.0000000015\ \text{F})(10^6\ \mu\text{F/F}) = \mathbf{0.0015\,\mu F}$

5. $W = \left(\dfrac{1}{2}\right)CV^2$

    $C = \dfrac{2W}{V^2} = \dfrac{2(10\ \text{mJ})}{(100\ \text{V})^2} = \mathbf{2\,\mu F}$

6. $C = \dfrac{A\varepsilon_r(8.85\times10^{-12}\ \text{F/m})}{d} = \dfrac{(0.002\ \text{m}^2)(5)(8.85\times10^{-12}\ \text{F/m})}{63.5\,\mu\text{m}} = \mathbf{1.39\ nF}$

7. $C = \dfrac{A\varepsilon_r(8.85\times10^{-12}\ \text{F/m})}{d}$

    $= \dfrac{(0.1\ \text{m}^2)(1.006)(8.85\times10^{-12}\ \text{F/m})}{0.01\,\text{m}} = 8.85\times10^{-11}\ \text{F} = \mathbf{88.5\ pF}$

8. $C = \dfrac{A\varepsilon_r(8.85\times10^{-12})}{d}$

$A = \dfrac{Cd}{\varepsilon_r(8.85\times10^{-12})} = \dfrac{(1)(8\times10^{-5})}{(2.5)(8.85\times10^{-12})} = 3.6\times10^6 \, \text{m}^2$

$l = \sqrt{A} = \sqrt{3.6\times10^6 \, \text{m}^2} = 1.9\times10^3 \, \text{m}$ (almost 1.2 miles on a side)

The capacitor is too large to be practical and, of course, will not fit in the Astrodome.

9. $C = \dfrac{A\varepsilon_r(8.85\times10^{-12})}{d} = \dfrac{(0.09)(2.5)(8.85\times10^{-12})}{8.0\times10^{-5}} = 24.9 \text{ nF} = \mathbf{0.0249 \ \mu F}$

10. $\Delta T = 50 \text{ C}°$
$(-200 \text{ ppm/}°\text{C})50 \text{ C}° = -10,000 \text{ ppm}$
$\Delta C = \left(\dfrac{1\times10^3}{1\times10^6}\right)(-10\times10^3 \text{ ppm}) = -10 \text{ pF}$
$C_{75°} = 1000 \text{ pF} - 10 \text{ pF} = \mathbf{990 \ pF}$

11. $\Delta T = 25 \text{ C}°$
$(500 \text{ ppm/}°\text{C})25 \text{ C}° = 12,500 \text{ ppm}$
$(1\times10^6 \text{ pF/}\mu\text{F})(0.001 \ \mu\text{F}) = 1000 \text{ pF}$
$\Delta C = \left(\dfrac{1000}{1\times10^6}\right)12,500 \text{ ppm} = \mathbf{12.5 \ pF}$

SECTION 9-2 Types of Capacitors

12. The plate area is increased by increasing the number of layers of plate and dielectric materials.

13. Ceramic has a higher dielectric constant than mica.

14. See Figure 9-1.

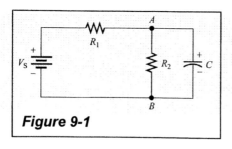

Figure 9-1

15. (a) 0.022 μF (b) 0.047 μF (c) 0.001 μF (d) 22 pF

16. Aluminum, tantalum; electrolytics are polarized, others are not.

17. (a) Encapsulation
    (b) Dielectric (ceramic disk)
    (c) Plate (metal disk)
    (d) Conductive leads

SECTION 9-3 Series Capacitors

18. $C_T = \dfrac{1000 \text{ pF}}{5} = \mathbf{200 \text{ pF}}$

19. (a) $C_T = \dfrac{1}{\dfrac{1}{1\,\mu\text{F}} + \dfrac{1}{2.2\,\mu\text{F}}} = \mathbf{0.69\,\mu F}$

    (b) $C_T = \dfrac{1}{\dfrac{1}{100\text{ pF}} + \dfrac{1}{560\text{ pF}} + \dfrac{1}{390\text{ pF}}} = \mathbf{69.7 \text{ pF}}$

    (c) $C_T = \dfrac{1}{\dfrac{1}{10\,\mu\text{F}} + \dfrac{1}{4.7\,\mu\text{F}} + \dfrac{1}{47\,\mu\text{F}} + \dfrac{1}{22\,\mu\text{F}}} = \mathbf{2.6\,\mu F}$

20. (a) $C_T = 0.69\,\mu\text{F}$

    $V_{1\mu\text{F}} = \left(\dfrac{C_T}{1\,\mu\text{F}}\right)10\text{ V} = \left(\dfrac{0.69\,\mu\text{F}}{1\,\mu\text{F}}\right)10\text{ V} = \mathbf{6.9 \text{ V}}$

    $V_{2.2\mu\text{F}} = \left(\dfrac{0.69\,\mu\text{F}}{2.2\,\mu\text{F}}\right)10\text{ V} = \mathbf{3.13 \text{ V}}$

    (b) $C_T = 69.7\text{ pF}$

    $V_{100\text{pF}} = \left(\dfrac{69.7\text{ pF}}{100\text{ pF}}\right)100\text{ V} = 69.7\text{ V}$

    $V_{560\text{pF}} = \left(\dfrac{69.7\text{ pF}}{560\text{ pF}}\right)100\text{ V} = 12.4\text{ V}$

    $V_{390\text{pF}} = \left(\dfrac{69.7\text{ pF}}{390\text{ pF}}\right)100\text{ V} = 17.9\text{ V}$

    (c) $C_T = 2.6\,\mu\text{F}$

    $V_{10\mu\text{F}} = \left(\dfrac{2.6\,\mu\text{F}}{10\,\mu\text{F}}\right)30\text{ V} = \mathbf{7.8 \text{ V}}$

$$V_{4.7\mu F} = \left(\frac{2.6\ \mu F}{4.7\ \mu F}\right)30\ V = \textbf{16.8 V}$$

$$V_{47\mu F} = \left(\frac{2.6\ \mu F}{47\ \mu F}\right)30\ V = \textbf{1.68 V}$$

$$V_{22\mu F} = \left(\frac{2.6\ \mu F}{22\ \mu F}\right)30\ V = \textbf{3.59 V}$$

21. $Q_T = Q_1 = Q_2 = Q_3 = Q_4 = 10\ \mu C$

$$V_1 = \frac{Q_1}{C_1} = \frac{10\ \mu C}{4.7\ \mu F} = \textbf{2.13 V}$$

$$V_2 = \frac{Q_2}{C_2} = \frac{10\ \mu C}{1\ \mu F} = \textbf{10 V}$$

$$V_3 = \frac{Q_3}{C_3} = \frac{10\ \mu C}{2.2\ \mu F} = \textbf{4.55 V}$$

$$V_4 = \frac{Q_4}{C_4} = \frac{10\ \mu C}{10\ \mu F} = \textbf{1 V}$$

SECTION 9-4 Parallel Capacitors

22. (a) $C_T = 47\ pF + 10\ pF + 1000\ pF = \textbf{1057 pF}$
    (b) $C_T = 0.1\ \mu F + 0.01\ \mu F + 0.001\ \mu F + 0.01\ \mu F = \textbf{0.121}\ \boldsymbol{\mu}\textbf{F}$

23. (a) $C_T = \dfrac{1}{\left(\dfrac{1}{10\ \mu F}\right) + \left(\dfrac{1}{10\ \mu F}\right) + \left(\dfrac{1}{2.2\ \mu F + 3.3\ \mu F}\right)} = \textbf{2.62}\ \boldsymbol{\mu}\textbf{F}$

   (b) $C_T = \left(\dfrac{1}{\dfrac{1}{100\ pF} + \dfrac{1}{100\ pF}}\right) + \left(\dfrac{1}{\dfrac{1}{1000\ pF} + \dfrac{1}{470\ pF}}\right) + \left(\dfrac{1}{\dfrac{1}{0.001\ \mu F} + \dfrac{1}{470\ pF}}\right)$

   $= 50\ pF + 319.7\ pF + 319.7\ pF = \textbf{689 pF}$

   (c) $C_T = \dfrac{1}{\left(\dfrac{1}{\dfrac{1}{1\ \mu F} + \dfrac{1}{1\ \mu F}} + 1\ \mu F\right) + \dfrac{1}{1\ \mu F}} + 1\ \mu F = \textbf{1.6}\ \boldsymbol{\mu}\textbf{F}$

24. (a) $C_T = 2.62\ \mu F$

   $$V_{AB} = \left(\frac{2.62\ \mu F}{5\ \mu F}\right)5\ V = \textbf{2.62 V}$$

(b)   For the part of the circuit in Figure 9-2:

$$C_T = \cfrac{1}{\left(\cfrac{1}{C_{0.001}}\right) + \left(\cfrac{1}{C_{470}}\right)} = \cfrac{1}{\left(\cfrac{1}{0.001\ \mu F}\right) + \left(\cfrac{1}{470\ pF}\right)}$$

$$= 319.7\ pF$$

$$V_{AB} = \left(\frac{319.7\ pF}{0.001\ \mu F}\right)10\ V = \mathbf{3.20\ V}$$

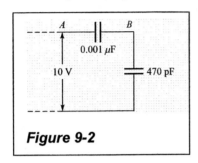

Figure 9-2

(c) $C_{AB} = 1.5\ \mu F$
For the part of the circuit shown in Figure 9-3:

$$C_T = \cfrac{1}{\cfrac{1}{1\ \mu F} + \cfrac{1}{1.5\ \mu F}} = 0.6\ \mu F$$

$$V_{AB} = \left(\frac{0.6\ \mu F}{1.5\ \mu F}\right)10\ V = \mathbf{4\ V}$$

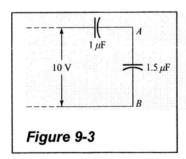

Figure 9-3

SECTION 9-5 Capacitors in DC Circuits

25.   (a) $\tau = RC = (100\ \Omega)(1\ \mu F) = \mathbf{100\ \mu s}$
       (b) $\tau = RC = (10\ M\Omega)(56\ pF) = \mathbf{560\ \mu s}$
       (c) $\tau = RC = (4.7\ k\Omega)(0.0047\ \mu F) = \mathbf{22.1\ \mu s}$
       (d) $\tau = RC = (1.5\ M\Omega)(0.01\ \mu F) = \mathbf{15\ ms}$

26.   (a) $5\tau = 5RC = 5(47\ \Omega)(47\ \mu F) = \mathbf{11.04\ ms}$
       (b) $5\tau = 5RC = 5(3300\ \Omega)(0.015\ \mu F) = \mathbf{248\ \mu s}$

(c) $5\tau = 5RC = 5(22 \text{ k}\Omega)(100 \text{ pF}) = \mathbf{11 \ \mu s}$

(d) $5\tau = 5RC = 5(4.7 \text{ M}\Omega)(10 \text{ pF}) = \mathbf{235 \ \mu s}$

27. $\tau = RC = (100 \ \Omega)(1 \ \mu\text{F}) = 10 \ \mu s$

    (a) $v_C = 15 \text{ V}(1 - e^{-t/RC}) = 15 \text{ V}(1 - e^{-10\mu s/10\mu s}) = 15 \text{ V}(1 - e^{-1}) = \mathbf{9.48 \ V}$

    (b) $v_C = 15 \text{ V}(1 - e^{-2}) = \mathbf{13.0 \ V}$

    (c) $v_C = 15 \text{ V}(1 - e^{-3}) = \mathbf{14.3 \ V}$

    (d) $v_C = 15 \text{ V}(1 - e^{-4}) = \mathbf{14.7 \ V}$

    (e) $v_C = 15 \text{ V}(1 - e^{-5}) = \mathbf{14.9 \ V}$

28. $\tau = RC = (1.0 \text{ k}\Omega)(1.5 \ \mu\text{F}) = 1.5 \text{ ms}$

    (a) $v_C = V_i e^{-t/RC} = 25e^{-1.5ms/1.5ms} = 25e^{-1} = \mathbf{9.2 \ V}$

    (b) $v_C = V_i e^{-t/RC} = 25e^{-4.5ms/1.5ms} = 25e^{-3} = \mathbf{1.24 \ V}$

    (c) $v_C = V_i e^{-t/RC} = 25e^{-6ms/1.5ms} = 25e^{-4} = \mathbf{458 \ mV}$

    (d) $v_C = V_i e^{-t/RC} = 25e^{-7.5ms/1.5ms} = 25e^{-5} = \mathbf{168 \ mV}$

29.   (a) $v_C = 15 \text{ V}(1 - e^{-t/RC}) = 15 \text{ V}(1 - e^{-2\mu s/10\mu s}) = 15 \text{ V}(1 - e^{-0.2}) = \mathbf{2.72 \ V}$

    (b) $v_C = 15 \text{ V}(1 - e^{-5\mu s/10\mu s}) = 15 \text{ V}(1 - e^{-0.5}) = \mathbf{5.90 \ V}$

    (c) $v_C = 15 \text{ V}(1 - e^{-15\mu s/10\mu s}) = 15 \text{ V}(1 - e^{-1.5}) = \mathbf{11.7 \ V}$

30.   (a) $v_C = V_i e^{-t/RC} = 25e^{-0.5ms/1.5ms} = 25e^{-0.33} = \mathbf{18.0 \ V}$

    (b) $v_C = V_i e^{-t/RC} = 25e^{-1ms/1.5ms} = 25e^{-0.67} = \mathbf{12.8 \ V}$

    (c) $v_C = V_i e^{-t/RC} = 25e^{-2ms/1.5ms} = 25e^{-1.33} = \mathbf{6.61 \ V}$

SECTION 9-6   Capacitors in AC Circuits

31.   (a) $X_C = \dfrac{1}{2\pi fC} = \dfrac{1}{2\pi(10 \text{ Hz})(0.047 \ \mu\text{F})} = \mathbf{339 \ k\Omega}$

    (b) $X_C = \dfrac{1}{2\pi fC} = \dfrac{1}{2\pi(250 \text{ Hz})(0.047 \ \mu\text{F})} = \mathbf{13.5 \ k\Omega}$

    (c) $X_C = \dfrac{1}{2\pi fC} = \dfrac{1}{2\pi(5 \text{ kHz})(0.047 \ \mu\text{F})} = \mathbf{677 \ \Omega}$

    (d) $X_C = \dfrac{1}{2\pi fC} = \dfrac{1}{2\pi(100 \text{ kHz})(0.047 \ \mu\text{F})} = \mathbf{33.9 \ \Omega}$

32.   (a) $X_C = \dfrac{1}{2\pi fC} = \dfrac{1}{2\pi(1 \text{ kHz})(0.047 \ \mu\text{F})} = \mathbf{3.39 \ k\Omega}$

    (b) $C_T = 10 \ \mu\text{F} + 15 \ \mu\text{F} = 25 \ \mu\text{F}$

        $X_C = \dfrac{1}{2\pi(1 \text{ Hz})(25 \ \mu\text{F})} = \mathbf{6.37 \ k\Omega}$

(c) $\quad C_T = \dfrac{1}{\dfrac{1}{1\,\mu F} + \dfrac{1}{1\,\mu F}} = 0.5\,\mu F$

$X_C = \dfrac{1}{2\pi(60\ \text{Hz})(0.5\,\mu F)} = \textbf{5.31 k}\boldsymbol{\Omega}$

33. C_T for each circuit was found in Problem 23.

(a) $\quad C_T = 2.62\ \mu F$

$X_C = \dfrac{1}{2\pi f C_T} = \dfrac{1}{2\pi(2\ \text{kHz})(2.62\,\mu F)} = \textbf{30.4}\ \boldsymbol{\Omega}$

(b) $\quad C_T = 689\ \text{pF}$

$X_C = \dfrac{1}{2\pi(2\ \text{kHz})(689\ \text{pF})} = \textbf{115 k}\boldsymbol{\Omega}$

(c) $\quad C_T = 1.6\ \mu F$

$X_C = \dfrac{1}{2\pi(2\ \text{kHz})(1.6\,\mu F)} = \textbf{49.7}\ \boldsymbol{\Omega}$

34. (a) For $X_C = 100\ \Omega$:

$f = \dfrac{1}{2\pi X_C C} = \dfrac{1}{2\pi(100\ \Omega)(0.047\,\mu F)} = \textbf{33.86 kHz}$

For $X_C = 1\ \text{k}\Omega$:

$f = \dfrac{1}{2\pi X_C C} = \dfrac{1}{2\pi(1\ \text{k}\Omega)(0.047\,\mu F)} = \textbf{3.386 kHz}$

(b) For $X_C = 100\ \Omega$:

$f = \dfrac{1}{2\pi X_C C} = \dfrac{1}{2\pi(100\ \Omega)(25\,\mu F)} = \textbf{63.7 Hz}$

For $X_C = 1\ \text{k}\Omega$:

$f = \dfrac{1}{2\pi X_C C} = \dfrac{1}{2\pi(1\ \text{k}\Omega)(25\,\mu F)} = \textbf{6.37 kHz}$

(c) For $X_C = 100\ \Omega$:

$f = \dfrac{1}{2\pi X_C C} = \dfrac{1}{2\pi(100\ \Omega)(0.5\,\mu F)} = \textbf{3.18 kHz}$

For $X_C = 1\ \text{k}\Omega$:

$f = \dfrac{1}{2\pi X_C C} = \dfrac{1}{2\pi(1\ \text{k}\Omega)(0.5\,\mu F)} = \textbf{318 Hz}$

35. $\quad X_C = \dfrac{V_{rms}}{I_{rms}} = \dfrac{20\ \text{V}}{100\ \text{mA}} = 0.2\ \text{k}\Omega = \textbf{200}\ \boldsymbol{\Omega}$

36. $V_{rms} = I_{rms} X_C$

$$X_C = \frac{1}{2\pi(10 \text{ kHz})(0.0047 \text{ } \mu\text{F})} = 3.39 \text{ k}\Omega$$

$V_{rms} = (1 \text{ mA})(3.39 \text{ k}\Omega) = \textbf{3.39 V}$

37. $X_C = \dfrac{1}{2\pi fC} = 3.39 \text{ k}\Omega$

$P_{true} = \textbf{0 W}$

$P_r = I_{rms}^2 X_C = (1 \text{ mA})^2 (3.39 \text{ k}\Omega) = \textbf{3.39 mVAR}$

SECTION 9-7 Capacitor Applications

38. The ripple voltage is reduced when the capacitance is increased.

39. $X_{C(bypass)}$ ideally should be **0 Ω** to provide a short to ground for ac.

ADVANCED PROBLEMS

40. $V_X = \left(\dfrac{C_T}{C_X}\right) V_S$

$$C_T = \frac{C_X V_X}{V_S} = \frac{(1 \text{ } \mu\text{F})(8 \text{ V})}{12 \text{ V}} = 0.667 \text{ } \mu\text{F}$$

$$C_X = \left(\frac{C_T}{V_X}\right) V_S = \left(\frac{0.667 \text{ } \mu\text{F}}{4 \text{ V}}\right) 12 \text{ V} = \textbf{2 } \boldsymbol{\mu}\textbf{F}$$

41. $v = v_i e^{-t/RC}$

$e^{-t/RC} = \dfrac{v}{V_i}$

$\ln(e^{-t/RC}) = \ln\left(\dfrac{V}{V_i}\right)$

$-\left(\dfrac{t}{RC}\right) = \ln\left(\dfrac{v}{V_i}\right)$

$t = -RC \ln\left(\dfrac{V}{V_i}\right)$

$t = -(1.0 \text{ k}\Omega)(1.5 \text{ } \mu\text{F}) \ln\left(\dfrac{3 \text{ V}}{25 \text{ V}}\right) = \textbf{3.18 ms}$

42. $v = V_F(1 - e^{-t/RC})$

$v = V_F - V_F e^{-t/RC}$

$V_F e^{-t/RC} = V_F - v$

$e^{-t/RC} = \dfrac{V_F - v}{V_F} = 1 - \dfrac{v}{V_F}$

$\ln(e^{-t/RC}) = \ln\left(1 - \dfrac{v}{V_F}\right)$

$-\left(\dfrac{t}{RC}\right) = \ln\left(1 - \dfrac{v}{V_F}\right)$

$t = -RC\, \ln\left(1 - \dfrac{v}{V_F}\right)$

$t = -(10\ \text{k}\Omega)(0.001\ \mu\text{F})\ln\left(1 - \dfrac{8\ \text{V}}{15\ \text{V}}\right) = \textbf{7.62 } \boldsymbol{\mu}\textbf{s}$

43. Looking from the capacitor, the Thevenin resistance is

$R_{\text{TH}} = R_4 + R_1 \parallel R_2 \parallel R_3 = 1471\ \Omega$

$\tau = R_{\text{TH}}C = (1471\ \Omega)(0.0022\ \mu\text{F}) = \textbf{3.24 } \boldsymbol{\mu}\textbf{s}$

44. $t = RC\, \ln\left(1 - \dfrac{v_C}{V_F}\right)$

$R = \dfrac{-t}{C\ln\left(1 - \dfrac{v_C}{V_F}\right)} = \dfrac{-10\ \mu\text{s}}{(1000\ \text{pF})\ln\left(1 - \dfrac{7.2}{10}\right)} = \textbf{7.86 k}\boldsymbol{\Omega}$

45. $\tau_1 = (R_1 + R_2)C = (55\ \text{k}\Omega)(1\ \mu\text{F}) = 55\ \text{ms}$

$\tau_2 = (R_2 + R_3)C = (43\ \text{k}\Omega)(1\ \mu\text{F})\ 43\ \text{ms}$

$5\tau_2 = 5(43\ \text{ms}) = 215\ \text{ms}$

$v_C = 20(1 - e^{-10\text{ms}/.55\text{ms}}) = 3.32\ \text{V}$

See Figure 9-4(a).

$v_C = 3.32e^{-5\text{ms}/43\text{ms}} = 2.96\ \text{V}$

See Figure 9-4(b).

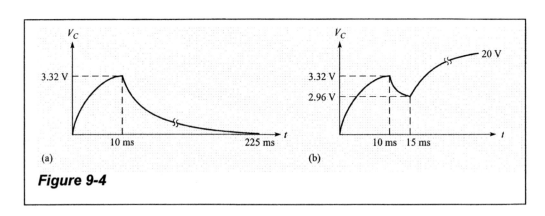

(a)

(b)

Figure 9-4

46. $C_{5\text{-}6} = 0.006\ \mu\text{F}$, $C_{4\text{-}5\text{-}6} = 0.053\ \mu\text{F}$, $C_{3\text{-}4\text{-}5\text{-}6} = 0.01169\ \mu\text{F}$, $C_{2\text{-}3\text{-}4\text{-}5\text{-}6} = 0.03369\ \mu\text{F}$

$C_T = 0.00771\ \mu\text{F}$, $X_{C(tot)} = 68.8\ \text{k}\Omega$

$$I_{C1} = \frac{V_s}{X_{C(tot)}} = \frac{10\ \text{V}}{68.8\ \text{k}\Omega} = \mathbf{145\ \mu A}$$

$$V_{C1} = \left(\frac{C_T}{C_1}\right)V_s = \left(\frac{0.00771\ \mu\text{F}}{0.01\ \mu\text{F}}\right)10\ \text{V} = \mathbf{7.71\ V}$$

$$V_{C2} = V_s - V_{C1} = 10\ \text{V} - 7.71\ \text{V} = \mathbf{2.29\ V}$$

$X_{C2} = 24.1\ \text{k}\Omega$

$$I_{C2} = \frac{V_{C2}}{X_{C2}} = \frac{2.29\ \text{V}}{24.1\ \text{k}\Omega} = \mathbf{95.0\ \mu A}$$

$$V_{C3} = \left(\frac{C_{3\text{-}4\text{-}5\text{-}6}}{C_3}\right)V_{C2} = \left(\frac{0.01183\ \mu\text{F}}{0.015\ \mu\text{F}}\right)2.29\ \text{V} = \mathbf{1.78\ V}$$

$X_{C3} = 35.4\ \text{k}\Omega$

$$I_{C3} = \frac{V_{C3}}{X_{C3}} = \frac{1.78\ \text{V}}{35.4\ \text{k}\Omega} = \mathbf{50.4\ \mu A}$$

$$V_{C4} = V_{C2} - V_{C3} = 2.29\ \text{V} - 1.78\ \text{V} = \mathbf{505\ mV}$$

$X_{C4} = 11.3\ \text{k}\Omega$

$$I_{C4} = \frac{V_{C4}}{X_{C4}} = \frac{505\ \text{mV}}{11.3\ \text{k}\Omega} = \mathbf{44.7\ \mu A}$$

$$V_{C5} = \left(\frac{C_{5\text{-}6}}{C_5}\right)V_{C4} = \left(\frac{0.006\ \mu\text{F}}{0.01\ \mu\text{F}}\right)505\ \text{mV} = \mathbf{303\ mV}$$

$X_{C5} = 53.1\ \text{k}\Omega$

$$I_{C5} = I_{C6} = \frac{V_{C5}}{X_{C5}} = \frac{303\ \text{mV}}{53.1\ \text{k}\Omega} = \mathbf{5.71\ \mu A}$$

$$V_{C6} = V_{C4} - V_{C5} = 505\ \text{mV} - 303\ \text{mV} = \mathbf{202\ mV}$$

47. $V_{C2} = V_{C3} = (4\ \text{mA})X_{C3} = (4\ \text{mA})(750\ \Omega) = 3\ \text{V}$

$$f = \frac{1}{2\pi X_{C3}C_3} = \frac{1}{2\pi(750\ \Omega)(0.0015\ \mu\text{F})} = 141.5\ \text{kHz}$$

$$X_{C2} = \frac{1}{2\pi f C_2} = \frac{1}{2\pi(141.5\ \text{kHz})(0.0022\ \mu\text{F})} = 511\ \Omega$$

$$I_{C2} = \frac{V_{C2}}{X_{C2}} = \frac{3\ \text{V}}{511\ \Omega} = 5.87\ \text{mA}$$

$I_{C1} = I_{C(tot)} = I_{C2} + I_{C3} = 5.87\ \text{mA} + 4\ \text{mA} = 9.87\ \text{mA}$

$V_{C1} = 5\ \text{V} - 3\ \text{V} = 2\ \text{V}$

$$X_{C1} = \frac{V_{C1}}{I_{C1}} = \frac{2\ \text{V}}{9.87\ \text{mA}} = 203\ \Omega$$

$$C_1 = \frac{1}{2\pi f X_{C1}} = \frac{1}{2\pi(141.5\ \text{kHz})(203\ \Omega)} = \mathbf{0.0056\ \mu F}$$

48. *Position 1*:

$$V_5 - \left(\frac{C_{T(1,5)}}{C_5}\right) 12\text{ V}$$

$$\frac{1}{C_{T(1,5)}} = \frac{1}{C_1} + \frac{1}{C_5} = \frac{1}{0.01\,\mu\text{F}} + \frac{1}{0.068\,\mu\text{F}} \qquad C_T = 0.0087\,\mu\text{F}$$

$$V_5 = \left(\frac{0.0087\,\mu\text{F}}{0.068\,\mu\text{F}}\right) 12\text{ V} = 1.54\text{ V}$$

$$\frac{1}{C_{T(3,6)}} = \frac{1}{C_3} + \frac{1}{C_6} = \frac{1}{0.047\,\mu\text{F}} + \frac{1}{0.056\,\mu\text{F}} \qquad C_{T(3,6)} = 0.0256\,\mu\text{F}$$

$$V_6 = \left(\frac{C_{T(3,6)}}{C_6}\right) 12\text{ V} = \left(\frac{0.0256\,\mu\text{F}}{0.056\,\mu\text{F}}\right) 12\text{ V} = 5.48\text{ V}$$

Position 2:

$$\frac{1}{C_{T(2,5)}} = \frac{1}{C_2} + \frac{1}{C_5} = \frac{1}{0.022\,\mu\text{F}} + \frac{1}{0.068\,\mu\text{F}} \qquad C_{T(2,5)} = 0.0166\,\mu\text{F}$$

$$V_5 = \left(\frac{C_{T(2,5)}}{C_5}\right) 12\text{ V} = \left(\frac{0.0166\,\mu\text{F}}{0.068\,\mu\text{F}}\right) 12\text{ V} = 2.93\text{ V}$$

$$\frac{1}{C_{T(4,6)}} = \frac{1}{C_4} + \frac{1}{C_6} = \frac{1}{0.015\,\mu\text{F}} + \frac{1}{0.056\,\mu\text{F}} \qquad C_{T(4,6)} = 0.0118\,\mu\text{F}$$

$$V_6 = \left(\frac{C_{T(4,6)}}{C_6}\right) 12\text{ V} = \left(\frac{0.0118\,\mu\text{F}}{0.056\,\mu\text{F}}\right) 12\text{ V} = 2.54\text{ V}$$

$\Delta V_5 = 2.93\text{ V} - 1.54\text{ V} = \textbf{1.39 V increase,} \qquad \Delta V_6 = 5.48\text{ V} - 2.54\text{ V} = \textbf{2.94 V decrease}$

49.

$$\frac{1}{C_{tot(3,5,6)}} = \frac{1}{C_3} + \frac{1}{C_5} + \frac{1}{C_6} = \frac{1}{0.015\,\mu\text{F}} + \frac{1}{0.01\,\mu\text{F}} + \frac{1}{0.015\,\mu\text{F}} \qquad C_{tot(3,5,6)} = 0.0043\,\mu\text{F}$$

$$C_{tot(2,3,5,6)} = 0.022\,\mu\text{F} + 0.0043\,\mu\text{F} = 0.0263\,\mu\text{F}$$

$$\frac{1}{C_{tot}} = \frac{1}{C_1} + \frac{1}{C_{tot(2,3,5,6)}} = \frac{1}{0.01\,\mu\text{F}} + \frac{1}{0.0263\,\mu\text{F}} \qquad C_{tot} = 0.00725\,\mu\text{F}$$

$$V_{C1} = \left(\frac{C_{tot}}{C_1}\right) 10\text{ V} = \left(\frac{0.00725\,\mu\text{F}}{0.01\,\mu\text{F}}\right) 10\text{ V} = \textbf{7.25 V}$$

$$V_{C2} = \left(\frac{C_{tot}}{C_{tot(2,3,5,6)}}\right) 10\text{ V} = \left(\frac{0.00725\,\mu\text{F}}{0.0263\,\mu\text{F}}\right) 10\text{ V} = \textbf{2.76 V}$$

$$V_{C3} = \left(\frac{C_{tot(3,5,6)}}{C_3}\right) V_{C2} = \left(\frac{0.0043\,\mu\text{F}}{0.015\,\mu\text{F}}\right) 2.76\text{ V} = \textbf{0.79 V}$$

$$V_{C5} = \left(\frac{C_{tot(3,5,6)}}{C_5}\right) V_{C2} = \left(\frac{0.0043\,\mu\text{F}}{0.01\,\mu\text{F}}\right) 2.76\text{ V} = \textbf{1.19 V}$$

$$V_{C6} = \left(\frac{C_{tot(3,5,6)}}{C_6}\right) V_{C2} = \left(\frac{0.0043\,\mu\text{F}}{0.015\,\mu\text{F}}\right) 2.76\text{ V} = \textbf{0.79 V}$$

$$V_{C4} = V_{C5} + V_{C6} = 1.19\text{ V} + 0.79\text{ V} = \textbf{1.98 V}$$

50. C_2 is leaky.

51. C_2 is open.

52. C_1 is shorted.

53. No fault

54. C_1 is shorted.

CHAPTER 10
RC CIRCUITS

BASIC PROBLEMS

SECTION 10-1 Sinusoidal Response of *RC* Circuits

1. Both voltages are also sine waves with the same **8 kHz** frequency as the source voltage.

2. The current is sinusoidal.

SECTION 10-2 Impedance and Phase Angle of Series *RC* Circuits

3. (a) $Z = \sqrt{R^2 + X_C^2} = \sqrt{(270\ \Omega)^2 + (100\ \Omega)^2} = \mathbf{288\ \Omega}$

    (b) $Z = \sqrt{R^2 + X_C^2} = \sqrt{(680\ \Omega)^2 + (1000\ \Omega)^2} = \mathbf{1209\ \Omega}$

4. (a) $R_{tot} = 100\ \text{k}\Omega + 47\ \text{k}\Omega = 147\ \text{k}\Omega$

    $$C_{tot} = \cfrac{1}{\cfrac{1}{0.01\ \mu\text{F}} + \cfrac{1}{0.022\ \mu\text{F}}} = 0.00688\ \mu\text{F}$$

    $$X_{C(tot)} = \frac{1}{2\pi f C_{tot}} = \frac{1}{2\pi(100\ \text{Hz})(0.00688\ \mu\text{F})} = 231\ \text{k}\Omega$$

    $$Z = \sqrt{R_{tot}^2 + X_{C(tot)}^2} = \sqrt{(147\ \text{k}\Omega)^2 + (231\ \text{k}\Omega)^2} = \mathbf{274\ k\Omega}$$

    $$\theta = \tan^{-1}\left(\frac{X_{C(tot)}}{R_{tot}}\right) = \tan^{-1}\left(\frac{231\ \text{k}\Omega}{147\ \text{k}\Omega}\right) = \mathbf{57.6°}\ (I \text{ leads } V)$$

    (b) $C_{tot} = 560\ \text{pF} + 560\ \text{pF} = 1120\ \text{pF}$

    $$X_{C(tot)} = \frac{1}{2\pi f C_{tot}} = \frac{1}{2\pi(20\ \text{kHz})(1120\ \text{pF})} = 7.11\ \text{k}\Omega$$

    $$Z = \sqrt{R_{tot}^2 + X_{C(tot)}^2} = \sqrt{(10\ \text{k}\Omega)^2 + (7.11\ \text{k}\Omega)^2} = \mathbf{12.3\ k\Omega}$$

    $$\theta = \tan^{-1}\left(\frac{X_{C(tot)}}{R}\right) = \tan^{-1}\left(\frac{7.11\ \text{k}\Omega}{10\ \text{k}\Omega}\right) = \mathbf{35.4°}\ (I \text{ leads } V)$$

5.   (a) $X_C = \dfrac{1}{2\pi f C} = \dfrac{1}{2\pi(100\ \text{Hz})(0.0022\ \mu\text{F})} = 723\ \text{k}\Omega$

           $Z = \sqrt{R^2 + X_C^2} = \sqrt{(56\ \text{k}\Omega)^2 + (723\ \text{k}\Omega)^2} = \mathbf{726\ k\Omega}$

   (b) $X_C = \dfrac{1}{2\pi f C} = \dfrac{1}{2\pi(500\ \text{Hz})(0.0022\ \mu\text{F})} = 145\ \text{k}\Omega$

           $Z = \sqrt{R^2 + X_C^2} = \sqrt{(56\ \text{k}\Omega)^2 + (145\ \text{k}\Omega)^2} = \mathbf{155\ k\Omega}$

   (c) $X_C = \dfrac{1}{2\pi f C} = \dfrac{1}{2\pi(1\ \text{kHz})(0.0022\ \mu\text{F})} = 72.3\ \text{k}\Omega$

           $Z = \sqrt{R^2 + X_C^2} = \sqrt{(56\ \text{k}\Omega)^2 + (72.3\ \text{k}\Omega)^2} = \mathbf{91.5\ k\Omega}$

   (d) $X_C = \dfrac{1}{2\pi f C} = \dfrac{1}{2\pi(2.5\ \text{kHz})(0.0022\ \mu\text{F})} = 28.9\ \text{k}\Omega$

           $Z = \sqrt{R^2 + X_C^2} = \sqrt{(56\ \text{k}\Omega)^2 + (31.8\ \text{k}\Omega)^2} = \mathbf{63.0\ k\Omega}$

6.   (a) $X_C = \dfrac{1}{2\pi f C} = \dfrac{1}{2\pi(100\ \text{Hz})(0.0047\ \mu\text{F})} = 339\ \text{k}\Omega$

           $Z = \sqrt{R^2 + X_C^2} = \sqrt{(56\ \text{k}\Omega)^2 + (339\ \text{k}\Omega)^2} = \mathbf{343\ k\Omega}$

   (b) $X_C = \dfrac{1}{2\pi f C} = \dfrac{1}{2\pi(500\ \text{Hz})(0.0047\ \mu\text{F})} = 67.7\ \text{k}\Omega$

           $Z = \sqrt{R^2 + X_C^2} = \sqrt{(56\ \text{k}\Omega)^2 + (67.7\ \text{k}\Omega)^2} = \mathbf{87.9\ k\Omega}$

   (c) $X_C = \dfrac{1}{2\pi f C} = \dfrac{1}{2\pi(1\ \text{kHz})(0.0047\ \mu\text{F})} = 33.9\ \text{k}\Omega$

           $Z = \sqrt{R^2 + X_C^2} = \sqrt{(56\ \text{k}\Omega)^2 + (33.9\ \text{k}\Omega)^2} = \mathbf{65.4\ k\Omega}$

   (d) $X_C = \dfrac{1}{2\pi f C} = \dfrac{1}{2\pi(2.5\ \text{kHz})(0.0047\ \mu\text{F})} = 13.5\ \text{k}\Omega$

           $Z = \sqrt{R^2 + X_C^2} = \sqrt{(56\ \text{k}\Omega)^2 + (13.5\ \text{k}\Omega)^2} = \mathbf{57.6\ k\Omega}$

SECTION 10-3   Analysis of Series *RC* Circuits

7.   (a) $I = \dfrac{V_s}{Z} = \dfrac{10\ \text{V}}{288\ \Omega} = \mathbf{34.7\ mA}$

   (b) $I = \dfrac{V_s}{Z} = \dfrac{5\ \text{V}}{1209\ \Omega} = \mathbf{4.14\ mA}$

8. (a) $I = \dfrac{V_s}{Z} = \dfrac{50\ \text{V}}{274\ \text{k}\Omega} = \mathbf{182\ \mu A}$

(b) $I = \dfrac{V_s}{Z} = \dfrac{8\ \text{V}}{12.3\ \text{k}\Omega} = \mathbf{652\ \mu A}$

9. See Figure 10-1.

$$C_{tot} = \dfrac{1}{\dfrac{1}{0.1\ \mu F} + \dfrac{1}{0.22\ \mu F}} = 0.0688\ \mu F$$

$$X_C = \dfrac{1}{2\pi(15\ \text{kHz})(0.0688\ \mu F)} = 154\ \Omega$$

$$Z = \sqrt{R_{tot}^2 + X_C^2} = \sqrt{(50\ \Omega)^2 + (154\ \Omega)^2} = 162\ \Omega$$

$$I_{tot} = \dfrac{V_s}{Z} = \dfrac{2\ \text{V}}{162\ \Omega} = \mathbf{12.3\ mA}$$

$$X_{C(0.1\mu F)} = \dfrac{1}{2\pi(15\ \text{kHz})(0.1\ \mu F)} = 106\ \Omega$$

$$X_{C(0.22\ \mu F)} = \dfrac{1}{2\pi(15\ \text{kHz})(0.22\ \mu F)} = 48.2\ \Omega$$

$V_{C1} = I_{tot}X_{C(0.1\mu F)} = (12.3\ \text{mA})(106\ \Omega) = \mathbf{1.31\ V}$

$V_{C2} = I_{tot}X_{C(0.22\mu F)} = (12.3\ \text{mA})(48.2\ \Omega) = \mathbf{0.595\ V}$

$V_R = I_{tot}R_{tot} = (12.3\ \text{mA})(50\ \Omega) = \mathbf{0.616\ V}$

$\theta = \tan^{-1}\left(\dfrac{X_C}{R_{tot}}\right) = \tan^{-1}\left(\dfrac{154\ \Omega}{50\ \Omega}\right) = \mathbf{72.0°}$ (I_{tot} leads V_s)

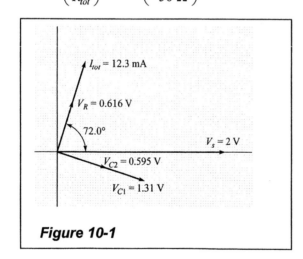

Figure 10-1

10. (a) $X_C = \dfrac{1}{2\pi(20\ \text{Hz})(100\ \mu F)} = 79.6\ \Omega$

$Z = \sqrt{R^2 + X_C^2} = \sqrt{(56\ \Omega)^2 + (79.6\ \Omega)^2} = \mathbf{97.3\ \Omega}$

(b) $I = \dfrac{10\ \text{V}}{97.3\ \Omega} = \textbf{103 mA}$

(c) $V_R = \left(\dfrac{R}{Z}\right)V_s = \left(\dfrac{56\ \Omega}{97.3\ \Omega}\right)10\ \text{V} = \textbf{5.76 V}$

(d) $V_C = \left(\dfrac{X_C}{Z}\right)V_s = \left(\dfrac{79.6\ \Omega}{97.3\ \Omega}\right)10\ \text{V} = \textbf{8.18 V}$

11. $Z = \dfrac{V_s}{I} = \dfrac{10\ \text{V}}{10\ \text{mA}} = 1\ \text{k}\Omega$

$X_C = \dfrac{1}{2\pi(10\ \text{kHz})(0.027\ \mu\text{F})} = 589\ \Omega$

$\sqrt{R^2 + X_C^2} = 1\ \text{k}\Omega$

$R^2 + (589\ \Omega)^2 = (1000\ \Omega)^2$

$R = \sqrt{(1000\ \Omega)^2 - (589\ \Omega)^2} = \textbf{808 }\boldsymbol{\Omega}$

$\theta = -\tan^{-1}\left(\dfrac{589\ \Omega}{808\ \Omega}\right) = \textbf{--36.1°}$

12. **(a)** $X_C = \dfrac{1}{2\pi(1\ \text{Hz})(0.039\ \mu\text{F})} = 4.08\ \text{M}\Omega$

$\phi = 90° - \tan^{-1}\left(\dfrac{X_C}{R}\right) = 90° - \tan^{-1}\left(\dfrac{4.08\ \text{M}\Omega}{3.9\ \text{k}\Omega}\right) = \textbf{0.0548°}$

(b) $X_C = \dfrac{1}{2\pi(100\ \text{Hz})(0.039\ \mu\text{F})} = 40.8\ \text{k}\Omega$

$\phi = 90° - \tan^{-1}\left(\dfrac{X_C}{R}\right) = 90° - \tan^{-1}\left(\dfrac{40.8\ \text{k}\Omega}{3.9\ \text{k}\Omega}\right) = \textbf{5.46°}$

(c) $X_C = \dfrac{1}{2\pi(1\ \text{kHz})(0.039\ \mu\text{F})} = 4.08\ \text{k}\Omega$

$\phi = 90° - \tan^{-1}\left(\dfrac{X_C}{R}\right) = 90° - \tan^{-1}\left(\dfrac{4.08\ \text{k}\Omega}{3.9\ \text{k}\Omega}\right) = \textbf{43.7°}$

(d) $X_C = \dfrac{1}{2\pi(10\ \text{kHz})(0.039\ \mu\text{F})} = 408\ \Omega$

$\phi = 90° - \tan^{-1}\left(\dfrac{X_C}{R}\right) = 90° - \tan^{-1}\left(\dfrac{408\ \Omega}{3.9\ \text{k}\Omega}\right) = \textbf{84.0°}$

13. (a) $X_C = \dfrac{1}{2\pi f C} = \dfrac{1}{2\pi(1\,\text{Hz})(10\,\mu\text{F})} = 15.9\,\text{k}\Omega$

$\phi = \tan^{-1}\left(\dfrac{X_C}{R}\right) = \tan^{-1}\left(\dfrac{15.9\,\text{k}\Omega}{10\,\Omega}\right) = \mathbf{90.0°}$

(b) $X_C = \dfrac{1}{2\pi f C} = \dfrac{1}{2\pi(100\,\text{Hz})(10\,\mu\text{F})} = 159\,\Omega$

$\phi = \tan^{-1}\left(\dfrac{X_C}{R}\right) = \tan^{-1}\left(\dfrac{159\,\Omega}{10\,\Omega}\right) = \mathbf{86.4°}$

(c) $X_C = \dfrac{1}{2\pi f C} = \dfrac{1}{2\pi(1\,\text{kHz})(10\,\mu\text{F})} = 15.9\,\Omega$

$\phi = \tan^{-1}\left(\dfrac{X_C}{R}\right) = \tan^{-1}\left(\dfrac{15.9\,\Omega}{10\,\Omega}\right) = \mathbf{57.8°}$

(d) $X_C = \dfrac{1}{2\pi f C} = \dfrac{1}{2\pi(10\,\text{kHz})(10\,\mu\text{F})} = 1.59\,\Omega$

$\phi = \tan^{-1}\left(\dfrac{X_C}{R}\right) = \tan^{-1}\left(\dfrac{1.59\,\Omega}{10\,\Omega}\right) = \mathbf{9.04°}$

SECTION 10-4 Impedance and Phase Angle of Parallel *RC* Circuits

14. $Z = \dfrac{RX_C}{\sqrt{R^2 + X_C^2}} = \dfrac{(1.2\,\text{k}\Omega)(2.2\,\text{k}\Omega)}{\sqrt{(1.2\,\text{k}\Omega)^2 + (2.2\,\text{k}\Omega)^2}} = \mathbf{1.05\,\text{k}\Omega}$

15. $B_C = 2\pi f C = 2.76\,\text{mS}$

$G = \dfrac{1}{750\,\Omega} = 1.33\,\text{mS}$

$Y = \sqrt{G^2 + B_C^2} = \sqrt{(1.33\,\text{mS})^2 + (2.76\,\text{mS})^2} = 3.07\,\text{mS}$

$Z = \dfrac{1}{Y} = \dfrac{1}{3.07\,\text{mS}} = \mathbf{326\,\Omega}$

$\theta = \tan^{-1}\left(\dfrac{2.76\,\text{mS}}{1.33\,\text{mS}}\right) = 64.3°\ \ (I \text{ leads } V)$

16. (a) $B_C = 2\pi(1.5\,\text{kHz})(0.22\,\mu\text{F}) = 2.07\,\text{mS}$

$Y = \sqrt{(1.33\,\text{mS})^2 + (2.07\,\text{mS})^2} = 2.47\,\text{mS}$

$Z = \dfrac{1}{Y} = \dfrac{1}{2.47\,\text{mS}} = \mathbf{405\,\Omega}$

$\theta = \tan^{-1}\left(\dfrac{2.07\,\text{mS}}{1.33\,\text{mS}}\right) = \mathbf{57.3°}$

(b)　$B_C = 2\pi(3 \text{ kHz})(0.22 \text{ }\mu\text{F}) = 4.15 \text{ mS}$

$Y = \sqrt{(1.33 \text{ mS})^2 + (4.15 \text{ mS})^2} = 4.36 \text{ mS}$

$Z = \dfrac{1}{Y} = \dfrac{1}{4.36 \text{ mS}} = \textbf{230 } \boldsymbol{\Omega}$

$\theta = \tan^{-1}\left(\dfrac{4.15 \text{ mS}}{1.33 \text{ mS}}\right) = \textbf{72.2°}$

(c)　$B_C = 2\pi(5 \text{ kHz})(0.22 \text{ }\mu\text{F}) = 6.91 \text{ mS}$

$Y = \sqrt{(1.33 \text{ mS})^2 + (6.91 \text{ mS})^2} = 7.04 \text{ mS}$

$Z = \dfrac{1}{Y} = \dfrac{1}{7.04 \text{ mS}} = \textbf{142 } \boldsymbol{\Omega}$

$\theta = \tan^{-1}\left(\dfrac{6.91 \text{ mS}}{1.33 \text{ mS}}\right) = \textbf{79.1°}$

(d)　$B_C = 2\pi(10 \text{ kHz})(0.22 \text{ }\mu\text{F}) = 13.8 \text{ mS}$

$Y = \sqrt{(1.33 \text{ mS})^2 + (13.8 \text{ mS})^2} = 13.9 \text{ mS}$

$Z = \dfrac{1}{Y} = \dfrac{1}{13.9 \text{ mS}} = \textbf{72.0 } \boldsymbol{\Omega}$

$\theta = \tan^{-1}\left(\dfrac{13.9 \text{ mS}}{1.33 \text{ mS}}\right) = \textbf{84.5°}$

17.　$B_C = 2\pi fC = 2\pi f(C_1 + C_2) = 2\pi(2 \text{ kHz})(0.32 \text{ }\mu\text{F}) = 4.02 \text{ mS}$

$G = \dfrac{1}{R_1 + R_2 + R_3} = \dfrac{1}{1480 \text{ }\Omega} = 0.676 \text{ mS}$

$Y = \sqrt{G^2 + B_C^2} = \sqrt{(0.676 \text{ mS})^2 + (4.02 \text{ mS})^2} = 4.08 \text{ mS}$

$Z = \dfrac{1}{Y} = \dfrac{1}{4.08 \text{ mS}} = \textbf{245 } \boldsymbol{\Omega}$

$\theta = \tan^{-1}\left(\dfrac{4.02 \text{ mS}}{0.676 \text{ mS}}\right) = \textbf{80.5°}$

SECTION 10-5　Analysis of Parallel *RC* Circuits

18.　$Z_{tot} = \dfrac{(68 \text{ }\Omega)(90 \text{ }\Omega)}{\sqrt{(68 \text{ }\Omega)^2 + (90 \text{ }\Omega)^2}} = 54.3 \text{ }\Omega$

$V_C = V_R = V_s = \textbf{10 V}$

$I_{tot} = \dfrac{10 \text{ V}}{54.3 \text{ }\Omega} = \textbf{184 mA}$

$I_R = \dfrac{10 \text{ V}}{68 \text{ }\Omega} = \textbf{147 mA}$

$I_C = \dfrac{10 \text{ }\Omega}{90 \text{ }\Omega} = \textbf{111 mA}$

19. $X_{C1} = \dfrac{1}{2\pi(50\,\text{kHz})(0.47\,\mu\text{F})} = 67.7\,\Omega$

$X_{C2} = \dfrac{1}{2\pi(50\,\text{kHz})(0.022\,\mu\text{F})} = 145\,\Omega$

$I_{C1} = \dfrac{V_s}{X_{C1}} = \dfrac{8\,\text{V}}{67.7\,\Omega} = \textbf{118 mA}$

$I_{C2} = \dfrac{V_s}{X_{C2}} = \dfrac{8\,\text{V}}{145\,\Omega} = \textbf{55.3 mA}$

$I_{R1} = \dfrac{V_s}{R_1} = \dfrac{8\,\text{V}}{220\,\Omega} = \textbf{36.4 mA}$

$I_{R2} = \dfrac{V_s}{R_2} = \dfrac{8\,\text{V}}{180\,\Omega} = \textbf{44.4 mA}$

$I_{tot} = \sqrt{I_{R(tot)}^2 + I_{C(tot)}^2} = \sqrt{(80.8\,\text{mA})^2 + (173.3\,\text{mA})^2} = \textbf{191 mA}$

$\theta = \tan^{-1}\left(\dfrac{I_{C(tot)}}{I_{R(tot)}}\right) = \tan^{-1}\left(\dfrac{173.3\,\text{mA}}{80.8\,\text{mA}}\right) = \textbf{65.0°}$

20. (a) $Z = \dfrac{(10\,\Omega)(21\,\Omega)}{\sqrt{(10\,\Omega)^2 + (21\,\Omega)^2}} = \textbf{9.03}\,\boldsymbol{\Omega}$

   (b) $I_R = \dfrac{V_s}{R} = \dfrac{100\,\text{mV}}{10\,\Omega} = \textbf{10 mA}$

   (c) $I_C = \dfrac{V_s}{X_C} = \dfrac{100\,\text{mV}}{21\,\Omega} = \textbf{4.76 mA}$

   (d) $I_{tot} = \dfrac{V_s}{Z} = \dfrac{100\,\text{mV}}{9.03\,\Omega} = \textbf{11.1 mA}$

   (e) $\theta = \tan^{-1}\left(\dfrac{10\,\Omega}{21\,\Omega}\right) = \textbf{25.5°}$ (I_{tot} leads V_s)

21. $X_C = \dfrac{1}{2\pi(500\,\text{Hz})(0.047\,\mu\text{F})} = 6.77\,\text{k}\Omega$

   (a) $Z = \dfrac{(4.7\,\text{k}\Omega)(6.77\,\text{k}\Omega)}{\sqrt{(4.7\,\text{k}\Omega)^2 + (6.77\,\text{k}\Omega)^2}} = \textbf{3.86 k}\boldsymbol{\Omega}$

   (b) $I_R = \dfrac{V_s}{R} = \dfrac{100\,\text{mV}}{4.7\,\text{k}\Omega} = \textbf{21.3}\,\boldsymbol{\mu}\textbf{A}$

   (c) $I_C = \dfrac{V_s}{X_C} = \dfrac{100\,\text{mV}}{6.77\,\text{k}\Omega} = \textbf{14.8}\,\boldsymbol{\mu}\textbf{A}$

   (d) $I_{tot} = \dfrac{V_s}{Z} = \dfrac{100\,\text{mV}}{3.86\,\text{k}\Omega} = \textbf{25.9}\,\boldsymbol{\mu}\textbf{A}$

   (e) $\theta = \tan^{-1}\left(\dfrac{4.7\,\text{k}\Omega}{6.77\,\text{k}\Omega}\right) = \textbf{34.8°}$

22. $R_{tot} = 22 \text{ k}\Omega$, $C_{tot} = 32.0 \text{ pF}$

$$X_{C(tot)} = \frac{1}{2\pi(100 \text{ kHz})(32.0 \text{ pF})} = 49.8 \text{ k}\Omega$$

$$Z = \frac{(22 \text{ k}\Omega)(49.8 \text{ k}\Omega)}{\sqrt{(22 \text{ k}\Omega)^2 + (49.8 \text{ k}\Omega)^2}} = 20.1 \text{ k}\Omega$$

$$\theta = \tan^{-1}\left(\frac{R_{tot}}{X_{C(tot)}}\right) = \tan^{-1}\left(\frac{22 \text{ k}\Omega}{49.8 \text{ k}\Omega}\right) = 23.8°$$

$R_{eq} = Z \cos\theta = (20.1 \text{ k}\Omega)\cos 23.8° = \textbf{18.4 k}\boldsymbol{\Omega}$

$X_{C(eq)} = Z \sin\theta = (20.1 \text{ k}\Omega)\sin 23.8° = 8.13 \text{ k}\Omega$

$$C_{eq} = \frac{1}{2\pi f X_{C(eq)}} = \textbf{196 pF}$$

SECTION 10-6 Analysis of Series-Parallel *RC* Circuits

23. $$X_{C1} = \frac{1}{2\pi(15 \text{ kHz})(0.1 \text{ μF})} = 106 \text{ }\Omega$$

$$X_{C2} = \frac{1}{2\pi(15 \text{ kHz})(0.047 \text{ μF})} = 226 \text{ }\Omega$$

$$X_{C3} = \frac{1}{2\pi(15 \text{ kHz})(0.22 \text{ μF})} = 48.2 \text{ }\Omega$$

The total resistance in the resistive branch is
$R_{tot} = R_1 + R_2 = 330 \text{ }\Omega + 180 \text{ }\Omega = 510 \text{ }\Omega$
The combined parallel capacitance of C_2 and C_3 is
$C_{(tot)p} = C_1 + C_2 = 0.047 \text{ μF} + 0.22 \text{ μF} = 0.267 \text{ μF}$

$$X_{C(tot)p} = \frac{1}{2\pi(15 \text{ kHz})(0.267 \text{ μF})} = 39.7 \text{ }\Omega$$

The impedance of R_{tot} in parallel with $C_{(tot)p}$ is
$$Z_p = \frac{R_{tot} X_{C(tot)p}}{\sqrt{R_{tot}^2 + X_{C(tot)p}^2}} = \frac{(510 \text{ }\Omega)(39.7 \text{ }\Omega)}{\sqrt{(510 \text{ }\Omega)^2 + (39.7 \text{ }\Omega)^2}} = 39.6 \text{ }\Omega$$

The angle associated with R_{tot} and $C_{(tot)p}$ in parallel is
$$\theta = \tan^{-1}\left(\frac{R_{tot}}{X_{C(tot)p}}\right) = \tan^{-1}\left(\frac{510 \text{ }\Omega}{39.7 \text{ }\Omega}\right) = \textbf{85.5°}$$

Converting from parallel to series:
$R_{eq} = Z_p \cos\theta = (39.6 \text{ }\Omega)\cos 85.5° = 3.08 \text{ }\Omega$
$X_{C(eq)} = Z_p \sin\theta = (39.6 \text{ }\Omega)\sin 85.5° = 39.5 \text{ }\Omega$
The total circuit impedance is
$$Z_{tot} = \sqrt{R_{eq}^2 + (X_{C1} + X_{C(eq)})^2} = \sqrt{(3.08 \text{ }\Omega)^2 + (145.6 \text{ }\Omega)^2} = 145.6 \text{ }\Omega$$

The voltage across the parallel branches is

$$V_{C2} = V_{C3} = V_{R1R2} = \left(\frac{Z_p}{Z_{tot}}\right)V_s = \left(\frac{39.6\ \Omega}{145.6\ \Omega}\right)12\ V = \textbf{3.26 V}$$

$$V_{R1} = \left(\frac{330\ \Omega}{510\ \Omega}\right)3.26\ V = \textbf{2.11 V}$$

$$V_{R2} = \left(\frac{180\ \Omega}{510\ \Omega}\right)3.26\ V = \textbf{1.15 V}$$

$$V_{C1} = \left(\frac{X_{C1}}{Z_{tot}}\right)12\ V = \left(\frac{106\ \Omega}{145.6\ \Omega}\right)12\ V = \textbf{8.74 V}$$

24. From Problem 23, $R_{eq} = 3.08\ \Omega$ and $X_{C1} + X_{C(eq)} = 145.6\ \Omega$.
Since $145.6\ \Omega > 3.08\ \Omega$, the circuit is predominantly **capacitive**.

25. Using data from Problem 23:

$$I_{tot} = \frac{V_s}{Z_{tot}} = \frac{12\ V}{145.6\ \Omega} = \textbf{82.4 mA}$$

$$I_{C2} = \frac{V_{C2}}{X_{C2}} = \frac{3.26\ V}{226\ \Omega} = \textbf{14.4 mA}$$

$$I_{C3} = \frac{V_{C3}}{X_{C3}} = \frac{3.26\ V}{48.2\ \Omega} = \textbf{67.6 mA}$$

$$I_{R1} = I_{R2} = \frac{3.26\ V}{510\ \Omega} = \textbf{6.39 mA}$$

26. $R_{tot} = R_1 + R_2 \parallel R_3 = 89.9\ \Omega$

$$X_C = \frac{1}{2\pi(1\ kHz)(0.47\ \mu F)} = 339\ \Omega$$

$$Z_{tot} = \sqrt{R_{tot}^2 + X_C^2} = \sqrt{(89.9\ \Omega)^2 + (339\ \Omega)^2} = 351\ \Omega$$

(a) $\quad I_{tot} = \dfrac{V_s}{Z_{tot}} = \dfrac{15\ V}{351\ \Omega} = \textbf{42.7 mA}$

(b) $\quad \theta = \tan^{-1}\left(\dfrac{X_C}{R_{tot}}\right) = \tan^{-1}\left(\dfrac{339\ \Omega}{89.9\ \Omega}\right) = \textbf{75.1°}\ (I_{tot}$ leads $V_s)$

(c) $\quad V_{R1} = \left(\dfrac{R_1}{Z_{tot}}\right)V_s = \left(\dfrac{47\ \Omega}{351\ \Omega}\right)15\ V = \textbf{2.01 V}$

(d) $\quad V_{R2} = \left(\dfrac{R_2 \parallel R_3}{Z_{tot}}\right)V_s = \left(\dfrac{42.9\ \Omega}{351\ \Omega}\right)15\ V = \textbf{1.83 V}$

(e) $\quad V_{R3} = V_{R2} = \textbf{1.83 V}$

(f) $\quad V_C = \left(\dfrac{X_C}{Z_{tot}}\right)V_s = \left(\dfrac{339\ \Omega}{351\ \Omega}\right)15\ V = \textbf{14.5 V}$

27. $P_a = \sqrt{P_{\text{true}}^2 + P_r^2} = \sqrt{(2 \text{ W})^2 + (3.5 \text{ VAR})^2} = \textbf{4.03 VA}$

28. From Problem 10: $I_{tot} = 103 \text{ mA}$, $X_C = 79.6 \text{ }\Omega$

   $P_{\text{rue}} = I_{tot}^2 R = (103 \text{ mA})^2 (56 \text{ }\Omega) = \textbf{0.591 W}$

   $P_r = I_{tot}^2 X_C = (103 \text{ mA})^2 (79.6 \text{ }\Omega) = \textbf{0.840 VAR}$

29. Using the results from Problem 22:

   $R_{\text{eq}} = 18.4 \text{ k}\Omega$

   $X_{C(\text{eq})} = \dfrac{1}{2\pi f C_{\text{eq}}} = \dfrac{1}{2\pi(100 \text{ kHz})(196 \text{ pF})} = 8.13 \text{ k}\Omega$

   $\theta = \tan^{-1}\left(\dfrac{X_{C(\text{eq})}}{R_{\text{eq}}}\right) = \tan^{-1}\left(\dfrac{8.13 \text{ k}\Omega}{18.4 \text{ k}\Omega}\right) = 23.8°$

   $PF = \cos\theta = \cos 23.8° = \textbf{0.915}$

30. From Problem 26: $I_{tot} = 42.7 \text{ mA}$, $R_{tot} = 89.9 \text{ }\Omega$, $X_C = 339 \text{ }\Omega$, $Z_{tot} = 351 \text{ }\Omega$

   $P_{\text{true}} = I_{tot}^2 R_{tot} = (42.7 \text{ mA})^2 (89.9 \text{ }\Omega) = \textbf{169 mW}$

   $P_r = I_{tot}^2 X_C = (42.7 \text{ mA})^2 (339 \text{ }\Omega) = \textbf{618 mVAR}$

   $P_a = I_{tot}^2 Z_{tot} = (42.7 \text{ mA})^2 (351 \text{ }\Omega) = \textbf{640 mVA}$

   $PF = \cos\theta = \cos(75.1°) = \textbf{0.257}$

SECTION 10-8 Basic Applications

31. Use the formula, $V_{out} = \left(\dfrac{X_C}{Z_{tot}}\right) 1 \text{ V}$. See Figure 10-2.

Frequency (kHz)	X_C (kΩ)	Z_{tot} (kΩ)	V_{out} (V)
0			1.000
1	4.08	5.64	0.723
2	2.04	4.40	0.464
3	1.36	4.13	0.329
4	1.02	4.03	0.253
5	0.816	3.98	0.205
6	0.680	3.96	0.172
7	0.583	3.94	0.148
8	0.510	3.93	0.130
9	0.453	3.93	0.115
10	0.408	3.92	0.104

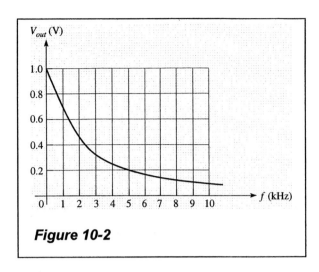

Figure 10-2

32. Use the formula, $V_{out} = \left(\dfrac{R}{Z_{tot}} \right) 10$ V. See Figure 10-3.

Frequency (kHz)	X_C (Ω)	Z_{tot} (Ω)	V_{out} (V)
0			0
1	15.9	18.79	5.32
2	7.96	12.78	7.82
3	5.31	11.32	8.83
4	3.98	10.76	9.29
5	3.18	10.49	9.53
6	2.65	10.35	9.67
7	2.27	10.26	9.75
8	1.99	10.20	9.81
9	1.77	10.16	9.85
10	1.59	10.13	9.88

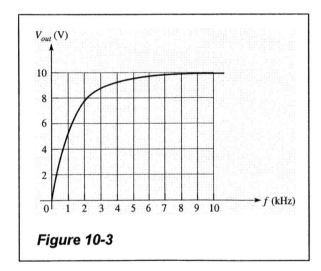

Figure 10-3

33. For Figure 10-75:

$$X_C = \frac{1}{2\pi(5 \text{ kHz})(0.039 \text{ }\mu\text{F})} = 816 \text{ }\Omega$$

$$Z = \sqrt{(3.9 \text{ k}\Omega)^2 + (816 \text{ }\Omega)^2} = 3.98 \text{ k}\Omega$$

$$\theta = \tan^{-1}\left(\frac{X_C}{R}\right) = \tan^{-1}\left(\frac{816 \text{ }\Omega}{3.9 \text{ k}\Omega}\right) = \mathbf{11.8°}$$

$$I = \frac{V_s}{Z} = \frac{1 \text{ V}}{3980 \text{ }\Omega} = 251 \text{ }\mu\text{A}$$

$V_R = IR = (251 \text{ }\mu\text{A})(3.9 \text{ k}\Omega) = \mathbf{979 \text{ mV}}$
$V_C = IX_C = (251 \text{ }\mu\text{A})(816 \text{ }\Omega) = \mathbf{205 \text{ mV}}$
The phasor diagram is shown is Figure 10-4(a).

For Figure 10-76:

$$X_C = \frac{1}{2\pi(5 \text{ kHz})(10 \text{ }\mu\text{F})} = 3.18 \text{ }\Omega$$

$$Z = \sqrt{(10 \text{ }\Omega)^2 + (3.18 \text{ }\Omega)^2} = 10.5 \text{ }\Omega$$

$$\theta = \tan^{-1}\left(\frac{X_C}{R}\right) = \tan^{-1}\left(\frac{3.18 \text{ }\Omega}{10 \text{ }\Omega}\right) = \mathbf{17.7°}$$

$$I = \frac{V_s}{Z} = \frac{1 \text{ V}}{10.5 \text{ }\Omega} = 95.3 \text{ mA}$$

$V_R = IR = (95.3 \text{ mA})(10 \text{ }\Omega) = \mathbf{953 \text{ mV}}$
$V_C = IX_C = (95.3 \text{ mA})(3.18 \text{ }\Omega) = \mathbf{303 \text{ mV}}$
The phasor diagram is shown in Figure 10-4(b).

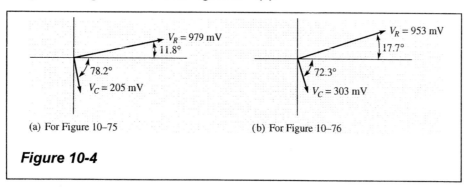

(a) For Figure 10–75   (b) For Figure 10–76

Figure 10-4

34. $$X_C = \frac{1}{2\pi(3 \text{ kHz})(0.047 \text{ }\mu\text{F})} = 1.13 \text{ k}\Omega$$

The signal loss is the voltage drop across C.

$$V_C = \left(\frac{X_C}{\sqrt{R_{in(B)}^2 + X_C^2}}\right)V_{out(A)} = \left(\frac{1.13 \text{ k}\Omega}{\sqrt{(10 \text{ k}\Omega)^2 + (1.13 \text{ k}\Omega)^2}}\right)50 \text{ mV} = \mathbf{5.61 \text{ mV}}$$

35. For Figure 10-75:

$$f_c = \frac{1}{2\pi RC} = \frac{1}{2\pi(3.9 \text{ k}\Omega)(0.039 \text{ }\mu\text{F})} = \textbf{1.05 kHz}$$

For Figure 10-76:

$$f_c = \frac{1}{2\pi RC} = \frac{1}{2\pi(10 \text{ }\Omega)(10 \text{ }\mu\text{F})} = \textbf{1.59 kHz}$$

36. $f_c = \dfrac{1}{2\pi RC} = \dfrac{1}{2\pi(3.9 \text{ k}\Omega)(0.039 \text{ }\mu\text{F})} = 1.05 \text{ kHz}$

Since this is a low-pass filter, $BW = f_c = \textbf{1.05 kHz}$

SECTION 10-9 Troubleshooting

37. After removing C, the circuit is reduced to Thevenin's equivalent:

$$R_{th} = \frac{(4.7 \text{ k}\Omega)(5 \text{ k}\Omega)}{9.7 \text{ k}\Omega} = 2.42 \text{ k}\Omega$$

$$V_{th} = \left(\frac{5 \text{ k}\Omega}{9.7 \text{ k}\Omega}\right)10 \text{ V} = 5.15 \text{ V}$$

Assuming no leakage in the capacitor:

$$X_C = \frac{1}{2\pi(10 \text{ Hz})(10 \text{ }\mu\text{F})} = 1592 \text{ }\Omega$$

$$V_{out} = \left(\frac{X_C}{\sqrt{R^2 + X_C^2}}\right)10 \text{ V} = \left(\frac{1592 \text{ }\Omega}{\sqrt{(4.7 \text{ k}\Omega)^2 + (1592 \text{ }\Omega)^2}}\right)10 \text{ V} = \textbf{3.21 V}$$

$$\theta = \tan^{-1}\left(\frac{1592 \text{ }\Omega}{4.7 \text{ k}\Omega}\right) = \textbf{18.7}°$$

With the leakage resistance taken into account:

$$V_{out} = \left(\frac{X_C}{\sqrt{R_{th}^2 + X_C^2}}\right)V_{th} = \left(\frac{1592 \text{ }\Omega}{\sqrt{(2.42 \text{ k}\Omega)^2 + (1592)^2}}\right)5.15 \text{ V} = \textbf{2.83 V}$$

$$\theta = \tan^{-1}\left(\frac{1592 \text{ }\Omega}{2.42 \text{ k}\Omega}\right) = \textbf{33.3}°$$

The leaky capacitor reduces the output voltage by 0.38 V and increases the phase angle by 14.6°.

38. (a) The leakage resistance effectively appears in parallel with R_2.
Thevenizing from the capacitor:

$$R_{th} = R_1 \| R_2 \| R_{leak} = 10 \text{ k}\Omega \| 10 \text{ k}\Omega \| 2 \text{ k}\Omega = 1.43 \text{ k}\Omega$$

$$V_{th} = \left(\frac{R_2 \| R_{leak}}{R_1 + R_2 \| R_{leak}}\right)V_{in} = \left(\frac{1.67 \text{ k}\Omega}{11.67 \text{ k}\Omega}\right)1 \text{ V} = 143 \text{ mV}$$

$$X_C = \frac{1}{2\pi(10\ \text{Hz})(4.7\ \mu\text{F})} = 3386\ \Omega$$

$$V_{out} = \left(\frac{X_C}{\sqrt{R_{th}^2 + X_C^2}}\right)V_{th} = \left(\frac{3386\ \Omega}{\sqrt{(1.43\ \text{k}\Omega)^2 + (3386\ \Omega)^2}}\right)143\ \text{mV} = \textbf{132 mV}$$

(b) $$X_C = \frac{1}{2\pi(100\ \text{kHz})(470\ \text{pF})} = 3386\ \Omega$$

$$R_{eq} = R_1 \parallel (R_2 + R_3) = 2.2\ \text{k}\Omega \parallel 2\ \text{k}\Omega = 1.05\ \text{k}\Omega$$

$$X_C \parallel R_{leak} = \frac{(R_{leak})(X_C)}{\sqrt{R_{leak}^2 + X_C^2}} = \frac{(2\ \text{k}\Omega)(3386\ \Omega)}{\sqrt{(2\ \text{k}\Omega)^2 + (3386\ \Omega)^2}} = 1722\ \Omega$$

$$V_{R1} = \left(\frac{R_{eq}}{X_C \parallel R_{leak} + R_{eq}}\right)V_{in} = 1.96\ \text{V}$$

$X_C \parallel R_{leak}$ consists of a reactive and a resistive term and cannot be added directly to R_{eq}.

$$V_{out} = \left(\frac{R_3}{R_2 + R_3}\right)V_{R1} = \left(\frac{1.0\ \text{k}\Omega}{2\ \text{k}\Omega}\right)1.96\ \text{V} = \textbf{0.978 V}$$

39.   (a) $V_{out} = \textbf{0 V}$ **(less than normal output)**

$$X_C = \frac{1}{2\pi(10\ \text{Hz})(4.7\ \mu\text{F})} = 3386\ \Omega$$

(b) $$V_{out} = \left(\frac{X_C}{\sqrt{R^2 + X_C^2}}\right)V_{in} = \left(\frac{3386\ \Omega}{10,494\ \Omega}\right)1\ \text{V} = \textbf{0.321 V}\ \textbf{(greater than normal output)}$$

(c) $$V_{out} = \left(\frac{R_2}{R_1 + R_2}\right)V_{in} = \left(\frac{10\ \text{k}\Omega}{20\ \text{k}\Omega}\right)1\ \text{V} = \textbf{0.5 V}\ \textbf{(greater than normal output)}$$

(d) $V_{out} = \textbf{0 V}$ **(less than normal output)**

40.   (a) $V_{out} = \textbf{0 V}$ **(less than normal)**

(b) $$V_{out} = \left(\frac{R_3}{R_2 + R_3}\right)V_{in} = \left(\frac{1.0\ \text{k}\Omega}{2\ \text{k}\Omega}\right)5\ \text{V} = \textbf{2.5 V}\ \textbf{(greater than normal output)}$$

$$X_C = 3386$$

(c) $$V_{out} = \left(\frac{R_3}{\sqrt{(R_2 + R_3)^2 + X_C^2}}\right)V_{in} = \left(\frac{1000\ \Omega}{3933\ \Omega}\right)5\ \text{V} = \textbf{1.27 V}\ \textbf{(greater than normal output)}$$

(d) $V_{out} = \textbf{0 V}$ **(less than normal output)**

(e) $$V_{out} = \left(\frac{R_1}{\sqrt{R_1^2 + X_C^2}}\right)V_{in} = \left(\frac{2.2\ \text{k}\Omega}{4038\ \Omega}\right)5\ \text{V} = \textbf{2.72 V}\ \textbf{(greater than normal output)}$$

ADVANCED PROBLEMS

41. (a) $I_{L(A)} = \dfrac{220 \text{ V}}{50 \ \Omega} = \mathbf{4.4 \ A}$

$I_{L(B)} = \dfrac{220 \text{ V}}{72 \ \Omega} = \mathbf{3.06 \ A}$

(b) $PF_A = \cos \theta = 0.85; \quad \theta = 31.8°$
$PF_B = \cos \theta = 0.95; \quad \theta = 18.19°$
$X_{C(A)} = (50 \ \Omega)\sin 31.8° = 26.3 \ \Omega$
$X_{C(B)} = (72 \ \Omega)\sin 18.19° = 22.48 \ \Omega$
$P_{r(A)} = I_{L(A)}X_{C(A)} = (4.4 \text{ A})^2(26.3 \ \Omega) = \mathbf{509 \ VAR}$
$P_{r(B)} = I_{L(B)}X_{C(B)} = (3.06 \text{ A})^2(22.48 \ \Omega) = \mathbf{211 \ VAR}$

(c) $R_A = (50 \ \Omega)\cos 31.8° = 42.5 \ \Omega$
$R_B = (72 \ \Omega)\cos 18.19° = 68.4 \ \Omega$
$P_{true(A)} = I_{L(A)}^2 R_A = (4.4 \text{ A})^2(42.5 \ \Omega) = \mathbf{823 \ W}$

$P_{true(B)} = I_{L(B)}^2 R_B = (3.06 \text{ A})^2(68.4 \ \Omega) = \mathbf{641 \ W}$

(d) $P_{a(A)} = \sqrt{(P_{true(A)})^2 + P_{r(A)}^2} = \sqrt{(823 \text{ W})^2 + (509 \text{ VAR})^2} = \mathbf{968 \ VA}$

$P_{a(B)} = \sqrt{(P_{true(B)})^2 + P_{r(B)}^2} = \sqrt{(641 \text{ W})^2 + (211 \text{ VAR})^2} = \mathbf{675 \ VA}$

(e) Load A has more voltage drop.

42. $\dfrac{V_{out1}}{V_{in1}} = \dfrac{R}{\sqrt{R^2 + X_C^2}} = 0.707$

$R = 0.707\sqrt{R^2 + X_C^2}$

$\sqrt{R^2 + X_C^2} = \dfrac{R}{0.707} = 1.414R$

$R^2 + X_C^2 = (1.414)^2 R^2 = 2R^2$

$X_C^2 = 2R^2 - R^2 = R^2(2-1) = R^2$

$X_C = R$

$\dfrac{1}{2\pi f C} = R$

$C = \dfrac{1}{2\pi f R} = \dfrac{1}{2\pi(20 \text{ Hz})(100 \text{ k}\Omega)} = \mathbf{0.08 \ \mu F}$

43. $X_C = \dfrac{1}{2\pi(1 \text{ kHz})(0.01 \ \mu F)} = 15.9 \text{ k}\Omega$

$\theta = \tan^{-1}\left(\dfrac{R_{tot}}{X_C}\right)$

$\left(\dfrac{R_{tot}}{X_C}\right) = \tan \theta$

106

$$R_{tot} = X_C \tan \theta = (15.9 \text{ k}\Omega)\tan 30° = 9.19 \text{ k}\Omega$$

$$R_{tot} = \frac{R_1 R_2}{R_1 + R_2}$$

$$R_{tot}(R_1 + R_2) = R_1 R_2$$

$$R_1 R_{tot} + R_2 R_{tot} = R_1 R_2$$

$$R_1(R_{tot} - R_2) = -R_2 R_{tot}$$

$$R_1 = \frac{R_2 R_{tot}}{R_2 - R_{tot}} = \frac{(47 \text{ k}\Omega)(9.19 \text{ k}\Omega)}{37.9 \text{ k}\Omega} = \textbf{11.4 k}\boldsymbol{\Omega}$$

44. $$X_{C1} = \frac{1}{2\pi(2.5 \text{ kHz})(0.015 \text{ μF})} = 4244 \ \Omega$$

$$X_{C2} = \frac{1}{2\pi(2.5 \text{ kHz})(0.047 \text{ μF})} = 1355 \ \Omega$$

$$R_4 \parallel X_{C2} = \frac{R_4 X_{C2}}{\sqrt{R_4^2 + X_{C2}^2}} = \frac{(910 \ \Omega)(1355 \ \Omega)}{\sqrt{(910 \ \Omega) + (1355 \ \Omega)}} = 756 \ \Omega$$

$$\theta_{R4C2} = \tan^{-1}\left(\frac{R_4}{X_{C2}}\right) = \tan^{-1}\left(\frac{910 \ \Omega}{1355 \ \Omega}\right) = 33.9°$$

The equivalent series R and X_C for $R_4 \parallel X_{C2}$:

$$R_{eq} = (R_4 \parallel X_{C2})\cos \theta_{R4C2} = (756 \ \Omega)\cos 33.9° = 627 \ \Omega$$

$$X_{C(eq)} = (R_4 \parallel X_{C2})\sin \theta_{R4C2} = (756 \ \Omega)\sin 33.9° = 422 \ \Omega$$

$$Z_{tot} = \sqrt{R_{tot}^2 + X_{C(tot)}^2} = \sqrt{(R_1 + R_2 + R_3 + R_{eq})^2 + (X_{C1} + X_{C(eq)})^2}$$

$$= \sqrt{(1.0 \text{ k}\Omega + 680 \ \Omega + 1.0 \text{ k}\Omega + 627 \ \Omega)^2 + (4244 \ \Omega + 422 \ \Omega)^2}$$

$$= \sqrt{(3307 \ \Omega)^2 + (4666 \ \Omega)^2} = 5719 \ \Omega$$

$$\theta = \tan^{-1}\left(\frac{X_{C(tot)}}{R_{tot}}\right) = \tan^{-1}\left(\frac{4666 \ \Omega}{3307 \ \Omega}\right) = \textbf{54.7°}$$

$$I_{tot} = \frac{V_s}{Z_{tot}} = \frac{10 \text{ V}}{5719 \ \Omega} = \textbf{1.75 mA}$$

I_{tot} leads V_s by 54.7°

$$I_{C1} = I_{R1} = I_{R2} = I_{R3} = I_{tot} = \textbf{1.75 mA}$$

$$I_{R4} = \left(\frac{X_{C2}}{\sqrt{R_4^2 + X_{C2}^2}}\right)I_{tot} = \left(\frac{1355 \ \Omega}{\sqrt{(910 \ \Omega)^2 + (1355 \ \Omega)^2}}\right)1.75 \text{ mA} = \textbf{1.45 mA}$$

$$I_{C2} = \left(\frac{R_4}{\sqrt{R_4^2 + X_{C2}^2}}\right)I_{tot} = \left(\frac{910 \ \Omega}{\sqrt{(910)^2 + (1355 \ \Omega)^2}}\right)1.75 \text{ mA} = \textbf{0.976 mA}$$

$$V_{C1} = I_{tot}X_{C1} = (1.75 \text{ mA})(4244 \ \Omega) = \textbf{7.43 V}$$
$$V_{R1} = I_{tot}R_1 = (1.75 \text{ mA})(1.0 \ \Omega) = \textbf{1.75 V}$$
$$V_{R2} = I_{tot}R_2 = (1.75 \text{ mA})(680 \ \Omega) = \textbf{1.19 V}$$
$$V_{R3} = I_{tot}R_3 = (1.75 \text{ mA})(1.0 \ \Omega) = \textbf{1.75 V}$$
$$V_{R4} = V_{C2} = I_{R4}R_4 = (1.45 \text{ mA})(910 \ \Omega) = \textbf{1.32 V}$$
V_{C1} lags I_{tot} by 90°.

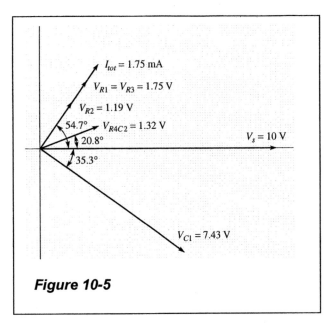

Figure 10-5

V_{R1}, V_{R2}, and V_{R3} are all in phase with I_{tot}.
V_{R4C2} lags I_{tot} by **33.9°**. See Figure 10-5.

45. $\theta = \cos^{-1}(0.75) = 41.4°$

$P_{\text{true}} = P_a\cos\theta$

$P_a = \dfrac{P_{\text{true}}}{PF} = \dfrac{1.5\,\text{kW}}{0.75} = \textbf{2 kVA}$

$P_r = P_a\sin\theta = (2\,\text{kVA})\sin 41.4° = \textbf{1.32 kVAR}$

46. $Z_{tot} = \dfrac{100\,\text{V}}{5\,\text{A}} = 20\,\Omega$

$P_{\text{true}} = I^2 R_{tot}$

$R_{tot} = \dfrac{P_{\text{true}}}{I^2} = \dfrac{400\,\text{W}}{(5\,\text{A})^2} = 16\,\Omega$

$R_x = R_{tot} - R_1 = 16\,\Omega - 4\,\Omega = \textbf{12 }\Omega$

$Z^2_{tot} = R^2_{tot} + X^2_C$

$X_C\sqrt{Z^2_{tot} - R^2_{tot}} = \sqrt{(20\,\Omega)^2 - (16\,\Omega)^2} = \sqrt{144} = 12\,\Omega$

$C_x = \dfrac{1}{2\pi(1\,\text{kHz})(12\,\Omega)} = \textbf{13.3 }\mu\textbf{F}$

47. For $I = 0$ A, $V_A = V_B$ and $V_{R1} = V_{R2}$

$X_{C1} = \dfrac{1}{2\pi(1\,\text{kHz})(0.047\,\mu\text{F})} = 3.39\,\text{k}\Omega$

$V_{R1} = V_{R2}$

$\left(\dfrac{2.2\,\text{k}\Omega}{\sqrt{(2.2\,\text{k}\Omega)^2 + (3.39\,\text{k}\Omega)^2}}\right)V_s = \left(\dfrac{1.0\,\text{k}\Omega}{\sqrt{(1.0\,\text{k}\Omega)^2 + X^2_{C2}}}\right)V_s$

Cancelling the V_s terms and solving for X_{C2}:

$$\left(\frac{2.2 \text{ k}\Omega}{\sqrt{(2.2 \text{ k}\Omega)^2 + (3.39 \text{ k}\Omega)^2}}\right) = \left(\frac{1.0 \text{ k}\Omega}{\sqrt{(1.0 \text{ k}\Omega)^2 + X_{C2}^2}}\right)$$

$$\sqrt{(1.0 \text{ k}\Omega)^2 + X_{C2}^2} = \frac{1.0 \text{ k}\Omega\sqrt{(2.2 \text{ k}\Omega)^2 + (3.39 \text{ k}\Omega)^2}}{2.2 \text{ k}\Omega}$$

$$(1.0 \text{ k}\Omega)^2 + X_{C2}^2 = \frac{(1.0 \text{ k}\Omega)^2\left((2.2 \text{ k}\Omega)^2 + (3.39 \text{ k}\Omega)^2\right)}{(2.2 \text{ k}\Omega)^2}$$

$$X_{C2} = \sqrt{\frac{(1.0 \text{ k}\Omega)^2\left((2.2 \text{ k}\Omega)^2 + (3.39 \text{ k}\Omega)^2\right)}{(2.2 \text{ k}\Omega)^2} - (1.0 \text{ k}\Omega)^2} = 1.54 \text{ k}\Omega$$

$$C_2 = \frac{1}{2\pi(1 \text{ kHz})(1.54 \text{ k}\Omega)} = \textbf{0.103 } \boldsymbol{\mu}\textbf{F}$$

48. See Figure 10-6.
V_{in} = 10 V peak

$$f = \frac{1}{10 \text{ }\mu\text{s}} = 100 \text{ kHz}$$

$$X_C = \frac{1}{2\pi(100 \text{ kHz})(0.1 \text{ }\mu\text{F})} = 15.9 \text{ }\Omega$$

X_C can be neglected because it is very small compared to 22 kΩ.
R_A = 22 kΩ || 18 kΩ || (8.2 kΩ + 1.0 kΩ) = 4.77 kΩ

$$V_{out} \cong V_A = \left(\frac{4.77 \text{ k}\Omega}{14.77 \text{ k}\Omega}\right)10 \text{ V} = 3.23 \text{ V peak}$$

The waveform on the scope is correct, so the circuit is OK.

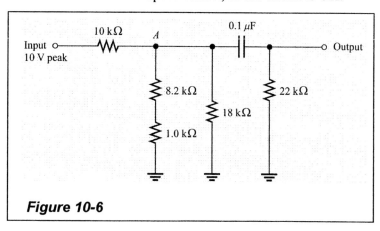

Figure 10-6

49. C is leaky.

50. C_2 is shorted.

51.   No fault

52. C is open.

53. R_2 is open.

54. C is shorted.

CHAPTER 11
INDUCTORS

BASIC PROBLEMS

SECTION 11-1 The Basic Inductor

1. (a) $1\,H \times 1000\,mH/H =$ **1000 mH**
    (b) $250\,\mu H \times 0.001\,mH/\mu H =$ **0.25 mH**
    (c) $10\,\mu H \times 0.001\,mH/\mu H =$ **0.01 mH**
    (d) $0.0005\,H \times 1000\,mH/H =$ **0.5 mH**

2. (a) $300\,mH \times 10^3\,\mu H/mH =$ **300,000 μH**
    (b) $0.08\,H \times 10^6\,\mu H/H =$ **80,000 μH**
    (c) $5\,mH \times 10^3\,\mu H/mH =$ **5000 μH**
    (d) $0.00045\,mH \times 10^3\,\mu H/mH =$ **0.45 μH**

3. $L = \dfrac{N^2 \mu A}{l}$

    $N = \sqrt{\dfrac{Ll}{\mu A}} = \sqrt{\dfrac{(30\,mH)(0.05\,m)}{(1.26 \times 10^{-6})(10 \times 10^{-5}\,m^2)}} =$ **3450 turns**

4. $I = \dfrac{V_{dc}}{R_W} = \dfrac{12\,V}{12\,\Omega} =$ **1 A**

5. $W = \left(\dfrac{1}{2}\right)LI^2 = \dfrac{(0.1\,H)(1\,A)^2}{2} =$ **50 mJ**

6. $v_{induced} = L \times (\text{rate of change of } I) = (100\,mH)(200\,mA/s) =$ **20 mV**

SECTION 11-3 Series and Parallel Inductors

7. $L_T = 5\,\mu H + 10\,\mu H + 20\,\mu H + 40\,\mu H + 80\,\mu H =$ **155 μH**

8. $L_x = 50\,mH - 10\,mH - 22\,mH =$ **18 mH**

9. $L_T = \dfrac{1}{\dfrac{1}{75\,\mu H} + \dfrac{1}{50\,\mu H} + \dfrac{1}{25\,\mu H} + \dfrac{1}{15\,\mu H}} = \textbf{7.14 } \boldsymbol{\mu}\textbf{H}$

10. $8\,mH = \dfrac{L_1(12\,mH)}{L_1 + 12\,mH}$

$(8\,mH)L_1 + (8\,mH)(12\,mH) = (12\,mH)L_1$

$(4\,mH)L_1 = 96\,mH^2$

$L_1 = \dfrac{96\,mH^2}{4\,mH} = \textbf{24 mH}$

11. (a) $L_T = 1\,H + \dfrac{(10\,H)(5\,H)}{10\,H + 5\,H} = \textbf{4.33 H}$

(b) $L_T = \dfrac{100\,mH}{2} = \textbf{50 mH}$

(c) $L_T = \dfrac{1}{\dfrac{1}{100\,\mu H} + \dfrac{1}{200\,\mu H} + \dfrac{1}{400\,\mu H}} = \textbf{57 } \boldsymbol{\mu}\textbf{H}$

12. (a) $L_T = \dfrac{(100\,mH)(50\,mH)}{150\,mH} + \dfrac{(60\,mH)(40\,mH)}{100\,mH} = 33.33\,mH + 24\,mH = \textbf{57.3 mH}$

(b) $L_T = \dfrac{(12\,mH)(6\,mH)}{18\,mH} = \textbf{4 mH}$

(c) $L_T = 4\,mH + \dfrac{(2\,mH)(4\,mH)}{6\,mH} = \textbf{5.33 mH}$

SECTION 11-4 Inductors in DC Circuits

13. (a) $\tau = \dfrac{L}{R} = \dfrac{100\,\mu H}{100\,\Omega} = \textbf{1 } \boldsymbol{\mu}\textbf{s}$

(b) $\tau = \dfrac{L}{R} = \dfrac{10\,mH}{4.7\,k\Omega} = \textbf{2.13 } \boldsymbol{\mu}\textbf{s}$

(c) $\tau = \dfrac{L}{R} = \dfrac{3\,H}{1.5\,M\Omega} = \textbf{2 } \boldsymbol{\mu}\textbf{s}$

14. (a) $5\tau = 5\left(\dfrac{L}{R}\right) = 5\left(\dfrac{50\,\mu H}{56\,\Omega}\right) = \textbf{4.46 } \boldsymbol{\mu}\textbf{s}$

(b) $5\tau = 5\left(\dfrac{L}{R}\right) = 5\left(\dfrac{15\,mH}{3300\,\Omega}\right) = \textbf{22.7 } \boldsymbol{\mu}\textbf{s}$

(c) $5\tau = 5\left(\dfrac{L}{R}\right) = 5\left(\dfrac{100\,mH}{22\,k\Omega}\right) = \textbf{22.7 } \boldsymbol{\mu}\textbf{s}$

15. $\tau = \dfrac{L}{R} = \dfrac{10\,mH}{1.0\,k\Omega} = 10\,\mu s$

(a) $v_L = V_i e^{-t/\tau} = 15e^{-10\mu s/10\mu s} = 15e^{-1} = \textbf{5.52 V}$

(b) $v_L = V_i e^{-t/\tau} = 15e^{-20\mu s/10\mu s} = 15e^{-2} = \textbf{2.03 V}$

112

(c) $v_L = V_i e^{-t/\tau} = 15e^{-30\mu s/10\mu s} = 15e^{-3} = \textbf{0.747 V}$

(d) $v_L = V_i e^{-t/\tau} = 15e^{-40\mu s/10\mu s} = 15e^{-4} = \textbf{0.275 V}$

(e) $v_L = V_i e^{-t/\tau} = 15e^{-50\mu s/10\mu s} = 15e^{-5} = \textbf{0.101 V}$

16. $\tau = \dfrac{L}{R} = \dfrac{75 \text{ mH}}{8.2 \text{ k}\Omega} = 9.15 \text{ } \mu s$

     $I_F = \dfrac{V_s}{R} = \dfrac{10 \text{ V}}{8.2 \text{ k}\Omega} = 1.22 \text{ mA}$

(a) $i = I_F \left(1 - e^{-10\mu s/9.15\mu s}\right) = \textbf{0.811 mA}$

(b) $i = I_F \left(1 - e^{-20\mu s/9.15\mu s}\right) = \textbf{1.08 mA}$

(c) $i = I_F \left(1 - e^{-30\mu s/9.15\mu s}\right) = \textbf{1.17 mA}$

SECTION 11-5 Inductors in AC Circuits

17.   The total inductance for each circuit was found in Problem 11.
     (a) $X_L = 2\pi f L_{tot} = 2\pi(5 \text{ kHz})(4.33 \text{ H}) = \textbf{136 k}\Omega$
     (b) $X_L = 2\pi f L_{tot} = 2\pi(5 \text{ kHz})(50 \text{ mH}) = \textbf{1.57 k}\Omega$
     (c) $X_L = 2\pi f L_{tot} = 2\pi(5 \text{ kHz})(57 \text{ } \mu\text{H}) = \textbf{1.79 }\Omega$

18.   The total inductance for each circuit was found in Problem 12.
     (a) $X_L = 2\pi f L_{tot} = 2\pi(400 \text{ Hz})(57.3 \text{ mH}) = \textbf{144 }\Omega$
     (b) $X_L = 2\pi f L_{tot} = 2\pi(400 \text{ Hz})(4 \text{ mH}) = \textbf{10.1 }\Omega$
     (c) $X_L = 2\pi f L_{tot} = 2\pi(400 \text{ Hz})(5.33 \text{ mH}) = \textbf{13.4 }\Omega$

19. $L_{tot} = L_1 + \dfrac{L_2 L_3}{L_2 + L_3} = 50 \text{ mH} + \dfrac{(20 \text{ mH})(40 \text{ mH})}{60 \text{ mH}} = 63.3 \text{ mH}$

     $X_{L(tot)} = 2\pi f L_{tot} = 2\pi(2.5 \text{ kHz})(63.3 \text{ mH}) = 994 \text{ }\Omega$

     $X_{L2} = 2\pi f L_{tot} = 2\pi(2.5 \text{ kHz})(20 \text{ mH}) = 314 \text{ }\Omega$

     $X_{L3} = 2\pi f L_{tot} = 2\pi(2.5 \text{ kHz})(40 \text{ mH}) = 628 \text{ }\Omega$

     $I_{tot} = \dfrac{V_{rms}}{X_{L(tot)}} = \dfrac{10 \text{ V}}{994 \text{ }\Omega} = \textbf{10.1 mA}$

     $I_{L2} = \left(\dfrac{X_{L3}}{X_{L2} + X_{L3}}\right) I_{tot} = \left(\dfrac{628 \text{ }\Omega}{314 \text{ }\Omega + 628 \text{ }\Omega}\right) 10.1 \text{ mA} = \textbf{6.7 mA}$

     $I_{L3} = \left(\dfrac{X_{L2}}{X_{L2} + X_{L3}}\right) I_{tot} = \left(\dfrac{314 \text{ }\Omega}{314 \text{ }\Omega + 628 \text{ }\Omega}\right) 10.1 \text{ mA} = \textbf{3.37 mA}$

20. (a) $L_{tot} = 57.33$ mH

$$X_L = \frac{V}{I} = \frac{10 \text{ V}}{500 \text{ mA}} = 20 \text{ }\Omega$$

$$X_L = 2\pi f L_{tot}$$

$$f = \frac{X_L}{2\pi L_{tot}} = \frac{20 \text{ }\Omega}{2\pi(57.3 \text{ mH})} = \textbf{55.6 Hz}$$

(b) $L_{tot} = 4$ mH, $X_L = 20$ Ω

$$f = \frac{X_L}{2\pi L_{tot}} = \frac{20 \text{ }\Omega}{2\pi(4 \text{ mH})} = \textbf{796 Hz}$$

(c) $L_{tot} = 5.33$ mH, $X_L = 20$ Ω

$$f = \frac{X_L}{2\pi L_{tot}} = \frac{20 \text{ }\Omega}{2\pi(5.33 \text{ mH})} = \textbf{597 Hz}$$

21. $X_{L(tot)} = 994$ Ω from Problem 19.

$$P_r = I_{rms}^2 X_{L(tot)} = (10.1 \text{ mA})^2(994 \text{ }\Omega) = \textbf{101 mVAR}$$

ADVANCED PROBLEMS

22. $R_{TH} = R_1 \| R_2 + R_3 \| R_4$

$\quad = 4.7$ k$\Omega \| 4.7$ k$\Omega + 3.3$ k$\Omega \| 6.8$ k$\Omega = 4.57$ kΩ

$$\tau = \frac{L}{R_{TH}} = \frac{3.3 \text{ mH}}{4.57 \text{ k}\Omega} = \textbf{0.722 }\boldsymbol{\mu}\textbf{s}$$

23. $$V_{TH} = \left(\frac{R_2}{R_1 + R_2}\right)V_S - \left(\frac{R_4}{R_3 + R_4}\right)V_S = \left(\frac{4.7 \text{ k}\Omega}{9.4 \text{ k}\Omega}\right)15 \text{ V} - \left(\frac{6.8 \text{ k}\Omega}{10.1 \text{ k}\Omega}\right)15 \text{ V} = -2.6 \text{ V}$$

$$I_F = \frac{V_{TH}}{R_{TH}} = \frac{2.6 \text{ V}}{4.57 \text{ k}\Omega} = 569 \text{ }\mu\text{A}$$

(a) $i = I_F\left(1 - e^{-t/\tau}\right) = 569 \text{ }\mu\text{A}\left(1 - e^{-1\mu s/0.722\mu s}\right) = \textbf{427 }\boldsymbol{\mu}\textbf{A}$

(b) $i = I_F = \textbf{569 }\boldsymbol{\mu}\textbf{A}$

24. $R_T = (R_1 + R_3) \| (R_2 + R_4) = 8$ k$\Omega \| 11.5$ k$\Omega = 4.72$ kΩ

$$\tau = \frac{L}{R} = \frac{3.3 \text{ mH}}{4.72 \text{ k}\Omega} = 0.699 \text{ }\mu\text{s}$$

$$i = I_i e^{-t/\tau} = (569 \text{ }\mu\text{A})e^{-1\mu s/0.699\mu s} = \textbf{136 }\boldsymbol{\mu}\textbf{A}$$

25. $X_{L1} = 2\pi(3 \text{ kHz})(5 \text{ mH}) = 94.2$ Ω

$X_{L3} = 2\pi(3 \text{ kHz})(3 \text{ mH}) = 56.5$ Ω

$V_{L3} = I_{L3}X_{L3} = (50 \text{ mA})(56.5 \text{ }\Omega) = 2.83$ V

$V_{L1} = 10 \text{ V} - 2.83 \text{ V} = 7.17$ V

$$I_{L1} = \frac{V_{L1}}{X_{L1}} = \frac{7.17 \text{ V}}{94.2 \text{ }\Omega} = 76.1 \text{ mA}$$

$$I_{L2} = I_{L1} - I_{L3} = 76.1 \text{ mA} - 50 \text{ mA} = \textbf{26.1 mA}$$

26.   *Position 1:*
       $L_\text{T} = 5 \text{ mH} + 1 \text{ mH} = \textbf{6 mH}$
       Position 2:
       $L_\text{T} = 5 \text{ mH} + 100 \text{ }\mu\text{H} \ 1 \text{ mH} = \textbf{6.1 mH}$
       Position 3:
       $L_\text{T} = 5 \text{ mH} + 1000 \text{ }\mu\text{H} + 100 \text{ }\mu\text{H} + 1 \text{ mH} = \textbf{7.1 mH}$
       Position 4:
       $L_\text{T} = 5 \text{ mH} + 10 \text{ mH} + 1000 \text{ }\mu\text{H} + 100 \text{ }\mu\text{H} + 1 \text{ mH} = \textbf{17.1 mH}$

Multisim Troubleshooting Problems

27. L_3 is open.

28. L_1 is shorted.

29.   No fault

30. L_2 is open.

31. L_3 is shorted.

CHAPTER 12
RL CIRCUITS

BASIC PROBLEMS

SECTION 12-1 Sinusoidal Response of *RL* Circuits

1. All the frequencies are **15 kHz**.

2. I, V_R, and V_L are all **sinusoidal**.

SECTION 12-2 Impedance and Phase Angle of Series *RL* Circuits

3. (a) $Z = \sqrt{R^2 + X_L^2} = \sqrt{(100\ \Omega)^2 + (50\ \Omega)^2} = \mathbf{112\ \Omega}$

   (b) $Z = \sqrt{R^2 + X_L^2} = \sqrt{(1.5\ k\Omega)^2 + (1\ k\Omega)^2} = \mathbf{1.8\ k\Omega}$

4. (a) $R_{tot} = 47\ \Omega + 10\ \Omega = 57\ \Omega$

   $L_{tot} = 50\ mH + 100\ mH = 150\ mH$

   $X_{L(tot)} = 2\pi f L_{tot} = 2\pi(100\ Hz)(150\ mH) = 94.2\ \Omega$

   $Z = \sqrt{R_{tot}^2 + X_{L(tot)}^2} = \sqrt{(57\ \Omega)^2 + (94.2\ \Omega)^2} = \mathbf{110\ \Omega}$

   $\theta = \tan^{-1}\left(\dfrac{X_{L(tot)}}{R_{tot}}\right) = \tan^{-1}\left(\dfrac{94.2\ \Omega}{57\ \Omega}\right) = \mathbf{58.8°}$

   (b) $L_{tot} = \dfrac{(5\ mH)(8\ mH)}{5\ mH + 8\ mH} = 3.08\ mH$

   $X_{L(tot)} = 2\pi f L_{tot} = 2\pi(20\ kHz)(3.08\ mH) = 387\ \Omega$

   $Z = \sqrt{R_{tot}^2 + X_{L(tot)}^2} = \sqrt{(470\ \Omega)^2 + (387\ \Omega)^2} = \mathbf{609\ \Omega}$

   $\theta = \tan^{-1}\left(\dfrac{X_{L(tot)}}{R_{tot}}\right) = \tan^{-1}\left(\dfrac{387\ \Omega}{470\ \Omega}\right) = \mathbf{39.5°}$

5. (a) $X_L = 2\pi f L = 2\pi(100\ Hz)(0.02\ H) = 12.6\ \Omega$

   $Z = \sqrt{R^2 + X_L^2} = \sqrt{(12\ \Omega)^2 + (12.6\ \Omega)^2} = \mathbf{17.4\ \Omega}$

   (b) $X_L = 2\pi f L = 2\pi(500\ Hz)(0.02\ H) = 62.8\ \Omega$

   $Z = \sqrt{R^2 + X_L^2} = \sqrt{(12\ \Omega)^2 + (62.8\ \Omega)^2} = \mathbf{64.0\ \Omega}$

(c) $X_L = 2\pi f L = 2\pi(1\text{ kHz})(0.02\text{ H}) = 126\ \Omega$

$Z = \sqrt{R^2 + X_L^2} = \sqrt{(12\ \Omega)^2 + (126\ \Omega)^2} = \mathbf{127\ \Omega}$

(d) $X_L = 2\pi f L = 2\pi(2\text{ kHz})(0.02\text{ H}) = 251\ \Omega$

$Z = \sqrt{R^2 + X_L^2} = \sqrt{(12\ \Omega)^2 + (251\ \Omega)^2} = \mathbf{251\ \Omega}$

6. (a) $R = Z\cos\theta = (20\ \Omega)\cos 45° = \mathbf{14.1\ \Omega}$

$X_L = Z\sin\theta = (20\ \Omega)\sin 45° = \mathbf{14.1\ \Omega}$

(b) $R = Z\cos\theta = (500\ \Omega)\cos 35° = \mathbf{410\ \Omega}$

$X_L = Z\sin\theta = (500\ \Omega)\sin 35° = \mathbf{287\ \Omega}$

(c) $R = Z\cos\theta = (2.5\text{ k}\Omega)\cos 72.5° = \mathbf{752\ \Omega}$

$X_L = Z\sin\theta = (2.5\text{ k}\Omega)\sin 72.5° = \mathbf{2.38\text{ k}\Omega}$

(d) $R = Z\cos\theta = (998\ \Omega)\cos 45° = \mathbf{706\ \Omega}$

$X_L = Z\sin\theta = (998\ \Omega)\sin 45° = \mathbf{706\ \Omega}$

SECTION 12-3 Analysis of Series *RL* Circuits

7. $R_{tot} = R_1 + R_2 = 47\ \Omega + 10\ \Omega = 57\ \Omega$

$L_{tot} = L_1 + L_2 = 50\text{ mH} + 100\text{ mH} = 150\text{ mH}$

$X_{L(tot)} = 2\pi f L_{tot} = 2\pi(1\text{ kHz})(150\text{ mH}) = 942\ \Omega$

$$V_{R(tot)} = \left(\frac{R_{tot}}{\sqrt{R_{tot}^2 + X_{L(tot)}^2}}\right)V_s = \left(\frac{57\ \Omega}{944\ \Omega}\right)5\text{ V} = \mathbf{0.302\text{ V}}$$

8. $R_{tot} = 470\ \Omega$

$$L_{tot} = \frac{1}{\dfrac{1}{L_1} + \dfrac{1}{L_2}} = \frac{1}{\dfrac{1}{5\text{ mH}} + \dfrac{1}{8\text{ mH}}} = 3.08\text{ mH}$$

$X_{L(tot)} = 2\pi f L_{tot} = 2\pi(20\text{ kHz})(3.08\text{ mH}) = 387\ \Omega$

$$V_{R(tot)} = \left(\frac{R_{tot}}{\sqrt{R_{tot}^2 + X_L^2}}\right)V_s = \left(\frac{470\ \Omega}{\sqrt{(470\ \Omega)^2 + (387\ \Omega)^2}}\right)8\text{ V} = \mathbf{6.18\text{ V}}$$

$$V_{L(tot)} = \left(\frac{X_{L(tot)}}{\sqrt{R_{tot}^2 + X_{L(tot)}^2}}\right)V_s = \left(\frac{387\ \Omega}{\sqrt{(470\ \Omega)^2 + (387\ \Omega)^2}}\right)8\text{ V} = \mathbf{5.08\text{ V}}$$

9. (a) $Z = 112\ \Omega$ from Problem 3.

$I = \dfrac{V_s}{Z} = \dfrac{10\text{ V}}{112\ \Omega} = \mathbf{89.3\text{ mA}}$

(b) $Z = 1.8\text{ k}\Omega$ from Problem 3.

$I = \dfrac{V_s}{Z} = \dfrac{5\text{ V}}{1.8\text{ k}\Omega} = \mathbf{2.78\text{ mA}}$

10. Using the results of Problem 4:

(a) $I = \dfrac{V_s}{Z} = \dfrac{5\,V}{110\,\Omega} = \textbf{45.5 mA}$

(b) $I = \dfrac{V_s}{Z} = \dfrac{8\,V}{609\,\Omega} = \textbf{13.1 mA}$

11. $X_L = 2\pi(60\ \text{Hz})(0.1\ \text{H}) = 37.7\ \Omega$

$\theta = \tan^{-1}\left(\dfrac{X_L}{R}\right) = \tan^{-1}\left(\dfrac{37.7\ \Omega}{47\ \Omega}\right) = \textbf{38.7°}$

12. $\theta = \tan^{-1}\left(\dfrac{X_L}{R}\right)$

$X_L = 2\pi(60\ \text{Hz})(0.1\ \text{H}) = 37.7\ \Omega$

$\theta = \tan^{-1}\left(\dfrac{37.7\ \Omega}{47\ \Omega}\right) = 38.7°$

Double L:

$X_L = 2\pi(60\ \text{Hz})(0.2\ \text{H}) = 75.4\ \Omega$

$\theta = \tan^{-1}\left(\dfrac{75.4\ \Omega}{47\ \Omega}\right) = 58.1°$

θ increases by 19.4° from 38.7° to 58.1°.

13. The circuit phase angle was determined to be 38.7° in Problem 11. This is the phase angle by which the source voltage leads the current; it is the same as the angle between the resistor voltage and the source voltage. The inductor voltage leads the resistor voltage by 90°. See Figure 12-1.

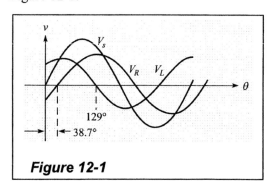

Figure 12-1

14. (a) $X_L = 2\pi(60\ \text{Hz})(100\ \text{mH}) = 37.7\ \Omega$

$Z = \sqrt{R^2 + X_L^2} = \sqrt{(150\ \Omega)^2 + (37.7\ \Omega)^2} = 155\ \Omega$

$V_R = \left(\dfrac{R}{Z}\right)V_s = \left(\dfrac{150\ \Omega}{155\ \Omega}\right)5\,V = \textbf{4.84 V}$

$V_L = \left(\dfrac{X_L}{Z}\right)V_s = \left(\dfrac{37.7\ \Omega}{155\ \Omega}\right)5\,V = \textbf{1.22 V}$

(b)　$X_L = 2\pi(200\ \text{Hz})(100\ \text{mH}) = 126\ \Omega$

$$Z = \sqrt{R^2 + X_L^2} = \sqrt{(150\ \Omega)^2 + (126\ \Omega)^2} = 196\ \Omega$$

$$V_R = \left(\frac{R}{Z}\right)V_s = \left(\frac{150\ \Omega}{196\ \Omega}\right)5\ \text{V} = \mathbf{3.83\ V}$$

$$V_L = \left(\frac{X_L}{Z}\right)V_s = \left(\frac{126\ \Omega}{196\ \Omega}\right)5\ \text{V} = \mathbf{3.21\ V}$$

(c)　$X_L = 2\pi(500\ \text{Hz})(100\ \text{mH}) = 314\ \Omega$

$$Z = \sqrt{R^2 + X_L^2} = \sqrt{(150\ \Omega)^2 + (314\ \Omega)^2} = 348\ \Omega$$

$$V_R = \left(\frac{R}{Z}\right)V_s = \left(\frac{150\ \Omega}{348\ \Omega}\right)5\ \text{V} = \mathbf{2.15\ V}$$

$$V_L = \left(\frac{X_L}{Z}\right)V_s = \left(\frac{314\ \Omega}{348\ \Omega}\right)5\ \text{V} = \mathbf{4.5\ V}$$

(d)　$X_L = 2\pi(1\ \text{kHz})(100\ \text{mH}) = 628\ \Omega$

$$Z = \sqrt{R^2 + X_L^2} = \sqrt{(150\ \Omega)^2 + (628\ \Omega)^2} = 646\ \Omega$$

$$V_R = \left(\frac{R}{Z}\right)V_s = \left(\frac{150\ \Omega}{646\ \Omega}\right)5\ \text{V} = \mathbf{1.16\ V}$$

$$V_L = \left(\frac{X_L}{Z}\right)V_s = \left(\frac{628\ \Omega}{646\ \Omega}\right)5\ \text{V} = \mathbf{4.86\ V}$$

15.　(a)　$X_L = 2\pi(1\ \text{Hz})(10\ \text{H}) = 62.8\ \Omega$

$$\phi = \tan^{-1}\left(\frac{X_L}{R}\right) = \tan^{-1}\left(\frac{62.83\ \Omega}{39\ \text{k}\Omega}\right) = \mathbf{0.092°}$$

(b)　$X_L = 2\pi(100\ \text{Hz})(10\ \text{H}) = 6.28\ \text{k}\Omega$

$$\phi = \tan^{-1}\left(\frac{X_L}{R}\right) = \tan^{-1}\left(\frac{6.28\ \text{k}\Omega}{39\ \text{k}\Omega}\right) = \mathbf{9.15°}$$

(c)　$X_L = 2\pi(1\ \text{kHz})(10\ \text{H}) = 62.8\ \text{k}\Omega$

$$\phi = \tan^{-1}\left(\frac{X_L}{R}\right) = \tan^{-1}\left(\frac{62.8\ \text{k}\Omega}{39\ \text{k}\Omega}\right) = \mathbf{58.2°}$$

(d)　$X_L = 2\pi(10\ \text{kHz})(10\ \text{H}) = 628\ \text{k}\Omega$

$$\phi = \tan^{-1}\left(\frac{X_L}{R}\right) = \tan^{-1}\left(\frac{628\ \text{k}\Omega}{39\ \text{k}\Omega}\right) = \mathbf{86.4°}$$

16.　(a)　$\phi = 90° - \tan^{-1}\left(\frac{X_L}{R}\right) = 90° - \tan^{-1}\left(\frac{62.8\ \Omega}{39\ \text{k}\Omega}\right) = \mathbf{89.9°}$

(b)　$\phi = 90° - \tan^{-1}\left(\frac{X_L}{R}\right) = 90° - \tan^{-1}\left(\frac{6.28\ \text{k}\Omega}{39\ \text{k}\Omega}\right) = \mathbf{80.9°}$

(c) $\phi = 90° - \tan^{-1}\left(\dfrac{X_L}{R}\right) = 90° - \tan^{-1}\left(\dfrac{62.8 \text{ k}\Omega}{39 \text{ k}\Omega}\right) = \mathbf{31.8°}$

(d) $\phi = 90° - \tan^{-1}\left(\dfrac{X_L}{R}\right) = 90° - \tan^{-1}\left(\dfrac{628 \text{ k}\Omega}{39 \text{ k}\Omega}\right) = \mathbf{3.55°}$

SECTION 12-4 Impedance and Phase Angle of *RL* Circuits

17. $X_L = 2\pi(2 \text{ kHz})(800 \text{ }\mu\text{H}) = 10 \text{ }\Omega$

$Y_{tot} = \sqrt{\left(\dfrac{1}{12 \text{ }\Omega}\right)^2 + \left(\dfrac{1}{10 \text{ }\Omega}\right)^2} = 0.13 \text{ S}$

$Z = \dfrac{1}{Y_{tot}} = \dfrac{1}{0.13 \text{ S}} = \mathbf{7.69 \text{ }\Omega}$

18. (a) $X_L = 2\pi(1.5 \text{ kHz})(800 \text{ }\mu\text{H}) = 7.54 \text{ }\Omega$

$Y = \sqrt{\left(\dfrac{1}{R}\right)^2 + \left(\dfrac{1}{X_L}\right)^2} = \sqrt{\left(\dfrac{1}{12 \text{ }\Omega}\right)^2 + \left(\dfrac{1}{7.54 \text{ }\Omega}\right)^2} = 0.157 \text{ S}$

$Z = \dfrac{1}{Y} = \dfrac{1}{0.157 \text{ S}} = \mathbf{6.37 \text{ }\Omega}$

(b) $X_L = 2\pi(3 \text{ kHz})(800 \text{ }\mu\text{H}) = 15.1 \text{ }\Omega$

$Y = \sqrt{\left(\dfrac{1}{R}\right)^2 + \left(\dfrac{1}{X_L}\right)^2} = \sqrt{\left(\dfrac{1}{12 \text{ }\Omega}\right)^2 + \left(\dfrac{1}{15.1 \text{ }\Omega}\right)^2} = 0.106 \text{ S}$

$Z = \dfrac{1}{Y} = \dfrac{1}{0.106 \text{ S}} = \mathbf{9.43 \text{ }\Omega}$

(c) $X_L = 2\pi(5 \text{ kHz})(800 \text{ }\mu\text{H}) = 25.1 \text{ }\Omega$

$Y = \sqrt{\left(\dfrac{1}{R}\right)^2 + \left(\dfrac{1}{X_L}\right)^2} = \sqrt{\left(\dfrac{1}{12 \text{ }\Omega}\right)^2 + \left(\dfrac{1}{25.1 \text{ }\Omega}\right)^2} = 0.092 \text{ S}$

$Z = \dfrac{1}{Y} = \dfrac{1}{0.092 \text{ S}} = \mathbf{10.9 \text{ }\Omega}$

(d) $X_L = 2\pi(10 \text{ kHz})(800 \text{ }\mu\text{H}) = 50.3 \text{ }\Omega$

$Y = \sqrt{\left(\dfrac{1}{R}\right)^2 + \left(\dfrac{1}{X_L}\right)^2} = \sqrt{\left(\dfrac{1}{12 \text{ }\Omega}\right)^2 + \left(\dfrac{1}{50.3 \text{ }\Omega}\right)^2} = 0.086 \text{ S}$

$Z = \dfrac{1}{Y} = \dfrac{1}{0.086 \text{ S}} = \mathbf{11.6 \text{ }\Omega}$

19. $X_L = 2\pi fL$

$$f = \frac{X_L}{2\pi L} = \frac{12\ \Omega}{2\pi(800\ \mu H)} = \textbf{2.39 kHz}$$

SECTION 12-5   Analysis of Parallel *RL* Circuits

20. $I_R = \dfrac{10\ V}{2.2\ k\Omega} = \textbf{4.55 mA}$

$I_L = \dfrac{10\ V}{3.5\ k\Omega} = \textbf{2.86 mA}$

$I_{tot} = \sqrt{(4.55\ mA)^2 + (2.86\ mA)^2} = \textbf{5.37 mA}$

21. (a) $X_L = 2\pi(2\ kHz)(25\ mH) = 314\ \Omega$

$$Z = \frac{RX_L}{\sqrt{R^2 + X_L^2}} = \frac{(560\ \Omega)(314\ \Omega)}{\sqrt{(560\ \Omega)^2 + (314\ \Omega)^2}} = \textbf{274}\ \boldsymbol{\Omega}$$

(b) $I_R = \dfrac{V_s}{R} = \dfrac{50\ V}{560\ \Omega} = \textbf{89.3 mA}$

(c) $I_L = \dfrac{V_s}{X_L} = \dfrac{50\ V}{314\ \Omega} = \textbf{159 mA}$

(d) $I_{tot} = \dfrac{V_s}{Z} = \dfrac{50\ V}{274\ \Omega} = \textbf{183 mA}$

(e) $\theta = \tan^{-1}\left(\dfrac{R}{X_L}\right) = \tan^{-1}\left(\dfrac{560\ \Omega}{314\ \Omega}\right) = \textbf{60.7°}$

22. $Z_{tot} = \dfrac{(R_1 + R_2)X_L}{\sqrt{(R_1 + R_2)^2 + X_L^2}} = \dfrac{(11.5\ k\Omega)(5\ k\Omega)}{12.54\ k\Omega} = 4.59\ k\Omega$

$\theta = \tan^{-1}\left(\dfrac{11.5\ k\Omega}{5\ k\Omega}\right) = 66.5°$

$R_{eq} = Z_{tot}\cos\theta = (4.59\ k\Omega)\cos 66.5° = \textbf{1.83 k}\boldsymbol{\Omega}$

$X_{L(eq)} = Z_{tot}\sin\theta = (4.59\ k\Omega)\sin 66.5° = \textbf{4.21 k}\boldsymbol{\Omega}$

SECTION 12-6   Analysis of Series-Parallel *RL* Circuits

23. $X_L = 2\pi(100\ kHz)(1\ mH) = 628\ \Omega$

$$Z_p = \frac{R_2 X_L}{\sqrt{R_2^2 + X_L^2}} = \frac{(1500\ \Omega)(628\ \Omega)}{\sqrt{(1500\ \Omega)^2 + (628\ \Omega)^2}} = 579\ \Omega$$

$\theta = \tan^{-1}\left(\dfrac{R_2}{X_L}\right) = \tan^{-1}\left(\dfrac{1500\ \Omega}{628\ \Omega}\right) = 67.3°$

$R_{eq} = Z_p\cos\,\theta = (579\ \Omega)\cos 67.3° = 224\ \Omega$

$X_{L(eq)} = Z_p\sin\,\theta = (579\ \Omega)\sin 67.3° = 534\ \Omega$

$Z_{tot} = \sqrt{(R_1 + R_{eq})^2 + X_{L(eq)}^2} = \sqrt{(444\ \Omega)^2 + (534\ \Omega)^2} = 694\ \Omega$

$I_{tot} = \dfrac{25\ V}{694\ \Omega} = 36\ mA$

$V_{R1} = I_{tot}R_1 = (36\ mA)(220\ \Omega) = \mathbf{7.92\ V}$

$V_{R2} = V_L = I_{tot}Z_p = (36\ mA)(579\ \Omega) = \mathbf{20.8\ V}$

24. The circuit is predominantly inductive because $X_{L(eq)} > R_{tot}$.

25. Using the results of Problem 23:

$I_{tot} = \mathbf{36\ mA}$

$I_L = \dfrac{V_L}{X_L} = \dfrac{20.8\ V}{628\ \Omega} = \mathbf{33.2\ mA}$

$I_{R2} = \dfrac{V_{R2}}{R_2} = \dfrac{20.8\ V}{1500\ \Omega} = \mathbf{13.9\ mA}$

SECTION 12-7 Power in *RL* Circuits

26. $P_a = \sqrt{P_{true}^2 + P_r^2} = \sqrt{(100\ mW)^2 + (340\ mVAR)^2} = \mathbf{354\ mVA}$

27. $X_L = 2\pi(60\ Hz)(0.1\ H) = 37.7\ \Omega$

$Z = \sqrt{R^2 + X_L^2} = \sqrt{(47\ \Omega)^2 + (37.7\ \Omega)^2} = 60.3\ \Omega$

$I_{tot} = \dfrac{V_s}{Z} = \dfrac{1\ V}{60.3\ \Omega} = 16.6\ mA$

$P_{true} = I_{tot}^2R = (16.6\ mA)^2(47\ \Omega) = \mathbf{13.0\ mW}$

$P_r = I_{tot}^2X_L = (16.6\ mA)^2(37.7\ \Omega) = \mathbf{10.4\ mVAR}$

28. $\theta = \tan^{-1}\left(\dfrac{R}{X_L}\right) = \tan^{-1}\left(\dfrac{2.2\ k\Omega}{3.5\ k\Omega}\right) = 32.2°$

$PF = \cos\,\theta = \cos 32.2° = \mathbf{0.846}$

29. Using the results of Problems 23 and 25:

$PF = \cos\,\theta = \cos 67.3° = \mathbf{0.386}$

$P_{true} = V_sI\cos\,\theta = (25\ V)(36\ mA)(0.386) = \mathbf{347\ mW}$

$P_r = I_L^2X_L = (33.2\ mA)^2(628\ \Omega) = \mathbf{692\ mVAR}$

$P_a = V_sI_{tot} = (25\ V)(36\ mA) = \mathbf{900\ mVA}$

30. Use the formula, $V_{out} = \left(\dfrac{R}{Z_{tot}}\right)V_{in}$. See Figure 12-2.

Frequency (kHz)	X_L (kΩ)	Z_{tot} (kΩ)	V_{out} (V)
0	0	39	1
1	62.8	73.9	0.53
2	126	132	0.30
3	189	193	0.20
4	251	254	0.15
5	314	316	0.12

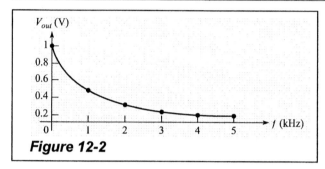

Figure 12-2

31. Use the formula, $V_{out} = \left(\dfrac{X_L}{Z_{tot}}\right)V_{in}$. See Figure 12-3.

Frequency (kHz)	X_L (kΩ)	Z_{tot} (kΩ)	V_{out} (mV)
0	0	39	0
1	62.8	73.9	42.5
2	126	132	47.7
3	189	193	49.0
4	251	254	49.4
5	314	316	49.7

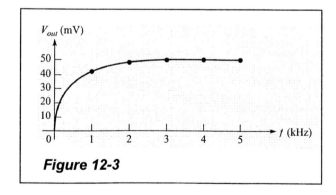

Figure 12-3

32. For Figure 12-58: See Figure 12-4(a).

$X_L = 2\pi(8 \text{ kHz})(10 \text{ H}) = 503 \text{ k}\Omega$

$Z = \sqrt{R^2 + X_L^2} = \sqrt{(39 \text{ k}\Omega)^2 + (503 \text{ k}\Omega)^2} = 505 \text{ k}\Omega$

$$\theta = \tan^{-1}\left(\frac{X_L}{R}\right) = \tan^{-1}\left(\frac{503 \text{ k}\Omega}{39 \text{ k}\Omega}\right) = \mathbf{85.6°}$$

$$V_R = \left(\frac{R}{Z}\right)V_{in} = \left(\frac{39 \text{ k}\Omega}{505 \text{ k}\Omega}\right)1 \text{ V} = \mathbf{77.2 \text{ mV}}$$

$$V_L = \left(\frac{X_L}{Z}\right)V_{in} = \left(\frac{503 \text{ k}\Omega}{505 \text{ k}\Omega}\right)1 \text{ V} = \mathbf{996 \text{ mV}}$$

For Figure 12-59: See Figure 12-4(b).

$$X_L = 2\pi(8 \text{ kHz})(10 \text{ H}) = 503 \text{ k}\Omega$$

$$Z = \sqrt{R^2 + X_L^2} = \sqrt{(39 \text{ k}\Omega)^2 + (503 \text{ k}\Omega)^2} = 505 \text{ k}\Omega$$

$$\theta = \tan^{-1}\left(\frac{X_L}{R}\right) = \tan^{-1}\left(\frac{503 \text{ k}\Omega}{39 \text{ k}\Omega}\right) = \mathbf{85.6°}$$

$$V_R = \left(\frac{R}{Z}\right)V_{in} = \left(\frac{39 \text{ k}\Omega}{505 \text{ k}\Omega}\right)50 \text{ mV} = \mathbf{3.86 \text{ mV}}$$

$$V_L = \left(\frac{X_L}{Z}\right)V_{in} = \left(\frac{503 \text{ k}\Omega}{505 \text{ k}\Omega}\right)50 \text{ mV} = \mathbf{49.8 \text{ mV}}$$

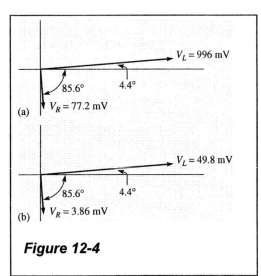

Figure 12-4

SECTION 12-9 Troubleshooting

33. $V_{R1} = V_{L1} = \mathbf{18 \text{ V}}$
    $V_{R2} = V_{R3} = V_{L2} = \mathbf{0 \text{ V}}$

34. (a) $V_{out} = \mathbf{0 \text{ V}}$
    (b) $V_{out} = \mathbf{0 \text{ V}}$
    (c) $V_{out} = \mathbf{0 \text{ V}}$
    (d) $V_{out} = \mathbf{0 \text{ V}}$

ADVANCED PROBLEMS

35. See Figure 12-5(a).

$R_{th} = R_3 + R_1 \| R_2 = 33\ \Omega + 56\ \Omega \| 22\ \Omega = 48.8\ \Omega$

$V_{th} = \left(\dfrac{R_2}{R_1 + R_2}\right) 25\ \text{V} = \left(\dfrac{22\ \Omega}{78\ \Omega}\right) 25\ \text{V} = 7.05\ \text{V}$

See Figure 12-5(b):

$L_{tot} = \dfrac{1}{\dfrac{1}{50\ \text{mH}} + \dfrac{1}{50\ \text{mH}}} = 25\ \text{mH}$

$X_{L(tot)} = 2\pi f L_{tot} = 2\pi(400\ \text{Hz})(25\ \text{mH}) = 62.8\ \Omega$

$V_L = \left(\dfrac{X_{L(tot)}}{\sqrt{R_{th}^2 + X_{L(tot)}^2}}\right) V_{th} = \left(\dfrac{62.8\ \Omega}{\sqrt{(48.8\ \Omega)^2 + (62.8\ \Omega)^2}}\right) 7.05\ \text{V} = \mathbf{5.57\ V}$

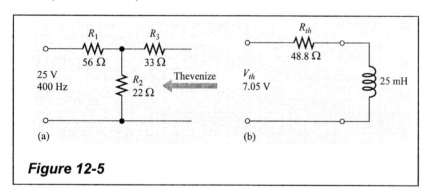

Figure 12-5

36. Since $X_{L(tot)} > R_{th}$, the circuit is predominantly **inductive**.

37. From Problem 35,

$X_{L(tot)} = 62.8\ \Omega$

$Z_{tot} = R_1 + R_2 \| \sqrt{R_3^2 + X_{L(tot)}^2} = 56\ \Omega + 22\ \Omega \| \sqrt{(33\ \Omega)^2 + (62.8\ \Omega)^2} = 72.8\ \Omega$

$I_{tot} = \dfrac{V_s}{Z_{tot}} = \dfrac{25\ \text{V}}{72.8\ \Omega} = \mathbf{343\ mA}$

38. (a) $X_L = 2\pi f L = 2\pi(80\ \text{kHz})(8\ \text{mH}) = 4.02\ \text{k}\Omega$

$Z_{tot} = R_1 \| \left(R_2 + R_3 \| \sqrt{R_4^2 + X_L^2}\right)$

$= 1.2\ \text{k}\Omega \| \left(1.0\ \text{k}\Omega + 3.3\ \text{k}\Omega \| \sqrt{(5.6\ \text{k}\Omega)^2 + (4.02\ \text{k}\Omega)^2}\right)$

$= \mathbf{875\ \Omega}$

(b) $I_{tot} = \dfrac{V_s}{Z_{tot}} = \dfrac{18\ \text{V}}{875\ \Omega} = \mathbf{20.6\ mA}$

(c) $R_{tot} = R_1 \| (R_2 + R_3) + R_4 = 1.2\ \text{k}\Omega \| 4.3\ \text{k}\Omega + 5.6\ \text{k}\Omega = 6.54\ \text{k}\Omega$

$$\theta = \tan^{-1}\left(\frac{X_L}{R_{tot}}\right) = \tan^{-1}\left(\frac{4.02\ k\Omega}{6.54\ k\Omega}\right) = \mathbf{31.6°}$$

(d)   See Figure 12-6(a).

$$R_{th} = R_4 + R_2 \parallel R_3 = 5.6\ k\Omega + 1.0\ k\Omega \parallel 3.3\ k\Omega = 6.37\ k\Omega$$

$$V_{th} = \left(\frac{R_3}{R_2 + R_3}\right)V_s = \left(\frac{3.3\ k\Omega}{4.3\ k\Omega}\right)18\ V = 13.8\ V$$

$$V_L = \left(\frac{X_L}{\sqrt{R_{th}^2 + X_L^2}}\right)V_{th} = \left(\frac{4.02\ k\Omega}{\sqrt{(6.37\ k\Omega)^2 + (4.02\ k\Omega)^2}}\right)13.8\ V = \mathbf{7.37\ V}$$

(e)   See Figure 12-6(b) and (c):

$$R_{th} = R_2 \parallel R_3 = 1.0\ k\Omega \parallel 3.3\ k\Omega = 767\ \Omega$$

$$V_{th} = \left(\frac{R_3}{R_2 + R_3}\right)V_s = \left(\frac{3.3\ k\Omega}{4.4\ k\Omega}\right)18\ V = 13.8\ V$$

The voltage across the R_4-L combination is the same as the voltage across R_3.

$$V_{R3} = \left(\frac{\sqrt{R_4^2 + X_L^2}}{\sqrt{(R_{th} + R_4)^2 + X_L^2}}\right)V_{th}$$

$$= \left(\frac{\sqrt{(5.6\ k\Omega)^2 + (4.02\ k\Omega)^2}}{\sqrt{(6.37\ k\Omega)^2 + (4.02\ k\Omega)^2}}\right)13.8\ V = \left(\frac{6.89\ k\Omega}{7.53\ k\Omega}\right)13.8\ V = \mathbf{12.6\ V}$$

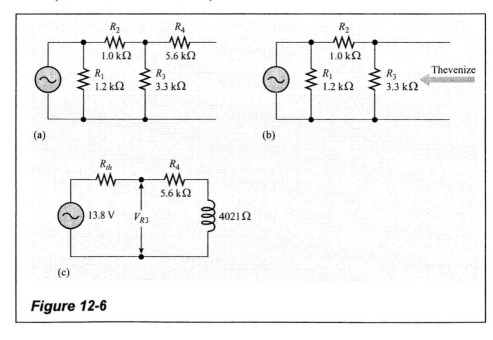

Figure 12-6

126

39. (a) $Z_{R2-X_{L1}} = \dfrac{R_2 X_{L1}}{\sqrt{R_2^2 + X_{L1}^2}} = \dfrac{(68\ \Omega)(100\ \Omega)}{\sqrt{(68\ \Omega)^2 + (100\ \Omega)^2}} = 56.2\ \Omega$

$\theta_{R2-X_{L1}} = \tan^{-1}\left(\dfrac{R_2}{X_{L1}}\right) = \tan^{-1}\left(\dfrac{68\ \Omega}{100\ \Omega}\right) = 34.2°$

Converting the parallel combination of R_2 and X_{L1} to an equivalent series form:

$R_{eq} = Z_{R2-X_{L1}} \cos\theta_{R2-X_{L1}} = (56.2\ \Omega)\cos 34.2° = 46.5\ \Omega$

$X_{L(eq)} = Z_{R2-X_{L1}} \sin\theta_{R2-X_{L1}} = (56.2\ \Omega)\sin 34.2° = 31.6\ \Omega$

$Z_B = \sqrt{(R_1 + R_{eq})^2 + X_{L(eq)}^2} = \sqrt{(47\ \Omega + 46.5\ \Omega)^2 + (31.6\ \Omega)^2} = 98.7\ \Omega$

$I_{R1} = \dfrac{V_s}{Z_B} = \dfrac{40\ \text{V}}{98.7\ \Omega} = \textbf{405 mA}$

(b) $I_{L1} = \left(\dfrac{R_2}{\sqrt{R_2^2 + X_{L1}^2}}\right) I_{R1} = \left(\dfrac{68\ \Omega}{\sqrt{(68\ \Omega)^2 + (100\ \Omega)^2}}\right) 405\ \text{mA} = \textbf{228 mA}$

(c) $X_{L2-L3} = X_{L2} + X_{L3} = 75\ \Omega + 45\ \Omega = 120\ \Omega$

$I_{L2} = \dfrac{V_s}{X_{L2-L3}} = \dfrac{40\ \text{V}}{120\ \Omega} = \textbf{333 mA}$

(d) $I_{R2} = \left(\dfrac{X_{L1}}{\sqrt{R_2^2 + X_{L1}^2}}\right) I_{R1} = \left(\dfrac{100\ \Omega}{\sqrt{(68\ \Omega)^2 + (100\ \Omega)^2}}\right) 405\ \text{mA} = \textbf{335 mA}$

40. $R_4 + R_5 = 3.9\ \text{k}\Omega + 6.8\ \text{k}\Omega = 10.7\ \text{k}\Omega$

$R_3 \parallel (R_4 + R_5) = 4.7\ \text{k}\Omega \parallel 10.7\ \text{k}\Omega = 3.27\ \text{k}\Omega$

$R_2 + R_3 \parallel (R_4 + R_5) = 5.6\ \text{k}\Omega + 3.27\ \text{k}\Omega = 8.87\ \text{k}\Omega$

$R_{tot} = R_1 \parallel (R_2 + R_3 \parallel (R_4 + R_5)) = 3.3\ \text{k}\Omega \parallel 8.87\ \text{k}\Omega = 2.41\ \text{k}\Omega$

$X_L = 2\pi(10\ \text{k}\Omega)(50\ \text{mH}) = 3.14\ \text{k}\Omega$

$\theta = \tan^{-1}\left(\dfrac{X_L}{R}\right) = \tan^{-1}\left(\dfrac{3.14\ \text{k}\Omega}{2.41\ \text{k}\Omega}\right) = \textbf{52.5°}\quad V_{out}\ \textbf{lags}\ V_{in}$

$V_{R1} = \left(\dfrac{R_{tot}}{\sqrt{R_{tot}^2 + X_L^2}}\right) V_{in} = \left(\dfrac{2.41\ \text{k}\Omega}{\sqrt{(2.41\ \text{k}\Omega)^2 + (3.14\ \text{k}\Omega)^2}}\right) 1\ \text{V} = 609\ \text{mV}$

$V_{R3} = \left(\dfrac{R_3 \parallel (R_4 + R_5)}{R_3 \parallel (R_4 + R_5) + R_2}\right) V_{R1} = \left(\dfrac{3.27\ \text{k}\Omega}{3.27\ \text{k}\Omega + 5.6\ \text{k}\Omega}\right) 609\ \text{mV} = 225\ \text{mV}$

$V_{out} = V_{R5} = \left(\dfrac{R_5}{R_4 + R_5}\right) V_{R3} = \left(\dfrac{6.8\ \text{k}\Omega}{3.9\ \text{k}\Omega + 6.8\ \text{k}\Omega}\right) 225\ \text{mV} = 143\ \text{mV}$

Attenuation $= \dfrac{V_{out}}{V_{in}} = \dfrac{143\ \text{mV}}{1\ \text{V}} = \textbf{0.143}$

41. $L_{tot} = \left((L_4 + L_5) \parallel L_3 + L_2\right) \parallel L_1$

$= \left((1\ \text{mH} + 1\ \text{mA}) \parallel 2\ \text{mH} + 1\ \text{mH}\right) \parallel 2\ \text{mH}$

$= (1\ \text{mH} + 1\ \text{mA}) \parallel 2\ \text{mH} = 2\ \text{mH} \parallel 2\ \text{mH} = 1\ \text{mH}$

$$X_{L(tot)} = 2\pi f L = 62.8 \ \Omega$$

$$V_{L(tot)} = \left(\frac{X_{L(tot)}}{\sqrt{R^2 + X_{L(tot)}^2}} \right) V_{in}$$

$$= \left(\frac{62.8 \ \Omega}{\sqrt{(100 \ \Omega)^2 + (62.8 \ \Omega)^2}} \right) 1 \ V = 0.532 \ V$$

$$V_{L3-4-5} = \left(\frac{62.8 \ \Omega}{125.6 \ \Omega} \right) 0.532 \ V = 0.265 \ V$$

$$V_{out} = \left(\frac{62.8 \ \Omega}{125.6 \ \Omega} \right) 0.265 \ V = 0.133 \ V$$

$$\text{Attenuation} = \frac{V_{out}}{V_{in}} = \frac{0.133 \ V}{1 \ V} = \textbf{0.133}$$

42. $$R_1 = \frac{12 \ V}{1 \ A} = 12 \ \Omega$$

$$R_2 = \frac{2.5 \ kV}{1 \ A} = 2.5 \ k\Omega$$

See Figure 12-7. When the switch is thrown from position 1 to position 2, the inductance will attempt to keep 1 A through R_2, thus a 2.5 kV spike is created across R_2 for a short time. This design neglects the arcing of the switch, assuming instantaneous closure from position 1 to position 2. The value of L is arbitrary since no time constant requirements are imposed.

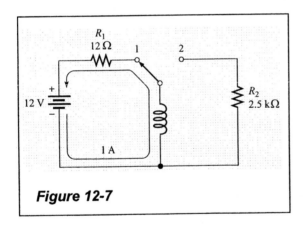

Figure 12-7

43. See Figure 12-8. The correct output voltage is calculated as follows:
$$X_L = 2\pi f L = 2\pi(10 \ kHz)(50 \ mH) = 3142 \ \Omega$$
3.9 kΩ + 6.8 kΩ = 10.7 kΩ
4.7 kΩ ‖ 10.7 kΩ = 3.27 kΩ
5.6 kΩ + 3.27 kΩ = 8.87 kΩ
3.3 kΩ ‖ 8.87 kΩ = 2.41 kΩ

$$V_A = \left(\frac{2.41 \ k\Omega}{\sqrt{(2.41 \ k\Omega)^2 + (3.142 \ k\Omega)^2}} \right) 1 \ V = 0.609 \ V$$

128

$$V_B = \left(\frac{3.27 \text{ k}\Omega}{3.27 \text{ k}\Omega + 5.6 \text{ k}\Omega}\right)0.609 \text{ V} = 0.225 \text{ V}$$

$$V_{out} = \left(\frac{6.8 \text{ k}\Omega}{6.8 \text{ k}\Omega + 3.9 \text{ k}\Omega}\right)0.225 \text{ V} = 0.143 \text{ V}$$

The measured output is approximately 0.3 V peak, which is incorrect.

After trial and error, we find that if **the 4.7 kΩ is open** we get:

$R_{tot} = 3.3 \text{ k}\Omega \parallel (5.6 \text{ k}\Omega + 3.9 \text{ k}\Omega + 6.8 \text{ k}\Omega) = 2.74 \text{ k}\Omega$

$$V_A = \left(\frac{2.74 \text{ k}\Omega}{\sqrt{(2.74 \text{ k}\Omega)^2 + (3.142 \text{ k}\Omega)^2}}\right)1 \text{ V} = 0.657 \text{ V}$$

$$V_{out} = \left(\frac{6.8 \text{ k}\Omega}{5.6 \text{ k}\Omega + 3.9 \text{ k}\Omega + 6.8 \text{ k}\Omega}\right)0.657 \text{ V} = 0.274 \text{ V}$$

This is relatively close to the measured value. Component tolerances could give us the scope reading.

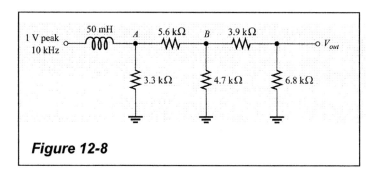

Figure 12-8

Multisim Troubleshooting Problems

44. R_2 is shorted.

45. L_2 is open.

46. L_1 is shorted.

47. R_2 is open.

48. No fault

49. L_1 is shorted.

CHAPTER 13
RLC CIRCUITS AND RESONANCE

BASIC PROBLEMS

SECTION 13-1 Impedance and Phase Angle of Series *RLC* Circuits

1. $X_C = \dfrac{1}{2\pi fC} = \dfrac{1}{2\pi(5 \text{ kHz})(0.047 \text{ }\mu\text{F})} = 677 \text{ }\Omega$

   $X_L = 2\pi fL = 2\pi(5 \text{ kHz})(5 \text{ mH}) = 157 \text{ }\Omega$

   $Z = \sqrt{R^2 + (X_C - X_L)^2}$

   $\quad = \sqrt{(10 \text{ }\Omega)^2 + (677 \text{ }\Omega - 157 \text{ }\Omega)^2} = \sqrt{(10 \text{ }\Omega)^2 + (520 \text{ }\Omega)^2} = \textbf{520 }\Omega$

   $\theta = \tan^{-1}\left(\dfrac{X_C - X_L}{R}\right) = \tan^{-1}\left(\dfrac{520 \text{ }\Omega}{10 \text{ }\Omega}\right) = \textbf{88.9°} \ (V_s \text{ lagging } I)$

   $X_{tot} = X_C - X_L = \textbf{520 }\Omega \ \textbf{Capacitive}$

2. $Z = \sqrt{R^2 + (X_L - X_C)^2} = \sqrt{(4.7 \text{ k}\Omega)^2 + (8.0 \text{ k}\Omega - 3.5 \text{ k}\Omega)^2} = \textbf{6.51 k}\Omega$

3. Doubling f doubles X_L and halves X_C, thus increasing the net reactance and, therefore, the **impedance increases.**

SECTION 13-2 Analysis of Series *RLC* Circuits

4. $Z_{tot} = \sqrt{R^2 + (X_L - X_C)^2} = \sqrt{(4.7 \text{ k}\Omega)^2 + (4.5 \text{ k}\Omega)^2} = 6.51 \text{ k}\Omega$

   $I_{tot} = \dfrac{V_s}{Z_{tot}} = \dfrac{4 \text{ V}}{6.51 \text{ k}\Omega} = \textbf{614 }\mu\text{A}$

   $V_R = I_{tot}R = (614 \text{ }\mu\text{A})(4.7 \text{ k}\Omega) = \textbf{2.89 V}$

   $V_L = I_{tot}X_L = (614 \text{ }\mu\text{A})(8.0 \text{ k}\Omega) = \textbf{4.91 V}$

   $V_C = I_{tot}X_C = (614 \text{ }\mu\text{A})(3.5 \text{ k}\Omega) = \textbf{2.15 V}$

5. $\theta = \tan^{-1}\left(\dfrac{X_{tot}}{R}\right) = \tan^{-1}\left(\dfrac{4.5 \text{ k}\Omega}{4.7 \text{ k}\Omega}\right) = 43.8°$

   The voltage values were determined in Problem 4. V_R lags V_s by 43.8° because it is in phase with I. V_L and V_C are each 90° away from V_R and 180° out of phase with each other. See Figure 13-1.

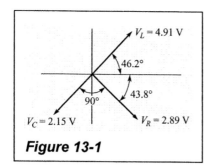

Figure 13-1

6. $R_{tot} = R_1 \parallel R_2 = 220\ \Omega \parallel 390\ \Omega = 141\ \Omega$
     $L_{tot} = L_1 + L_2 = 0.5\ \text{mH} + 1.0\ \text{mH} = 1.5\ \text{mH}$
     $C_{tot} = C_1 + C_2 = 0.01\ \mu\text{F} + 1800\ \text{pF} = 0.0118\ \mu\text{F}$
     $X_{L(tot)} = 236\ \Omega$
     $X_{C(tot)} = 540\ \Omega$
     $Z_{tot} = \sqrt{R_{tot}^2 + (X_{L(tot)} - X_{C(tot)})^2} = \sqrt{(141\ \Omega)^2 + (304\ \Omega)^2} = 335\ \Omega$

   (a) $I_{tot} = \dfrac{V_s}{Z_{tot}} = \dfrac{12\ \text{V}}{335\ \Omega} = \textbf{35.8 mA}$

   (b) $P_{\text{true}} = I_{tot}^2 R_{tot} = (35.8\ \text{mA})^2(141\ \Omega) = \textbf{181 mW}$

   (c) $P_r = I_{tot}^2 X_{tot} = (35.8\ \text{mA})^2(304\ \Omega) = \textbf{390 mVAR}$

   (d) $P_a = \sqrt{(P_{\text{true}})^2 + (P_r)^2} = \textbf{430 mVA}$

SECTION 13-3   Series Resonance

7.   Because $X_C < X_L$, f_r is less than the frequency indicated.

8. $X_C = X_L$ at resonance.
     $V_R = V_s = \textbf{12 V}$

9. $f_r = \dfrac{1}{2\pi\sqrt{LC}} = \dfrac{1}{2\pi\sqrt{(1\ \text{mH})(47\ \text{pF})}} = 734\ \text{kHz}$

     $X_L = 2\pi f_r L = 2\pi(734\ \text{kHz})(1\ \text{mH}) = \textbf{4.61 k}\boldsymbol{\Omega}$
     $X_C = X_L = \textbf{4.61 k}\boldsymbol{\Omega}$
     $Z_{tot} = R = \textbf{220 }\boldsymbol{\Omega}$
     $I = \dfrac{V_s}{Z_{tot}} = \dfrac{12\ \text{V}}{220\ \Omega} = \textbf{54.5 mA}$

10. $V_C = V_L = 100\ \text{V}$ at resonance
      $Z = R = \dfrac{V_s}{I_{max}} = \dfrac{10\ \text{V}}{50\ \text{mA}} = \textbf{200 }\boldsymbol{\Omega}$

      $X_L = X_C = \dfrac{V_L}{I_{max}} = \dfrac{100\ \text{V}}{50\ \text{mA}} = \textbf{2 k}\boldsymbol{\Omega}$

11. $f_r = \dfrac{1}{2\pi\sqrt{LC}} = \dfrac{1}{2\pi\sqrt{(8\ \mu H)(0.015\ \mu F)}} = \textbf{459 kHz}$

$X_L = 2\pi(459\ \text{kHz})(8\ \mu H) = 23.1\ \Omega$

$Q = \dfrac{X_L}{R} = \dfrac{23.1\ \Omega}{10\ \Omega} = 2.31$

$BW = \dfrac{f_r}{Q} = \dfrac{459\ \text{kHz}}{2.31} = 199\ \text{kHz}$

$f_{c1} = f_r - \dfrac{BW}{2} = 459\ \text{kHz} - \dfrac{199\ \text{kHz}}{2} = \textbf{360 kHz}$

$f_{c2} = f_r + \dfrac{BW}{2} = 459\ \text{kHz} + \dfrac{199\ \text{kHz}}{2} = \textbf{559 kHz}$

12. $I_{max} = \dfrac{V_s}{R} = \dfrac{7.07\ \text{V}}{10\ \Omega} = 707\ \text{mA at resonance}$

$I_{half\text{-}power} = 0.707 I_{max} = 0.707(707\ \text{mA}) = \textbf{500 mA}$

SECTION 13-4 Series Resonant Filters

13. (a) $f_r = \dfrac{1}{2\pi\sqrt{LC}} = \dfrac{1}{2\pi\sqrt{(12\ \text{mH})(0.01\ \mu F)}} = \textbf{14.5 kHz}$

(b) $f_r = \dfrac{1}{2\pi\sqrt{LC}} = \dfrac{1}{2\pi\sqrt{(2\ \text{mH})(0.022\ \mu F)}} = \textbf{24.0 kHz}$

These are bandpass filters.

14. (a) $R_{tot} = 10\ \Omega + 75\ \Omega = 85\ \Omega$

$f_r = \dfrac{1}{2\pi\sqrt{LC}} = \dfrac{1}{2\pi\sqrt{(12\ \text{mH})(0.01\ \mu F)}} = 14.5\ \text{kHz}$

$X_L = 2\pi(14.5\ \text{kHz})(12\ \text{mH}) = 1.09\ \text{k}\Omega$

$Q = \dfrac{X_L}{R_{tot}} = \dfrac{1.09\ \text{k}\Omega}{85\ \Omega} = 13$

$BW = \dfrac{f_r}{Q} = \dfrac{14.5\ \text{kHz}}{13} = \textbf{1.12 kHz}$

(b) $R_{tot} = 10\ \Omega + 22\ \Omega = 32\ \Omega$

$f_r = \dfrac{1}{2\pi\sqrt{LC}} = \dfrac{1}{2\pi\sqrt{(2\ \text{mH})(0.022\ \mu F)}} = 24.0\ \text{kHz}$

$X_L = 2\pi(24.0\ \text{kHz})(2\ \text{mH}) = 302\ \Omega$

$Q = \dfrac{X_L}{R_{tot}} = \dfrac{302\ \Omega}{32\ \Omega} = 9.44$

$BW = \dfrac{f_r}{Q} = \dfrac{24.0\ \text{kHz}}{9.44} = \textbf{2.54 kHz}$

15. (a) $f_r = \dfrac{1}{2\pi\sqrt{LC}} = \dfrac{1}{2\pi\sqrt{(100\,\mu H)(0.0022\,\mu F)}} = \mathbf{339\ kHz}$

$X_L = 2\pi(339\,\text{kHz})(100\,\mu H) = 213\ \Omega$

$Q = \dfrac{X_L}{R} = \dfrac{213\ \Omega}{150\ \Omega} = 1.42$

$BW = \dfrac{f_r}{Q} = \dfrac{339\,\text{kHz}}{1.42} = \mathbf{239\ kHz}$

(b) $f_r = \dfrac{1}{2\pi\sqrt{LC}} = \dfrac{1}{2\pi\sqrt{(5\,\text{mH})(0.047\,\mu F)}} = \mathbf{10.4\ kHz}$

$X_L = 2\pi(10.4\,\text{kHz})(5\,\text{mH}) = 327\ \Omega$

$Q = \dfrac{X_L}{R} = \dfrac{327\ \Omega}{82\ \Omega} = 3.99$

$BW = \dfrac{f_r}{Q} = \dfrac{10.4\,\text{kHz}}{3.99} = \mathbf{2.61\ kHz}$

SECTION 13-5 Parallel *RLC* Circuits

16. $X_L = 2\pi f L = 2\pi(12\,\text{kHz})(15\,\text{mH}) = 1.13\ \text{k}\Omega$

$X_C = \dfrac{1}{2\pi f C} = \dfrac{1}{2\pi(12\,\text{kHz})(0.022\,\mu F)} = 603\ \Omega$

$Y = \sqrt{\left(\dfrac{1}{R}\right)^2 + \left(\dfrac{1}{X_C} - \dfrac{1}{X_L}\right)^2} = \sqrt{\left(\dfrac{1}{100\ \Omega}\right)^2 + \left(\dfrac{1}{603\ \Omega} - \dfrac{1}{1.13\ \text{k}\Omega}\right)^2}$

$= \sqrt{(0.01\,\text{S})^2 + (16.58\times10^{-4}\,\text{S} - 8.84\times10^{-4}\,\text{S})^2} = 10.03\ \text{mS}$

$Z_{tot} = \dfrac{1}{Y} = \dfrac{1}{10.03\,\text{mS}} = \mathbf{99.7\ \Omega}$

17. $X_L = 2\pi(12\,\text{kHz})(15\,\text{mH}) = 1.13\ \text{k}\Omega$

$X_C = \dfrac{1}{2\pi(12\,\text{kHz})(0.022\,\mu F)} = 603\ \Omega$

Since $X_C < X_L$, the parallel circuit is **predominantly capacitive**.
The smaller reactance in a parallel circuit dominates the circuit response because it has the largest current.

18. $I_{tot} = \dfrac{V_s}{Z_{tot}} = \dfrac{5\,\text{V}}{99.7\ \Omega} \cong \mathbf{50.2\ mA}$ $\qquad I_R = \dfrac{V_s}{R} = \dfrac{5\,\text{V}}{100\ \Omega} = \mathbf{50.0\ mA}$

$I_L = \dfrac{V_s}{X_L} = \dfrac{5\,\text{V}}{1.13\ \text{k}\Omega} = \mathbf{4.42\ mA}$ $\qquad I_C = \dfrac{V_s}{X_C} = \dfrac{5\,\text{V}}{603\ \Omega} = \mathbf{8.29\ mA}$

$V_R = V_L = V_C = V_s = \mathbf{5\ V}$

19. $X_C = \dfrac{1}{2\pi f C} = \dfrac{1}{2\pi(60 \text{ Hz})(0.022 \text{ μF})} = 121 \text{ k}\Omega$

$X_L = 2\pi f L = 2\pi(60 \text{ Hz})(2 \text{ H}) = 754 \text{ }\Omega$

$R_W = 47 \text{ }\Omega$

$Q = \dfrac{X_L}{R_W} = \dfrac{754 \text{ }\Omega}{47 \text{ }\Omega} = 16$

$R_{p(eq)} = R_W(Q^2 + 1) = 47 \text{ }\Omega(16^2 + 1) = 12.1 \text{ k}\Omega$

$L_{eq} = \left(\dfrac{Q^2 + 1}{Q}\right)L \cong 2 \text{ H}$

The equivalent circuit is shown in Figure 13-2.

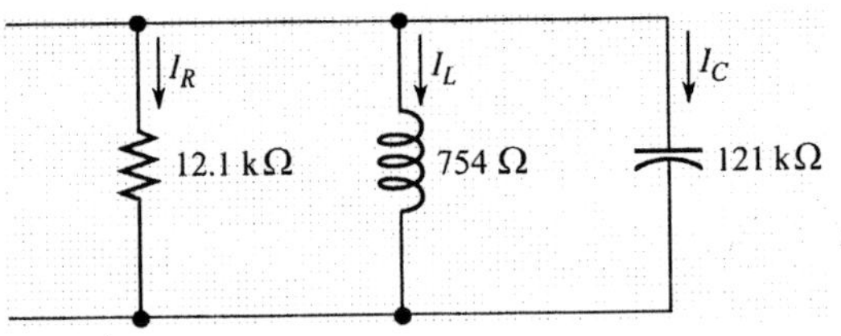

$I_R = \dfrac{5 \text{ V}}{12.1 \text{ k}\Omega} = 413 \text{ μA}$

$I_{L(eq)} = \dfrac{5 \text{ V}}{754 \text{ }\Omega} = 6.63 \text{ mA}$

$I_C = \dfrac{5 \text{ V}}{121 \text{ k}\Omega} = 41.3 \text{ μA}$

Figure 13-2

$I_{LC} = I_{L(eq)} - I_C = 6.59 \text{ mA}$

$I_{tot} = \sqrt{I_R^2 + I_{LC}^2} = \sqrt{(413 \text{ μA})^2 + (6.59 \text{ mA})^2} = 6.60 \text{ mA}$

$Z_{tot} = \dfrac{5 \text{ V}}{6.60 \text{ mA}} = \mathbf{758 \text{ }\Omega}$

SECTION 13-6 Parallel Resonance

20. Z_r is infinitely large.

21. $f_r = \dfrac{\sqrt{1 - \dfrac{R_W^2 C}{L}}}{2\pi\sqrt{LC}} = \dfrac{\sqrt{1 - \dfrac{(20 \text{ }\Omega)^2(47 \text{ pF})}{50 \text{ mH}}}}{2\pi\sqrt{(50 \text{ mH})(47 \text{ pF})}} = \mathbf{104 \text{ kHz}}$

$X_L = 2\pi f_r L = 2\pi(103.82 \text{ kHz})(50 \text{ mH}) = 32.6 \text{ k}\Omega$

$Q = \dfrac{X_L}{R_W} = \dfrac{32.6 \text{ k}\Omega}{20 \text{ }\Omega} = 1630$

$Z_r = R_W(Q^2 + 1) = 20 \text{ }\Omega(1630^2 + 1) = \mathbf{53.1 \text{ M}\Omega}$

22. From Problem 21: $Z_r = 53.1 \text{ M}\Omega$ and $f_r = 104 \text{ kHz}$

$I_{tot} = \dfrac{V_s}{Z_r} = \dfrac{6.3 \text{ V}}{53.1 \text{ M}\Omega} = \mathbf{119 \text{ nA}}$

$I_C = I_L = \dfrac{6.3 \text{ V}}{\sqrt{(20 \text{ }\Omega)^2 + 32.6 \text{ k}\Omega)^2}} = \mathbf{193 \text{ μA}}$

23. $Q = \dfrac{X_L}{R} = \dfrac{2 \text{ k}\Omega}{25 \ \Omega} = 80$

   $BW = \dfrac{f_r}{Q} = \dfrac{5 \text{ kHz}}{80} = \textbf{62.5 Hz}$

24. $BW = f_{c2} - f_{c1} = 2800 \text{ Hz} - 2400 \text{ Hz} = \textbf{400 Hz}$

25. $P = (0.5)P_r = (0.5)(2.75 \text{ W}) = \textbf{1.38 W}$

26. $Q = \dfrac{f_r}{BW} = \dfrac{8 \text{ kHz}}{800 \text{ Hz}} = 10$

   $X_{L(res)} = QR_W = 10(10 \ \Omega) = 100 \ \Omega$

   $L = \dfrac{X_L}{2\pi f_r} = \dfrac{100 \ \Omega}{2\pi(8 \text{ kHz})} = \textbf{1.99 mH}$

   $X_C = X_L$ at resonance

   $C = \dfrac{1}{2\pi f_r X_C} = \dfrac{1}{2\pi(8 \text{ kHz})(100 \ \Omega)} = \textbf{0.199 } \boldsymbol{\mu}\textbf{F}$

27. Since $BW = \dfrac{f_r}{Q}$, the bandwidth is halved when Q is doubled.

   So, when Q is increased from 50 to 100, BW decreases from 400 Hz to **200 Hz.**

ADVANCED PROBLEMS

28. (a) $20 \log\left(\dfrac{V_{out}}{V_{in}}\right) = 20 \log\left(\dfrac{1 \text{ V}}{1 \text{ V}}\right) = \textbf{0 dB}$

   (b) $20 \log\left(\dfrac{V_{out}}{V_{in}}\right) = 20 \log\left(\dfrac{3 \text{ V}}{5 \text{ V}}\right) = \textbf{--4.4 dB}$

   (c) $20 \log\left(\dfrac{V_{out}}{V_{in}}\right) = 20 \log\left(\dfrac{7.07 \text{ V}}{10 \text{ V}}\right) = \textbf{--3 dB}$

   (d) $20 \log\left(\dfrac{V_{out}}{V_{in}}\right) = 20 \log\left(\dfrac{5 \text{ V}}{25 \text{ V}}\right) = \textbf{--14 dB}$

29.

$$X_{L(tot)} = \cfrac{1}{\left(\cfrac{1}{X_{L1}} + \cfrac{1}{X_{L2}}\right)} = \cfrac{1}{\left(\cfrac{1}{5\ k\Omega} + \cfrac{1}{10\ k\Omega}\right)} = 3.33\ k\Omega$$

$$Z_p = X_{L(tot)} \parallel R_2 = \cfrac{R_2 X_{L(tot)}}{\sqrt{R_2^2 + X_{L(tot)}^2}} = \cfrac{(10\ k\Omega)(3.33\ k\Omega)}{\sqrt{(10\ k\Omega)^2 + (3.33\ k\Omega)^2}} = 3.16\ k\Omega$$

$$\theta_p = \tan^{-1}\left(\cfrac{R_2}{X_{L(tot)}}\right) = \tan^{-1}\left(\cfrac{10\ k\Omega}{3.33\ k\Omega}\right) = 71.6°$$

Converting the parallel combination of R_2, X_{L1}, and X_{L2} to an equivalent series circuit:

$R_{eq} = Z_p \cos \theta_p = (3.16\ k\Omega)\cos 71.6° = 997\ \Omega$

$X_{L(eq)} = Z_p \sin \theta = (3.16\ k\Omega)\sin 71.6° = 3\ k\Omega$

$Z_{(tot)} = \sqrt{(R_1 + R_{eq}^2)^2 + (X_{L(eq)} + X_C)^2} + \sqrt{(4297\ \Omega)^2 + (2000\ \Omega)^2} = 4740\ \Omega$

$I_{tot} = I_{R1} = I_C = \cfrac{V_s}{Z_{tot}} = \cfrac{10\ V}{4740\ \Omega} = \textbf{2.11 mA}$

$V_{R1} = I_{tot}R_1 = (2.11\ mA)(3.3\ k\Omega) = \textbf{6.96 V}$

$V_C = I_{tot}X_C = (2.11\ mA)(1.0\ k\Omega) = \textbf{2.11 V}$

$V_{L1-L2-R2} = I_{tot}Z_p = (2.11\ mA)(3.16\ k\Omega) = \textbf{6.67 V}$

$I_{L1} = \cfrac{V_{L1}}{X_{L1}} = \cfrac{6.67\ V}{5\ k\Omega} = \textbf{1.33 mA}$

$I_{L2} = \cfrac{V_{L2}}{X_{L2}} = \cfrac{6.67\ V}{10\ k\Omega} = \textbf{667 μA}$

$I_{R2} = \cfrac{V_{R2}}{R_2} = \cfrac{6.67\ V}{10\ k\Omega} = \textbf{667 μA}$

30. For $V_{ab} = 0\ V$, $V_a = V_b$ in both magnitude and phase angle.

$X_{L1} = 226\ \Omega; \quad X_{L2} = 151\ \Omega$

$$V_a = V_{L1} = \left(\cfrac{226\ \Omega}{\sqrt{(180\ \Omega)^2 + (226\ \Omega)^2}}\right)12\ V = 9.38\ V$$

It is not possible for V_{ab} to be 0 V because the LC branch has no resistance; thus, the voltage from a to b can only have a phase angle of 0°, 90°, or –90° (the branch will be either resonant, purely inductive, or purely capacitive depending on the value of X_C). Therefore, it is not possible for V_a to equal V_b in both magnitude and phase angle, which are necessary conditions.

31.

$$X_C = \cfrac{1}{2\pi(3\ kHz)(0.22\ \mu F)} = 241\ \Omega$$

$X_{L1} = 2\pi(3\ kHz)(12\ mH) = 226\ \Omega$

$X_{L2} = 2\pi(3\ kHz)(8\ mH) = 151\ \Omega$

$$I_{R1-L1} = \cfrac{V_s}{\sqrt{R_1^2 + X_{L1}^2}} = \cfrac{12\ V}{\sqrt{(180\ \Omega)^2 + (226\ \Omega)^2}} = \textbf{41.5 mA}$$

$$I_{C-L2} = \cfrac{V_s}{X_C - X_{L2}} = \cfrac{12\ V}{241\ \Omega - 151\ \Omega} = \textbf{133 mA}$$

$$\theta_{R1-L1} = \tan^{-1}\left(\frac{X_{L1}}{R_1}\right) = \tan^{-1}\left(\frac{226\ \Omega}{180\ \Omega}\right) = 51.5°$$

The resistive component of current in the left branch is:

$I_R = I_{R1-L1}\cos\theta_{R1-L1} = (41.5\ \text{mA})\cos 51.5° = 25.8\ \text{mA}$

The reactive component of current in the left branch is:

$I_X = I_{R1-L1}\sin\theta_{R1-L1} = (41.5\ \text{mA})\sin 57.5° = 32.5\ \text{mA}$

In the right branch $X_C > X_{L2}$, so I_{C-L2} is totally reactive and is $180°$ out of phase with I_X in the left branch.

$$I_{tot} = \sqrt{I_R^2 + (I_{C-L2} - I_X)^2} = \sqrt{(25.8\ \text{mA})^2 + (133\ \text{mA} - 32.5\ \text{mA})^2} = \textbf{104 mA}$$

32. *For parallel resonance:* $f_r = \dfrac{\sqrt{1 - \dfrac{R_W^2 C}{L_2}}}{2\pi\sqrt{L_2 C}} \cong \dfrac{1}{2\pi(25\ \text{mH})(0.15\ \mu\text{F})} = \textbf{2.6 kHz}$

$X_{L2} = 2\pi(2.6\ \text{kHz})(25\ \text{mH}) = 408\ \Omega$ $\qquad Q_p = \dfrac{X_{L2}}{R_{W2}} = \dfrac{408\ \Omega}{4\ \Omega} = 102$

$Z_r = R_{W2}\left(Q_p^2 + 1\right) = 4\ \Omega(102^2 + 1) = 41.6\ \text{k}\Omega$

$X_{L1} = 2\pi(2.6\ \text{kHz})(10\ \text{mH}) = 163\ \Omega$

Since Z_r is much greater than R, R_{W1}, or X_{L1} and is resistive, the output voltage is:

$V_{out} \cong V_s = \textbf{10 V}$

For series resonance: $f_r = \dfrac{1}{2\pi\sqrt{L_1 C}} = \dfrac{1}{2\pi\sqrt{(10\ \text{mH})(0.15\ \mu\text{F})}} = \textbf{4.1 kHz}$

and

$X_C = X_{L1} = 2\pi(4.1\ \text{kHz})(10\ \text{mH}) = 258\ \Omega$

$X_{L2} = 2\pi(4.1\ \text{kHz})(25\ \text{mH}) = 644\ \Omega$

Since $X_C < X_{L2}$, the parallel portion of the circuit is capacitive.

$$Z_r = \sqrt{R_{W1}^2 + X_{L1}^2} - \frac{X_C\left(\sqrt{R_{W2}^2 + X_{L2}^2}\right)}{\sqrt{R_{W2}^2 + (X_{L2} - X_C)^2}} \cong 172\ \Omega$$

Assuming that Z_r is almost totally reactive:

$$V_{out} \cong \left(\frac{Z_r}{\sqrt{R^2 + Z_r^2}}\right)V_s = \left(\frac{172\ \Omega}{\sqrt{(860\ \Omega)^2 + (172\ \Omega)^2}}\right)10\ \text{V} = \textbf{1.96 V}$$

33. $f_r = BW \times Q = (500\ \text{Hz})(40) = 20\ \text{kHz}$

$X_C = \dfrac{2.5\ \text{V}}{20\ \text{mA}} = 125\ \Omega$

$C = \dfrac{1}{2\pi f_r X_C} = \dfrac{1}{2\pi(20\ \text{kHz})(125\ \Omega)} = \textbf{0.064}\ \mu\textbf{F}$

$Q = \dfrac{X_L}{R_W} = 40$

$R_W = \dfrac{X_L}{Q} = \left(\dfrac{1}{40}\right)X_L = 0.025X_L = 0.025(2\pi f_r L)$

$$f_r = \frac{\sqrt{1 - \dfrac{R_W^2 C}{L}}}{2\pi\sqrt{LC}}$$

$$f_r^2 = \frac{1 - \left(\dfrac{R_W^2 C}{L}\right)}{4\pi^2 LC} = \frac{1 - \left(\dfrac{(0.025(2\pi f_r L))^2 C}{L}\right)}{4\pi^2 LC} = \frac{1 - 0.025 f_r^2 LC}{4\pi^2 LC}$$

In the above derivation, the term $(0.025(2\pi))^2 \cong 0.025$

$$f_r^2 4\pi^2 LC = 1 - 0.025 f_r^2 LC$$

$$f_r^2 LC(4\pi^2 + 0.025) = 1$$

$$L = \frac{1}{f_r^2 C(4\pi^2 + 0.025)} = \textbf{989 μH}$$

34. Refer to Figure 13-3.

$$f_r = \frac{1}{2\pi\sqrt{LC}} \qquad \text{Choose } C = 0.001 \ \mu F$$

$$f_r^2 = \frac{1}{4\pi^2 LC}$$

(a) $f_r = 500$ kHz: $L_1 = \dfrac{1}{4\pi^2 f_r^2 C} = \dfrac{1}{4\pi^2 (500 \text{ kHz})^2 (0.001 \ \mu F)} = \textbf{101 μH}$

(b) $f_r = 1000$ kHz: $L_2 = \dfrac{1}{4\pi^2 f_r^2 C} = \dfrac{1}{4\pi^2 (1000 \text{ kHz})^2 (0.001 \ \mu F)} = \textbf{25.3 μH}$

(c) $f_r = 1500$ kHz: $L_3 = \dfrac{1}{4\pi^2 f_r^2 C} = \dfrac{1}{4\pi^2 (1500 \text{ kHz})^2 (0.001 \ \mu F)} = \textbf{11.3 μH}$

(d) $f_r = 2000$ kHz: $L_4 = \dfrac{1}{4\pi^2 f_r^2 C} = \dfrac{1}{4\pi^2 (2000 \text{ kHz})^2 (0.001 \ \mu F)} = \textbf{6.3 μH}$

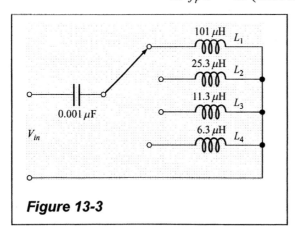

Figure 13-3

35. See Figure 13-4. The winding resistance is neglected because it contributes negligibly to the outcome of the calculations.

$$f_r = \frac{1}{2\pi\sqrt{LC}}$$

$$f_r^2 = \frac{1}{4\pi^2 LC}$$

$$C = \frac{1}{4\pi^2 f_r^2 L}$$

For $f_r = 8$ MHz, 9 MHz, 10 MHz, and 11 MHz:

$$C_1 = \frac{1}{4\pi^2 (8\ \text{MHz})^2 (10\ \mu\text{H})} = \textbf{40 pF}$$

$$C_2 = \frac{1}{4\pi^2 (9\ \text{MHz})^2 (10\ \mu\text{H})} = \textbf{31 pF}$$

$$C_3 = \frac{1}{4\pi^2 (10\ \text{MHz})^2 (10\ \mu\text{H})} = \textbf{25 pF}$$

$$C_4 = \frac{1}{4\pi^2 (11\ \text{MHz})^2 (10\ \mu\text{H})} = \textbf{21 pF}$$

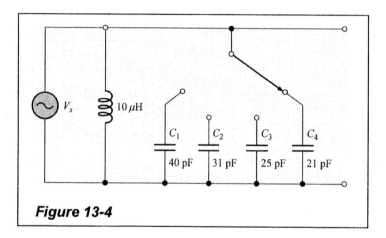

Figure 13-4

Multisim Troubleshooting Problems

36. L is open.

37. No fault

38. C is open.

39. L is shorted.

40. C is shorted.

41. L is shorted.

CHAPTER 14
TRANSFORMERS

BASIC PROBLEMS

SECTION 14-1 Mutual Inductance

1. $L_M = k\sqrt{L_1 L_2} = 0.75\sqrt{(1\ \mu H)(4\ \mu H)} = \mathbf{1.5\ \mu H}$

2. $L_M = k\sqrt{L_1 L_2}$

$k = \dfrac{L_M}{\sqrt{L_1 L_2}} = \dfrac{1\ \mu H}{\sqrt{(8\ \mu H)(2\ \mu H)}} = \mathbf{0.25}$

SECTION 14-2 The Basic Transformer

3. $n = \dfrac{N_{sec}}{N_{pri}} = \dfrac{360}{120} = \mathbf{3}$

4.   (a) $n = \dfrac{N_{sec}}{N_{pri}} = \dfrac{1000}{250} = \mathbf{4}$

(b) $n = \dfrac{N_{sec}}{N_{pri}} = \dfrac{100}{400} = \mathbf{0.25}$

5.   (a)   In phase   (b)   Out of phase   (c)   Out of phase

SECTION 14-3 Step-Up and Step-Down Transformers

6. $n = \dfrac{N_{sec}}{N_{pri}} = \dfrac{150}{100} = 1.5$

$V_{sec} = 1.5 V_{pri} = 1.5(120\ V) = \mathbf{180\ V}$

7. $N_{sec} = 2N_{pri} = 2(250\ \text{turns}) = \mathbf{500\ turns}$

8. $n = \dfrac{N_{sec}}{N_{pri}} = \dfrac{V_{sec}}{V_{pri}} = 10$

$V_{pri} = \left(\dfrac{1}{n}\right)V_{sec} = \left(\dfrac{1}{10}\right)60\text{ V} = \mathbf{6\ V}$

9. See Figure 14-1(a).

(a) $V_{sec} = nV_{pri} = \left(\dfrac{N_{sec}}{N_{pri}}\right)V_{pri} = 10(10\text{ V}) = \mathbf{100\ V\ rms}$

See Figure 14-1(b).

(b) $V_{sec} = nV_{pri} = \left(\dfrac{N_{sec}}{N_{pri}}\right)V_{pri} = 2(50\text{ V}) = \mathbf{100\ V\ rms}$

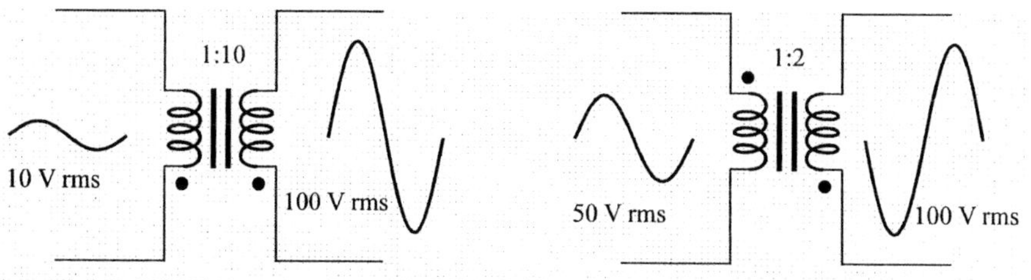

1:10   100 V rms   1:2   100 V rms

10 V rms   50 V rms

(a) In-phase   (b) 180 degrees out-of-phase

Figure 14-1

10. $\dfrac{V_{sec}}{V_{pri}} = \dfrac{N_{sec}}{N_{pri}}$

$n = \dfrac{N_{sec}}{N_{pri}} = \dfrac{30\text{ V}}{120\text{ V}} = \mathbf{0.25}$

11. $V_{sec} = (0.2)(1200\text{ V}) = \mathbf{240\ V}$

12. $\dfrac{V_{sec}}{V_{pri}} = \dfrac{N_{sec}}{N_{pri}} = n = 0.1$

$V_{pri} = \left(\dfrac{1}{n}\right)V_{sec} = \left(\dfrac{1}{0.1}\right)(6\text{ V}) = \mathbf{60\ V}$

13. (a) $V_L = nV_{pri} = \left(\dfrac{N_{sec}}{N_{pri}}\right)V_{pri} = \left(\dfrac{1}{20}\right)120\text{ V} = \mathbf{6\ V}$

(b) $V_L = \mathbf{0\ V}$ (The transformer does not couple constant dc voltage)

(c) $V_L = nV_{pri} = \left(\dfrac{N_{sec}}{N_{pri}}\right)V_{pri} = 4(10\text{ V}) = \mathbf{40\ V}$

14. No, the voltages would not change.

15. (a) $V_L = (0.1)V_{sec} = (0.1)(100 \text{ V}) = \mathbf{10 \text{ V}}$
    (b) $V_{pri} = 20V_L = 20(12 \text{ V}) = \mathbf{240 \text{ V}}$

16. Meter would indicate **10 V**.

SECTION 14-4 Loading the Secondary

17. $\dfrac{I_{sec}}{I_{pri}} = \dfrac{N_{pri}}{N_{sec}} = \dfrac{1}{n} = \dfrac{1}{3}$

$I_{sec} = \left(\dfrac{1}{n}\right)I_{pri} = \left(\dfrac{1}{3}\right)100 \text{ mA} = \mathbf{33.3 \text{ mA}}$

18. $\dfrac{V_{sec}}{V_{pri}} = \dfrac{I_{pri}}{I_{sec}}$

    (a) $V_{sec} = nV_{pri} = \left(\dfrac{N_{sec}}{N_{pri}}\right)V_{pri} = \left(\dfrac{1}{2}\right)30 \text{ V} = \mathbf{15 \text{ V}}$

    (b) $I_{sec} = \dfrac{V_{sec}}{R_L} = \dfrac{15 \text{ V}}{300 \ \Omega} = \mathbf{50 \text{ mA}}$

    (c) $I_{pri} = \left(\dfrac{V_{sec}}{V_{pri}}\right)I_{sec} = \left(\dfrac{15 \text{ V}}{30 \text{ V}}\right)50 \text{ mA} = \mathbf{25 \text{ mA}}$

    (d) $P_L = I_{sec}^2 R_L = (50 \text{ mA})^2(300 \ \Omega) = \mathbf{0.75 \text{ W}}$

SECTION 14-5 Reflected Load

19. $R_{pri} = \left(\dfrac{1}{n}\right)^2 R_L = \left(\dfrac{1}{5}\right)^2 680 \ \Omega = \left(\dfrac{1}{25}\right)680 \ \Omega = \mathbf{27.2 \ \Omega}$

20. $n = \dfrac{1}{50}$

$R_{pri} = \left(\dfrac{1}{n}\right)^2 R_L = 50^2(8 \ \Omega) = \mathbf{20 \text{ k}\Omega}$

21. $I_{pri} = \dfrac{V_{sec}}{R_{pri}} = \dfrac{115 \text{ V}}{20 \text{ k}\Omega} = \mathbf{5.75 \text{ mA}}$

22. $R_{pri} = 300 \ \Omega; \ R_L = 1.0 \ k\Omega$

$$n^2 = \frac{R_L}{R_{pri}}$$

$$n = \sqrt{\frac{R_L}{R_{pri}}} = \sqrt{\frac{1.0 \ k\Omega}{300 \ \Omega}} = \mathbf{1.83}$$

SECTION 14-6 Impedance Matching

23. $R_{pri} = \left(\frac{1}{n}\right)^2 R_L$

$$\left(\frac{1}{n}\right)^2 = \frac{R_{pri}}{R_L}$$

$$\frac{1}{n} = \sqrt{\frac{R_{pri}}{R_L}} = \sqrt{\frac{16 \ \Omega}{4 \ \Omega}} = \sqrt{4} = 2$$

$$n = \frac{1}{2} = \mathbf{0.5}$$

24. $n = 0.5$ from Problem 23.

$$R_{pri} = \left(\frac{1}{n}\right)^2 R_{speaker} = \left(\frac{1}{0.25}\right)4 \ \Omega = 16 \ \Omega$$

$$I_{pri} = \frac{25 \ V}{16 \ \Omega} = 1.56 \ A$$

$$I_{sec} = \left(\frac{1}{n}\right)I_{pri} = 2(1.56 \ A) = 3.12 \ A$$

$$P_{speaker} = I_{sec}^2 R_{speaker} = (3.12 \ A)^2(4 \ \Omega) = \mathbf{38.9 \ W}$$

25. $n = 10 \qquad n = \sqrt{\frac{R_L}{R_{pri}}} \qquad n^2 = \frac{R_L}{R_{pri}}$

$$R_L = n^2 R_{pri} = 10^2(50 \ \Omega) = 100(50 \ \Omega) = \mathbf{5 \ k\Omega}$$

26. $R_{pri} = \left(\frac{1}{n}\right)^2 R_L = \left(\frac{1}{10}\right)^2 R_L = (0.01)R_L$

For $R_L = 1 \ k\Omega, \ R_{pri} = (0.01)(1 \ k\Omega) = 10 \ \Omega$

$$V_{R(pri)} = \left(\frac{10 \ \Omega}{60 \ \Omega}\right)10 \ V = 1.67 \ V$$

$$P = \frac{(1.67 \ V)^2}{10 \ \Omega} = \mathbf{0.278 \ W}$$

For $R_L = 2\ \text{k}\Omega$, $R_{pri} = (0.01)(2\ \text{k}\Omega) = 20\ \Omega$

$$V_{R(pri)} = \left(\frac{20\ \Omega}{70\ \Omega}\right)10\ \text{V} = 2.86\ \text{V}$$

$$P = \frac{(2.86\ \text{V})^2}{20\ \Omega} = \mathbf{0.408\ W}$$

For $R_L = 3\ \text{k}\Omega$, $R_{pri} = (0.01)(3\ \text{k}\Omega) = 30\ \Omega$

$$V_{R(pri)} = \left(\frac{30\ \Omega}{80\ \Omega}\right)10\ \text{V} = 3.75\ \text{V}$$

$$P = \frac{(3.75\ \text{V})^2}{30\ \Omega} = \mathbf{0.469\ W}$$

For $R_L = 4\ \text{k}\Omega$, $R_{pri} = 40\ \Omega$

$$V_{R(pri)} = \left(\frac{40\ \Omega}{90\ \Omega}\right)10\ \text{V} = 4.44\ \text{V}$$

$$P = \frac{(4.44\ \text{V})^2}{40\ \Omega} = \mathbf{0.494\ W}$$

For $R_L = 5\ \text{k}\Omega$, $R_{pri} = 50\ \Omega$

$$V_{R(pri)} = \left(\frac{50\ \Omega}{100\ \Omega}\right)10\ \text{V} = 5\ \text{V}$$

$$P = \frac{(5\ \text{V})^2}{50\ \Omega} = \mathbf{0.500\ W}$$

For $R_L = 6\ \text{k}\Omega$, $R_{pri} = 60\ \Omega$

$$V_{R(pri)} = \left(\frac{60\ \Omega}{110\ \Omega}\right)10\ \text{V} = 5.45\ \text{V}$$

$$P = \frac{(5.45\ \text{V})^2}{60\ \Omega} = \mathbf{0.496\ W}$$

For $R_L = 7\ \text{k}\Omega$, $R_{pri} = 70\ \Omega$

$$V_{R(pri)} = \left(\frac{70\ \Omega}{120\ \Omega}\right)10\ \text{V} = 5.83\ \text{V}$$

$$P = \frac{(5.83\ \text{V})^2}{70\ \Omega} = \mathbf{0.486\ W}$$

For $R_L = 8\ \text{k}\Omega$, $R_{pri} = 80\ \Omega$

$$V_{R(pri)} = \left(\frac{80\ \Omega}{130\ \Omega}\right)10\ \text{V} = 6.15\ \text{V}$$

$$P = \frac{(6.15\ \text{V})^2}{80\ \Omega} = \mathbf{0.473\ W}$$

For $R_L = 9$ kΩ, $R_{pri} = 90$ Ω

$$V_{R(pri)} = \left(\frac{90 \ \Omega}{140 \ \Omega} \right) 10 \ V = 6.43 \ V$$

$$P = \frac{(6.43 \ V)^2}{90 \ \Omega} = \textbf{0.459 W}$$

For $R_L = 10$ kΩ, $R_{pri} = 100$ Ω

$$V_{R(pri)} = \left(\frac{100 \ \Omega}{150 \ \Omega} \right) 10 \ V = 6.67 \ V$$

$$P = \frac{(6.67 \ V)^2}{100 \ \Omega} = \textbf{0.444 W}$$

See Figure 14-2.

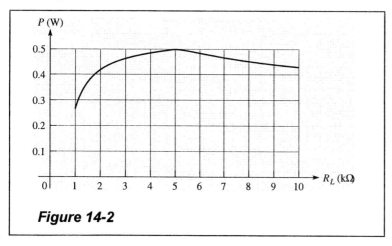

Figure 14-2

SECTION 14-7 Nonideal Transformer Characteristics

27. $P_L = P_{pri} - P_{lost} = 100 \ W - 5.5 \ W = \textbf{94.5 W}$

28. % efficiency $= \left(\dfrac{P_{out}}{P_{in}} \right) 100\% = \left(\dfrac{94.5 \ W}{100 \ W} \right) 100\% = \textbf{94.5 \%}$

29. Coefficient of coupling $= 1 - 0.02 = \textbf{0.98}$

30. (a) $I_{L(max)} = \dfrac{P_a}{V_{sec}} = \dfrac{1\,kVA}{600\,V} = \textbf{1.67 A}$

(b) $R_{L(min)} = \dfrac{V_{sec}}{I_{L(max)}} = \dfrac{600\,V}{1.67\,A} = \textbf{359 }\boldsymbol{\Omega}$

(c) $X_C = \dfrac{V_{sec}}{I_L} = \textbf{359 }\boldsymbol{\Omega}$

$C_{max} = \dfrac{1}{2\pi f X_C} = \dfrac{1}{2\pi(60\,Hz)(359\,\Omega)} = \textbf{7.4 }\boldsymbol{\mu}\textbf{F}$

31. kVA rating = (2.5 kV)(10 A) = **25 kVA**

SECTION 14-8 Tapped and Multiple-Winding Transformers

32. $V_1 = \left(\dfrac{50}{500}\right)115\,V = \textbf{11.5 V}$

$V_2 = \left(\dfrac{100}{500}\right)115\,V = \textbf{23 V}$

$V_3 = \left(\dfrac{100}{500}\right)115\,V = \textbf{23 V}$

$V_4 = V_2 + V_3 = \textbf{46 V}$

33. *For secondary 1:*
$n = \dfrac{V_{sec}}{V_{pri}} = \dfrac{24\,V}{12\,V} = \textbf{2}$

For secondary 2:
$n = \dfrac{V_{sec}}{V_{pri}} = \dfrac{6\,V}{12\,V} = \textbf{0.5}$

For secondary 3:
$n = \dfrac{V_{sec}}{V_{pri}} = \dfrac{3\,V}{12\,V} = \textbf{0.25}$

34. (a) See Figure 14-3.

(b) 100 turns: $V_{sec} = \left(\dfrac{100}{2000}\right)240\,V = \textbf{12 V}$

200 turns: $V_{sec} = \left(\dfrac{200}{2000}\right)240\,V = \textbf{24 V}$

500 turns: $V_{sec} = \left(\dfrac{500}{2000}\right)240\,V = \textbf{60 V}$

1000 turns: $V_{sec} = \left(\dfrac{1000}{2000}\right)240\,V = \textbf{120 V}$

146

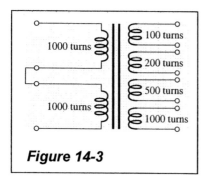

Figure 14-3

35. For both primaries:

Top secondary: $n = \dfrac{100}{1000} = \mathbf{0.1}$

Next secondary: $n = \dfrac{200}{1000} = \mathbf{0.2}$

Third secondary: $n = \dfrac{500}{1000} = \mathbf{0.5}$

Bottom secondary: $n = \dfrac{1000}{1000} = \mathbf{1}$

SECTION 14-9 Troubleshooting

36. Open primary winding. Replace transformer.

37. If the primary shorts, excessive current is drawn which potentially can burn out the source and/or the transformer unless the primary is fused.

38. Some, but not all, of the secondary windings are shorted.

ADVANCED PROBLEMS

39. (a) $N_{sec} = 400 \text{ turns} + 300 \text{ turns} = 700 \text{ turns}$

$$V_{L1} = nV_{pri} = \left(\frac{N_{sec}}{N_{pri}}\right)V_{pri} = \left(\frac{700}{1200}\right)60 \text{ V} = \mathbf{35\ V}$$

$$I_{L1} = \frac{V_{L1}}{R_{L1}} = \frac{35 \text{ V}}{12\ \Omega} = \mathbf{2.92\ A}$$

$$V_{L2} = \left(\frac{300}{1200}\right)60 \text{ V} = \mathbf{15\ V}$$

$$I_{L2} = \frac{V_{L2}}{R_{L2}} = \frac{15 \text{ V}}{10\ \Omega} = \mathbf{1.5\ A}$$

(b) $\dfrac{1}{Z_{pri}} = \dfrac{1}{\left(\dfrac{N_{pri}}{N_{700}}\right)^2 R_{L1}} + \dfrac{1}{\left(\dfrac{N_{pri}}{N_{300}}\right)^2 R_{L2}} = \dfrac{1}{(2.94)(12\ \Omega)} + \dfrac{1}{(16)(10\ \Omega)}$

$= \dfrac{1}{35.3\ \Omega} + \dfrac{1}{160\ \Omega} = 0.0283\ \text{S} + 0.00625\ \text{S} = 0.0346\ \text{S}$

$Z_{pri} = \dfrac{1}{0.0346\ \text{S}} = \textbf{28.9 } \boldsymbol{\Omega}$

40. (a) $V_{pri} = 2400\ \text{V}$

$n = \dfrac{N_{sec}}{N_{pri}} = \dfrac{V_{sec}}{V_{pri}} = \dfrac{120\ \text{V}}{2400\ \text{V}} = \textbf{0.05}$

(b) $I_{sec} = \dfrac{P_a}{V_{sec}} = \dfrac{5\ \text{kVA}}{120\ \text{V}} = \textbf{41.7 A}$

(c) $I_{pri} = nI_{sec} = (0.05)(41.7\ \text{A}) = \textbf{2.09 A}$

41. (a) The lower 100 Ω resistor is shorted out by the meter ground; so, the full secondary voltage measured by the meter is:

$V_{meter} = V_{sec} = nV_{pri} = \left(\dfrac{N_{sec}}{N_{pri}}\right)120\ \text{V} = \left(\dfrac{1}{6}\right)120\ \text{V} = \textbf{20 V}$

(b) The common point between the 100 Ω resistors is ground. Both resistors are still in the secondary with one-half of the secondary voltage across each.

$V_{meter} = \left(\dfrac{1}{2}\right)V_{sec} = \left(\dfrac{1}{2}\right)20\ \text{V} = \textbf{10 V}$

42. *Position 1:*

$R_L = 560\ \Omega + 220\ \Omega + 1.0\ \text{k}\Omega = 1780\ \Omega$

$n = \sqrt{\dfrac{R_L}{R_{pri}}} = \sqrt{\dfrac{1780\ \Omega}{10\ \Omega}} = \textbf{13.3}$

$N_{sec} = N_{sec1} + N_{sec2} + N_{sec3} = nN_{pri} = 13.3 \times 100 = \textbf{1330 turns}$

Position 2:

$R_L = 220\ \Omega + 1.0\ \text{k}\Omega = 1220\ \Omega$

$n = \sqrt{\dfrac{R_L}{R_{pri}}} = \sqrt{\dfrac{1220\ \Omega}{10\ \Omega}} = \textbf{11.0}$

$N_{sec} = N_{sec2} + N_{sec3} = nN_{pri} = 11.0 \times 100 = \textbf{1100 turns}$

Position 3:

$R_L = 1.0\ \text{k}\Omega$

$n = \sqrt{\dfrac{R_L}{R_{pri}}} = \sqrt{\dfrac{1000\ \Omega}{10\ \Omega}} = \textbf{10}$

$N_{sec} = N_{sec3} = nN_{pri} = 10 \times 100 = \textbf{1000 turns}$

43. $R_{pri} = \dfrac{115 \text{ V}}{3 \text{ mA}} = 38.3 \text{ k}\Omega$

$R_{pri} = \left(\dfrac{1}{n}\right)^2 R_L$

$n^2 = \dfrac{R_L}{R_{pri}}$

$n = \sqrt{\dfrac{R_L}{R_{pri}}} = \sqrt{\dfrac{8 \ \Omega}{38.3 \text{ k}\Omega}} = \mathbf{0.0145}$

This is 69.2 primary turns for each secondary turn.

44. $n = \dfrac{12.6 \text{ V}}{110 \text{ V}} = 0.115$

$I_{pri(max)} = \dfrac{10 \text{ VA}}{110 \text{ V}} = 90.9 \text{ mA}$

$I_{sec(max)} = \dfrac{90.9 \text{ mA}}{0.115} = \mathbf{794 \text{ mA}}$

$R_{L(min)} = \dfrac{12.6 \text{ V}}{794 \text{ mA}} = \mathbf{15.9 \ \Omega}$

45. $n = \dfrac{10 \text{ V}}{110 \text{ V}} = 0.0909$

$I_{pri(max)} = (0.0909)(1 \text{ A}) = 90.9 \text{ mA}$

A fuse rated at **90 mA** or less should be used.

Multisim Troubleshooting Problems

46. Partial short in transformer.

47. Secondary is open.

48. No fault

49. Primary is open.

CHAPTER 15
TIME RESPONSE OF REACTIVE CIRCUITS

BASIC PROBLEMS

SECTION 15-1 The *RC* Integrator

1. $\tau = RC = (2.2 \text{ k}\Omega)(0.047 \text{ μF}) = \textbf{103 μs}$

2. (a) $5RC = 5(47 \text{ Ω})(47 \text{ μF}) = \textbf{11.0 ms}$
   (b) $5RC = 5(3300 \text{ k}\Omega)(0.015 \text{ μF}) = \textbf{248 μs}$
   (c) $5RC = 5(22 \text{ k}\Omega)(100 \text{ pF}) = \textbf{11 μs}$
   (d) $5RC = 5(4.7 \text{ M}\Omega)(10 \text{ pF}) = \textbf{235 μs}$

3. $\tau = 6 \text{ ms}, C = 0.22 \text{ μF}$
   $\tau = RC$
   $$R = \frac{\tau}{C} = \frac{6 \text{ ms}}{0.22 \text{ μF}} = 27.3 \text{ k}\Omega$$
   Use a standard **27 kΩ** resistor.

4. $t_{W(\text{min})} = 5\tau = 5(6 \text{ ms}) = \textbf{30 ms}$

SECTION 15-2 Response of *RC* Integrators to a Single Pulse

5. $v_C = 0.63(20 \text{ V}) = \textbf{12.6 V}$

6. (a) $v = 0.86(20 \text{ V}) = \textbf{17.2 V}$
   (b) $v = 0.95(20 \text{ V}) = \textbf{19 V}$
   (c) $v = 0.98(20 \text{ V}) = \textbf{19.6 V}$
   (d) $v = 0.99(20 \text{ V}) = \textbf{19.8 V}$ (considered 20 V)

7. See Figure 15-1.

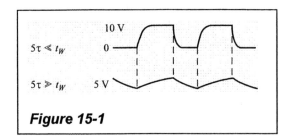

Figure 15-1

8. $\tau = RC = (1.0 \text{ k}\Omega)(1 \text{ μF}) = 1 \text{ ms}$
$v_{out} = 0.632(8 \text{ V}) = \textbf{5.06 V}$
The time to reach steady-state with repetitive pulses is **5 ms**.
See Figure 15-2 for output wave shape.

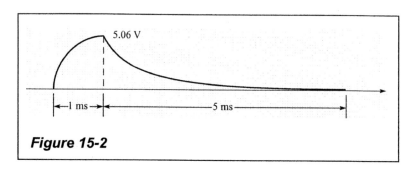

5.06 V

←1 ms→ ←————5 ms————→

Figure 15-2

SECTION 15-3 Response of *RC* Integrators to Repetitive Pulses

9. $\tau = (4.7 \text{ k}\Omega)(10 \text{ μF}) = 47 \text{ ms}$
$5\tau = 235 \text{ ms}$
See Figure 15-3.

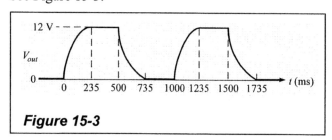

12 V

V_{out}

0   235 500 735 1000 1235 1500 1735 t (ms)

Figure 15-3

10. $T = \dfrac{1}{f} = \dfrac{1}{10 \text{ kHz}} = 100 \text{ μs}$ $t_W = 0.25(100 \text{ μs}) = 25 \text{ μs}$

1st pulse: 0.632(1 V) = 632 mV
Between 1st and 2nd pulses: 0.05(632 mV) = 31.6 mV
2nd pulse: 0.632(1 V − 31.6 mV) + 31.6 mV = 644 mV
Between 2nd and 3rd pulses: 0.05(644 mV) = 32.2 mV
3rd pulse: 0.632(1 V − 32.2 mV) + 32.2 mV = 644 mV

See Figure 15-4.

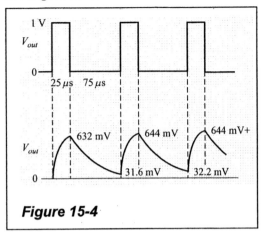

Figure 15-4

11.   The steady-state output equals the average value of the input which is
       15 V with a small ripple.

SECTION 15-4 Response of *RC* Differentiators to a Single Pulse

12.   See Figure 15-5.

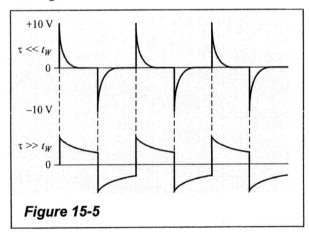

Figure 15-5

13. $\tau = (1.0 \text{ k}\Omega)(1 \text{ }\mu\text{F}) = 1 \text{ ms}$
       See Figure 15-6. Steady-state is reached in **5 ms**.

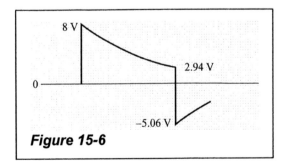

Figure 15-6

14. $\tau = (1.0 \text{ k}\Omega)(1 \text{ μF}) = 1 \text{ ms}$
     See Figure 15-7.

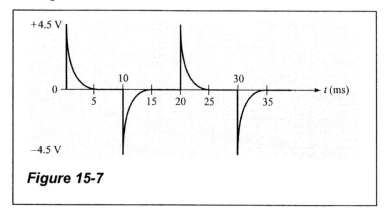

Figure 15-7

15. The output voltage is approximately the same wave shape as the input voltage but with an average value of **0 V**.

SECTION 15-6 Response of *RL* Integrators to Pulse Inputs

16. $\tau = \dfrac{10 \text{ mH}}{10 \text{ k}\Omega} = 1 \text{ μs}$

     $5\tau = 5 \text{ μs}$
     $V_{out(max)} = 0.632(8 \text{ V}) = 5.06 \text{ V}$
     See Figure 15-8.

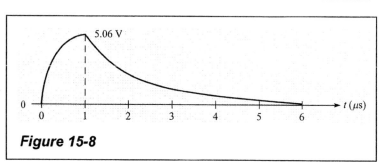

Figure 15-8

17. $\tau = \dfrac{50 \text{ mH}}{1.0 \text{ k}\Omega} = 50 \text{ μs}$

     $5\tau = 250 \text{ μs}$
     $V_{out(max)} = 12 \text{ V}$
     See Figure 15-9.

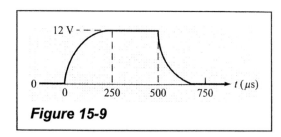

Figure 15-9

153

18. (a) $\tau = \dfrac{100 \ \mu H}{22 \ k\Omega} = 4.55 \ ns$

   (b) At end of pulse,
   $v_{out} = (10 \ V)e^{-2.2} = 1.11 \ V$
   See Figure 15-10.

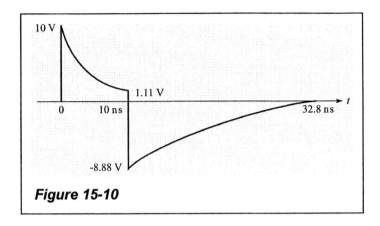

Figure 15-10

19. $\tau = \dfrac{100 \ \mu H}{22 \ k\Omega} = 4.55 \ ns$

   $5\tau = 22.75 \ ns$
   See Figure 15-11.

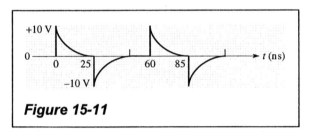

Figure 15-11

SECTION 15-8 Applications

20. $\tau = RC = (22 \ k\Omega)(0.001 \ \mu F) = 22 \ \mu s$
   $v_B = V_F(1 - e^{-t/RC}) = 10 \ V(1 - e^{-440\mu s/22\mu s}) = \mathbf{10.0 \ V}$

21. The output of the integrator is ideally a dc level which equals the average value of the input signal, **6 V** in this case.

SECTION 15-9 Troubleshooting

22. $\tau = RC = (3.3 \ k\Omega)(0.22 \ \mu F) = 726 \ \mu s$
   $5\tau = 5RC = 5(726 \ \mu s) = 3.63 \ ms$
   (b) Since the output looks like the input, the **capacitor must be open** or the resistor shorted because there is no charging time.
   (c) The zero output could be caused by an **open resistor or a shorted capacitor.**

23. $\tau = 726 \ \mu s; \ 5\tau = 5(726 \ \mu s) = 3.63 \ ms$
   (b) **No fault.**
   (c) **Open capacitor or shorted resistor.**

ADVANCED PROBLEMS

24. (a) Looking from the source and capacitor,

$$R_{tot} = \frac{(2.2 \text{ k}\Omega)(1.0 \text{ k}\Omega + 1.0 \text{ k}\Omega)}{4.2 \text{ k}\Omega} = 1.05 \text{ k}\Omega$$

$$\tau = R_{tot}C = (1.05 \text{ k}\Omega)(560 \text{ pF}) = 588 \text{ ns} = 0.588 \text{ } \mu s$$

(b) See Figure 15-12.

$$v = 10e^{-2.6\mu s/0.588\mu s} = 120 \text{ mV}$$

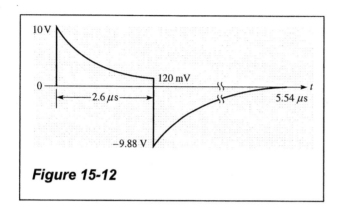

Figure 15-12

25. (a) Looking from the capacitor, the Thevenin resistance is 5 kΩ.

$$\tau = (5 \text{ k}\Omega)(4.7 \text{ } \mu F) = \textbf{23.5 ms}; \quad 5\tau = 5(23.5 \text{ ms}) = 118 \text{ ms}$$

(b) See Figure 15-13.

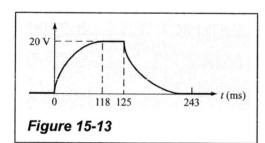

Figure 15-13

26. $L_{tot} = 8 \text{ } \mu H + 4 \text{ } \mu H = 12 \text{ } \mu H$

$$R_{tot} = \frac{(10 \text{ k}\Omega)(14.7 \text{ k}\Omega)}{24.7 \text{ k}\Omega} = 5.95 \text{ k}\Omega$$

$$\tau = \frac{L_{tot}}{R_{tot}} = \frac{12 \text{ } \mu H}{5.95 \text{ k}\Omega} = 2.02 \text{ ns}$$

This circuit is an **integrator.**

27. $v = V_F(1 - e^{-t/\tau})$

$2.5 = 5(1 - e^{-t/\tau})$

$2.5 = 5 - 5e^{-t/\tau}$

$5e^{-t/\tau} = 5 - 2.5$

$e^{-t/\tau} = \dfrac{2.5}{5} = 0.5$

$\ln e^{-t/\tau} = \ln 0.5$

$-\dfrac{t}{\tau} = -0.693$

$\tau = \dfrac{t}{0.693} = \dfrac{1\text{ s}}{0.693} = \mathbf{1.44\ s}$

28. The scope display is correct. See Figure 15-14.

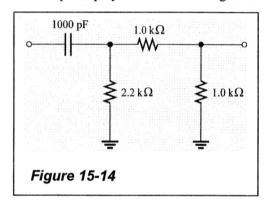

Figure 15-14

Multisim Troubleshooting Problems

29. Capacitor is open.

30. R_2 is open.

31. No fault

32. L_1 is open.

CHAPTER 16
DIODES AND APPLICATIONS

SECTION 16-1 Introduction to Semiconductors

1. Two types of semiconductor materials are **silicon** and **germanium**.

2. Semiconductors have **4** valence electrons.

3. In a silicon crystal, a single atom forms **4** covalent bonds.

4. When heat is added to silicon, **the number of free electrons increases.**

5. Current in silicon is produced at the **conduction band** and the **valence band** levels.

6. Doping is the process of adding trivalent or pentavalent elements to an intrinsic semiconductor in order to increase the effective number of free electrons or holes, respectively.

7. Antimony is an *n*-**type** impurity. Boron is a *p*-**type** impurity.

8. A hole is the absence of an electron in the valence band of an atom.

9. Recombination is the process in which an electron that has crossed the *pn* junction falls into a hole in the *p*-region, creating a negative ion.

SECTION 16-2 The Diode

10. The electric field across a *pn* junction is created by the diffusion of free electrons from the *n*-type material across the barrier and their recombination with holes in the *p*-type material. This results in a net negative charge on the *p* side of the junction and a net positive charge on the *n* side of the junction, forming an electric field.

11. **A diode cannot be used as a voltage source** using the barrier potential because the potential opposes any further charge movement and is an equilibrium condition, not an energy source.

12. Forward biasing of a *pn* junction is accomplished by connecting the positive terminal of a battery to the *p*-**type** material.

13. A series resistor is necessary to limit the diode current when a diode is forward-biased to prevent overheating.

14. To generate the forward bias portion of the diode characteristic curve, use the set-up shown in Figure 16-1.

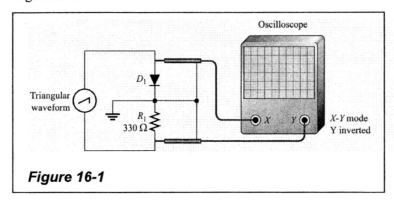

Figure 16-1

15. The barrier potential would decrease from 0.7 V to 0.6 V is there were an **increase in junction temperature.**

16. (a) The diode is **reverse-biased** because the anode is at 5 V and the cathode is at 8 V.
    (b) The diode is **forward-biased** because the anode is at ground and the cathode is at −100 V.
    (c) The diode is **forward-biased** by the positive voltage produced by the voltage divider.
    (d) The diode is **forward-biased** because its cathode is more negative than the anode due to the −20 V source.

17. (a) $V_R = 8\ V - 5\ V = 3\ V$ (reversed biased) (b) $V_F = 0.7\ V$
    (c) $V_F = 0.7\ V$ (d) $V_F = 0.7\ V$

18. (a) The diode should be forward-biased with $V_F = 0.7\ V$. The 25 V measurement indicates an **open** diode.
    (b) The diode should be forward-biased with $V_F = 0.7\ V$. The 15 V measurement indicates an **open** diode.
    (c) The diode should be reverse-biased and the measured voltage should be 0 V. The 2.5 V reading indicates that the diode is **shorted**.
    (d) The diode is reverse-biased. The 0 V reading across the resistor indicates there is no current. From this, it cannot be determined whether the diode is functioning properly or is open.

19. $V_A = V_{S1} = \mathbf{25\ V}$
    $V_B = V_A - 0.7\ V = 25\ V - 0.7\ V = \mathbf{24.3\ V}$
    $V_C = V_{S2} + 0.7\ V = 8\ V + 0.7\ V = \mathbf{8.7\ V}$
    $V_D = V_{S2} = \mathbf{8\ V}$

20. $V_{\text{AVG}} = \dfrac{V_p}{\pi} = \dfrac{200 \text{ V}}{\pi} = \textbf{63.7 V}$

21. $V_{L(\text{peak})} = 50 \text{ V} - 0.7 \text{ V} = \textbf{49.3 V}$

$I_{L(\text{peak})} = \dfrac{49.3 \text{ V}}{100 \text{ }\Omega} = \textbf{493 mA}$

See Figure 16-2.

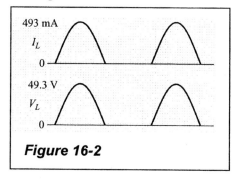

Figure 16-2

22. **Yes**, a diode with a PIV rating of 50 V can be used because the maximum reverse voltage is 50 V.

23. $V_{sec} = nV_{pri} = \left(\dfrac{N_{sec}}{N_{pri}}\right)115 \text{ V} = (0.5)115 \text{ V} = 57.5 \text{ V rms}$

$V_{sec(\text{peak})} = 1.414(57.5 \text{ V}) = 81.3 \text{ V}$

$V_{RL(\text{peak})} = V_{sec(\text{peak})} - 0.7 \text{ V} = \textbf{80.6 V}$

24. $V_{\text{AVG}} = \dfrac{2V_p}{\pi} = \dfrac{2(75 \text{ V})}{\pi} = \textbf{47.7 V}$

25. (a) **Center-tapped full-wave rectifier.**
     (b) $V_{sec} = 0.25(80 \text{ V}) = 20 \text{ V rms}$
          $V_{sec(\text{peak})} = 1.414(20 \text{ V}) = \textbf{28.3 V}$
     (c) $\dfrac{V_{sec(\text{peak})}}{2} = \dfrac{28.3 \text{ V}}{2} = \textbf{14.2 V}$
     (d) See Figure 16-3.
     (e) $I_{F(\text{peak})} = \dfrac{V_{sec(\text{peak})}}{2} - \dfrac{0.7 \text{ V}}{R_L} = \dfrac{14.2 \text{ V} - 0.7 \text{ V}}{1.0 \text{ k}\Omega} = \dfrac{13.5 \text{ V}}{1.0 \text{ k}\Omega} = \textbf{13.5 mA}$

(f) $PIV = 2V_{p(out)} = 2(13.5 \text{ V}) = \textbf{27.0 V}$

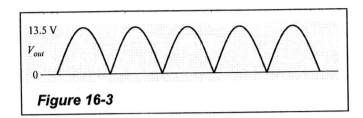

Figure 16-3

26. $V_{AVG} = = \dfrac{110 \text{ V}}{2} = 55 \text{ V}$ for each half of the transformer

$V_{AVG} = \dfrac{V_p}{\pi}$

$V_p = \pi V_{AVG} = \pi(55 \text{ V}) = \textbf{173 V}$

27. See Figure 16-4.

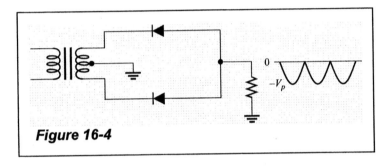

Figure 16-4

28. $PIV = V_p = \dfrac{\pi V_{AVG}}{2} = \dfrac{\pi(50 \text{ V})}{2} = \textbf{78.5 V}$

SECTION 16-5 Power Supplies

29. The ideal dc output voltage of a capacitor filter is the **peak value** of the rectified input.

30. $V_{sec(peak)} = 1.414(12 \text{ V})(3) = 50.9 \text{ V}$
      See Figure 16-5.

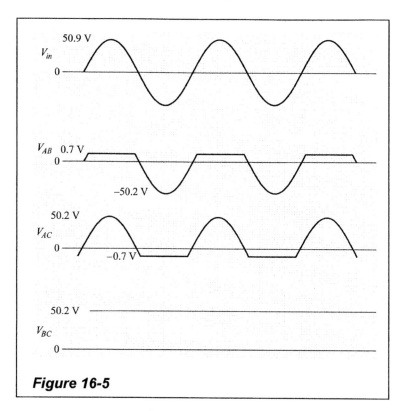

50.9 V

V_{in}

0

V_{AB} 0.7 V

0

−50.2 V

50.2 V

V_{AC}

0

−0.7 V

50.2 V

V_{BC}

0

Figure 16-5

31. % load regulation $= \left(\dfrac{V_{NL} - V_{FL}}{V_{FL}} \right) 100\%$

$= \left(\dfrac{12.6\text{ V} - 12.1\text{ V}}{12.1\text{ V}} \right) 100\%$

$= \mathbf{4.13\%}$

32. % line regulation $= \left(\dfrac{\Delta V_{OUT}}{\Delta V_{IN}} \right) 100\%$

$= \left(\dfrac{4.85\text{ V} - 4.65\text{ V}}{9.35\text{ V} - 6.48\text{ V}} \right) 100\%$

$= \mathbf{6.97\%}$

SECTION 16-6 Special-Purpose Diodes

33. See Figure 16-6.

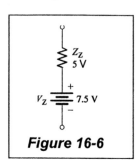

Z_Z
5 V

+

V_Z 7.5 V

−

Figure 16-6

34. $$Z_Z = \frac{\Delta V_Z}{\Delta I_Z} = \frac{38\,\text{mV}}{1\,\text{mA}} = \mathbf{38\ \Omega}$$

35. At 5 V; $C = 20$ pF
    At 20 V; $C = 11$ pF
    $\Delta C = 20$ pF $- 11$ pF $= \mathbf{9\ pF}$ **(decrease)**

36. From the graph, the diode reverse voltage that produces a capacitance of 25 pF is $V_R \cong \mathbf{3\ V}$.

37. The microammeter reading will **increase** because the photodiode will conduct current when the LED is turned on.

38. The reverse current in a photodiode with no incident light is called **dark current.**

SECTION 16-7 Troubleshooting

39. $$V_{\text{AVG}} = \frac{2V_p}{\pi} = \frac{2(115\,\text{V})(1.414)}{\pi} \cong 103\ \text{V}$$

    The output of the bridge is correct. However, the 0 V output from the filter indicates that the **capacitor is shorted** or R_{surg} **is open**.

40. (a) Output is correct.
    (b) Incorrect, open diode.
    (c) Output is correct.
    (d) Incorrect, open or faulty capacitor.

41. (a) Readings are correct.
    (b) Zener diode is open.
    (c) Fuse is blown or switch is open.
    (d) C_1 is open.
    (e) Transformer winding is open or the bridge is open.

42. (a) Fuse is open. Replace fuse.
    (b) Open transformer winding or connection. Verify and replace transformer.
    (c) Open transformer winding or connection. Verify and replace transformer.
    (d) Transformer has some primary turns shorted creating an effective turns ratio greater than one. Replace the transformer.
    (e) Transformer has some secondary turns shorted creating an effective turns ratio less than one. Replace the transformer.
    (f) C_1 is open. Replace capacitor.
    (g) C_1 leaky. Replace capacitor.
    (h) A diode is open. Isolate and replace.
    (i) Fuse is blown or C_2 is shorted or IC regulator is bad or transformer is open or at least two bridge diodes are open. Isolate and replace.

43. The diode is open.

44. D_2 is shorted.

45. No fault

46. D_2 is open.

47. D_1 is leaky.

48. Diode is shorted.

49. D_2 is open.

50. A bridge diode is shorted.

51. No fault

52. Zener diode D is open.

CHAPTER 17
TRANSISTORS AND APPLICATIONS

SECTION 17-1 DC Operation of Bipolar Junction Transistors

1. $I_C = I_E - I_B = 5.34 \text{ mA} - 475 \text{ μA} = \textbf{4.87 mA}$

2. $\alpha_{DC} = \dfrac{I_C}{I_E} = \dfrac{8.23 \text{ mA}}{8.69 \text{ mA}} = \textbf{0.947}$

3. $\beta_{DC} = \dfrac{I_C}{I_B} = \dfrac{25 \text{ mA}}{200 \text{ μA}} = \textbf{125}$

4. $I_B = 0.02 I_E = 0.02(30 \text{ mA}) = 0.6 \text{ mA}$
   $I_C = I_E - I_B = 30 \text{ mA} - 0.6 \text{ mA} = \textbf{29.4 mA}$

5. $V_B = 2 \text{ V}$
   $V_E = V_B - V_{BE} = 2 \text{ V} - 0.7 \text{ V} = 1.3 \text{ V}$
   $I_E = \dfrac{V_E}{R_E} = \dfrac{1.3 \text{ V}}{1.0 \text{ k}\Omega} = \textbf{1.3 mA}$
   $I_C = \alpha_{DC} I_E = (0.98)(1.3 \text{ mA}) = \textbf{1.27 mA}$
   $I_B = \dfrac{I_C}{\beta_{DC}} = \dfrac{1.27 \text{ mA}}{49} = \textbf{25.9 μA}$

6. $V_B = 2 \text{ V}$
   $V_E = V_B - V_{BE} = 2 \text{ V} - 0.7 \text{ V} = 1.3 \text{ V}$
   $I_E = \dfrac{V_E}{R_E} = \dfrac{1.3 \text{ V}}{1.0 \text{ k}\Omega} = \textbf{1.3 mA}$
   $I_C = \alpha_{DC} I_E = (0.98)(1.3 \text{ mA}) = \textbf{1.27 mA}$
   $I_B = \dfrac{I_C}{\beta_{DC}} = \dfrac{1.27 \text{ mA}}{100} = \textbf{12.7 μA}$

7. $V_E = V_B - V_{BE} = 2 \text{ V} - 0.7 \text{ V} = \textbf{1.3 V}$

8. (a) $V_B = V_{BB} = \textbf{10 V}$
       $V_C = V_{CC} = \textbf{20 V}$
       $V_E = V_B - V_{BE} = 10 \text{ V} - 0.7 \text{ V} = \textbf{9.3 V}$
       $V_{CE} = V_C - V_E = 20 \text{ V} - 9.3 \text{ V} = \textbf{10.7 V}$
       $V_{BE} = \textbf{0.7 V}$
       $V_{BC} = V_B - V_C = 10 \text{ V} - 20 \text{ V} = \textbf{-10 V}$

(b) $V_B = V_{BE} = \mathbf{0.7\ V}$

$V_E = \mathbf{0\ V}$

$V_{R_B} = 4\ V - 0.7\ V = 3.3\ V$

$I_B = \dfrac{V_{R_B}}{R_B} = \dfrac{3.3\ V}{4.7\ k\Omega} = 702\ \mu A$

$I_C = \beta_{DC}I_B = 50(702\ \mu A) = 35.1\ mA$

$V_C = V_{CE} = V_{CC} - I_CR_C = 24\ V - (35.1\ mA)(430\ \Omega) = \mathbf{8.91\ V}$

$V_{BC} = V_B - (V_{CC} - I_CR_C) = 0.7\ V - 8.91\ V = \mathbf{-8.21\ V}$

9. $I_B = \dfrac{1\ V - 0.7\ V}{22\ k\Omega} = \dfrac{0.3\ V}{22\ k\Omega} = \mathbf{13.6\ \mu A}$

$I_C = \beta_{DC}I_B = 50(13.6\ \mu A) = \mathbf{680\ \mu A}$

$V_C = 10\ V - (680\ \mu A)(1.0\ k\Omega) = \mathbf{9.32\ V}$

10. $V_B = \left(\dfrac{R_2\ \|\ \beta_{DC}R_E}{R_1 + R_2\ \|\ \beta_{DC}R_E}\right)V_{CC} = \left(\dfrac{10\ k\Omega\ \|\ (100)(100\ \Omega)}{22\ k\Omega + 10\ k\Omega\ \|\ (100)(100\ \Omega)}\right)12\ V = \left(\dfrac{5\ k\Omega}{27\ k\Omega}\right)12\ V$

$= \mathbf{2.22\ V}$

$V_E = V_B - V_{BE} = 2.22\ V - 0.7\ V = \mathbf{1.52\ V}$

$I_E = \dfrac{V_E}{R_E} = \dfrac{1.52\ V}{100\ \Omega} = \mathbf{15.2\ mA}$

$I_B = \dfrac{I_E}{\beta + 1} = \dfrac{15.2\ mA}{101} = 151\ \mu A$

$I_C \cong I_E = \mathbf{15.2\ mA}$

$V_C = V_{CC} - I_CR_C = 12\ V - (15.2\ mA)(470\ \Omega) = 12\ V - 7.14\ V = \mathbf{4.86\ V}$

11. $V_E = 1.52\ V$, $V_C = 4.86\ V$, $I_C = 15.2\ mA$

$V_{CE} = V_C - V_E = 4.86\ V - 1.52\ V = \mathbf{3.34\ V}$

Q-point: $I_C = \mathbf{15.2\ mA}$, $V_{CE} = \mathbf{3.34\ V}$

SECTION 17-2 BJT Class A Amplifiers

12. $V_{out} = A_vV_{in} = 50(100\ mV) = \mathbf{5\ V}$

13. $A_v = \dfrac{V_{out}}{V_{in}} = \dfrac{10\ V}{300\ mV} = \mathbf{33.3}$

14. $A_v = \dfrac{R_C}{R_E} = \dfrac{500\ \Omega}{100\ \Omega} = 5$

$V_c = A_vV_b = 5(50\ mV) = \mathbf{250\ mV}$

15. $V_B = \left(\dfrac{4.7\ k\Omega}{4.7\ k\Omega + 22\ k\Omega}\right)15\ V = 2.64\ V$

$V_E = V_B - V_{BE} = 2.64\ V - 0.7\ V = 1.94\ V$

$$I_E = \frac{V_E}{R_E} = \frac{1.94 \text{ V}}{390 \text{ }\Omega} = 4.97 \text{ mA}$$

$$r_e = \frac{25 \text{ mV}}{4.97 \text{ mA}} = 5.03 \text{ }\Omega$$

$$A_v = \frac{R_C}{r_e} = \frac{1.0 \text{ k}\Omega}{5.03 \text{ }\Omega} = \mathbf{199}$$

16. $V_B = \mathbf{2.64 \text{ V}}$ From Problem 15.
    $V_E = \mathbf{1.94 \text{ V}}$ From Problem 15.
    $I_C \cong I_E = 4.97 \text{ mA}$
    $V_C = 15 \text{ V} - (4.97 \text{ mA})(1.0 \text{ k}\Omega) = \mathbf{10.03 \text{ V}}$

17. (a) $V_B = \left(\dfrac{R_2 \parallel \beta_{DC} R_E}{R_1 + R_2 \parallel \beta_{DC} R_E} \right) V_{CC} = \left(\dfrac{12 \text{ k}\Omega \parallel (75)(1.0 \text{ k}\Omega)}{47 \text{ k}\Omega + 12 \text{ k}\Omega \parallel (75)(1.0 \text{ k}\Omega)} \right) 18 \text{ V} = \mathbf{3.25 \text{ V}}$

   (b) $V_E = V_B - V_{BE} = 3.25 \text{ V} - 0.7 \text{ V} = \mathbf{2.55 \text{ V}}$

   (c) $I_E = \dfrac{V_E}{R_E} = \dfrac{2.55 \text{ V}}{1.0 \text{ k}\Omega} = \mathbf{2.55 \text{ mA}}$

   (d) $I_C \cong I_E = \mathbf{2.55 \text{ mA}}$
   (e) $V_C = V_{CC} - I_C R_C = 18 \text{ V} - (2.55 \text{ mA})(3.3 \text{ k}\Omega) = \mathbf{9.59 \text{ V}}$
   (f) $V_{CE} = V_C - V_E = 9.59 \text{ V} - 2.55 \text{ V} = \mathbf{7.04 \text{ V}}$

18. (a) From Problem 17, $I_E = 2.55 \text{ mA}$

   $$R_{in} = \beta r_e = \beta_{ac} \left(\frac{25 \text{ mV}}{I_E} \right) = 70 \left(\frac{25 \text{ mV}}{2.55 \text{ mA}} \right) = \mathbf{686 \text{ }\Omega}$$

   (b) $R_{in(tot)} = R_1 \parallel R_2 \parallel R_{in} = 47 \text{ k}\Omega \parallel 12 \text{ k}\Omega \parallel 686 \text{ }\Omega = \mathbf{640 \text{ }\Omega}$

   (c) $A_v = \dfrac{R_C}{r_e} = \dfrac{3.3 \text{ k}\Omega}{9.8 \text{ }\Omega} = \mathbf{337}$

   (d) $I_s = \dfrac{V_{in}}{R_{in(tot)}} = \dfrac{10 \text{ mV}}{6.40 \text{ }\Omega} = 15.6 \text{ }\mu\text{A}$

   $$I_b = \left(\frac{R_1 \parallel R_2}{R_{in} + R_1 \parallel R_2} \right) I_s = \left(\frac{47 \text{ k}\Omega \parallel 12 \text{ k}\Omega}{47 \text{ k}\Omega + 12 \text{ k}\Omega} \right) 15.6 \text{ }\mu\text{A} = 2.51 \text{ }\mu\text{A}$$

   $$I_c = \beta_{ac} I_b = 70(2.51 \text{ }\mu\text{A}) = 175 \text{ }\mu\text{A}$$

   $$A_i = \frac{I_c}{I_s} = \frac{175 \text{ }\mu\text{A}}{15.6 \text{ }\mu\text{A}} = \mathbf{11.2}$$

   (e) $A_p = A_v A_i = (337)(11.2) = \mathbf{3774}$

19. $V_B = \left(\dfrac{R_2 \parallel \beta_{DC} R_E}{R_1 + R_2 \parallel \beta_{DC} R_E} \right) V_{CC} = \left(\dfrac{3.3 \text{ k}\Omega \parallel (150)(100 \text{ }\Omega)}{12 \text{ k}\Omega + 3.3 \text{ k}\Omega \parallel (150)(100 \text{ }\Omega)} \right) 8 \text{ V} = 1.47 \text{ V}$

$$I_E = \frac{V_B - V_{BE}}{R_E} = \frac{1.47 \text{ V} - 0.7 \text{ V}}{100 \text{ }\Omega} = 7.7 \text{ mA}$$

$$r_e = \frac{25 \text{ mV}}{I_e} = \frac{25 \text{ mV}}{7.7 \text{ mA}} = 3.25 \text{ }\Omega$$

$$A_{v(min)} = \frac{R_C}{(R_E + r_e)} = \frac{300 \ \Omega}{103.25 \ \Omega} = \textbf{2.91}$$

$$A_{v(max)} = \frac{R_C}{r_e} = \frac{300 \ \Omega}{3.25 \ \Omega} = \textbf{92.3}$$

20. $$A_{v(max)} = \frac{R_C \parallel R_L}{r_e} = \frac{300 \ \Omega \parallel 600 \ \Omega}{3.25 \ \Omega} = \textbf{61.5}$$

21. $$V_B = \left(\frac{R_2 \parallel \beta R_E}{R_1 + R_2 \parallel \beta R_E} \right) V_{CC} = \left(\frac{4.7 \ k\Omega \parallel 100 \ k\Omega}{10 \ k\Omega + 4.7 \ k\Omega \parallel 100 \ k\Omega} \right) 5.5 \ V = 1.70 \ V$$

$$I_E = \left(\frac{V_B - V_{BE}}{R_E} \right) = \left(\frac{1.70 \ V - 0.7 \ V}{1.0 \ k\Omega} \right) = 1.0 \ mA$$

$$r_e = \frac{25 \ mV}{1.0 \ mA} = 25 \ \Omega$$

$$A_v = \frac{R_E}{R_E + r_e} = \frac{1.0 \ k\Omega}{1.0 \ k\Omega + 25 \ \Omega} = \textbf{0.976}$$

22. $$R_{in(tot)} = R_1 \parallel R_2 \parallel \beta(R_E + r_e) \cong R_1 \parallel R_2 \parallel \beta R_E = 10 \ k\Omega \parallel 4.7 \ k\Omega \parallel 100 \ k\Omega = \textbf{3.1 k}\Omega$$
$$V_{OUT} = V_E = V_B - V_{BE} = 1.70 \ V - V_{BE} = 1.70 \ V - 0.7 \ V = \textbf{1.63 V}$$

23. The voltage gain is reduced.

SECTION 17-3 BJT Class B Amplifiers

24. *Bias current*

$$I_T = \frac{V_{CC} - 1.4 \ V}{R_1 + R_2} = \frac{20 \ V - 1.4 \ V}{780 \ \Omega} = 23.85 \ mA$$

$V_{B1} = V_{CC} - I_T R_1 = 20 \ V - (23.85 \ mA)(390 \ \Omega) = \textbf{10.7 V}$
$V_{E1} = V_{B1} - V_{BE} = 10.7 \ V - 0.7 \ V = \textbf{10 V}$
$V_{B2} = V_{B1} - 1.4 \ V = 10.7 \ V - 1.4 \ V = \textbf{9.3 V}$
$V_{E2} = V_{B2} + 0.7 \ V = 9.3 \ V + 0.7 \ V = \textbf{10 V}$
$V_{CEQ1} = V_{C1} - V_{E1} = 20 \ V - 10 \ V = \textbf{10 V}$
$V_{CEQ2} = V_{E2} - V_{C2} = 10 \ V - 0 \ V = \textbf{10 V}$

25. $$V_{p(out)} = V_{CEQ} = \frac{V_{CC}}{2} = \frac{20 \ V}{2} = \textbf{10 V}$$

$$I_{p(load)} \cong I_{c(sat)} = \frac{V_{CEQ}}{R_L} = \frac{10 \ V}{16 \ \Omega} = \textbf{625 mA}$$

26. Efficiency $= \dfrac{P_{out}}{P_{in}}$

$P_{out} = (0.71)(16.3 \ W) = \textbf{11.6 W}$

27. $I_{C(sat)} = \dfrac{V_{CC}}{R_C} = \dfrac{5\ V}{10\ k\Omega} = \mathbf{0.5\ mA}$

$I_{B(min)} = \dfrac{I_{C(sat)}}{\beta_{DC}} = \dfrac{0.5\ mA}{150} = \mathbf{3.33\ \mu A}$

$I_{B(min)} = \dfrac{V_{IN(min)} - 0.7\ V}{R_B}$

$V_{IN(min)} = R_B\left(I_{B(min)} + \dfrac{0.7\ V}{R_B}\right)$

$V_{IN(min)} = I_{B(min)}R_B + 0.7\ V = (3.33\ \mu A)(100\ k\Omega) + 0.7\ V = \mathbf{1.03\ V}$

28. $I_{C(sat)} = \dfrac{15\ V}{1.2\ k\Omega} = 12.5\ mA$

$I_{B(min)} = \dfrac{I_{C(sat)}}{\beta_{DC}} = \dfrac{12.5\ mA}{150} = 83.3\ \mu A$

$R_{B(min)} = \dfrac{V_{IN} - 0.7\ V}{I_{B(min)}} = \dfrac{4.3\ V}{83.3\ \mu A} = 51.6\ k\Omega$

SECTION 17-5 DC Operation of Field-Effect Transistors (FETs)

29. (a) The depletion region **narrows** when V_{GS} is increased from 1 V to 3 V.
     (b) The resistance **increases** when V_{GS} is increased from 1 V to 3 V.

30. The gate-to-source voltage of an N-channel JFET must be zero or negative in order to maintain the required reverse-bias condition.

31. See Figure 17-1.

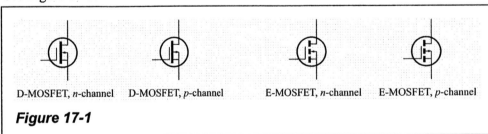

D-MOSFET, n-channel   D-MOSFET, p-channel   E-MOSFET, n-channel   E-MOSFET, p-channel

Figure 17-1

32. The gate is insulated from the channel by an SiO_2 layer.

33. The n-channel D-MOSFET operates in **enhancement mode** when positive V_{GS} is applied.

34. $V_{GS(min)} = V_{GS(th)} = \mathbf{3\ V}$

35. (a) $V_S = (1 \text{ mA})(1.0 \text{ k}\Omega) = 1 \text{ V}$
$V_D = 12 \text{ V} - (1 \text{ mA})(4.7 \text{ k}\Omega) = 7.3 \text{ V}$
$V_G = 0 \text{ V}$
$V_{DS} = V_D - V_S = 7.3 \text{ V} - 1 \text{ V} = \textbf{6.3 V}$
$V_{GS} = V_G - V_S = 0 \text{ V} - 1 \text{ V} = \textbf{–1 V}$

(b) $V_S = (3 \text{ mA})(100 \text{ }\Omega) = 0.3 \text{ V}$
$V_D = 9 \text{ V} - (3 \text{ mA})(470 \text{ }\Omega) = 7.59 \text{ V}$
$V_G = 0 \text{ V}$
$V_{DS} = V_D - V_S = 7.59 \text{ V} - 0.3 \text{ V} = \textbf{7.29 V}$
$V_{GS} = V_G - V_S = 0 \text{ V} - 0.3 \text{ V} = \textbf{–0.3 V}$

(c) $V_S = (-5 \text{ mA})(470 \text{ }\Omega) = -2.35 \text{ V}$
$V_D = -15 \text{ V} - (-5 \text{ mA})(2.2 \text{ k}\Omega) = -4 \text{ V}$
$V_G = 0 \text{ V}$
$V_{DS} = V_D - V_S = -4 \text{ V} - (-2.35 \text{ V}) = \textbf{–1.65 V}$
$V_{GS} = V_G - V_S = 0 \text{ V} - (-2.35 \text{ V}) = \textbf{2.35 V}$

36. (a) Depletion   (b) Enhancement
(c) Zero bias   (d) Enhancement

37. (a) $V_{GS} = \left(\dfrac{10 \text{ M}\Omega}{14.7 \text{ M}\Omega} \right) 10 \text{ V} = 6.8 \text{ V}$ **This one is on.**

(b) $V_{GS} = \left(\dfrac{1.0 \text{ M}\Omega}{11 \text{ M}\Omega} \right) (-25 \text{ V}) = -2.27 \text{ V}$ **This one is off.**

SECTION 17-6 FET Amplifiers

38. (a) $A_v = g_m R_D = (3.8 \text{ mS})(1.2 \text{ k}\Omega) = \textbf{4.56}$
(b) $A_v = g_m R_D = (5.5 \text{ mS})(2.2 \text{ k}\Omega \parallel 10 \text{ k}\Omega) = \textbf{9.92}$

39. (a) $A_v = \dfrac{g_m R_S}{1 + g_m R_S} = \dfrac{(3000 \text{ μS})(4.7 \text{ k}\Omega)}{1 + (3000 \text{ μS})(4.7 \text{ k}\Omega)} = \textbf{0.934}$

(b) $A_v = \dfrac{g_m R_S}{1 + g_m R_S} = \dfrac{(4300 \text{ μS})(100 \text{ }\Omega)}{1 + (4300 \text{ μS})(100 \text{ }\Omega)} = \textbf{0.301}$

40. (a) $A_v = \dfrac{g_m R_S}{1 + g_m R_S} = \dfrac{(3000 \text{ μS})(4.7 \text{ k}\Omega \parallel 10 \text{ k}\Omega)}{1 + (3000 \text{ μS})(4.7 \text{ k}\Omega \parallel 10 \text{ k}\Omega)} = \textbf{0.906}$

(b) $A_v = \dfrac{g_m R_S}{1 + g_m R_S} = \dfrac{(4300 \text{ μS})(100 \text{ }\Omega \parallel 10 \text{ k}\Omega)}{1 + (4300 \text{ μS})(100 \text{ }\Omega \parallel 10 \text{ k}\Omega)} = \textbf{0.299}$

41. Unity gain around the closed loop is required for sustained oscillation.
$$A_{cl} = A_V B = 1$$

$$B = \frac{1}{A_v} = \frac{1}{75} = 0.0133$$

42. To ensure start up:
$$A_{cl} > 1$$
Since $A_v = 75$, **B must be greater than 1/75** in order to produce the condition.
$$A_v B > 1.$$
For example, if $B = 1/50$,
$$A_v B = 75(1/50) = 1.5$$

43. (a) $\quad C_{eq} = \dfrac{C_1 C_2}{C_1 + C_2} = 909 \text{ pF}$

$$f_r = \frac{1}{2\pi\sqrt{LC_{eq}}} = \frac{1}{2\pi\sqrt{(0.1\,\text{mH})(909\,\text{pF})}} = \textbf{528 kHz}$$

Oscillator is Colpitts.

(b) $\quad L_{eq} = L_1 + L_2 = 22 \;\mu\text{H}$

$$f_r = \frac{1}{2\pi\sqrt{L_{eq}C}} = \frac{1}{2\pi\sqrt{(22\,\mu\text{H})(0.002\,\mu\text{F})}} = \textbf{759 kHz}$$

Oscillator is Hartley.

44. If R_5 opens, $V_{B2} \cong 0$ V and Q_2 will be in **cutoff**.
$$V_{C2} = \textbf{10 V}$$

45. (a) If the bypass capacitor, C_2, opens, the voltage gain of the first stage and thus the overall gain decreases. The dc voltages and the currents are not affected.

(b) If the coupling capacitor, C_3, opens, the signal will not reach the second stage so $V_{out} = 0$ V. The voltage gain of the first stage increases due to reduced loading. The dc voltages and currents are not affected.

(c) If the bypass capacitor, C_4, opens, the voltage gain of the second stage and thus the overall gain decreases. The dc voltages and currents are not affected.

(d) If C_2 shorts, R_4 is shorted, resulting in the dc bias voltages of the first stage being changed.

(e) If the BC junction of Q_1 opens, the signal will not pass through the first stage. The dc voltages at the base, emitter, and collector of Q_1 will change. The dc voltages and currents in the second stage are not affected.

(f) If the BE junction of Q_2 opens, the signal will not pass through the second stage. The dc voltages at the base, emitter, and collector of Q_2 will change. The dc voltages and currents in the first stage are not affected.

46. (a) Q_1 open drain to source: $V_{S1} = 0$ V, $V_{D1} = +V_{DD}$, no signal at Q_1 drain.
    (b) R_3 open: $V_{S1} = 0$ V, V_{D1} floating, no signal at Q_2 gate.
    (c) C_2 shorted: $V_{GS} = 0$ V, $I_D \cong I_{DSS}$.
    (d) C_3 shorted: $V_{G2} = V_{D1}$, improperly biasing Q_2
    (e) Q_2 open drain to source: $V_{S2} = 0$ V, $V_{D2} = +V_{DD}$, no signal at Q_2 drain

Multisim Troubleshooting Problems

47. Base-collector junction is open.

48. No fault

49. Drain and source are shorted.

50. R_2 is open.

51. No fault

52. C_2 is open.

53. C_1 is open.

CHAPTER 18
THE OPERATIONAL AMPLIFIER

SECTION 18-1 Introduction to the Operational Amplifier

1. **Practical op-amp**: High open-loop gain, high input impedance, low output impedance, and high CMRR.
    Ideal op-amp: Infinite open-loop gain, infinite input impedance, zero output impedance, and infinite CMRR.

2. Op-amp 2 is more desirable because it has a higher input impedance, a lower output impedance, and a higher open-loop gain.

SECTION 18-2 The Differential Amplifier

3. (a) Single-ended input, differential output
    (b) Single-ended input, single-ended output
    (c) Differential input, single-ended output
    (d) Differential input, differential output

4. $V_{E1} = V_{E2} = -0.7$ V

$$I_{RE} = \frac{-0.7 \text{ V} - (-15 \text{ V})}{2.2 \text{ k}\Omega} = \frac{14.3 \text{ V}}{2.2 \text{ k}\Omega} = 6.5 \text{ mA}$$

$$I_{E1} = I_{E2} = \frac{6.5 \text{ mA}}{2} = 3.25 \text{ mA}$$

$$\alpha_1 = \frac{I_{C1}}{I_{E1}} = 0.98$$

$$\alpha_2 = \frac{I_{C2}}{I_{E2}} = 0.975$$

$I_{C1} = 0.98(3.25 \text{ mA}) = 3.19 \text{ mA}$
$I_{C2} = 0.975(3.25 \text{ mA}) = 3.17 \text{ mA}$
$V_{C1} = 15 \text{ V} - (3.19 \text{ mA})(3.3 \text{ k}\Omega) = 4.47 \text{ V}$
$V_{C2} = 15 \text{ V} - (3.17 \text{ mA})(3.3 \text{ k}\Omega) = 4.54 \text{ V}$
$V_{OUT} = V_{C2} - V_{C1} = 4.54 \text{ V} - 4.47 \text{ V} = 0.07 \text{ V} = \mathbf{70 \text{ mV}}$

5. (a) Single-ended mode
    (b) Differential mode
    (c) Common mode

6.   See Figure 18-1. $V_{in1} = V_{in2}$

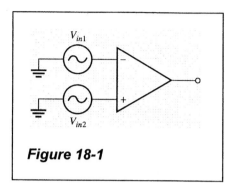

Figure 18-1

SECTION 18-3 Op-Amp Parameters

7. $I_{BIAS} = \dfrac{8.3\ \mu A + 7.9\ \mu A}{2} = \mathbf{8.1\ \mu A}$

8.   Input bias current is the average of the two input currents.
      Input offset current is the *difference* of the two input currents.
      $I_{OS} = |I_1 - I_2| = |8.3\ \mu A - 7.9\ \mu A| = \mathbf{0.4\ \mu A}$

9.   CMRR = 20 log 250,000 = **108 dB**

10. $CMRR = 20\log\left(\dfrac{A_{ol}}{A_{cm}}\right) = 20\ \log\left(\dfrac{175,000}{0.18}\right) = \mathbf{120\ dB}$

11. $CMRR = \dfrac{A_{ol}}{A_{cm}}$

      $A_{cm} = \dfrac{A_{ol}}{CMRR} = \dfrac{90,000}{300,000} = \mathbf{0.3}$

12.   Slew rate $= \dfrac{24\ V}{15\ \mu s} = \mathbf{1.6\ V/\mu s}$

13. $\Delta t = \dfrac{\Delta V_{out}}{\text{slew rate}} = \dfrac{20\ V}{0.5\ V/\mu s} = \mathbf{40\ \mu s}$

SECTION 18-5 Op-Amp Configurations with Negative Feedback

14.   (a)   Voltage-follower   (b)   Noninverting   (c)   Inverting

15. (a) $A_{cl(NI)} = \dfrac{1}{B} = \dfrac{1}{1.5\ k\Omega/561.5\ k\Omega} = \textbf{374}$

(b) $V_{out} = A_{cl(NI)}V_{in} = (374)(10\ mV) = \textbf{3.74 V}$

(c) $V_f = \left(\dfrac{1.5\ k\Omega}{561.5\ k\Omega}\right)3.74\ V = \textbf{10 mV}$

16. (a) $A_{cl(NI)} = \dfrac{1}{B} = \dfrac{1}{4.7\ k\Omega/51.7\ k\Omega} = \textbf{11}$

(b) $A_{cl(NI)} = \dfrac{1}{B} = \dfrac{1}{10\ k\Omega/1.01\ M\Omega} = \textbf{101}$

(c) $A_{cl(NI)} = \dfrac{1}{B} = \dfrac{1}{4.7\ k\Omega/224.7\ k\Omega} = \textbf{47.8}$

(d) $A_{cl(NI)} = \dfrac{1}{B} = \dfrac{1}{1.0\ k\Omega/23\ k\Omega} = \textbf{23}$

17. (a) $A_{cl(NI)} = \dfrac{1}{B} = \dfrac{1}{R_i/(R_f + R_i)} = \dfrac{R_f + R_i}{R_i}$

$R_f + R_i = R_i A_{cl(NI)}$
$R_f = R_i A_{cl(NI)} - R_i$
$R_f = R_i(A_{cl(NI)} - 1) = 1.0\ k\Omega(49) = \textbf{49 k}\Omega$

(b) $A_{cl(I)} = -\left(\dfrac{R_f}{R_i}\right)$

$R_f = -A_{cl(I)}R_i = -(-300)(10\ k\Omega) = \textbf{3 M}\Omega$

(c) $R_f = R_i(A_{cl(NI)} - 1) = 12\ k\Omega(7) = \textbf{84 k}\Omega$

(d) $R_f = -A_{cl(I)}R_i = -(-75)(2.2\ k\Omega) = \textbf{165 k}\Omega$

18. (a) $A_{cl(VF)} = \textbf{1}$

(b) $A_{cl(I)} = -\left(\dfrac{R_f}{R_i}\right) = -\left(\dfrac{100\ k\Omega}{100\ k\Omega}\right) = \textbf{-1}$

(c) $A_{cl(NI)} = \dfrac{1}{R_i/(R_i + R_f)} = \dfrac{1}{47\ k\Omega/(47\ k\Omega + 1.0\ M\Omega)} = \textbf{22.3}$

(d) $A_{cl(I)} = -\left(\dfrac{R_f}{R_i}\right) = -\left(\dfrac{330\ k\Omega}{33\ k\Omega}\right) = \textbf{-10}$

19. (a) $V_{out} = V_{in} = \textbf{10 mV, in-phase}$

(b) $V_{out} = A_{cl}V_{in} = -\left(\dfrac{R_f}{R_i}\right)V_{in} = -1(10\ mV) = \textbf{-10 mV, 180° out-of-phase}$

(c) $V_{out} = \left(\dfrac{1}{R_i/(R_f + R_i)}\right)V_{in} = \left(\dfrac{1}{47\ k\Omega/1.047\ M\Omega}\right)10\ mV = \textbf{223 mV, in-phase}$

(d) $V_{out} = -\left(\dfrac{R_f}{R_i}\right)V_{in} = -\left(\dfrac{330\ k\Omega}{33\ k\Omega}\right)10\ mV = \textbf{-100 mV, 180° out-of-phase}$

20. (a) $I_{in} = \dfrac{V_{in}}{R_{in}} = \dfrac{1\text{ V}}{2.2\text{ k}\Omega} = \textbf{455 }\boldsymbol{\mu}\textbf{A}$

(b) $I_f = I_{in} = \textbf{455 }\boldsymbol{\mu}\textbf{A}$

(c) $V_{out} = -I_f R_f = -(455\ \mu\text{A})(22\text{ k}\Omega) = \textbf{-10 V}$

(d) $A_{cl(\text{I})} = -\left(\dfrac{R_f}{R_i}\right) = -\left(\dfrac{22\text{ k}\Omega}{2.2\text{ k}\Omega}\right) = \textbf{-10}$

SECTION 18-6 Op-Amp Impedances

21. (a) $B = \dfrac{2.7\text{ k}\Omega}{562.7\text{ k}\Omega} = 0.0048$

$Z_{in(\text{NI})} = (1 + A_{ol}B)Z_{in} = (1 + 175{,}000 \times 0.0048)10\text{ M}\Omega = \textbf{8410 M}\boldsymbol{\Omega}$

$Z_{out(\text{NI})} = \dfrac{Z_{out}}{(1 + A_{ol}B)} = \dfrac{75\ \Omega}{(1 + 175{,}000 \times 0.0048)} = \textbf{89.2 m}\boldsymbol{\Omega}$

(b) $B = \dfrac{1.5\text{ k}\Omega}{48.5\text{ k}\Omega} = 0.0309$

$Z_{in(\text{NI})} = (1 + A_{ol}B)Z_{in} = (1 + 200{,}000 \times 0.0309)1.0\text{ M}\Omega = \textbf{6181 M}\boldsymbol{\Omega}$

$Z_{out(\text{NI})} = \dfrac{Z_{out}}{(1 + A_{ol}B)} = \dfrac{25\ \Omega}{(1 + 200{,}000 \times 0.0309)} = \textbf{4.04 m}\boldsymbol{\Omega}$

(c) $B = \dfrac{56\text{ k}\Omega}{1.056\text{ M}\Omega} = 0.053$

$Z_{in(\text{NI})} = (1 + A_{ol}B)Z_{in} = (1 + 50{,}000 \times 0.053)2\text{ M}\Omega = \textbf{5302 M}\boldsymbol{\Omega}$

$Z_{out(\text{NI})} = \dfrac{Z_{out}}{(1 + A_{ol}B)} = \dfrac{50\ \Omega}{(1 + 50{,}000 \times 0.053)} = \textbf{18.9 m}\boldsymbol{\Omega}$

22. (a) $Z_{in(\text{VF})} = (1 + A_{ol})Z_{in} = (1 + 220{,}000)6.0\text{ M}\Omega = 1.32 \times 10^{12}\ \Omega = \textbf{1.32 T}\boldsymbol{\Omega}$

$Z_{out(\text{VF})} = \dfrac{Z_{out}}{1 + A_{ol}} = \dfrac{100\ \Omega}{1 + 220{,}000} = \textbf{0.455 m}\boldsymbol{\Omega}$

(b) $Z_{in(\text{VF})} = (1 + A_{ol})Z_{in} = (1 + 100{,}000)5.0\text{ M}\Omega = 500 \times 10^{9}\ \Omega = \textbf{500 G}\boldsymbol{\Omega}$

$Z_{out(\text{VF})} = \dfrac{Z_{out}}{1 + A_{ol}} = \dfrac{60\ \Omega}{1 + 100{,}000} = \textbf{0.6 m}\boldsymbol{\Omega}$

(c) $Z_{in(\text{VF})} = (1 + A_{ol})Z_{in} = (1 + 50{,}000)800\text{ k}\Omega = \textbf{40 G}\boldsymbol{\Omega}$

$Z_{out(\text{VF})} = \dfrac{Z_{out}}{1 + A_{ol}} = \dfrac{75\ \Omega}{1 + 50{,}000} = \textbf{1.5 m}\boldsymbol{\Omega}$

23. (a) $Z_{in(\text{I})} \cong R_i = \textbf{10 k}\boldsymbol{\Omega}$

$Z_{out(\text{I})} = Z_{out} = \textbf{5.12 m}\boldsymbol{\Omega}$

(b) $Z_{in(\text{I})} \cong R_i = \textbf{100 k}\boldsymbol{\Omega}$

$Z_{out(\text{I})} = Z_{out} = \textbf{67.2 m}\boldsymbol{\Omega}$

(c) $Z_{in(\text{I})} \cong R_i = \textbf{470 }\boldsymbol{\Omega}$

$Z_{out(\text{I})} = Z_{out} = \textbf{6.24 m}\boldsymbol{\Omega}$

24. (a) Faulty op-amp or open R_1
     (b) R_2 is open, forcing open-loop operation.
     (c) Nonzero output offset voltage. R_4 is faulty or needs adjustment.

25. The closed-loop voltage gain will increase to:
     $$A_{cl} = \frac{100 \text{ k}\Omega}{1 \text{ k}\Omega} = \textbf{100}$$
     This increase is because the feedback resistance becomes the maximum potentiometer resistance (100 kΩ).

Multisim Troubleshooting Problems

26. R_2 is open.

27. R_1 is open.

28. No fault

29. The op-amp is faulty.

30. C is open.

CHAPTER 19
BASIC OP-AMP CIRCUITS

SECTION 19-1 Comparators

1. (a) Maximum negative
    (b) Maximum positive
    (c) Maximum negative

2. $V_{p(out)} = A_{ol}V_{in} = (80,000)(0.15 \text{ mV})(1.414) = 16.9 \text{ V}$
    Since 12 V is the peak limit,
    $V_{pp(out)} = \textbf{24 V}$

3. See Figure 19-1.

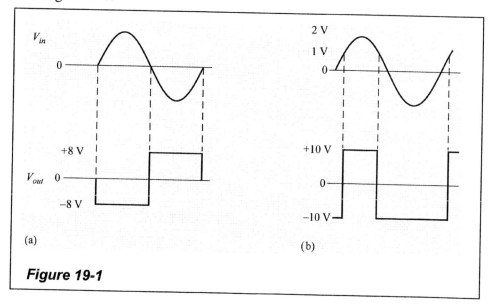

Figure 19-1

SECTION 19-2 Summing Amplifiers

4. (a) $V_{OUT} = -(1 \text{ V} + 1.5 \text{ V}) = \textbf{--2.5 V}$

    (b) $V_{OUT} = -\left(\dfrac{R_f}{R}\right)(-0.1 \text{ V} + 1 \text{ V} + 0.5 \text{ V}) = -2.2(1.4 \text{ V}) = \textbf{--3.08 V}$

5. (a) $V_{R1} = \textbf{1 V}$
        $V_{R2} = \textbf{1.8 V}$

177

(b) $I_{R1} = \dfrac{1\,V}{22\,k\Omega} = 45.5\ \mu A$

$I_{R2} = \dfrac{1.8\,V}{22\,k\Omega} = 81.8\ \mu A$

$I_f = I_{R1} + I_{R2} = 45.45\ \mu A + 81.82\ \mu A = \mathbf{127\ \mu A}$

(c) $V_{OUT} = I_f R_f = -(127\ \mu A)(22\,k\Omega) = \mathbf{-2.8\ V}$

6. $5V_{in} = \left(\dfrac{R_f}{R}\right)V_{in}$

$\dfrac{R_f}{R} = 5$

$R_f = 5R = 5(22\,k\Omega) = \mathbf{110\ k\Omega}$

7. $V_{OUT} = -\left(\left(\dfrac{R_f}{R_1}\right)V_1 + \left(\dfrac{R_f}{R_2}\right)V_2 + \left(\dfrac{R_f}{R_3}\right)V_3 + \left(\dfrac{R_f}{R_4}\right)V_4\right)$

$= \left(\left(\dfrac{10\,k\Omega}{10\,k\Omega}\right)2\,V + \left(\dfrac{10\,k\Omega}{33\,k\Omega}\right)3\,V + \left(\dfrac{10\,k\Omega}{91\,k\Omega}\right)3\,V + \left(\dfrac{10\,k\Omega}{180\,k\Omega}\right)6\,V\right)$

$= -(2\,V + 0.91\,V + 0.33\,V + 0.33\,V) = \mathbf{-3.57\ V}$

$I_f = \dfrac{V_{OUT}}{R_f} = \dfrac{3.57\,V}{10\,k\Omega} = \mathbf{357\ \mu A}$

8. $R_f = 100\ k\Omega$, $R_1 = \mathbf{100\ k\Omega}$, $R_2 = \mathbf{50\ k\Omega}$, $R_3 = \mathbf{25\ k\Omega}$, $R_4 = \mathbf{12.5\ k\Omega}$, $R_5 = \mathbf{6.25\ k\Omega}$, $R_6 = \mathbf{3.125\ k\Omega}$

SECTION 19-3 Integrators and Differentiators

9. $\dfrac{\Delta V_{OUT}}{\Delta t} = \dfrac{-V_{IN}}{RC} = \dfrac{-5\,V}{(56\,k\Omega)(0.022\,\mu F)} = \mathbf{-4.06\ mV/\mu s}$

10. See Figure 19-2.

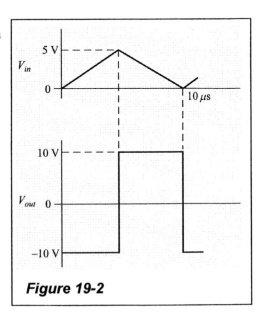

Figure 19-2

11. $\dfrac{V_{out}}{V_{in}} = \dfrac{1}{3}$

    $V_{out} = \left(\dfrac{1}{3}\right)V_{in} = \dfrac{2.2\ \text{V}}{3} = \textbf{733 mV}$

12. $f_r = \dfrac{1}{2\pi RC} = \dfrac{1}{2\pi(6.2\ \text{k}\Omega)(0.022\ \mu\text{F})} = \textbf{1.17 kHz}$

13. $\dfrac{R_f + R_{DS} + R_3}{R_{DS} + R_3} = 3$

    $3(R_{DS} + R_3) = R_f + R_{DS} + R_3$

    $3R_{DS} + 3.0\ \text{k}\Omega = 12\ \text{k}\Omega + R_{DS} + 1.0\ \text{k}\Omega$

    $3R_{DS} - R_{DS} = 13\ \text{k}\Omega - 3\ \text{k}\Omega$

    $R_{DS} = \dfrac{10\ \text{k}\Omega}{2} = \textbf{5 k}\Omega$

14. Negative excursions of V_{OUT} forward-bias D_1 causing C_3 to charge to a negative voltage, which increases the drain-source resistance of the JFET and reduces the gain.

15. $f_r = \dfrac{1}{2\pi RC} = \dfrac{1}{2\pi(15\ \text{k}\Omega)(0.01\ \mu\text{F})} = \textbf{1.06 kHz}$

16. The circuit produces a triangular waveform.

    $f = \dfrac{1}{4R_1 C}\left(\dfrac{R_2}{R_3}\right) = \dfrac{1}{4(22\ \text{k}\Omega)(0.022\ \mu\text{F})}\left(\dfrac{56\ \text{k}\Omega}{18\ \text{k}\Omega}\right) = \textbf{1.61 kHz}$

17. Change the frequency to 10 kHz by changing R_1 as follows:
    The circuit produces a triangular waveform.

    $f = \dfrac{1}{4R_1 C}\left(\dfrac{R_2}{R_3}\right)$

    $R_1 = \dfrac{1}{4fC}\left(\dfrac{R_2}{R_3}\right) = \dfrac{1}{4(10\ \text{kHz})(0.022\ \mu\text{F})}\left(\dfrac{56\ \text{k}\Omega}{18\ \text{k}\Omega}\right) = \textbf{3.54 k}\Omega$

SECTION 19-5 Active Filters

18. (a) One pole, low pass
    (b) One pole, high pass
    (c) Two poles, band pass

19. (a) $f_c = \dfrac{1}{2\pi RC} = \dfrac{1}{2\pi(4.7~\text{k}\Omega)(0.022~\mu\text{F})} = \textbf{1.54 kHz}$

(b) $f_c = \dfrac{1}{2\pi RC} = \dfrac{1}{2\pi(4.7~\text{k}\Omega)(0.0047~\mu\text{F})} = \textbf{7.20 kHz}$

(c) $f_c = \dfrac{1}{2\pi\sqrt{R_1 R_2 C_1 C_2}} = \dfrac{1}{2\pi\sqrt{(12~\text{k}\Omega)^2(0.022~\mu\text{F})(0.01~\mu\text{F})}} = \textbf{894 Hz}$

20. (a) *For the low-pass stage:*

$f_c = \dfrac{1}{2\pi\sqrt{R^2 C_1 C_2}} = \dfrac{1}{2\pi\sqrt{(10~\text{k}\Omega)^2(0.01~\mu\text{F})(0.0047~\mu\text{F})}} = 2.32~\text{kHz}$

For the high-pass stage:

$f_c = \dfrac{1}{2\pi\sqrt{R_3 R_4 C^2}} = \dfrac{1}{2\pi\sqrt{(22~\text{k}\Omega)(10~\text{k}\Omega)(0.01~\mu\text{F})^2}} = 1.07~\text{kHz}$

$BW = 2.32~\text{kHz} - 1.07~\text{kHz} = \textbf{1.25 kHz}$

$f_r = \sqrt{(2.32~\text{kHz})(1.07~\text{kHz})} = \textbf{1.58 kHz}$

(b) *For the low-pass stage:*

$f_c = \dfrac{1}{2\pi\sqrt{R^2 C_1 C_2}} = \dfrac{1}{2\pi\sqrt{(15~\text{k}\Omega)^2(2200~\text{pF})(1000~\text{pF})}} = 7.15~\text{kHz}$

For the high-pass stage:

$f_c = \dfrac{1}{2\pi\sqrt{R_1 R_2 C^2}} = \dfrac{1}{2\pi\sqrt{(56~\text{k}\Omega)(27~\text{k}\Omega)(1500~\text{pF})^2}} = 2.73~\text{kHz}$

$BW = 7.15~\text{kHz} - 2.73~\text{kHz} = \textbf{4.42 kHz}$

$f_r = \sqrt{(7.15~\text{kHz})(2.73~\text{kHz})} = \textbf{4.42 kHz}$

SECTION 19-6 Voltage Regulators

21. $V_{\text{OUT}} = \left(1 + \dfrac{R_2}{R_3}\right)V_{\text{REF}} = \left(1 + \dfrac{4.7~\text{k}\Omega}{1.8~\text{k}\Omega}\right)2~\text{V} = \textbf{7.22 V}$

22. For $R_3 = 1.8~\text{k}\Omega$:

$V_{\text{OUT}} = \left(1 + \dfrac{R_2}{R_3}\right)V_{\text{REF}} = \left(1 + \dfrac{4.7~\text{k}\Omega}{1.8~\text{k}\Omega}\right)2~\text{V} = 7.22~\text{V}$

For $R_3 = 2(1.8~\text{k}\Omega) = 3.6~\text{k}\Omega$:

$V_{\text{OUT}} = \left(1 + \dfrac{4.7~\text{k}\Omega}{3.6~\text{k}\Omega}\right)2~\text{V} = 4.61~\text{V}$

The output voltage **decreases by 2.61 V** when R_3 is changed from 1.8 kΩ to 3.6 kΩ.

23. $V_{OUT} = \left(1 + \dfrac{4.7 \text{ k}\Omega}{1.8 \text{ k}\Omega}\right) 2.7 \text{ V} = \mathbf{9.75 \text{ V}}$

24. $I_{L(max)} = \dfrac{0.7 \text{ V}}{R_4}$

$R_4 = \dfrac{0.7 \text{ V}}{I_{L(max)}} = \dfrac{0.7 \text{ V}}{250 \text{ mA}} = \mathbf{2.8 \ \Omega}$

$P_{max} = I_{L(max)}^2 R_4 = (250 \text{ mA})^2(2.8 \ \Omega) = \mathbf{175 \text{ mW}}$

Use a 0.25 W resistor.

25. $R_4 = \dfrac{2.8 \ \Omega}{2} = 1.4 \ \Omega$

$I_{L(max)} = \dfrac{0.7 \text{ V}}{R_4} = \dfrac{0.7 \text{ V}}{1.4 \ \Omega} = \mathbf{500 \text{ mA}}$

26. Q_1 conducts more when the load current increases, assuming that the output voltage attempts to increase. When the output voltage tries to increase due to a change in load current, the attempted increase is sensed by R_3 and R_4 and applied to the op-amp's noninverting input. The resulting difference voltage increases the op-amp's output, driving Q_1 more, and thus increasing its collector current.

27. $\Delta I_C = \dfrac{\Delta V_{R1}}{R_1} = \dfrac{1 \text{ V}}{100 \ \Omega} = \mathbf{10 \text{ mA}}$

28. $V_{OUT} = \left(1 + \dfrac{R_3}{R_4}\right) V_{REF} = \left(1 + \dfrac{8.2 \text{ k}\Omega}{3.9 \text{ k}\Omega}\right) 5 \text{ V} = 15.5 \text{ V}$

$I_{L1} = \dfrac{V_{OUT}}{R_{L1}} = \dfrac{15.5 \text{ V}}{1.0 \text{ k}\Omega} = 15.5 \text{ mA}$

$I_{L2} = \dfrac{V_{OUT}}{R_{L2}} = \dfrac{15.5 \text{ V}}{1.2 \text{ k}\Omega} = 12.9 \text{ mA}$

$\Delta I_L = 12.9 \text{ mA} - 15.5 \text{ mA} = -2.6 \text{ mA}$

$\Delta I_S = -\Delta I_L = \mathbf{2.6 \text{ mA}}$ (increase)

Multisim Troubleshooting Problems

29. R_2 is open.

30. Op-amp open.

31. No fault

32. C_1 is open.

CHAPTER 20
SPECIAL-PURPOSE OP-AMP CIRCUITS

SECTION 20-1 Instrumentation Amplifiers

1. $A_{v(1)} = 1 + \dfrac{R_1}{R_G} = 1 + \dfrac{100\,\text{k}\Omega}{1.0\,\text{k}\Omega} = \mathbf{101}$

   $A_{v(2)} = 1 + \dfrac{R_2}{R_G} = 1 + \dfrac{100\,\text{k}\Omega}{1.0\,\text{k}\Omega} = \mathbf{101}$

2. $A_{cl} = 1 + \dfrac{2R}{R_G} = 1 + \dfrac{200\,\text{k}\Omega}{1.0\,\text{k}\Omega} = \mathbf{201}$

3. $V_{out} = A_{cl}(V_{in(2)} - V_{in(1)}) = 201(10\,\text{mV} - 5\,\text{mV}) = \mathbf{1.005\ V}$

4. $A_v = 1 + \dfrac{2R}{R_G}$

   $\dfrac{2R}{R_G} = A_v - 1$

   $R_G = \dfrac{2R}{A_v - 1} = \dfrac{2(100\,\text{k}\Omega)}{1000 - 1} = \dfrac{200\,\text{k}\Omega}{999} = 200.2\ \Omega \cong \mathbf{200\ \Omega}$

5. $R_G = \dfrac{50.5\,\text{k}\Omega}{A_v - 1}$

   $A_v = \dfrac{50.5\,\text{k}\Omega}{1.0\,\text{k}\Omega} + 1 = \mathbf{51.5}$

6. Using the graph in textbook Figure 20-6,
   $BW \cong \mathbf{300\ kHz}$

7. Change R_G to
   $R_G = \dfrac{50.5\,\text{k}\Omega}{A_v - 1} = \dfrac{50.5\,\text{k}\Omega}{24 - 1} \cong \mathbf{2.2\ k\Omega}$

8. $R_G = \dfrac{50.5\,\text{k}\Omega}{A_v - 1} = \dfrac{50.5\,\text{k}\Omega}{20 - 1} \cong \mathbf{2.7\ k\Omega}$

9. $A_{v(total)} = (30)(10) = \mathbf{300}$

10.   (a) $A_{v1} = \dfrac{R_{f1}}{R_{i1}} + 1 = \dfrac{18\text{ k}\Omega}{8.2\text{ k}\Omega} + 1 = 3.2$

         $A_{v2} = \dfrac{R_{f2}}{R_{i2}} + 1 = \dfrac{150\text{ k}\Omega}{15\text{ k}\Omega} + 1 = 11$

         $A_{v(tot)} = A_{v1}A_{v2} = (3.2)(11) = \mathbf{35.2}$

     (b) $A_{v1} = \dfrac{R_{f1}}{R_{i1}} + 1 = \dfrac{330\text{ k}\Omega}{1.0\text{ k}\Omega} + 1 = 331$

         $A_{v2} = \dfrac{R_{f2}}{R_{i2}} + 1 = \dfrac{47\text{ k}\Omega}{15\text{ k}\Omega} + 1 = 4.13$

         $A_{v(tot)} = A_{v1}A_{v2} = (331)(4.13) = \mathbf{1{,}367}$

11. $A_{v2} = 11$ (from Problem 10)

     $A_{v1}A_{v2} = 100$

     $\dfrac{R_{f1}}{R_{i1}} + 1 = A_{v1} = \dfrac{100}{11} = 9.09$

     Change R_{f1} (18 kΩ) to 66.3 kΩ.

     Use **66.5 kΩ** $\pm$ 1% standard value resistor.

12. $A_{v1} = 331$ (from Problem 10)

     $A_{v1}A_{v2} = 440$

     $\dfrac{R_{f2}}{R_{i2}} + 1 = A_{v2} = \dfrac{440}{331} = 1.33$

     Change R_f (47 kΩ) to 3.3 kΩ.

     Change R_i (15 kΩ) to 10 kΩ.

13.   Connect pin 6 to pin 10 and pin 14 to pin 15.

SECTION 20-3 Operational Transconductance Amplifiers (OTAs)

14. $g_m = \dfrac{I_{out}}{V_{in}} = \dfrac{10\ \mu\text{A}}{10\text{ mV}} = \mathbf{1\ mS}$

15. $I_{out} = g_m V_{in} = (5000\ \mu\text{S})(100\text{ mV}) = \mathbf{500\ \mu A}$

     $V_{out} = I_{out}R_L = (500\ \mu\text{A})(10\text{ k}\Omega) = \mathbf{5\ V}$

16. $g_m = \dfrac{I_{out}}{V_{in}}$

     $I_{out} = g_m V_{in} = (4000\ \mu\text{S})(100\text{ mV}) = 400\ \mu\text{A}$

     $R_L = \dfrac{V_{out}}{I_{out}} = \dfrac{3.5\text{ V}}{400\ \mu\text{A}} = \mathbf{8.75\ k\Omega}$

17. $$I_{BIAS} = \frac{+12\,V - (-12\,V) - 0.7\,V}{R_{BIAS}} = \frac{+12\,V - (-12\,V) - 0.7\,V}{220\,k\Omega} = \frac{23.3\,V}{220\,k\Omega} = 106\,\mu A$$

From the graph in Figure 20-49:

$$g_m = KI_{BIAS} \cong (16\,\mu S/\mu A)(106\,\mu A) = 1.70\,mS$$

$$A_v = \frac{V_{out}}{V_{in}} = \frac{I_{out}R_L}{V_{in}} = g_m R_L = (1.70\,mS)(6.8\,k\Omega) = \textbf{11.6}$$

18. The maximum voltage gain occurs when the 10 kΩ potentiometer is set to 0 Ω and was determined in Problem 17.

$$A_{v(max)} = \textbf{11.6}$$

The minimum voltage gain occurs when the 10 kΩ potentiometer is set to 10 kΩ.

$$I_{BIAS} = \frac{+12\,V - (-12\,V) - 0.7\,V}{220\,k\Omega + 10\,k\Omega} = \frac{23.3\,V}{230\,k\Omega} = 101\,\mu A$$

$$g_m \cong (16\,\mu S/\mu A)(101\,\mu A) = 1.62\,mS$$

$$A_{v(min)} = g_m R_L = (1.62\,mS)(6.8\,k\Omega) = \textbf{11.0}$$

19. The V_{MOD} waveform is applied to the bias input.
The gain and output voltage for each value of V_{MOD} is determined as follows using $K = 16\,\mu S/\mu A$. The output waveform is shown in Figure 20-1.

For $V_{MOD} = +8\,V$:

$$I_{BIAS} = \frac{+8\,V - (-9\,V) - 0.7\,V}{39\,k\Omega} = \frac{16.3\,V}{39\,k\Omega} = 418\,\mu A$$

$$g_m = KI_{BIAS} \cong (16\,\mu S/\mu A)(418\,\mu A) = 6.69\,mS$$

$$A_v = \frac{V_{out}}{V_{in}} = \frac{I_{out}R_L}{V_{in}} = g_m R_L = (6.69\,mS)(10\,k\Omega) = 66.9$$

$$V_{out} = A_v V_{in} = (66.9)(100\,mV) = \textbf{6.69\,V}$$

For $V_{MOD} = +6\,V$:

$$I_{BIAS} = \frac{+6\,V - (-9\,V) - 0.7\,V}{39\,k\Omega} = \frac{14.3\,V}{39\,k\Omega} = 367\,\mu A$$

$$g_m = KI_{BIAS} \cong (16\,\mu S/\mu A)(367\,\mu A) = 5.87\,mS$$

$$A_v = \frac{V_{out}}{V_{in}} = \frac{I_{out}R_L}{V_{in}} = g_m R_L = (5.87\,mS)(10\,k\Omega) = 58.7$$

$$V_{out} = A_v V_{in} = (58.7)(100\,mV) = \textbf{5.87\,V}$$

For $V_{MOD} = +4$ V:

$$I_{BIAS} = \frac{+4\text{ V} - (-9\text{ V}) - 0.7\text{ V}}{39\text{ k}\Omega} = \frac{12.3\text{ V}}{39\text{ k}\Omega} = 315\ \mu\text{A}$$

$$g_m = KI_{BIAS} \cong (16\ \mu\text{S}/\mu\text{A})(315\ \mu\text{A}) = 5.04\text{ mS}$$

$$A_v = \frac{V_{out}}{V_{in}} = \frac{I_{out}R_L}{V_{in}} = g_mR_L = (5.04\text{ mS})(10\text{ k}\Omega) = 50.4$$

$$V_{out} = A_vV_{in} = (50.4)(100\text{ mV}) = \textbf{5.04 V}$$

For $V_{MOD} = +2$ V:

$$I_{BIAS} = \frac{+2\text{ V} - (-9\text{ V}) - 0.7\text{ V}}{39\text{ k}\Omega} = \frac{10.3\text{ V}}{39\text{ k}\Omega} = 264\ \mu\text{A}$$

$$g_m = KI_{BIAS} \cong (16\ \mu\text{S}/\mu\text{A})(264\ \mu\text{A}) = 4.22\text{ mS}$$

$$A_v = \frac{V_{out}}{V_{in}} = \frac{I_{out}R_L}{V_{in}} = g_mR_L = (4.22\text{ mS})(10\text{ k}\Omega) = 42.2$$

$$V_{out} = A_vV_{in} = (42.2)(100\text{ mV}) = \textbf{4.22 V}$$

For $V_{MOD} = +1$ V:

$$I_{BIAS} = \frac{+1\text{ V} - (-9\text{ V}) - 0.7\text{ V}}{39\text{ k}\Omega} = \frac{9.3\text{ V}}{39\text{ k}\Omega} = 238\ \mu\text{A}$$

$$g_m = KI_{BIAS} \cong (16\ \mu\text{S}/\mu\text{A})(238\ \mu\text{A}) = 3.81\text{ mS}$$

$$A_v = \frac{V_{out}}{V_{in}} = \frac{I_{out}R_L}{V_{in}} = g_mR_L = (3.81\text{ mS})(10\text{ k}\Omega) = 38.1$$

$$V_{out} = A_vV_{in} = (38.1)(100\text{ mV}) = \textbf{3.81 V}$$

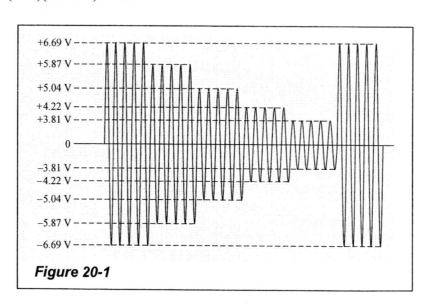

Figure 20-1

20. $$I_{BIAS} = \frac{+9\text{V} - (-9\text{ V}) - 0.7\text{ V}}{39\text{ k}\Omega} = \frac{17.3\text{ V}}{39\text{ k}\Omega} = 444\ \mu\text{A}$$

$$V_{TRIG(+)} = I_{BIAS}R_1 = (444\ \mu\text{A})(10\text{ k}\Omega) = \textbf{+4.44 V}$$

$$V_{TRIG(-)} = -I_{BIAS}R_1 = (-444\ \mu\text{A})(10\text{ k}\Omega) = \textbf{--4.44 V}$$

21.   See Figure 20-2.

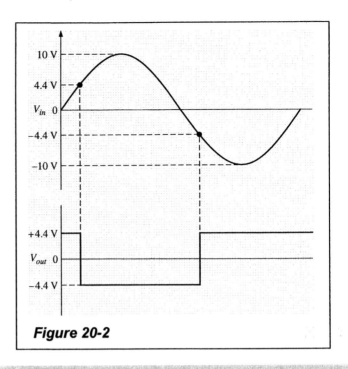

Figure 20-2

SECTION 20-4 Active Diode Circuits

22.   (a)   A sine wave with a positive peak at +0.7 V, a negative peak at −7.3 V, and a dc value of −3.3 V.

       (b)   A sine wave with a positive peak at +29.3 V, a negative peak at −0.7 V, and a dc value of +14.3 V.

23.   See Figure 20-3.

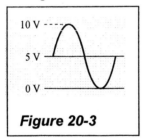

Figure 20-3

24.   See Figure 20-4.

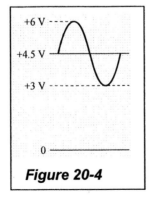

Figure 20-4

25.   (a) See Figure 20-5(a).
        (b) See Figure 20-5(b).

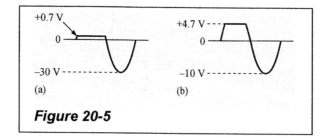

Figure 20-5

26.   See Figure 20-6.

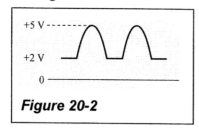

Figure 20-2

27.   See Figure 20-7.

$$A_v = \frac{R_2}{R_1} = \frac{180\text{ k}\Omega}{10\text{ k}\Omega} = 18$$

$$V_{out(p)} = A_v V_{in(p)} = 18(0.5\text{ V}) = 9\text{ V}$$

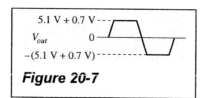

Figure 20-7

28. $A_v = \dfrac{R_2}{R_1} = \dfrac{180\text{ k}\Omega}{10\text{ k}\Omega} = 18$

        $V_{out(p)} = A_v V_{in(p)} = 18(50\text{ mV}) = 0.9\text{ V}$

    No limiting will occur because the peak output must be greater than 5.1 V + 0.7 V = 5.8 V.

29. $V_{out} = V_{p(in)} = 1.414(2.5\text{ V}) = 3.54\text{ V}$

30.   (a) $V_{IN} = V_Z = 4.7 \text{ V}$

$$I_L = \frac{V_{IN}}{R_i} = \frac{4.7 \text{ V}}{1.0 \text{ k}\Omega} = \textbf{4.7 mA}$$

(b) $V_{IN} = \left(\dfrac{10 \text{ k}\Omega}{20 \text{ k}\Omega} \right) 12 \text{ V} = 6 \text{ V}$

$R_i = 10 \text{ k}\Omega \parallel 10 \text{ k}\Omega + 100 \text{ }\Omega = 5.1 \text{ k}\Omega$

$$I_L = \frac{V_{IN}}{R_i} = \frac{6 \text{ V}}{5.1 \text{ k}\Omega} = \textbf{1.18 mA}$$

31.   See Figure 20-8.

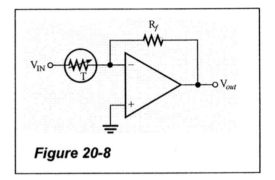

Figure 20-8

32. R_G leaky

33. D_2 shorted

34.   Diode is shorted.

35.   Zener diode open

36. R_4 is open.

CHAPTER 21
Measurement, Conversion, and Control

SECTION 21-1 Temperature Measurement

1. Assuming all are of the same type, the thermocouple exposed to the highest temperature (thermocouple C) produces the highest output. Note that thermocouple voltages are significantly different for different types as indicated in Figure 21-2 in the text.

2. The letters indicate the temperature range, coefficient, and voltage characteristic.

3. $V_{Thermocouple} = 20.869$ mV (from Table 21-1 in the text)
   $V_{Ambientjunction} = 0.25(4.277$ mV$) = 1.069$ mV
   The voltage across the op-amp inputs:
   $V_{Thermocouple} - V_{Ambientjunction} = 20.869$ mV $- 1.069$ mV $= 19.80$ mV
   For the inverting amplifier:
   $$A_v = -\frac{R_f}{R_i} = \frac{220 \text{ k}\Omega}{1.0 \text{ k}\Omega} = -220$$
   $V_{out} = (-220)(19.80$ mV$) = \mathbf{-4.36}$ **V**

4. When properly compensated, the input voltage to the amplifier is equal to the thermocouple voltage of 20.869 mV, so the output voltage is:

   $$V_{out} = -\frac{R_f}{R_i}V_{in} = \frac{220 \text{ k}\Omega}{1.0 \text{ k}\Omega}(20.869 \text{ mV}) = \mathbf{-4.59} \text{ V}$$

5. The bridge is balanced when
   $R_W + R_{RTD} + R_W = 560 \ \Omega$
   $R_{RTD} = 560 \ \Omega - 2R_W = 560 \ \Omega - 20 \ \Omega = \mathbf{540} \ \mathbf{\Omega}$

6. The bridge is balanced when
   $R_W + R_{RTD} = 560 \ \Omega + R_W$
   $R_{RTD} = 560 \ \Omega + R_W - R_W = 560 \ \Omega - 0 \ \Omega = \mathbf{560} \ \mathbf{\Omega}$

7. The results of problems 5 and 6 differ because in the three-wire circuit (text Figure 21-47), R_W has been added to both the RTD and the 560 Ω arms of the bridge which cancels the effect of R_W. In the two-wire circuit (text Figure 21-46), $2R_W$ appears only in the RTD arm of the bridge.

8. At the point in the bridge between R_1 and R_2:

$$V_{1\text{-}2} = \left(\frac{R_2}{R_1 + R_2}\right)(+15\text{ V}) = \left(\frac{10\text{ k}\Omega}{10\text{ k}\Omega + 10\text{ k}\Omega}\right)(+15\text{ V}) = +7.50\text{ V}$$

At a point in the bridge between R_3 and the RTD:

$$V_{3\text{-RTD}} = \left(\frac{R_{RTD}}{R_{RTD} + R_{32}}\right)(+15\text{ V}) = \left(\frac{697\,\Omega}{697\,\Omega + 750\,\Omega}\right)(+15\text{ V}) = +7.23\text{ V}$$

The bridge voltage applied to the inputs (across pins 1 and 3) of the amplifier is:

$V_{in} = V_{1\text{-}2} - V_{3\text{-RTD}} = 7.500\text{ V} - 7.225\text{ V} = 0.275\text{ V}$

The amplifier gain is:

$$A_v = \frac{50.5\text{ k}\Omega}{12\text{ k}\Omega} + 1 = 5.21$$

The amplifier output voltage is

$V_{out} = A_v V_{in} = (5.21)(0.275\text{ V}) = \mathbf{1.43\text{ V}}$

SECTION 21-2 Strain, Pressure, and Flow Rate Measurements

9. $\Delta R = (GF)(R)(\varepsilon) = (2.5)(600\,\Omega)(3 \times 10^6) = \mathbf{4.5\text{ m}\Omega}$

10. A strain gauge can be used to measure pressure by mounting it on a flexible diaphragm. As the diaphragm distends from increasing pressure, the strain gauge detects it.

11. The symbol in Figure 21-1(a) represents an absolute pressure transducer, which measures pressure relative to a vacuum.
    The symbol in Figure 21-1(b) represents a gauge pressure transducer, which measures pressure relative to ambient pressure.
    The symbol in Figure 21-1(c) represents a differential pressure transducer, which measures pressure relative to the other input.

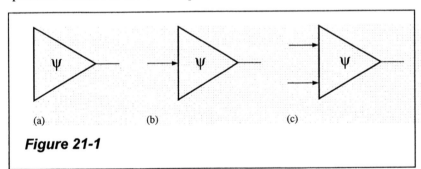

(a)   (b)   (c)

Figure 21-1

12.   See Figure 21-2.

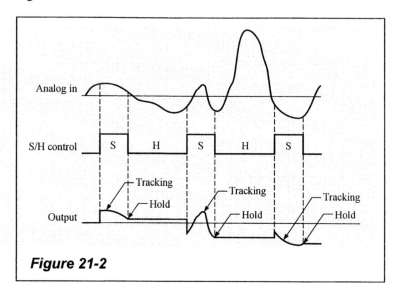

Figure 21-2

13.   See Figure 21-3.

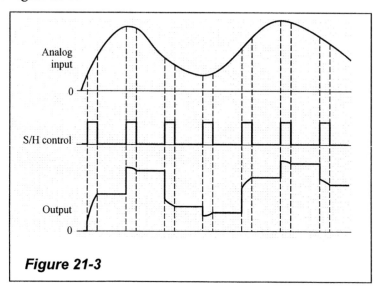

Figure 21-3

14. An SCR can be triggered into forward conduction by a pulse on the gate terminal if the anode is positive with respect to the cathode. An SCR can also be triggered into forward conduction if the forward voltage exceeds the forward breakover-voltage.

15. See Figure 21-4.

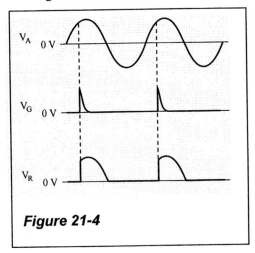

Figure 21-4

16. The output of the comparator is a square wave that is "in-phase" with the input sine wave with a peak voltage of approximately ±9 V. The output of the circuit is a series of positive triggers that rise from 0 V to 9 V, then decay in about 2 ms (measured on the 741 although the calculated is less). The positive triggers correspond to the rising edge of the sine wave.

17. Reverse the comparator inputs.

PART TWO

Solutions to Application Assignments

Step 1. The Circuit

Circuit (c) in Figure 2-59 is the only circuit that meets the requirements. See Figure AA-1. In circuit (a), all lamps are on when the switch is closed. In circuit (b), all lamps are on when the switch is closed. In circuit (d), to turn on a given lamp, the rotary switch may have to be moved through other positions thus turning on other lamps momentarily.

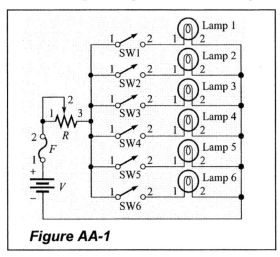

Figure AA-1

Purpose of each component in the circuit:

Battery — Supplies voltage and current to light the selected lamp.

Fuse — Protects the circuit from excessive current.

Rheostat — Controls the amount of current and thus the brightness of the selected lamp.

Switches — Each switch, when closed, allows current through the selected lamp. For only one lamp to be on, all switches except one must be open.

Lamp — Produces light when current is through the filament.

Step 2. Connecting the Circuit

The components required are: 1 battery, 1 fuse, 1 rheostat, and 6 SPST switches, and 6 lamps. The point-to-point connection list is as follows (See Figure AA-1 for labeling):

From	To	From	To
V+	F-1	SW4-2	Lamp 4-1
F-2	R-1	SW5-2	Lamp 5-1
R-1	R-2	SW6-2	Lamp 6-1
R-3	SW1-1	Lamp 1-2	Lamp 2-2
SW1-1	SW2-1	Lamp 2-2	Lamp 3-2
SW2-1	SW3-1	Lamp 3-2	Lamp 4-2
SW3-1	SW4-1	Lamp 4-2	Lamp 5-2
SW4-1	SW5-1	Lamp 5-2	Lamp 6-2
SW5-1	SW6-1	Lamp 6-2	V-
SW1-2	Lamp 1-1		
SW2-2	Lamp 2-1		
SW3-2	Lamp 3-1		

Step 3. Determining the Current Rating of the Fuse

Only one lamp is on at a time, so the maximum current is approximately 5 A. Use a 6 A fuse to allow the current to exceed 5 A by only 1 A. The use of a 5 A fuse is too marginal.

Step 4. Determining the Capacity of the Battery

The battery must supply 5 A for 4 hours:

$$\text{Minimum ampere-hour rating} = (5\ A)(4\ h) = \textbf{20 Ah}$$

Step 5. Troubleshooting the Circuit

Test procedure:
1. Set all six switches to the off position (open).
2. Observe that all lamps are off.
3. Set the rheostat to minimum resistance.
4. Turn switch 1 on and observe that lamp 1 is illuminated. Adjust rheostat to its maximum resistance and observe that lamp 1 dims.
5. Repeat step 4 and step 5 for the remaining five switches and lamps.

Symptoms and probable causes:
1. Each lamp can be turned on except one: **Bulb is burned out or the switch is faulty.**
2. None of the lamps can be turned on: **The fuse is open or the battery is dead.**
3. Each lamp is too dim and cannot be brightened by adjusting the rheostat: **The rheostat is faulty**.
4. Each lamp is too dim, however, the brightness can be varied with the rheostat: **The battery voltage is low**.

Step 1. Inspecting the Existing Resistance Box

No results required.

Step 2. Drawing the Schematic

See Figure AA-2.

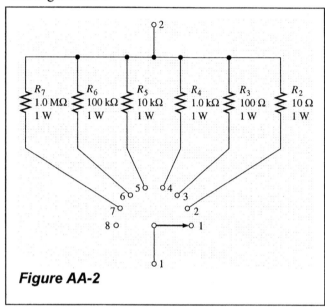

Figure AA-2

Step 3. Modifying the Schematic for the New Requirements

See Figure AA-3.

Calculations for the new current-limiting resistors R_1 and R_8:

$$R_1 = \frac{4\ V}{10\ mA} = 400\ \Omega \quad \text{Use nearest standard value of } \textbf{390 } \boldsymbol{\Omega}.$$

$$R_8 = \frac{4\ V}{5\ mA} = 800\ \Omega \quad \text{Use nearest standard value of } \textbf{820 } \boldsymbol{\Omega}.$$

Calculations of power for each resistor:

$$P_1 = \frac{(4\ V)^2}{390\ \Omega} = \textbf{41 mW}$$

$$P_2 = \frac{(4\ V)^2}{10\ \Omega} = \textbf{1.6 W}$$

$$P_3 = \frac{(4\ V)^2}{100\ \Omega} = \textbf{160 mW}$$

$$P_4 = \frac{(4\ V)^2}{1.0\ k\Omega} = \textbf{16 mW}$$

$$P_5 = \frac{(4\ V)^2}{10\ k\Omega} = \textbf{1.6 mW}$$

$$P_6 = \frac{(4\,V)^2}{100\,k\Omega} = \textbf{160 }\boldsymbol{\mu}\textbf{W}$$

$$P_7 = \frac{(4\,V)^2}{1.0\,M\Omega} = \textbf{16 }\boldsymbol{\mu}\textbf{W}$$

$$P_8 = \frac{(4\,V)^2}{820\,\Omega} = \textbf{19.5 mW}$$

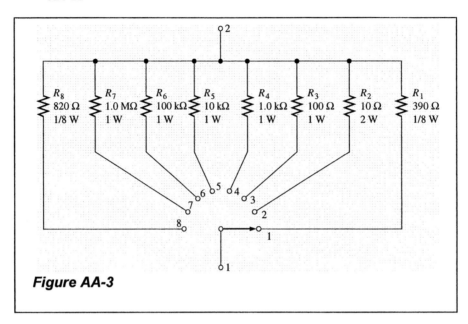

Figure AA-3

Step 4. Modifying the Circuit

1. R_2: The power rating must be increased to 2 W to handle the 1.6 W dissipation.
2. R_3 through R_7: The existing resistors have the correct resistance and the power ratings are more than adequate.
3. Add $R_1 = 390\ \Omega$ and $R_8 = 820\ \Omega$. 1/8 W ratings are more than adequate.
4. Label the leftmost switch position as viewed from the top of the box, *10 mA*. Label the rightmost switch position *5 mA*.

Step 5. Developing a Test Procedure
1. Connect an ohmmeter from terminal 1 to terminal 2.
2. Check the resistance value for each switch position as follows:

SW Position	Resistance	
$2 - R_2$	10 Ω	1
$3 - R_3$	100 Ω	
$4 - R_4$	1.0 kΩ	
$5 - R_5$	10 kΩ	
$6 - R_6$	100 kΩ	
$7 - R_7$	1.0 MΩ	8

3. Disconnect the ohmmeter and connect a 4 V dc source and a series ammeter from terminal 1 to terminal 2.
4. Place the switch in the *10 mA* position and read 10 mA on the ammeter.
5. Place the switch in the *5 mA* position and read 5 mA on the ammeter.

Step 6. Troubleshooting the Circuit

1. The ohmmeter shows an infinitely high resistance when the switch is in position 3: **Resistor R_3 open or a connection to the resistor is open.**
2. The ohmmeter shows an infinitely high resistance in all switch positions: **A connection to terminal 1 or terminal 2 on the box is open.**
3. The ohmmeter shows an incorrect value of resistance when the switch is in position 6: **Resistor R_6 has the wrong value.**

Step 1. Drawing the Schematic
See Figure AA-4.

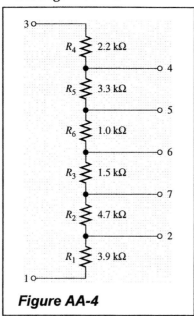

Figure AA-4

Step 2. Determining the Voltages
The total resistance:
$R_T = R_1 + R_2 + R_3 + R_4 + R_5 + R_6$
$= 3.9 \text{ k}\Omega + 4.7 \text{ k}\Omega + 1.5 \text{ k}\Omega + 1.0 \text{ k}\Omega + 3.3 \text{ k}\Omega + 2.2 \text{ k}\Omega = 16.6 \text{ k}\Omega$

Calculations of output voltages:

$$V_2 = \left(\frac{R_1}{R_T} \right) V_S = \left(\frac{3.9 \text{ k}\Omega}{16.6 \text{ k}\Omega} \right) 12 \text{ V} = \mathbf{2.82 \text{ V}}$$

$$V_7 = \left(\frac{R_1 + R_2}{R_T} \right) V_S = \left(\frac{8.6 \text{ k}\Omega}{16.6 \text{ k}\Omega} \right) 12 \text{ V} = \mathbf{6.22 \text{ V}}$$

$$V_6 = \left(\frac{R_1 + R_2 + R_3}{R_T} \right) V_S = \left(\frac{10.1 \text{ k}\Omega}{16.6 \text{ k}\Omega} \right) 12 \text{ V} = \mathbf{7.30 \text{ V}}$$

$$V_5 = \left(\frac{R_1 + R_2 + R_3 + R_6}{R_T} \right) V_S = \left(\frac{11.1 \text{ k}\Omega}{16.6 \text{ k}\Omega} \right) 12 \text{ V} = \mathbf{8.02 \text{ V}}$$

$$V_4 = \left(\frac{R_1 + R_2 + R_3 + R_6 + R_5}{R_T} \right) V_S = \left(\frac{14.4 \text{ k}\Omega}{16.6 \text{ k}\Omega} \right) 12 \text{ V} = \mathbf{10.4 \text{ V}}$$

All voltages are within 5% of specified values.

Step 3. Modifying the Existing Circuit (if necessary)

Since the output voltages of the existing circuit meet the specifications, no resistor value changes are required.

The maximum power occurs in R_2.

$$I = \frac{12\ V}{R_T} = \frac{12\ V}{16.6\ k\Omega} = 723\ \mu A$$

$P_{max} = I^2 R_2 = (723\ \mu A)^2\ 4.7\ k\Omega = \mathbf{2.46\ mW}$

The 1/4 W rating of each resistor is more than adequate.

Step 4. Determining the Life of the Battery

$(723\ \mu A)(h) = 6.5\ Ah$

$$h = \frac{6.5\ Ah}{723\ \mu A} = 8990\ h$$

$$\text{Number of days} = \frac{8990\ h}{24\ h/day} = \mathbf{374.6\ days}$$

Step 5. Developing a Test Procedure

Equipment: A 12 V dc source and a voltmeter.

1. Connect the positive terminal of the 12 V source to pin 3 of the circuit board. Connect the negative terminal of the source to pin 1 of the circuit board.
2. Measure the voltage at each of the pins as follows:

    Pin 1: 0 V

    Pin 2: 2.8 V $\pm$ 5%

    Pin 3: 12 V

    Pin 4: 10.4 V $\pm$ 5%

    Pin 5: 8.0 V $\pm$ 5%

    Pin 6: 7.3 V $\pm$ 5%

    Pin 7: 6.2 V $\pm$ 5%

Step 6. Troubleshooting the Circuit

1. No voltage at any of the pins on the circuit board: **The battery is dead or the connection from the battery to pin 3 is open.**
2. 12 V at pins 3 and 4. All other pins have 0 V: **Resistor R_5 is open.**
3. 12 V at all pins except 0 V at pin 1: **Resistor R_1 is open.**
4. 12 V at pin 6 and 0 V at pin 7: **Resistor R_3 is open.**
5. 3.3 V at pin 2: **The battery voltage is too high (14.3 V instead of 12 V) or resistors R_1 and R_2 are reversed ($R_1 = 4.7\ k\Omega$ and $R_2 = 3.9\ k\Omega$). This is shown by the following calculation:**

$$V_2 = \left(\frac{4.7\ k\Omega}{16.6\ k\Omega} \right) 12\ V = 3.4\ V$$

▪ **Determine the maximum power dissipated by R_{SH} in Figure 5-55 for each range setting.**

For the 25 mA range, no power is dissipated because there is no current in R_{SH}.
For the 250 mA range, the maximum current in R_{SH} is 225 mA and the voltage is 150 mV.

$$P = IV = (225 \text{ mA})(150 \text{ mV}) = 33.8 \text{ mW}$$

For the 2.5 A range, the maximum current in R_{SH} is 2.475 A and the voltage across it is 150 mV.

$$P = IV = (2.475 \text{ mA})(150 \text{ mV}) = 371 \text{ mW}$$

▪ **How much voltage is there from A to B in Figure 5-55 when the switch is set to the 2.5 A range and the current is 1 A?**

In the 2.5 A range the fraction of the total current in the meter is 25 mA/2.5 A = 1%. The meter current is thus 1% of 1 A = 10 mA, which is in both R_1 and the meter. The meter resistance is 6 Ω and the resistance of R_1 is 60.4 Ω. The voltage from A to B is

$$V_{AB} = I(R_1 + R_M) = (10 \text{ mA})(66.4 \text{ Ω}) = 66.4 \text{ mV}$$

▪ **The meter indicates 250 mA. How much does the voltage across the meter circuit from A to B change when the switch is moved from the 250 mA position to the 2.5 A position?**

In the 250 mA position, the voltage between A and B is 150 mV, as given previously. In the 2.5 A position, the actual current in the meter is 1% of the input current. Thus, when the input current is 250 mA, the meter current is 2.5 mA. In this case,

$$V_{AB} = I(R_M) = (2.5 \text{ mA})(6 \text{ Ω}) = 15 \text{ mV}$$

The change is 150 mV − 15 mV = 135 mV.

▪ **Assume the meter movement has a resistance of 4 Ω instead of 6 Ω. Specify any changes necessary in the circuit of Figure 5-55.**

The meter will drop 100 mV at maximum current for any switch position.

$$R_{SH} = \frac{100 \text{ mV}}{225 \text{ mA}} = 444 \text{ mΩ} \quad (2/3 \text{ of its former value})$$
$$V_{AB} = (2.475)(444 \text{ mΩ}) = 1.1 \text{ V}$$

The voltage across R_1 is

$$V_{R1} = 1.1 \text{ V} - 100 \text{ mV} = 1.0 \text{ V}$$
$$R_1 = \frac{1.0 \text{ V}}{25 \text{ mA}} = 40 \text{ Ω}$$

Step 1. The Schematic

See Figure AA-5.

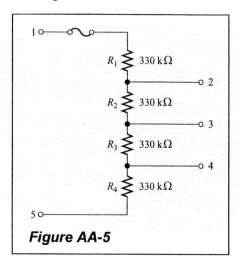

Figure AA-5

Step 2. Connecting the 12 V Power Supply

Connect the positive terminal of the power supply to pin 1 on the voltage divider board and the negative terminal to pin 5.

Step 3. Determining the Unloaded Output Voltages

$R_T = 4(330 \text{ k}\Omega) = 1.32 \text{ M}\Omega$

$$V_{OUT(2)} = \left(\frac{R_2 + R_3 + R_4}{R_T} \right) V_S = \left(\frac{990 \text{ k}\Omega}{1.32 \text{ M}\Omega} \right) 12 \text{ V} = \mathbf{9 \text{ V}}$$

$$V_{OUT(3)} = \left(\frac{R_3 + R_4}{R_T} \right) V_S = \left(\frac{660 \text{ k}\Omega}{1.32 \text{ M}\Omega} \right) 12 \text{ V} = \mathbf{6 \text{ V}}$$

$$V_{OUT(4)} = \left(\frac{R_4}{R_T} \right) V_S = \left(\frac{330 \text{ k}\Omega}{1.32 \text{ M}\Omega} \right) 12 \text{ V} = \mathbf{3 \text{ V}}$$

Step 4. Determining the Loaded Output Voltages

1. A 10 MΩ load resistor connected from pin 2 to ground:

$(R_2 + R_3 + R_4) \| R_L = 990 \text{ k}\Omega \| 10 \text{ M}\Omega = 901 \text{ k}\Omega$

$$V_{OUT(2)} = \left(\frac{(R_2 + R_3 + R_4) \| R_L}{R_1 + (R_2 + R_3 + R_4) \| R_L} \right) V_S = \left(\frac{901 \text{ k}\Omega}{1.23 \text{ M}\Omega} \right) 12 \text{ V} = \mathbf{8.79 \text{ V}}$$

$$V_{OUT(3)} = \left(\frac{R_3 + R_4}{R_2 + R_3 + R_4} \right) V_{OUT(2)} = \left(\frac{660 \text{ k}\Omega}{990 \text{ k}\Omega} \right) 8.79 \text{ V} = \mathbf{5.86 \text{ V}}$$

$$V_{\text{OUT}(4)} = \left(\frac{R_4}{R_3 + R_4}\right)V_{\text{OUT}(3)} = \left(\frac{330 \text{ k}\Omega}{660 \text{ k}\Omega}\right)5.86 \text{ V} = \textbf{2.93 V}$$

2. A 10 MΩ load resistor connected from pin 3 to ground:

$(R_3 + R_4) \parallel R_L = 660 \text{ k}\Omega \parallel 10 \text{ M}\Omega = 619 \text{ k}\Omega$

$$V_{\text{OUT}(2)} = \left(\frac{R_2 + (R_3 + R_4) \parallel R_L}{R_1 + R_2 + (R_3 + R_4) \parallel R_L}\right)V_S = \left(\frac{949 \text{ k}\Omega}{1.279 \text{ M}\Omega}\right)12 \text{ V} = \textbf{8.90 V}$$

$$V_{\text{OUT}(3)} = \left(\frac{(R_3 + R_4) \parallel R_L}{R_2 + (R_3 + R_4) \parallel R_L}\right)V_{\text{OUT}(2)} = \left(\frac{619 \text{ k}\Omega}{949 \text{ k}\Omega}\right)8.90 \text{ V} = \textbf{5.81 V}$$

$$V_{\text{OUT}(4)} = \left(\frac{R_4}{R_3 + R_4}\right)V_{\text{OUT}(3)} = \left(\frac{330 \text{ k}\Omega}{660 \text{ k}\Omega}\right)5.81 \text{ V} = \textbf{2.91 V}$$

3. A 10 MΩ load resistor connected from pin 4 to ground:

$R_4 \parallel R_L = 330 \text{ k}\Omega \parallel 10 \text{ M}\Omega = 319 \text{ k}\Omega$

$$V_{\text{OUT}(2)} = \left(\frac{R_2 + R_3 + R_4 \parallel R_L}{R_1 + R_2 + R_3 + R_4 \parallel R_L}\right)V_S = \left(\frac{979 \text{ k}\Omega}{1.31 \text{ M}\Omega}\right)12 \text{ V} = \textbf{8.98 V}$$

$$V_{\text{OUT}(3)} = \left(\frac{R_3 + R_4 \parallel R_L}{R_2 + R_3 + R_4 \parallel R_L}\right)V_{\text{OUT}(2)} = \left(\frac{649 \text{ k}\Omega}{979 \text{ k}\Omega}\right)8.98 \text{ V} = \textbf{5.95 V}$$

$$V_{\text{OUT}(4)} = \left(\frac{R_4 \parallel R_L}{R_3 + R_4 \parallel R_L}\right)V_{\text{OUT}(3)} = \left(\frac{319 \text{ k}\Omega}{649 \text{ k}\Omega}\right)5.95 \text{ V} = \textbf{2.93 V}$$

4. 10 MΩ load resistors connected from pin 2 and pin 3 to ground:

$(R_3 + R_4) \parallel R_{L3} = 660 \text{ k}\Omega \parallel 10 \text{ M}\Omega = 619 \text{ k}\Omega$

$(R_2 + (R_3 + R_4) \parallel R_{L3}) \parallel R_{L2} = 949 \text{ k}\Omega \parallel 10 \text{ M}\Omega = 867 \text{ k}\Omega$

$$V_{\text{OUT}(2)} = \left(\frac{(R_2 + (R_3 + R_4) \parallel R_{L3}) \parallel R_{L2}}{R_1 + (R_2 + (R_3 + R_4) \parallel R_{L3}) \parallel R_{L2}}\right)V_S = \left(\frac{867 \text{ k}\Omega}{1.197 \text{ M}\Omega}\right)12 \text{ V} = \textbf{8.69 V}$$

$$V_{\text{OUT}(3)} = \left(\frac{(R_3 + R_4) \parallel R_{L3}}{R_2 + (R_3 + R_4) \parallel R_{L3}}\right)V_{\text{OUT}(2)} = \left(\frac{619 \text{ k}\Omega}{949 \text{ k}\Omega}\right)8.69 \text{ V} = \textbf{5.67 V}$$

$$V_{\text{OUT}(4)} = \left(\frac{R_4}{R_3 + R_4}\right)V_{\text{OUT}(3)} = \left(\frac{330 \text{ k}\Omega}{660 \text{ k}\Omega}\right)5.67 \text{ V} = \textbf{2.84 V}$$

5. 10 MΩ load resistors connected from pin 2 and pin 4 to ground:

$R_4 \parallel R_{L4} = 330 \text{ k}\Omega \parallel 10 \text{ M}\Omega = 319 \text{ k}\Omega$

$(R_2 + R_3 + R_4 \parallel R_{L4}) \parallel R_{L2} = 979 \text{ k}\Omega \parallel 10 \text{ M}\Omega = 892 \text{ k}\Omega$

$$V_{\text{OUT}(2)} = \left(\frac{(R_2 + R_3 + R_4 \parallel R_{L4}) \parallel R_{L2}}{R_1 + (R_2 + R_3 + R_4 \parallel R_{L4}) \parallel R_{L2}}\right)V_S = \left(\frac{892 \text{ k}\Omega}{1.222 \text{ M}\Omega}\right)12 \text{ V} = \textbf{8.76 V}$$

$$V_{\text{OUT}(3)} = \left(\frac{R_3 + R_4 \parallel R_{L4}}{R_2 + R_3 + R_4 \parallel R_{L4}}\right)V_{\text{OUT}(2)} = \left(\frac{649 \text{ k}\Omega}{979 \text{ k}\Omega}\right)8.76 \text{ V} = \textbf{5.81 V}$$

$$V_{OUT(4)} = \left(\frac{R_4 \parallel R_{L4}}{R_3 + R_4 \parallel R_{L4}} \right) V_{OUT(3)} = \left(\frac{319 \text{ k}\Omega}{649 \text{ k}\Omega} \right) 5.81 \text{ V} = \textbf{2.86 V}$$

6.   10 MΩ load resistors connected from pin 3 and pin 4 to ground:

$R_4 \parallel R_{L4} = 330 \text{ k}\Omega \parallel 10 \text{ M}\Omega = 319 \text{ k}\Omega$

$(R_3 + R_4 \parallel R_{L4}) \parallel R_{L3} = 649 \text{ k}\Omega \parallel 10 \text{ M}\Omega = 609 \text{ k}\Omega$

$$V_{OUT(2)} = \left(\frac{R_2 + (R_3 + R_4 \parallel R_{L4}) \parallel R_{L3}}{R_1 + R_2 + (R_3 + R_4 \parallel R_{L4}) \parallel R_{L3}} \right) V_S = \left(\frac{939 \text{ k}\Omega}{1.269 \text{ M}\Omega} \right) 12 \text{ V} = \textbf{8.88 V}$$

$$V_{OUT(3)} = \left(\frac{(R_3 + R_4 \parallel R_{L4}) \parallel R_{L3}}{R_2 + (R_3 + R_4 \parallel R_{L4}) \parallel R_{L3}} \right) V_{OUT(2)} = \left(\frac{609 \text{ k}\Omega}{939 \text{ k}\Omega} \right) 8.88 \text{ V} = \textbf{5.76 V}$$

$$V_{OUT(4)} = \left(\frac{R_4 \parallel R_{L4}}{R_3 + R_4 \parallel R_{L4}} \right) V_{OUT(3)} = \left(\frac{319 \text{ k}\Omega}{649 \text{ k}\Omega} \right) 5.76 \text{ V} = \textbf{2.83 V}$$

7.   10 MΩ load resistors connected from pin 2, pin 3, and pin 4 to ground:

$R_4 \parallel R_{L4} = 330 \text{ k}\Omega \parallel 10 \text{ M}\Omega = 319 \text{ k}\Omega$

$(R_3 + R_4 \parallel R_{L4}) \parallel R_{L3} = 649 \text{ k}\Omega \parallel 10 \text{ M}\Omega = 609 \text{ k}\Omega$

$(R_2 + (R_3 + R_4 \parallel R_{L4}) \parallel R_{L3}) \parallel R_{L2} = 939 \text{ k}\Omega \parallel 10 \text{ M}\Omega = 858 \text{ k}\Omega$

$$V_{OUT(2)} = \left(\frac{\left(R_2 + (R_3 + R_4 \parallel R_{L4}) \parallel R_{L3}\right) \parallel R_{L2}}{R_1 + \left(R_2 + (R_3 + R_4 \parallel R_{L4}) \parallel R_{L3}\right) \parallel R_{L2}} \right) V_S = \left(\frac{858 \text{ k}\Omega}{1.188 \text{ M}\Omega} \right) 12 \text{ V} = \textbf{8.67 V}$$

$$V_{OUT(3)} = \left(\frac{(R_3 + R_4 \parallel R_{L4}) \parallel R_{L3}}{R_2 + (R_3 + R_4 \parallel R_{L4}) \parallel R_{L3}} \right) V_{OUT(2)} = \left(\frac{609 \text{ k}\Omega}{939 \text{ k}\Omega} \right) 8.67 \text{ V} = \textbf{5.62 V}$$

$$V_{OUT(4)} = \left(\frac{R_4 \parallel R_{L4}}{R_3 + R_4 \parallel R_{L4}} \right) V_{OUT(3)} = \left(\frac{319 \text{ k}\Omega}{649 \text{ k}\Omega} \right) 5.62 \text{ V} = \textbf{2.76 V}$$

Step 5. Determining the Percent Deviation of the Output Voltages

1.   A 10 MΩ load resistor connected from pin 2 to ground.

$$\% \text{ deviation} = \left(\frac{9 \text{ V} - 8.79 \text{ V}}{9 \text{ V}} \right) 100\% = \textbf{2.33\%}$$

2.   A 10 MΩ load resistor connected from pin 3 to ground.

$$\% \text{ deviation} = \left(\frac{6 \text{ V} - 5.81 \text{ V}}{6 \text{ V}} \right) 100\% = \textbf{3.17\%}$$

3.   A 10 MΩ load resistor connected from pin 4 to ground.

$$\% \text{ deviation} = \left(\frac{3 \text{ V} - 2.93 \text{ V}}{3 \text{ V}} \right) 100\% = \textbf{2.33\%}$$

4.   10 MΩ load resistors connected from pin 2 and pin 3 to ground.

$$\% \text{ deviation(2)} = \left(\frac{9 \text{ V} - 8.69 \text{ V}}{9 \text{ V}} \right) 100\% = \textbf{3.44\%}$$

$$\% \text{ deviation(3)} = \left(\frac{6 \text{ V} - 5.67 \text{ V}}{6 \text{ V}} \right) 100\% = \textbf{5.50\%}$$

5. 10 MΩ load resistors connected from pin 2 and pin 4 to ground.

$$\% \text{ deviation}(2) = \left(\frac{9\,V - 8.76\,V}{9\,V}\right)100\% = \mathbf{2.67\%}$$

$$\% \text{ deviation}(4) = \left(\frac{3\,V - 2.86\,V}{3\,V}\right)100\% = \mathbf{4.67\%}$$

6. 10 MΩ load resistors connected from pin 3 and pin 4 to ground.

$$\% \text{ deviation}(3) = \left(\frac{6\,V - 5.76\,V}{6\,V}\right)100\% = \mathbf{4.00\%}$$

$$\% \text{ deviation}(4) = \left(\frac{3\,V - 2.83\,V}{3\,V}\right)100\% = \mathbf{5.67\%}$$

7. 10 MΩ load resistors connected from pin 2, 3, and pin 4 to ground.

$$\% \text{ deviation}(2) = \left(\frac{9\,V - 8.67\,V}{9\,V}\right)100\% = \mathbf{3.67\%}$$

$$\% \text{ deviation}(3) = \left(\frac{6\,V - 5.62\,V}{6\,V}\right)100\% = \mathbf{6.33\%}$$

$$\% \text{ deviation}(4) = \left(\frac{3\,V - 2.76\,V}{3\,V}\right)100\% = \mathbf{8.00\%}$$

Step 6. Determining the Load Currents

1. $I_{\text{LOAD}(2)} = \dfrac{V_{\text{OUT}(2)}}{R_{L2}} = \dfrac{8.79\,V}{10\,M\Omega} = \mathbf{879\ nA}$

2. $I_{\text{LOAD}(3)} = \dfrac{V_{\text{OUT}(3)}}{R_{L3}} = \dfrac{5.81\,V}{10\,M\Omega} = \mathbf{581\ nA}$

3. $I_{\text{LOAD}(4)} = \dfrac{V_{\text{OUT}(4)}}{R_{L4}} = \dfrac{2.93\,V}{10\,M\Omega} = \mathbf{293\ nA}$

4. $I_{\text{LOAD}(2)} = \dfrac{V_{\text{OUT}(2)}}{R_{L2}} = \dfrac{8.69\,V}{10\,M\Omega} = \mathbf{869\ nA}$

   $I_{\text{LOAD}(3)} = \dfrac{V_{\text{OUT}(3)}}{R_{L3}} = \dfrac{5.67\,V}{10\,M\Omega} = \mathbf{567\ nA}$

5. $I_{\text{LOAD}(2)} = \dfrac{V_{\text{OUT}(2)}}{R_{L2}} = \dfrac{8.76\,V}{10\,M\Omega} = \mathbf{876\ nA}$

   $I_{\text{LOAD}(4)} = \dfrac{V_{\text{OUT}(4)}}{R_{L4}} = \dfrac{2.86\,V}{10\,M\Omega} = \mathbf{286\ nA}$

6. $I_{\text{LOAD}(3)} = \dfrac{V_{\text{OUT}(3)}}{R_{L3}} = \dfrac{5.76\,V}{10\,M\Omega} = \mathbf{576\ nA}$

   $I_{\text{LOAD}(4)} = \dfrac{V_{\text{OUT}(4)}}{R_{L4}} = \dfrac{2.83\,V}{10\,M\Omega} = \mathbf{283\ nA}$

7. $I_{\text{LOAD}(2)} = \dfrac{V_{\text{OUT}(2)}}{R_{L2}} = \dfrac{8.67\,V}{10\,M\Omega} = \mathbf{867\ nA}$

$$I_{\text{LOAD}(3)} = \frac{V_{\text{OUT}(3)}}{R_{L3}} = \frac{5.62 \text{ V}}{10 \text{ M}\Omega} = \textbf{562 nA}$$

$$I_{\text{LOAD}(4)} = \frac{V_{\text{OUT}(4)}}{R_{L4}} = \frac{2.76 \text{ V}}{10 \text{ M}\Omega} = \textbf{276 nA}$$

The maximum current occurs when all loads are connected.

$R_T = 1.188 \text{ M}\Omega$

$$I_T = \frac{12 \text{ V}}{1.188 \text{ M}\Omega} = 10.1 \text{ }\mu\text{A}$$

Fuses in the µA range are generally not available. The approach for this circuit is to use a standard fuse with the smallest available rating (0.25 A or 0.5 A) to protect against a catastrophic short circuit condition.

Step 7. Troubleshooting the Circuit Board

Case 1: **No supply voltage**
Case 2: **Fuse open**
Case 3: R_1 **open**
Case 4: R_2 **open**
Case 5: R_3 **open**
Case 6: R_4 **open**
Case 7: **Pin 3 shorted to ground**
Case 8: **Pin 4 shorted to ground**

Step 1. Connecting the System

The system is connected according to the following point-to-point wiring list with reference to the components in Figure 7-43.

From	*To*
Battery-**I**	Relay Bd.-**C**
Relay Bd.-**C**	Relay Bd.-**E**
Relay Bd.-**E**	Mag. Sw.-**M**
Mag. Sw.-**M**	Mag. Sw.-**O**
Mag. Sw.-**O**	Mag. Sw.-**Q**
Battery-**J**	Tog. Sw.-**U**
Tog. Sw.-**U**	Siren-**S**
Siren-**T**	Relay Bd.-**D**
Relay Bd.-**A**	Relay Bd.-**F**
Relay Bd.-**F**	Mag. Sw.-**N**
Mag. Sw.-**N**	Mag. Sw.-**P**
Mag. Sw.-**P**	Mag. Sw.-**R**
Relay Bd.-**B**	Tog. Sw.-**V**
Relay Bd.-**G**	Wall Sw.-**K**
Relay Bd.-**H**	Wall Sw.-**L**

Step 2. Testing the System

A test procedure is as follows:

1. Turn the system ON/OFF switch to the ON position.
2. Turn the wall switch off.
3. Close the first magnetic switch to simulate the opening of a window or door.
4. Verify that the alarm and the house lights are on.
5. Turn the system ON/OFF switch to the OFF position.
6. Repeat procedures 1 through 5 for each remaining magnetic switch.

Step 1. Familiarization with the Function Generator
No results required.

Step 2. Measuring the Sinusoidal Output

Minimum values from the scope display (Figure 8-70(a)):
V_p = 3 div × 10 mV/div = **30 mV**
V_{rms} = 0.707V_p = 0.707(30 mV) = **21.2 mV**
T = 10 div × 0.1 s/div = **1 s**
$f = \dfrac{1}{T} = \dfrac{1}{1\,\text{s}}$ = **1 Hz**

Minimum frequency setting on the function generator:
Frequency range switches: **Set to 1 Hz**
Frequency adjustment control: **Set to 0.2**
The frequency should be: f = **1 Hz × 0.2 = 0.2 Hz**

Maximum values from the scope display (Figure 8-70(b)):
V_p = 2.2 div × 10 V/div = **22 V**
V_{rms} = 0.707V_p = 0.707(22 V) = **15.6 V**
T = 8 div × 0.1 μs/div = **0.8 μs**
$f = \dfrac{1}{T} = \dfrac{1}{0.8\,\mu\text{s}}$ = **1.25 MHz**

Maximum frequency setting on the function generator:
Frequency range switches: **Set to 1 MHz**
Frequency adjustment control: **Set to 2.0**
The frequency should be: f = **1 MHz × 2.0 = 2 MHz**

Conclusion: There is a problem with the function generator in terms of the disagreement between the frequency settings and the actual output frequency.

Step 3. Measuring the DC Offset

Maximum positive dc offset (Figure 8-71(a)):
2 div × 2 V/div = **4 V**
Maximum negative dc offset (Figure 8-71(b)):
1 div × (–2 V/div) = **–2 V**

Step 4. Measuring the Triangular Output

Minimum values from the scope display (Figure 8-72(a)):

$V_p = 3$ div $\times$ 20 mV/div = **60 mV**

$T/2 = 6$ div $\times$ 0.1 s/div = 0.6 s

$T = $ **1.2 s**

$$f = \frac{1}{T} = \frac{1}{1.2\text{ s}} = \textbf{0.833 Hz}$$

Maximum values from the scope display (Figure 8-72(b)):

$V_p = 2.5$ div $\times$ 10 V/div = **25 V**

$T = 10$ div $\times$ 0.1 μs/div = **1 μs**

$$f = \frac{1}{T} = \frac{1}{1\text{ μs}} = \textbf{1 MHz}$$

Step 5. Measuring the Pulse Output

Minimum values from the scope display (Figure 8-73(a)):

$V_p = 2.2$ div $\times$ 10 mV/div = **22 mV**

$T = 8$ div $\times$ 0.1 s/div = **0.8 s**

$$f = \frac{1}{T} = \frac{1}{0.8\text{ s}} = \textbf{1.25 Hz}$$

$$t_W = \left(\frac{3}{5}\right)\text{DIV} \times 0.1\text{ s} = 0.06\text{ s}$$

$$\% \text{ duty cycle} = \left(\frac{t_W}{T}\right)100\% = \left(\frac{0.06\text{ s}}{0.8\text{ s}}\right)100\% = \textbf{7.5\%}$$

Maximum values from the scope display (Figure 8-73(b)):

$V_p = 3$ div $\times$ 5 V/div = **15 V**

$T = 6$ div $\times$ 0.1 μs/div = **0.6 μs**

$$f = \frac{1}{T} = \frac{1}{0.6\text{ μs}} = \textbf{1.67 MHz}$$

$$\% \text{ duty cycle} = \left(\frac{t_W}{T}\right)100\% = \left(\frac{0.3\text{ μs}}{0.6\text{ μs}}\right)100\% = \textbf{50\%}$$

Step 1. Comparing the Printed Circuit Board with the Schematic
The circuit board and schematic in Figure 9-56 agree.

Step 2. Testing the Input to Board 1

Oscilloscope measurements (Figure 9-57):
$V_{DC} = 5.1$ div $\times$ 1 V/div = **5.1 V**
$V_{pp} = 2.8$ div $\times$ 1 V/div = **2.8 V**
$V_{rms} = 0.707V_p = 0.707(1.4$ V$) \cong$ **1 V**
$T = 2$ div $\times$ 0.1 ms/div = **0.2 ms**
$$f = \frac{1}{T} = \frac{1}{0.2 \text{ ms}} = \textbf{5 kHz}$$
The ac and dc voltages at the base should be:
A 1 V rms signal is applied to the circuit board and coupled through C_1 to the base.
$$V_B = \left(\frac{27 \text{ k}\Omega}{127 \text{ k}\Omega} \right) 24 \text{ V} = 5.1 \text{ V}$$

The frequency should be 5 kHz.
The signal displayed on the scope is correct.

Step 3. Testing the Input to Board 2

Oscilloscope measurements (Figure 9-58):
$V_{DC} = 5.1$ div $\times$ 1 V/div = **5.1 V**
$V_{rms} =$ **0 V**
The ac and dc voltages at the base should be:
A 1 V rms signal is applied to the circuit board and coupled through C_1 to the base.
$$V_B = \left(\frac{27 \text{ k}\Omega}{127 \text{ k}\Omega} \right) 24 \text{ V} = 5.1 \text{ V}$$

The dc voltage at the base is correct but the signal voltage is missing. This indicates that the coupling capacitor C_1 is open or there is no signal at the input terminal of the printed circuit board.

Step 4. Testing the Input to Board 3

Oscilloscope measurements (Figure 9-59):
$V_{DC} =$ **0 V**
$V_p = 1.4$ div $\times$ 1 V/div = **1.4 V**
$V_{rms} = 0.707V_p = 0.707(1.4$ V$) \cong$ **1 V**
$T = 2$ div $\times$ 2 μs = **4 μs**
$$f = \frac{1}{T} = \frac{1}{4 \text{ } \mu s} = \textbf{250 kHz}$$

The ac and dc voltages at the base should be:
A 1 V rms signal is applied to the circuit board and coupled through C_1 to the base.

$$V_B = \left(\frac{27 \text{ k}\Omega}{127 \text{ k}\Omega}\right)24 \text{ V} = 5.1 \text{ V}$$

The ac voltage is correct but there is no dc level. This indicates that R_1 is open or there is no dc supply voltage.

Step 1. Evaluating the Amplifier Input Circuit

$$R_{in} = R_1 \parallel R_2 = 10 \text{ k}\Omega \parallel 47 \text{ k}\Omega = \cfrac{1}{\cfrac{1}{10 \text{ k}\Omega} + \cfrac{1}{47 \text{ k}\Omega}} = \textbf{8.2 k}\Omega$$

Step 2. Measuring the Response at Frequency f_1

The channel 2 scope probe is connected to the amplifier input (point B in Figure 10-64(a)).

The frequency is:

$T = 5 \text{ div} \times 0.2 \text{ ms/div} = 1 \text{ ms}$

$$f_1 = \frac{1}{T} = \frac{1}{1 \text{ ms}} = \textbf{1 kHz}$$

The scope is ac coupled so the dc voltage at point B is not displayed.
The peak-to-peak voltage at point B that should be displayed on channel 2 is:

$$X_C = \frac{1}{2\pi f_1 C} = \frac{1}{2\pi(1 \text{ kHz})(0.1 \text{ }\mu\text{F})} = 1.59 \text{ k}\Omega$$

$$V_{B(pp)} = \left(\frac{R_{in}}{\sqrt{R_{in}^2 + X_C^2}}\right)V_{in}$$

$$= \left(\frac{8.2 \text{ k}\Omega}{\sqrt{(8.2 \text{ k}\Omega)^2 + (1.59 \text{ k}\Omega)^2}}\right)1 \text{ V} = 0.98 \text{ V} \cong \textbf{1 V}$$

Step 3. Measuring the Response at Frequency f_2

The frequency is:

$T = 5 \text{ div} \times 2 \text{ ms/div} = 10 \text{ ms}$

$$f_2 = \frac{1}{T} = \frac{1}{10 \text{ ms}} = \textbf{100 Hz}$$

The scope is ac coupled so the dc voltage at point B is not displayed.
The peak-to-peak voltage at point B that should be displayed on channel 2 is:

$$X_C = \frac{1}{2\pi f_2 C} = \frac{1}{2\pi(100 \text{ Hz})(0.1 \text{ }\mu\text{F})} = 15.9 \text{ k}\Omega$$

$$V_{B(pp)} = \left(\frac{R_{in}}{\sqrt{R_{in}^2 + X_C^2}}\right)V_{in}$$

$$= \left(\frac{8.2 \text{ k}\Omega}{\sqrt{(8.2 \text{ k}\Omega)^2 + (15.9 \text{ k}\Omega)^2}}\right)1 \text{ V} = \textbf{0.46 V}$$

The ac voltage at point B is less at 100 Hz than at 1 kHz because the reactance has increased.

Step 4. Measuring the Response at Frequency f_3

The frequency is:

$T = 4 \text{ div} \times 5 \text{ ms/div} = 20 \text{ ms}$

$f_3 = \dfrac{1}{T} = \dfrac{1}{20 \text{ ms}} = \textbf{50 Hz}$

The scope is ac coupled so the dc voltage at point B is not displayed.
The peak-to-peak voltage at point B that should be displayed on channel 2 is:

$X_C = \dfrac{1}{2\pi f_3 C} = \dfrac{1}{2\pi(50 \text{ Hz})(0.1 \text{ μF})} = 31.8 \text{ k}\Omega$

$V_{B(pp)} = \left(\dfrac{R_{in}}{\sqrt{R_{in}^2 + X_C^2}} \right) V_{in}$

$= \left(\dfrac{8.2 \text{ k}\Omega}{\sqrt{(8.2 \text{ k}\Omega)^2 + (31.8 \text{ k}\Omega)^2}} \right) 1 \text{ V} = \textbf{0.25 V}$

The ac voltage at point B is less at 50 Hz than at 100 Hz because the reactance has increased.

Step 5. Ploting a Response Curve

At the cutoff (critical) frequency,

$X_C = R_{in} = 8.2 \text{ k}\Omega$

$\dfrac{1}{2\pi f_c C} = 8.2 \text{ k}\Omega$

$f_c = \dfrac{1}{2\pi X_C C} = \dfrac{1}{2\pi(8.2 \text{ k}\Omega)(0.1 \text{ μF})} = \textbf{194 Hz}$

$V_{B(pp)} = 0.707(1 \text{ V}) = \textbf{0.707 V}$

The response curve is shown in Figure AA-6. The high-pass characteristic of the input circuit is indicated by the increase in voltage as the frequency increases. The cutoff frequency can be decreased by increasing the value of the coupling capacitor.

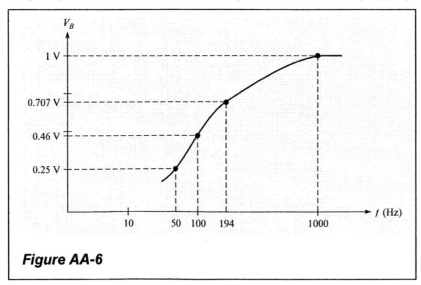

Figure AA-6

214

Step 1. Measuring the Coil Resistance and Selecting a Series Resistor

These are given as $R_W = 85\ \Omega$ and $R = 10\ \text{k}\Omega$.

Step 2. Determining the Inductance of Coil 1

Oscilloscope measurement (Figure 11-38):

$5\tau = 7\ \text{div} \times 0.5\ \mu\text{s/div} = 3.5\ \mu\text{s}$

$\tau = \dfrac{L}{R} = \dfrac{3.5\ \mu\text{s}}{5} = 0.7\ \mu\text{s}$

$L \cong (10\ \text{k}\Omega)(0.7\ \mu\text{s}) = \mathbf{7\ mH}$

Step 3. Determining the Inductance of Coil 2

Oscilloscope measurement (Figure 11-39):

$5\tau = 7\ \text{div} \times 20\ \mu\text{s/div} = 140\ \mu\text{s}$

$\tau = \dfrac{L}{R} = \dfrac{140\ \mu\text{s}}{5} = 28\ \mu\text{s}$

$L \cong (10\ \text{k}\Omega)(28\ \mu\text{s}) = \mathbf{280\ mH}$

Step 4. Another Way to Find Unknown Inductance

1. Apply a sinusoidal signal of known amplitude and frequency to the *RL* circuit.
2. Measure the voltage across the resistor.
3. Calculate the current: $I = V_R/R$
4. Calculate the impedance magnitude: $Z = V_s/I$
5. Calculate the inductive reactance: $X_L = \sqrt{Z^2 - R^2}$
6. Calculate the inductance: $L = X_L/2\pi f$

Step 1. Resistance Measurements of Module 1

The resistance measurements are:

1.61 kΩ from input to ground

1.50 kΩ from output to ground

The larger resistance measurement has to be the series combination of the resistor and the winding resistance of the coil. The smaller resistance measurement has to be the resistor value. Therefore, the values are as follows:

$R = $ **1.50 kΩ**

$R_W = 1.61 \text{ kΩ} - 1.50 \text{ kΩ} = $ **110 Ω**

See Figure AA-7.

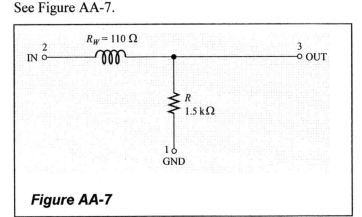

Figure AA-7

Step 2. AC Measurements of Module 1

The frequency of the input and output signals is

$T = 2.5 \text{ div} \times 5 \text{ μs/div} = 12.5 \text{ μs}$

$$f = \frac{1}{T} = \frac{1}{12.5 \ \mu s} = 80 \text{ kHz}$$

The peak-to-peak voltages are

$V_{in(pp)} = 1 \text{ V}$ (channel 2 on the scope)

$V_{out(pp)} \cong 0.707 \text{ V}$ (channel 1 on the scope)

Since V_{out} is 70.7% of V_{in}, the measurements are at the cutoff frequency.

Therefore,

$X_L = R = 1.61 \text{ kΩ}$

$2\pi f_c L = 1.61 \text{ kΩ}$

$$L = \frac{1.61 \text{ kΩ}}{2\pi(80 \text{ kHz})} = \textbf{3.2 mH}$$

Step 3. Resistance Measurements of Module 2

The resistance measurements are:

22.1 kΩ from input to ground

100 Ω from output to ground

The smaller resistance measurement has to be the winding resistance of the coil. The larger resistance measurement has to be the resistor value:

$R = \textbf{22 k}\boldsymbol{\Omega}$

$R_W = \textbf{100 }\boldsymbol{\Omega}$

See Figure AA-8.

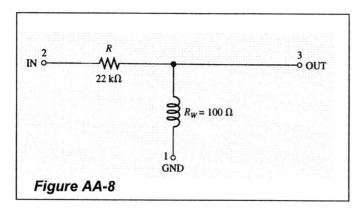

Figure AA-8

Step 4. AC Measurements of Module 2

The frequency of the input and output signals is

$T = 3.2 \text{ div} \times 0.1 \text{ ms/div} = 0.32 \text{ ms}$

$$f = \frac{1}{T} = \frac{1}{0.32 \text{ ms}} = 3.13 \text{ kHz}$$

The peak-to-peak voltages are

$V_{in(pp)} = 1 \text{ V}$ (channel 2 on the scope)

$V_{out(pp)} \cong 0.707 \text{ V}$ (channel 1 on the scope)

Since V_{out} is 70.7% of V_{in}, the measurements are at the cutoff frequency.

Therefore,

$X_L = R = 22 \text{ k}\Omega$

$2\pi f_c L = 22 \text{ k}\Omega$

$$L = \frac{22 \text{ k}\Omega}{2\pi(3.13 \text{ kHz})} = \textbf{1.12 H}$$

Step 1. Measuring the Frequency Response

The frequency and voltages indicated on the oscilloscope screens in Figure 13-64 are as follows:

Top left screen:

$R = 2.5$ div $\times$ 50 µs/div = 125 µs

$$f = \frac{1}{T} = \frac{1}{125 \ \mu s} = \textbf{8 kHz}$$

$V_{out(pp)} = 4.1$ div $\times$ 0.2 V/div = **0.82 V**

Top middle screen:

$T = 2.2$ div $\times$ 50 µs/div = 110 µs

$$f = \frac{1}{T} = \frac{1}{110 \ \mu s} = \textbf{9.1 kHz}$$

$V_{out(pp)} = 7$ div $\times$ 0.2 V/div = **1.4 V**

Top right screen:

$T = 5$ div $\times$ 20 µs/div = 100 µs

$$f = \frac{1}{T} = \frac{1}{100 \ \mu s} = \textbf{10 kHz}$$

$V_{out(pp)} = 4$ div $\times$ 0.5 V/div = **2 V**

Bottom left screen:

$T = 4.5$ div $\times$ 20 µs/div = 90 µs

$$f = \frac{1}{T} = \frac{1}{90 \ \mu s} = \textbf{11 kHz}$$

$V_{out(pp)} = 7$ div $\times$ 0.2 V/div = **1.4 V**

Bottom right screen:

$T = 4.2$ div $\times$ 20 µs/div = 84 µs

$$f = \frac{1}{T} = \frac{1}{84 \ \mu s} = \textbf{12 kHz}$$

$V_{out(pp)} = 4.8$ div $\times$ 0.2 V/div = **0.96 V**

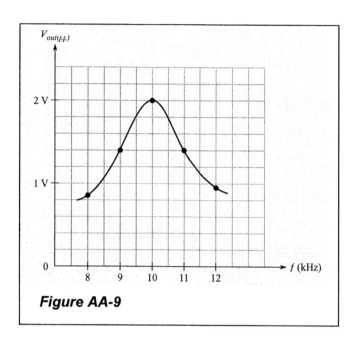

Figure AA-9

Step 2. Analyzing the Response Curve

The filter has a **bandpass** response as shown in Figure AA-9.
The resonant or center frequency is
$f_r = \textbf{10 kHz}$
The cutoff frequencies are at 9 kHz and 11 kHz because the output voltage
is $0.707 \times 2\text{ V} \cong 1.4\text{ V}$
$f_{c1} = \textbf{9 kHz}, f_{c2} = \textbf{11 kHz}$
$BW = 11\text{ kHz} - 9\text{ kHz} = \textbf{2 kHz}$

Step 1. Familiarization with the Power Supply
No results required.

Step 2. Measuring Voltages on Power Supply Board 1
The voltages on the meters in Figure 14-39 are correct. The power supply is working properly.

Step 3. Measuring Voltages on Power Supply Boards 2, 3, and 4
Board 2: The 110 V ac is applied to the circuit but there is no voltage on the primary.
The fuse is open.
Board 3: There are 10 V ac across the secondary but no dc voltage from the regulator.
The circuit board is faulty (cannot be isolated to a component with these measurements).
Board 4: There is no secondary voltage.
The transformer has an open winding.

Step 1. Capacitor Values

$$v_{thresh} = 5\ \text{V}\left(1 - e^{-t_d / RC}\right)$$

$$3.5\ \text{V} = 5\ \text{V} - (5\ \text{V})e^{-t_d / RC}$$

$$-1.5\ \text{V} = -(5\ \text{V})e^{-t_d / RC}$$

$$\ln\left(\frac{1.5}{5}\right) = \ln\left(e^{-t_d / RC}\right)$$

$$-1.2 = -\frac{t_d}{RC}$$

$$RC = \frac{t_d}{1.2}$$

$$C = \frac{t_d}{(1.2)(47\ \text{k}\Omega)}$$

Switch position A (specified delay time = 10 ms)

$$C_1 = \frac{10\ \text{ms}}{(1.2)(47\ \text{k}\Omega)} = \textbf{0.18 } \boldsymbol{\mu}\textbf{F}$$

$t_d = 1.2(4.7\ \text{k}\Omega)(0.18\ \mu\text{F}) = \textbf{10.2 ms}$

Switch position B (specified delay time = 25 ms)

$$C_2 = \frac{25\ \text{ms}}{(1.2)(47\ \text{k}\Omega)} = 0.44\ \mu\text{F}\ \ (\text{use } \textbf{0.47 } \boldsymbol{\mu}\textbf{F})$$

$t_d = 1.2(47\ \text{k}\Omega)(0.47\ \mu\text{F}) = \textbf{26.5 ms}$

Switch position C (specified delay time = 40 ms)

$$C_3 = \frac{40\ \text{ms}}{(1.2)(47\ \text{k}\Omega)} = 0.71\ \mu\text{F}\ (\text{use } \textbf{0.68 } \boldsymbol{\mu}\textbf{F})$$

$t_d = 1.2(47\ \text{k}\Omega)(0.68\ \mu\text{F}) = \textbf{38.4 ms}$

Switch position D (specified delay time = 65 ms)

$$C_4 = \frac{65\ \text{ms}}{(1.2)(47\ \text{k}\Omega)} = 1.15\ \mu\text{F}\ (\text{use } \textbf{1.2 } \boldsymbol{\mu}\textbf{F})$$

$t_d = 1.2(47\ \text{k}\Omega)(1.2\ \mu\text{F}) = \textbf{67.7 ms}$

Switch position E (specified delay time = 85 ms)

$$C_5 = \frac{85\ \text{ms}}{(1.2)(47\ \text{k}\Omega)} = 1.51\ \mu\text{F}\ (\text{use } \textbf{1.5 } \boldsymbol{\mu}\textbf{F})$$

$t_d = 1.2(47\ \text{k}\Omega)(1.5\ \mu\text{F}) = \textbf{84.6 ms}$

Step 2. Circuit Connections

From	To
1	5
3	9
4	8
6	14
7	10
8	19
15	2
16	13
17	15
18	12
19	17
20	11
21	1
22	14

Step 3. Test Procedure and Instrument Settings

For each switch position, the pulse waveform must be set so the pulse width is equal to the delay time for that position and the frequency is set to a value to allow sufficient time between pulses for the capacitor to completely discharge. During the pulse, the output voltage should increase to 3.5 V for each switch setting and then decrease to 0 V before the next pulse. See Figure AA-10.

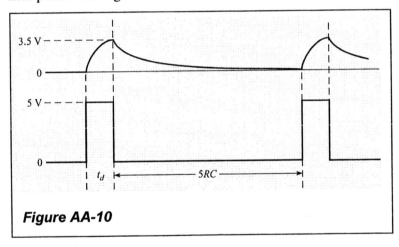

Figure AA-10

Test Procedure:

1. Set the function generator to produce a pulse waveform output.
2. Adjust the frequency of the function generator to a value equal to or less than required for the maximum time delay and capacitor discharge time determined as follows:

Maximum delay time = 85 ms
time constant used to produce the maximum delay time:
$\tau = RC = 47 \text{ k}\Omega \times 1.5 \text{ }\mu\text{F} = 70.5 \text{ ms}$
$T_{max} = t_{d(max)} + 5RC = 85 \text{ ms} + 5(70.5 \text{ ms}) = 437.5 \text{ ms}$
$$f_{min} = \frac{1}{437.5 \text{ ms}} = 2.29 \text{ Hz}$$

3. Adjust the duty cycle of the pulse waveform for each switch posotion according to the following table and verify on the scope that the output voltage reaches 3.5 V at the end of the pulse in each case.

Switch Position	Delay Time	Pulse Width	Duty Cycle	Scope Sec/Div
A	10 ms	10 ms	2.28%	1 ms
B	25 ms	25 ms	5.69%	5 ms
C	40 ms	40 ms	9.11%	5 ms
D	65 ms	65 ms	14.8%	10 ms
E	85 ms	85 ms	19.4%	10 ms

Step 4. Measurement
1. Connect the circuit in Figure 15–55 as determined in Step 2.
2. Set the instruments as determined in Step 3 for each switch setting.
3. Verify that the output waveform reaches a peak of 3.5 V on each pulse input for each switch setting.

Step 1. Identifying the Components

No results required.

Step 2. Relating the PC Boards to the Schematics

The PC boards agree with the schematics.

Step 3. Analyzing the Power Supply and IR Emitter

$$V_1 \cong V_{sec(p)} - 1.4 \text{ V} = \left(\frac{110 \text{ V} \times 1.414}{10} \right) - 1.4 \text{ V} = \mathbf{14.2 \text{ V}}$$

$$V_2 = V_Z = \mathbf{5.1 \text{ V}}$$

$$V_3 = V_2 - 0.7 \text{ V} = \mathbf{4.4 \text{ V}}$$

Step 4. Analyzing the IR Detector

With light blocked from the photodiode, it is not conducting:
$V_4 = \mathbf{5.1 \text{ V}}$

Step 5. Testing the Total System

When the units are linked by the IR from the LED, the photodiode is on and the voltage at point 4 is
$V_4 = 5.1 \text{ V} - (10 \text{ } \mu\text{A})(270 \text{ k}\Omega) = 5.1 \text{ V} - 2.7 \text{ V} = \mathbf{2.4 \text{ V}}$
When an object passes between the units and blocks the IR, the photodiode is off and the voltage at point 4 is 5.1 V.
The voltage at point 4 goes from 2.4 V to 5.1 V and back to 2.4 V as an object moves between the units and on down the conveyor belt.

Step 6. Troubleshooting the System

1. The fuse is blown, a transformer winding is open, C_1 shorted, or at least two bridge diodes are open.
2. Any fault in item 1, R_1 open, or short from point 2 to ground
3. C_1 open.
4. Zener diode is open.
5. Wrong zener diode (4.3 V instead of 5.1 V)
6. R_1 on IR detector is open.
7. Photodiode is open.
8. Short from point 4 to ground

Step 1. Relating the PC Board to the Schematic

See Figure AA-11.

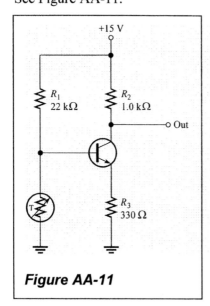

+15 V

R_1
22 kΩ

R_2
1.0 kΩ

o Out

R_3
330 Ω

T

Figure AA-11

Step 2. Analyzing the Circuit

$$R_{IN(base)} = \beta_{DC}R_3 = 100(330\ \Omega) = 33\ k\Omega$$

$$V_B = \left(\frac{R_{Therm}\ \|\ R_{IN(base)}}{R_1 + R_{Therm}\ \|\ R_{IN(base)}} \right)V_{CC}$$

$$V_E = V_B - 0.7\ V$$

$$I_C \cong I_E = \frac{V_E}{R_3}$$

$$V_{OUT} = V_{CC} - I_C R_2$$

At $T = 50°$ C:

$$V_B = \left(\frac{2.75\ k\Omega\ \|\ 33\ k\Omega}{22\ k\Omega + 2.75\ k\Omega\ \|\ 33\ k\Omega} \right)15\ V = 1.55\ V$$

$$V_E = 1.55\ V - 0.7\ V = 0.85\ V$$

$$I_C \cong I_E = \frac{0.85\ V}{330\ \Omega} = 2.58\ mA$$

$$V_{OUT} = 15\ V - (2.58\ mA)(1.0\ k\Omega) = \textbf{12.4 V}$$

At $T = 49°$ C:

$$V_B = \left(\frac{3.1\ k\Omega \parallel 33\ k\Omega}{22\ k\Omega + 3.1\ k\Omega \parallel 33\ k\Omega} \right) 15\ V = 1.71\ V$$

$V_E = 1.71\ V - 0.7\ V = 1.01\ V$

$$I_C \cong I_E = \frac{1.01\ V}{330\ \Omega} = 3.06\ mA$$

$V_{OUT} = 15\ V - (3.06\ mA)(1.0\ k\Omega) = \mathbf{11.9\ V}$

At $T = 51°$ C:

$$V_B = \left(\frac{2.5\ k\Omega \parallel 33\ k\Omega}{22\ k\Omega + 2.5\ k\Omega \parallel 33\ k\Omega} \right) 15\ V = 1.43\ V$$

$V_E = 1.43\ V - 0.7\ V = 0.73\ V$

$$I_C \cong I_E = \frac{0.73\ V}{330\ \Omega} = 2.21\ mA$$

$V_{OUT} = 15\ V - (2.21\ mA)(1.0\ k\Omega) = \mathbf{12.8\ V}$

The voltages are not significantly affected by the input resistance of the A/D converter.

Step 3. Checking Output Over Temperature Range

At $T = 30°$ C, $R_{Therm} \cong 9.75\ k\Omega$

$$V_B = \left(\frac{9.75\ k\Omega \parallel 33\ k\Omega}{22\ k\Omega + 9.75\ k\Omega \parallel 33\ k\Omega} \right) 15\ V = 3.82\ V$$

$V_E = 3.82\ V - 0.7\ V = 3.12\ V$

$$I_C \cong I_E = \frac{3.12\ V}{330\ \Omega} = 9.45\ mA$$

$V_{OUT} = 15\ V - (9.45\ mA)(1.0\ k\Omega) = \mathbf{5.55\ V}$

At $T = 50°$ C

$V_{OUT} = \mathbf{12.8\ V}$ (as determined in Step 2)

At $T = 70°$ C, $R_{Therm} \cong 2\ k\Omega$

$$V_B = \left(\frac{2\ k\Omega \parallel 33\ k\Omega}{22\ k\Omega + 2\ k\Omega \parallel 33\ k\Omega} \right) 15\ V = 1.19\ V$$

$V_E = 1.19\ V - 0.7\ V = 0.490\ V$

$$I_C \cong I_E = \frac{0.490\ V}{330\ \Omega} = 1.48\ mA$$

$V_{OUT} = 15\ V - (1.48\ mA)(1.0\ k\Omega) = \mathbf{13.5\ V}$

At $T = 90° \text{ C}$, $R_{\text{Therm}} \cong 1.8 \text{ k}\Omega$

$$V_B = \left(\frac{1.8 \text{ k}\Omega \,\|\, 33 \text{ k}\Omega}{22 \text{ k}\Omega + 1.8 \text{ k}\Omega \,\|\, 33 \text{ k}\Omega} \right) 15 \text{ V} = 1.08 \text{ V}$$

$V_E = 1.08 \text{ V} - 0.7 \text{ V} = 0.38 \text{ V}$

$I_C \cong I_E = \dfrac{0.38 \text{ V}}{330 \text{ }\Omega} = 1.15 \text{ mA}$

$V_{\text{OUT}} = 15 \text{ V} - (1.15 \text{ mA})(1.0 \text{ k}\Omega) = \mathbf{13.9 \text{ V}}$

At $T = 110° \text{ C}$, $R_{\text{Therm}} \cong 1.5 \text{ k}\Omega$

$$V_B = \left(\frac{1.5 \text{ k}\Omega \,\|\, 33 \text{ k}\Omega}{22 \text{ k}\Omega + 1.5 \text{ k}\Omega \,\|\, 33 \text{ k}\Omega} \right) 15 \text{ V} = 0.92 \text{ V}$$

$V_E = 0.92 \text{ V} - 0.7 \text{ V} = 0.22 \text{ V}$

$I_C \cong I_E = \dfrac{0.38 \text{ V}}{330 \text{ }\Omega} = 0.67 \text{ mA}$

$V_{\text{OUT}} = 15 \text{ V} - (0.67 \text{ mA})(1.0 \text{ k}\Omega) = \mathbf{14.3 \text{ V}}$

Step 4. Troubleshooting the Circuit Board

1. The termistor is open causing the transistor to saturate.
2. The transistor is off. Either the collector is internally open or resistor R_1 or R_3 is open.
3. Check circuit board for open contacts or bad connections. Test Q_1 in circuit. Lift one lead of R_1 and/or R_3 and check for open.

Step 1. Relating the PC Board to a Schematic
See Figure AA-12.

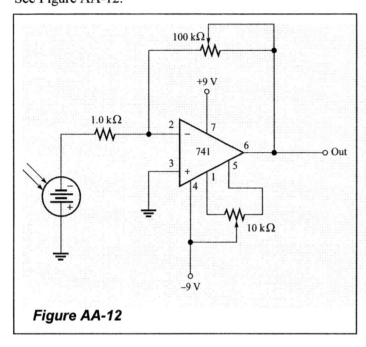

Figure AA-12

Step 2. Analyzing the Circuit

1. $\dfrac{R_f}{R_i} = A_v$

$R_f = R_i A_v = (1.0\ \text{k}\Omega)(10) = \mathbf{10\ k\Omega}$

2. $A_v = \dfrac{V_{out(\text{max})}}{V_{in(\text{max})}} = \dfrac{8\ \text{V}}{0.5\ \text{V}} = \mathbf{16}$

$R_f = (1.0\ \text{k}\Omega)(16) = \mathbf{16\ k\Omega}$

3. If $V_{photo} = 0.5$ V at 700 nm, which is approximately 89% of the maximum response at 800 nm, then

$V_{photo(\text{max})} = \dfrac{0.5\ \text{V}}{0.89} = 0.562\ \text{V}$

At 400 nm:
$V_{out} \cong 0.03 A_v V_{photo(\text{max})} = 0.03(16)(0.562\ \text{V}) = \mathbf{0.270\ V}$

At 450 nm:
$V_{out} \cong 0.1 A_v V_{photo(\text{max})} = 0.1(16)(0.562\ \text{V}) = \mathbf{0.899\ V}$

At 500 nm:
$V_{out} \cong 0.25 A_v V_{photo(\text{max})} = 0.25(16)(0.562\ \text{V}) = \mathbf{2.25\ V}$

At 550 nm:
$$V_{out} \cong 0.42 A_v V_{photo(\text{max})} = 0.42(16)(0.562 \text{ V}) = \textbf{3.78 V}$$

At 600 nm:
$$V_{out} \cong 0.59 A_v V_{photo(\text{max})} = 0.59(16)(0.562 \text{ V}) = \textbf{5.31 V}$$

At 650 nm:
$$V_{out} \cong 0.77 A_v V_{photo(\text{max})} = 0.77(16)(0.562 \text{ V}) = \textbf{6.92 V}$$

At 700 nm:
$$V_{out} \cong 0.89 A_v V_{photo(\text{max})} = 0.89(16)(0.562 \text{ V}) = \textbf{8.00 V}$$

See Figure AA-13.

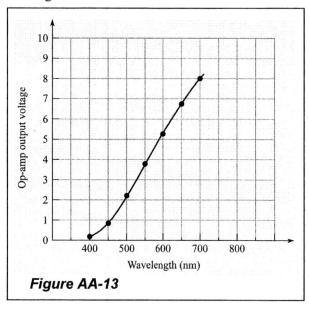

Figure AA-13

Step 3. Troubleshooting the Circuit
1. Op-amp output faulty, photocell shorted, or feedback pot shorted.
2. Op-amp faulty, Feedback pot open.
3. Op-amp faulty. 1.0 kΩ resistor open.

CHAPTER 19 Application Assignment

Step 1. Relating the PC Board to a Schematic

See Figure AA-14.

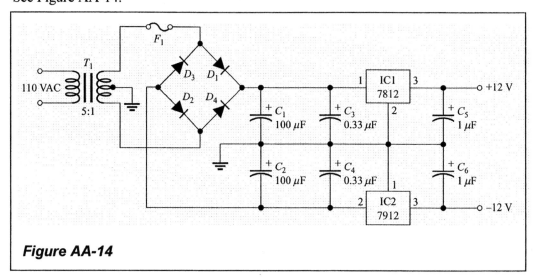

Figure AA-14

Step 2. Analyzing the Power Supply Circuits

1. $V_{sec} = \dfrac{1}{5}(110 \text{ V} \times 1.414) = 31 \text{ V}$

$\dfrac{V_{sec}}{2} = \dfrac{31 \text{ V}}{2} = 15.5 \text{ V}$

At the cathode of D_3:

$V_{K(D3)} = \dfrac{V_{sec}}{2} = \textbf{15.3 V peak ac}$

At the cathode of D_2:

$V_{K(D2)} = \dfrac{V_{sec}}{2} = \textbf{15.3 V peak ac}$

At the cathode of D_4:

$V_{K(D4)} = \dfrac{V_{sec}}{2} - 0.7 \text{ V} = \textbf{14.8 V dc}$

At the cathode of D_1:

$V_{K(D1)} = \dfrac{V_{sec}}{2} - 0.7 \text{ V} = \textbf{14.8 V dc}$

2. $PIV = 15.5 \text{ V} - (-14.8 \text{ V}) = \textbf{30.3 V}$

230

3. See Figure AA-15 for the voltage across D_1 during one cycle.

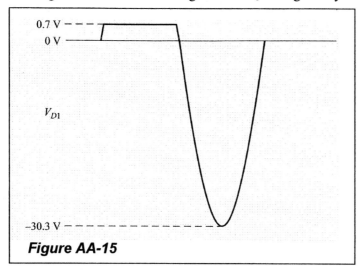

0.7 V

0 V

V_{D1}

−30.3 V

Figure AA-15

Step 3. Troubleshooting the Power Supply

1. Fuse has blown, there is no ac input, or a transformer winding is open.
2. IC1 regulator is defective.
3. IC2 regulator is defective.
4. Filter capacitor C_1 is open.

The voltage at each of the corners of the diode bridge for the following faults are:
1. With D_1 open there should be 15.5 V peak ac voltages at the D_1 and D_4 anodes, a positive voltage of approximately 14.8 V with a greater than normal ripple voltage at 60 Hz at the D_1 cathode resulting from half-wave rectification, and a negative voltage of approximately −14.8 V with a normal 120 Hz ripple voltage at the D_2 anode.

2. With C_2 open, there should be a full-wave rectified voltage with a peak of −14.8 V at the anode of D_2 and a normal +14.8 V dc at the cathode of D_1. There should be 15.5 V peak ac voltages at the anode of D_1 and the cathode of D_2.

Step 1. Checking the amplifier board
1. The board agrees with the schematic.
2. See Figure AA-16.

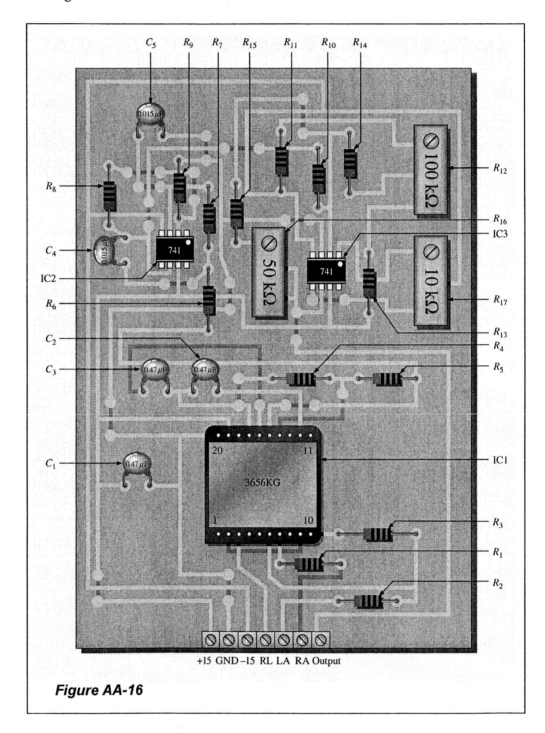

Figure AA-16

Step 2. Analyzing the Circuits

1. Isolation amplifier gain:

$$A_{v1} = \frac{R_3}{R_1} + 1 = \frac{330\,k\Omega}{86\,k\Omega} + 1 = 4.8; \quad A_{v2} = \frac{R_5}{R_4} + 1 = \frac{120\,k\Omega}{100\,k\Omega} + 1 = 2.2; \quad A_{v(tot)} = 10.56$$

2. Filter bandwidth: ≈ 106 Hz
   Filter gain: $A_v = 1.59$
3. Postamplifier gain: $A_{v(min)} = -100$, $A_{v(max)} = -150$
4. Amplifier gain range: $A_{v(min)} = -1750$, $A_{v(max)} = -2620$
5. Voltage range at position pot wiper: $V_{min} = -59.7$ mV, $V_{max} = +59.7$ mV

Step 3. Troubleshooting the Circuits

Board 1: Several faults can produce no output including R_{10} open or IC3 output faulty or open.
Board 2: R_6 or R_7 open
Board 3: R_{10} open.
Board 4: R_{15} or R_{16} open.

Step 1. Checking the Circuit Board

1. The circuit board agrees with the schematic.

2. See Figure AA-17.

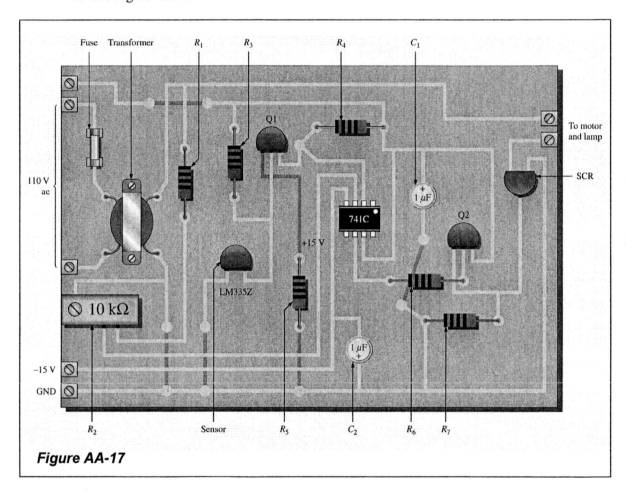

Figure AA-17

234

Step 2. Analyzing the Circuit

1. Voltage at collector of Q_1:

$$V_E = 2.93 \text{ V} - 0.7 \text{ V} = 2.23 \text{ V}$$

$$I_E = \frac{V_E}{R_5} = \frac{2.23 \text{ V}}{2.7 \text{ k}\Omega} = 0.826 \text{ mA}$$

$$I_C \cong I_E = 0.826 \text{ mA}$$

$$V_C = 15 \text{ V} - (0.826 \text{ mA})(10 \text{ k}\Omega)$$
$$= 15 \text{ V} - 8.26 \text{ V}$$
$$= \mathbf{6.74 \text{ V}}$$

Voltage at inverting input of 741C is V_C.

2. $K = 273 + °C = 273 + 50 = 323 \text{ K}$
$V_{+20°C} = 2.93 \text{ V}$
$\Delta K = 323 \text{ K} - 293 \text{ K} = 30 \text{ K}$
$V_{+50°C} = 2.93 \text{ V} + (10 \text{ mV/K})(30 \text{ K})$
$\quad\quad = 2.93 \text{ V} + 0.3 \text{ V} = \mathbf{3.23 \text{ V}}$

3. $V_{peak} = V_- = \mathbf{6.74 \text{ V}}$

Step 3. Testing the Circuit Board

1. • Apply 120 Vac to primary of transformer.
    • Check +15 Vdc and −15 Vdc.
    • Check for 12.6 V rms across transformer secondary.
    • Check for approximately 2.93 Vdc at the inverting input of the op-amp comparator.
    • Adjust potentiometer until the motor runs. Then back down to the point where the motor turns off.
    • Apply heat to the zener temperature sensor to turn the motor on.
    • Remove heat to turn the motor off.

2. $V_{sec} = 12.6 \text{ Vrms}$, $V_{Q_1 base} = 2.93 \text{ Vdc}$ @ 20°C,

$V_{Q_1 collector} = 6.74 \text{ Vdc}$ @ 20°C, $V_{-(741C)} = 6.74 \text{ Vdc}$ @ 20°C,

$V_{out(741C)} \cong \pm 14 \text{ V}$

Step 4. Troubleshooting the Circuits

1. Q_1 open or LM335Z shorted.

2. SCR bad or Q_2 faulty

3. 741C inverting input shorted to ground.

4. Motor shorted or it has a mechanical fault.

PART THREE

Summary of Multisim Circuit Results

Chapter	Circuit	MultiSIM 2001	MultiSIM 7	MultiSIM 8
3	P03-66	$I_T = 0.011$ mA$_{DC}$ $V_R = 12.000$ V$_{DC}$ R is open	$I_T = 0.011$ mA$_{DC}$ $V_R = 12.000$ V$_{DC}$ R is open	$I_T = 0.011$ mA$_{DC}$ $V_R = 12.000$ V$_{DC}$ R is open
	P03-67	$I_T = 9.091$ mA$_{DC}$ No fault	$I_T = 9.091$ mA$_{DC}$ No fault	$I_T = 9.091$ mA$_{DC}$ No fault
	P03-68	$V_{R1} = 0.010$ nV$_{DC}$ $V_{R2} = 10.000$ V$_{DC}$ R_1 is shorted	$V_{R1} = 0.010$ nV$_{DC}$ $V_{R2} = 10.000$ V$_{DC}$ R_1 is shorted	$V_{R1} = 0.010$ mV$_{DC}$ $V_{R2} = 10.000$ V$_{DC}$ R_1 is shorted
	P03-69	$V_{L1} = 4.000$ V$_{DC} = V_{L2} =$ V_{L3} $V_{L4} = 0.278$ nV$_{DC}$ Lamp 4 is shorted	$V_{L1} = 4.000$ V$_{DC} = V_{L2} =$ V_{L3} $V_{L4} = 0.278$ nV$_{DC}$ Lamp 4 is shorted	$V_{L1} = 4.000$ V$_{DC} = V_{L2} =$ V_{L3} $V_{L4} = 0.278$ nV$_{DC}$ Lamp 4 is shorted
	P03-70	$V_{L6} = 23.997$ V$_{DC}$ Lamp 6 is open	$V_{L6} = 23.997$ V$_{DC}$ Lamp 6 is open	$V_{L6} = 23.997$ V$_{DC}$ Lamp 6 is open
4	P04-56	$V_{R1} = 9.990$ V$_{DC}$ R_1 is open	$V_{R1} = 9.990$ V$_{DC}$ R_1 is open	$V_{R1} = 9.990$ V$_{DC}$ R_1 is open
	P04-57	$I_T = 0.075$ mA$_{DC}$ $V_{R6} = 0.076$ pV$_{DC}$ R_6 is shorted	$I_T = 0.075$ mA$_{DC}$ $V_{R6} = 0.076$ pV$_{DC}$ R_6 is shorted	$I_T = 0.075$ mA$_{DC}$ $V_{R6} = 0.076$ pV$_{DC}$ R_6 is shorted
	P04-58	$V_{R2} = 11.999$ V$_{DC}$ R_2 is open	$V_{R2} = 11.999$ V$_{DC}$ R_2 is open	$V_{R2} = 11.999$ V$_{DC}$ R_2 is open
	P04-59	$V_{LAMP} = 48.000$ V$_{DC}$ Lamp is open	$V_{LAMP} = 48.000$ V$_{DC}$ Lamp is open	$V_{LAMP} = 48.000$ V$_{DC}$ Lamp is open
	P04-60	$I_T = 0.073$ mA$_{DC}$ $V_{R6} = 0.597$ V$_{DC}$ No fault	$I_T = 0.073$ mA$_{DC}$ $V_{R6} = 0.597$ V$_{DC}$ No fault	$I_T = 0.073$ mA$_{DC}$ $V_{R6} = 0.597$ V$_{DC}$ No fault
	P04-61	$V_{82\Omega} = 0.021$ nV$_{DC}$ $I_T = 0.021$ A$_{DC}$ 82 Ω resistor is shorted	$V_{82\Omega} = 0.021$ nV$_{DC}$ $I_T = 0.021$ A$_{DC}$ 82 Ω resistor is shorted	$V_{82\Omega} = 0.021$ nV$_{DC}$ $I_T = 0.021$ A$_{DC}$ 82 Ω resistor is shorted
5	P05-48	$I_{R1} = 0.000$ A$_{DC}$ $I_{R2} = 6.667$ mA$_{DC}$ $I_{R3} = 5.455$ mA$_{DC}$ R_1 is open	$I_{R1} = 0.000$ A$_{DC}$ $I_{R2} = 6.667$ mA$_{DC}$ $I_{R3} = 5.455$ mA$_{DC}$ R_1 is open	$I_{R1} = 0.000$ A$_{DC}$ $I_{R2} = 6.667$ mA$_{DC}$ $I_{R3} = 5.455$ mA$_{DC}$ R_1 is open
	P05-49	$I_{R1} = 0.041$ A$_{DC}$ $I_{R2} = 0.027$ A$_{DC}$ $I_{R3} = 0.000$ A$_{DC}$ $I_{R4} = 0.016$ A$_{DC}$ R_3 is open	$I_{R1} = 0.041$ A$_{DC}$ $I_{R2} = 0.027$ A$_{DC}$ $I_{R3} = 0.000$ A$_{DC}$ $I_{R4} = 0.016$ A$_{DC}$ R_3 is open	$I_{R1} = 0.041$ A$_{DC}$ $I_{R2} = 0.027$ A$_{DC}$ $I_{R3} = 0.000$ A$_{DC}$ $I_{R4} = 0.016$ A$_{DC}$ R_3 is open
	P05-50	$R_T = 284.892$ kΩ No fault	$R_T = 284.892$ kΩ No fault	$R_T = 284.892$ kΩ No fault
	P05-51	$R_{1,4} = 340.146$ kΩ $R_{2,3} = 9.624$ kΩ $R_{1,4}$ is correct $R_{2,3}$ is correct	$R_{1,4} = 340.146$ kΩ $R_{2,3} = 9.624$ kΩ $R_{1,4}$ is correct $R_{2,3}$ is correct	$R_{1,4} = 340.146$ kΩ $R_{2,3} = 9.624$ kΩ $R_{1,4}$ is correct $R_{2,3}$ is correct
6	P06-62	$I_T = 4.286$ mA$_{DC} = I_{R1}$ $I_{R2} = 4.285$ mA$_{DC}$ $I_{R3} = 0.888$ μA$_{DC}$ R_3 is open	$I_T = 4.286$ mA$_{DC} = I_{R1}$ $I_{R2} = 4.285$ mA$_{DC}$ $I_{R3} = 0.888$ μA$_{DC}$ R_3 is open	$I_T = 4.286$ mA$_{DC} = I_{R1}$ $I_{R2} = 4.285$ mA$_{DC}$ $I_{R3} = 0.888$ μA$_{DC}$ R_3 is open

	P06-63	$I_{R2} = 10.000$ mA$_{DC}$ $I_{R3} = 0.000$ A$_{DC} = I_{R4}$ $V_{R2} = 0.010$ nV$_{DC}$ R_2 is open	$I_{R2} = 10.000$ mA$_{DC}$ $I_{R3} = 0.000$ A$_{DC} = I_{R4}$ $V_{R2} = 0.010$ nV$_{DC}$ R_2 is open	$I_{R2} = 10.000$ mA$_{DC}$ $I_{R3} = 0.000$ A$_{DC} = I_{R4}$ $V_{R2} = 0.010$ nV$_{DC}$ R_2 is open
	P06-64	$V_{R1} = 24.000$ V$_{DC}$ $I_{R1} = 3.553$ µA$_{DC}$ $I_{R2} = 0.240$ A$_{DC}$ R_1 is open	$V_{R1} = 24.000$ V$_{DC}$ $I_{R1} = 3.553$ µA$_{DC}$ $I_{R2} = 0.240$ A$_{DC}$ R_1 is open	$V_{R1} = 24.000$ V$_{DC}$ $I_{R1} = 3.553$ µA$_{DC}$ $I_{R2} = 0.240$ A$_{DC}$ R_1 is open
	P06-65	$I_T = 0.490$ mA$_{DC}$ $V_{R1} = 4.898$ V$_{DC}$ $V_{R2} = 4.102$ V$_{DC}$ $V_{R3} = 2.126$ V$_{DC}$ $V_{R4} = 1.976$ V$_{DC}$ $V_{R5} = 0.790$ V$_{DC}$ $V_{R6} = 1.185$ V$_{DC}$ No fault	$I_T = 0.490$ mA$_{DC}$ $V_{R1} = 4.898$ V$_{DC}$ $V_{R2} = 4.102$ V$_{DC}$ $V_{R3} = 2.126$ V$_{DC}$ $V_{R4} = 1.976$ V$_{DC}$ $V_{R5} = 0.790$ V$_{DC}$ $V_{R6} = 1.185$ V$_{DC}$ No fault	$I_T = 0.490$ mA$_{DC}$ $V_{R1} = 4.898$ V$_{DC}$ $V_{R2} = 4.102$ V$_{DC}$ $V_{R3} = 2.126$ V$_{DC}$ $V_{R4} = 1.976$ V$_{DC}$ $V_{R5} = 0.790$ V$_{DC}$ $V_{R6} = 1.185$ V$_{DC}$ No fault
	P06-66	$I_{R6} = 1.776$ µA$_{DC}$ $V_{R6} = 5.242$ V$_{DC}$ R_6 is open	$I_{R6} = 1.776$ µA$_{DC}$ $V_{R6} = 5.242$ V$_{DC}$ R_6 is open	$I_{R6} = 1.776$ µA$_{DC}$ $V_{R6} = 5.242$ V$_{DC}$ R_6 is open
	P06-67	$I_{R4} = 3.736$ mA$_{DC}$ $V_{R4} = 3.736$ pV$_{DC}$ R4 is shorted	$I_{R4} = 3.736$ mA$_{DC}$ $V_{R4} = 3.736$ pV$_{DC}$ R4 is shorted	$I_{R4} = 3.736$ mA$_{DC}$ $V_{R4} = 3.736$ pV$_{DC}$ R4 is shorted
	P06-68	$I_{R3} = 0.000$ A$_{DC}$ $I_{R1} = -0.020$ A$_{DC} = I_{R2}$ $I_{R4} = 0.020$ A$_{DC} = I_{R5}$ R_3 is open	$I_{R3} = 0.000$ A$_{DC}$ $I_{R1} = -0.020$ A$_{DC} = I_{R2}$ $I_{R4} = 0.020$ A$_{DC} = I_{R5}$ R_3 is open	$I_{R3} = 0.000$ A$_{DC}$ $I_{R1} = -0.020$ A$_{DC} = I_{R2}$ $I_{R4} = 0.020$ A$_{DC} = I_{R5}$ R_3 is open
	P06-69	$V_{R3} = 6.000$ V$_{DC} = V_{R4}$ $R_5 = 0$ Ω R_5 is shorted	$V_{R3} = 6.000$ V$_{DC} = V_{R4}$ $R_5 = 0$ Ω R_5 is shorted	$V_{R3} = 6.000$ V$_{DC} = V_{R4}$ $R_5 = 0$ Ω R_5 is shorted
7	P07-24	Switch closed: $I_{UPPER} = 0.000$ A$_{DC}$ $I_{LOWER} = 1.111$ A$_{DC}$ $I_T = 1.111$ A$_{DC}$ Switch open: $I_{UPPER} = 0.000$ A$_{DC}$ $I_{LOWER} = 9.000$ nA$_{DC}$ $I_T = 9.000$ nA$_{DC}$ Upper lamp is open	Switch closed: $I_{UPPER} = 0.000$ A$_{DC}$ $I_{LOWER} = 1.111$ A$_{DC}$ $I_T = 1.111$ A$_{DC}$ Switch open: $I_{UPPER} = 0.000$ A$_{DC}$ $I_{LOWER} = 9.000$ nA$_{DC}$ $I_T = 9.000$ nA$_{DC}$ Upper lamp is open	Switch closed: $I_{UPPER} = 0.000$ A$_{DC}$ $I_{LOWER} = 1.111$ A$_{DC}$ $I_T = 1.111$ A$_{DC}$ Switch open: $I_{UPPER} = 0.000$ A$_{DC}$ $I_{LOWER} = 9.000$ nA$_{DC}$ $I_T = 9.000$ nA$_{DC}$ Upper lamp is open
	P07-25	The design is flawed. 12 V is too little voltage to operate two 12V relays in series but 24 V is too much to operate a 12V lamp. Install a separate 12V power supply for the lamps and change 12V supply to 24 V for the relays.	The design is flawed. 12 V is too little voltage to operate two 12V relays in series but 24 V is too much to operate a 12V lamp. Install a separate 12V power supply for the lamps and change 12V supply to 24 V for the relays.	The design is flawed. 12 V is too little voltage to operate two 12V relays in series but 24 V is too much to operate a 12V lamp. Install a separate 12V power supply for the lamps and change 12V supply to 24 V for the relays.
8	P08-48	$V_R = 70.7$ V$_{PP} = 35.4$ V$_P$ $\tau = 1$ ms	$V_R = 70.7$ V$_{PP} = 35.4$ V$_P$ $\tau = 1$ ms	$V_R = 70.7$ V$_{PP} = 35.4$ V$_P$ $\tau = 1$ ms
	P08-49	$V_{R3} = 119.999$ V$_{RMS}$ R_3 is open	$V_{R3} = 119.999$ V$_{RMS}$ R_3 is open	$V_{R3} = 120.000$ V$_{RMS}$ R_3 is open

	P08-50	$I_{R1} = 1.023\ \mu V_{RMS}$ $I_{R2} = 0.050\ A_{RMS}$ $I_{R3} = 0.015\ A_{RMS}$ R_1 is open	$I_{R1} = 1.023\ \mu V_{RMS}$ $I_{R2} = 0.050\ A_{RMS}$ $I_{R3} = 0.015\ A_{RMS}$ R_1 is open	$I_{R1} = 1.024\ \mu V_{RMS}$ $I_{R2} = 0.050\ A_{RMS}$ $I_{R3} = 0.015\ A_{RMS}$ R_1 is open
	P08-51	$V_R = 5.0\ V_{PP}$ $\tau = 1\ ms$	$V_R = 5.0\ V_{PP}$ $\tau = 1\ ms$	$V_R = 5.0\ V_{PP}$ $\tau = 1\ ms$
	P08-52	$V_S = 5.0\ V_P$ $V_{R3} = 1.8\ V_P$ $\tau = 100\ \mu s$ Duty cycle = 30% No fault	$V_S = 5.0\ V_P$ $V_{R3} = 1.8\ V_P$ $\tau = 100\ \mu s$ Duty cycle = 30% No fault	$V_S = 5.0\ V_P$ $V_{R3} = 1.8\ V_P$ $\tau = 100\ \mu s$ Duty cycle = 29.6% No fault
9	P09-50	$V_{C1} = 10.000\ V_{RMS}$ $V_{C2} = 4.433\ V_{RMS}$ No fault	$V_{C1} = 10.000\ V_{RMS}$ $V_{C2} = 4.433\ V_{RMS}$ No fault	$V_{C1} = 10.000\ V_{RMS}$ $V_{C2} = 4.433\ V_{RMS}$ No fault
	P09-51	$I_T = 0.013\ A_{RMS}$ $I_{C2} = 2.876\ \mu A_{RMS}$ C_2 is open	$I_T = 0.013\ A_{RMS}$ $I_{C2} = 2.876\ \mu A_{RMS}$ C_2 is open	$I_T = 0.013\ A_{RMS}$ $I_{C2} = 2.918\ \mu A_{RMS}$ C_2 is open
	P09-52	$V_{C1} = 0.014\ nV_{RMS}$ $I_{C2} = 4.545\ mA_{RMS}$ $I_{C3} = 9.825\ mA_{RMS}$ C_1 is shorted	$V_{C1} = 0.014\ nV_{RMS}$ $I_{C2} = 4.511\ mA_{RMS}$ $I_{C3} = 9.823\ mA_{RMS}$ C_1 is shorted	$V_{C1} = 0.014\ nV_{RMS}$ $I_{C2} = 4.524\ mA_{RMS}$ $I_{C3} = 9.953\ mA_{RMS}$ C_1 is shorted
	P09-53	$\tau_{RC} \approx 500\ \mu s$ No fault	$\tau_{RC} \approx 500\ \mu s$ No fault	$\tau_{RC} \approx 500\ \mu s$ No fault
	P09-54	$V_{C1} = 0.000\ V_{DC}$ $V_{C2} = 4.727\ V_{DC}$ C_1 is shorted	$V_{C1} = 0.000\ V_{DC}$ $V_{C2} = 4.727\ V_{DC}$ C_1 is shorted	$V_{C1} = 0.000\ V_{DC}$ $V_{C2} = 4.706\ V_{DC}$ (after 75 minutes of simulation) C_1 is shorted
10	P10-49	$V_R = 17.057\ V_{RMS}$ $V_C = 0.945\ V_{RMS}$ C is leaky	$V_R = 17.057\ V_{RMS}$ $V_C = 0.945\ V_{RMS}$ C is leaky	$V_R = 17.057\ V_{RMS}$ $V_C = 0.945\ V_{RMS}$ C is leaky
	P10-50	$V_{C2} = 0.019\ nV_{RMS}$ C_2 is shorted	$V_{C2} = 0.019\ nV_{RMS}$ C_2 is shorted	$V_{C2} = 0.019\ nV_{RMS}$ C_2 is shorted
	P10-51	$I_{C1} = 0.145\ A_{RMS}$ $V_{C1} = 38.333\ V_{RMS}$ $I_{R1} = 0.082\ A_{RMS}$ $I_{C1,R2} = 0.030\ A_{RMS}$ $I_{C2} = 0.128\ A_{RMS}$ $V_{C2} = 72.067\ V_{RMS}$ No fault	$I_{C1} = 0.145\ A_{RMS}$ $V_{C1} = 38.333\ V_{RMS}$ $I_{R1} = 0.082\ A_{RMS}$ $I_{C1,R2} = 0.030\ A_{RMS}$ $I_{C2} = 0.128\ A_{RMS}$ $V_{C2} = 72.067\ V_{RMS}$ No fault	$I_{C1} = 0.145\ A_{RMS}$ $V_{C1} = 38.333\ V_{RMS}$ $I_{R1} = 0.082\ A_{RMS}$ $I_{C1,R2} = 0.030\ A_{RMS}$ $I_{C2} = 0.128\ A_{RMS}$ $V_{C2} = 72.067\ V_{RMS}$ No fault
	P10-52	$V_C = 2.500\ V_{RMS}$ $V_{OSC} = 4.500\ V_{DC}$ C is open	$V_C = 2.500\ V_{RMS}$ $V_{OSC} = 4.500\ V_{DC}$ C is open	$V_C = 2.500\ V_{RMS}$ $V_{OSC} = 4.500\ V_{DC}$ C is open
	P10-53	$I_{R2} = 0.316\ \mu A_{RMS}$ $I_C = 0.573\ mA_{RMS}$ R_2 is open	$I_{R2} = 0.320\ \mu A_{RMS}$ $I_C = 0.572\ mA_{RMS}$ R_2 is open	$I_{R2} = 0.320\ \mu A_{RMS}$ $I_C = 0.573\ mA_{RMS}$ R_2 is open
	P10-54	$V_A = 5\ V_{PP}, \tau = 100\ \mu s$ $V_B = 5\ V_{PP}, \tau = 100\ \mu s$ C is shorted	$V_A = 5\ V_{PP}, \tau = 100\ \mu s$ $V_B = 5\ V_{PP}, \tau = 100\ \mu s$ C is shorted	$V_A = 5\ V_{PP}, \tau = 100\ \mu s$ $V_B = 5\ V_{PP}, \tau = 100\ \mu s$ C is shorted
11	P11-27	$I_{L2} = 0.491\ A_{RMS}$ $I_{L3} = 1.229\ \mu A_{RMS}$ L_3 is open	$I_{L2} = 0.491\ A_{RMS}$ $I_{L3} = 1.229\ \mu A_{RMS}$ L_3 is open	$I_{L2} = 0.491\ A_{RMS}$ $I_{L3} = 1.229\ \mu A_{RMS}$ L_3 is open
	P11-28	V_{L1} (open) $= 0.000\ V_{RMS}$ V_{L2} (closed) $= 0.305\ nV_{RMS}$ L1 is shorted	V_{L1} (open) $= 0.000\ V_{RMS}$ V_{L2} (closed) $= 0.305\ nV_{RMS}$ L1 is shorted	V_{L1} (open) $= 0.000\ V_{RMS}$ V_{L2} (closed) $= 0.305\ nV_{RMS}$ L1 is shorted

	P11-29	$V_R = 4.918$ V_{RMS} $V_L = 0.209$ V_{RMS} Switch to left: Lamp 1 blinking, Lamp 2 on Switch to right: Lamp 1 on, Lamp 2 blinking No fault	$V_R = 4.918$ V_{RMS} $V_L = 0.209$ V_{RMS} Switch to left: Lamp 1 blinking, Lamp 2 on Switch to right: Lamp 1 on, Lamp 2 blinking No fault	$V_R = 4.918$ V_{RMS} $V_L = 0.209$ V_{RMS} Switch to left: Lamp 1 blinking, Lamp 2 on Switch to right: Lamp 1 on, Lamp 2 blinking No fault
	P11-30	$I_T = 0.022$ $mA_{RMS} = I_{L1}$ $I_{L2} = 0.000$ mA_{RMS} $I_{L3} = 0.022$ mA_{RMS} L_2 is open	$I_T = 0.022$ $mA_{RMS} = I_{L1}$ $I_{L2} = 0.000$ mA_{RMS} $I_{L3} = 0.022$ mA_{RMS} L_2 is open	$I_T = 0.022$ $mA_{RMS} = I_{L1}$ $I_{L2} = 0.000$ mA_{RMS} $I_{L3} = 0.022$ mA_{RMS} L_2 is open
	P11-31	$V_{L3} = 2.357$ nV_{RMS} L_3 is shorted	$V_{L3} = 2.357$ nV_{RMS} L_3 is shorted	$V_{L3} = 2.357$ nV_{RMS} L_3 is shorted
12	P12-44	$I_T = 8.001$ $mA_{RMS} = I_{R1}$ $I_{R2} = 8.000$ mA_{RMS} $I_L = 0.000$ A_{RMS} R_2 is shorted	$I_T = 8.001$ $mA_{RMS} = I_{R1}$ $I_{R2} = 8.000$ mA_{RMS} $I_L = 0.000$ A_{RMS} R_2 is shorted	$I_T = 8.000$ $mA_{RMS} = I_{R1}$ $I_{R2} = 8.000$ mA_{RMS} $I_L = 0.000$ A_{RMS} R_2 is shorted
	P12-45	$I_R = 0.080$ A_{RMS} $I_{L2} = 0.000$ A_{RMS} L_2 is open	$I_R = 0.080$ A_{RMS} $I_{L2} = 0.000$ A_{RMS} L_2 is open	$I_R = 0.080$ A_{RMS} $I_{L2} = 0.000$ A_{RMS} L_2 is open
	P12-46	$V_{L1} = 0.135$ nV_{RMS} L_1 is shorted	$V_{L1} = 0.135$ nV_{RMS} L_1 is shorted	$V_{L1} = 0.135$ nV_{RMS} L_1 is shorted
	P12-47	$I_{R2} = 1.391$ μA_{RMS} $I_{R4} = 1.075$ mA_{RMS} R_2 is open	$I_{R2} = 1.391$ μA_{RMS} $I_{R4} = 1.075$ mA_{RMS} R_2 is open	$I_{R2} = 1.386$ μA_{RMS} $I_{R4} = 1.073$ mA_{RMS} R_2 is open
	P12-48	$V_{L1} = 2.605$ V_{RMS} $V_{L2} = 2.261$ V_{RMS} $V_{R1} = 1.297$ V_{RMS} $V_{L3} = 2.212$ V_{RMS} $V_{R2} = 1.208$ V_{RMS} No fault	$V_{L1} = 2.605$ V_{RMS} $V_{L2} = 2.261$ V_{RMS} $V_{R1} = 1.297$ V_{RMS} $V_{L3} = 2.212$ V_{RMS} $V_{R2} = 1.208$ V_{RMS} No fault	$V_{L1} = 2.604$ V_{RMS} $V_{L2} = 2.261$ V_{RMS} $V_{R1} = 1.297$ V_{RMS} $V_{L3} = 2.211$ V_{RMS} $V_{R2} = 1.208$ V_{RMS} No fault
	P12-49	$V_{L1} = 2.432$ pV_{RMS} V_{L1} (diff.) $= 0$ V_{DC} L_1 is shorted	$V_{L1} = 2.432$ pV_{RMS} V_{L1} (diff.) $= 0$ V_{DC} L_1 is shorted	$V_{L1} = 2.432$ pV_{RMS} V_{L1} (diff.) $= 0$ V_{DC} L_1 is shorted
13	P13-36	$V_L = 7.000$ V_{RMS} L is open	$V_L = 7.000$ V_{RMS} L is open	$V_L = 7.000$ V_{RMS} L is open
	P13-37	$I_{R1} = 0.016$ A_{RMS} $I_{R2} = 9.129$ μA_{RMS} $I_{C1} = 0.014$ A_{RMS} $I_{C2} = 2.502$ mA_{RMS} No fault	$I_{R1} = 0.016$ A_{RMS} $I_{R2} = 9.129$ μA_{RMS} $I_{C1} = 0.014$ A_{RMS} $I_{C2} = 2.502$ mA_{RMS} No fault	$I_{R1} = 0.016$ A_{RMS} $I_{R2} = 9.129$ μA_{RMS} $I_{C1} = 0.014$ A_{RMS} $I_{C2} = 2.502$ mA_{RMS} No fault
	P13-38	$I_{C \parallel L} = 4.364$ mA_{RMS} $I_C = 0.000$ A_{RMS} C is open	$I_{C \parallel L} = 4.364$ mA_{RMS} $I_C = 0.000$ A_{RMS} C is open	$I_{C \parallel L} = 4.364$ mA_{RMS} $I_C = 0.000$ A_{RMS} C is open
	P13-39	$I_{L1} = 0.106$ A_{RMS} $V_C = 0.106$ nV_{RMS} L_1 is shorted	$I_{L1} = 0.106$ A_{RMS} $V_C = 0.106$ nV_{RMS} L_1 is shorted	$I_{L1} = 0.106$ A_{RMS} $V_C = 0.106$ nV_{RMS} L_1 is shorted
	P13-40	$I_C = 0.079$ $A_{RMS} = I_L$ $V_C = 0.079$ nV_{RMS} C is shorted	$I_C = 0.079$ $A_{RMS} = I_L$ $V_C = 0.079$ nV_{RMS} C is shorted	$I_C = 0.079$ $A_{RMS} = I_L$ $V_C = 0.079$ nV_{RMS} C is shorted

	P13-41	$I_{R1} = 0.289$ mA$_{RMS}$ = I_{R2} = I_L $V_L = 0.089$ pV$_{RMS}$ L is shorted	$I_{R1} = 0.289$ mA$_{RMS}$ = I_{R2} = I_L $V_L = 0.089$ pV$_{RMS}$ L is shorted	$I_{R1} = 0.288$ mA$_{RMS}$ = I_{R2} = I_L $V_L = 0.288$ pV$_{RMS}$ L is shorted
14	P14-29	V_{IN} and V_{OUT} are both 500 Hz 5V square waves Capacitor is open	V_{IN} and V_{OUT} are both 500 Hz 5V square waves Capacitor is open	V_{IN} and V_{OUT} are both 500 Hz 5V square waves Capacitor is open
	P14-30	$R_2 = 999.99$ GΩ Output shows partial RC charging and discharging with $\tau \approx$ 4.7 µs R_2 is open	R_2 = -r- Output shows partial RC charging and discharging with $\tau \approx$ 4.7 µs R_2 is open	R_2 = -r- Output shows partial RC charging and discharging with $\tau \approx$ 4.7 µs R_2 is open
	P14-31	$\tau \approx 7.8$ µs No fault	$\tau \approx 7.526$ µs No fault	$\tau \approx 7.663$ µs No fault
	R14-32	$R_{L1} = 999.999$ GΩ $\tau \approx 20$ ns L_1 is open	R_{L1} = -r- $\tau \approx 19.898$ ns L_1 is open	R_{L1} = -r- $\tau \approx 20.101$ ns L_1 is open
15	P15-46	$V_{RL} = 108.7$ V$_{PP}$ = 54.3 V$_P$ Partial short in transformer	$V_{RL} = 108.8$ V$_{PP}$ = 54.4 V$_P$ Partial short in transformer	$V_{RL} = 108.8$ V$_{PP}$ = 54.4 V$_P$ Partial short in transformer
	P15-47	$V_{IN} = 4.9$ V$_{PP}$ $V_{OUT} = 0$ V Secondary is open	$V_{IN} = 4.95$ V$_{PP}$ $V_{OUT} = 0$ V Secondary is open	$V_{IN} = 4.943$ V$_{PP}$ $V_{OUT} = 0$ V Secondary is open
	P15-48	$V_{IN} = 27.2$ V$_{PP}$ $V_{OUT} = 54.4$ V$_{PP}$ No fault	$V_{IN} = 27.179$ V$_{PP}$ $V_{OUT} = 54.350$ V$_{PP}$ No fault	$V_{IN} = 27.174$ V$_{PP}$ $V_{OUT} = 54.344$ V$_{PP}$ No fault
	P15-49	$V_{IN} = 14.0$ V$_{PP}$ $V_{OUT} = 0$ V Primary is open	$V_{IN} = 13.998$ V$_{PP}$ $V_{OUT} = 0$ V Primary is open	$V_{IN} = 13.984$ V$_{PP}$ $V_{OUT} = 0$ V Primary is open
16	P16-43	$V_D = 5.000$ V$_{DC}$ Diode is open	$V_D = 5.000$ V$_{DC}$ Diode is open	$V_D = 5.000$ V$_{DC}$ Diode is open
	P16-44	$V_{D2} = 1.043$ pV$_{DC}$ D_2 is shorted	$V_{D2} = 1.043$ pV$_{DC}$ D_2 is shorted	$V_{D2} = 1.043$ pV$_{DC}$ D_2 is shorted
	P16-45	$V_{R1} = 3.645$ V$_{DC}$ $V_{R2} = 3.645$ V$_{DC}$ $V_{R3} = 2.710$ V$_{DC}$ $V_D = 0.653$ V$_{DC}$ $V_{R4} = 2.057$ V$_{DC}$ No fault	$V_{R1} = 3.645$ V$_{DC}$ $V_{R2} = 3.645$ V$_{DC}$ $V_{R3} = 2.710$ V$_{DC}$ $V_D = 0.653$ V$_{DC}$ $V_{R4} = 2.057$ V$_{DC}$ No fault	$V_{R1} = 3.645$ V$_{DC}$ $V_{R2} = 3.645$ V$_{DC}$ $V_{R3} = 2.710$ V$_{DC}$ $V_D = 0.653$ V$_{DC}$ $V_{R4} = 2.057$ V$_{DC}$ No fault
	P16-46	$V_{D2} = 1.970$ V$_{DC}$ D_2 is open	$V_{D2} = 1.970$ V$_{DC}$ D_2 is open	$V_{D2} = 1.970$ V$_{DC}$ D_2 is open
	P16-47	$V_{D1} = 0.240$ V$_{DC}$ $V_{D2} = 0.688$ V$_{DC}$ $V_{D3} = 0.693$ V$_{DC}$ D_1 is leaky	$V_{D1} = 0.240$ V$_{DC}$ $V_{D2} = 0.688$ V$_{DC}$ $V_{D3} = 0.693$ V$_{DC}$ D_1 is leaky	$V_{D1} = 0.240$ V$_{DC}$ $V_{D2} = 0.688$ V$_{DC}$ $V_{D3} = 0.693$ V$_{DC}$ D_1 is leaky
	P16-48	$V_D = 5.055$ pV$_{RMS}$ $V_R = 70.7$ V$_P$ = V_{IN} Diode is shorted	$V_D = 4.984$ pV$_{RMS}$ $V_R = 70.708$ V$_P$ = V_{IN} Diode is shorted	$V_D = 4.996$ pV$_{RMS}$ $V_R = 70.655$ V$_P$ = V_{IN} Diode is shorted
	P16-49	V_{OUT} is a half-wave rectified ouput $R_{D2} = 1.000$ TΩ D_2 is open	V_{OUT} is a half-wave rectified ouput R_{D2} = -r- D_2 is open	V_{OUT} is a half-wave rectified ouput R_{D2} = -r- D_2 is open
	P16-50	$R_{1,2} = 0.000$ Ω A bridge diode is shorted	$R_{1,2} = 0$ Ω A bridge diode is shorted	$R_{1,2} = 0$ Ω A bridge diode is shorted

	P16-51	$V_{OUT} = V_{IN}$ clipped at ±5.7 V No fault	$V_{OUT} = V_{IN}$ clipped at ±5.743 V No fault	$V_{OUT} = V_{IN}$ clipped at ±5.743 V No fault
	P16-52	$V_{R2} = V_D = 9.901$ V_{DC}	$V_{R2} = V_D = 9.901$ V_{DC}	$V_{R2} = V_D = 9.901$ V_{DC}
17	P17-47	$R_{BC} = 2.000$ TΩ Base-collector junction is open	R_{BC} = -r- Base-collector junction is open	R_{BC} = -r- Base-collector junction is open
	P17-48	$V_{OUT} = 680.5$ mV$_P$ No fault	$V_{OUT} = 682.156$ mV$_P$ No fault	$V_{OUT} = 677.237$ mV$_P$ No fault
	P17-49	$V_{DS} = 0.012$ nV$_{DC}$ Drain and source are shorted	$V_{DS} = 0.012$ nV$_{DC}$ Drain and source are shorted	$V_{DS} = 0.012$ nV$_{DC}$ Drain and source are shorted
	P17-50	$V_{R1} = 14.310$ V_{DC} $V_{R2} = 0.690$ V_{DC} $V_{R3} = 14.837$ V_{DC} $V_{BE} = 0.690$ V_{DC} R_2 is open	$V_{R1} = 14.310$ V_{DC} $V_{R2} = 0.690$ V_{DC} $V_{R3} = 14.837$ V_{DC} $V_{BE} = 0.690$ V_{DC} R_2 is open	$V_{R1} = 14.310$ V_{DC} $V_{R2} = 0.690$ V_{DC} $V_{R3} = 14.837$ V_{DC} $V_{BE} = 0.690$ V_{DC} R_2 is open
	P17-51	$V_{IN} = 706.4$ mV$_P$ $V_{OUT} = 690.6$ mV$_P$ No fault	$V_{IN} = 690.238$ mV$_P$ $V_{OUT} = 683.646$ mV$_P$ No fault	$V_{IN} = 673.134$ mV$_P$ $V_{OUT} = 673.134$ mV$_P$ No fault
	P17-52	$V_{IN} = 13.9$ mV$_P$ $V_{OUT} = 5.0$ mV$_P$ C_2 is open	$V_{IN} = 13.960$ mV$_P$ $V_{OUT} = 5.048$ mV$_P$ C_2 is open	$V_{IN} = 13.968$ mV$_P$ $V_{OUT} = 5.052$ mV$_P$ C_2 is open
	P17-53	$V_{IN} = 1.4$ V$_P$ $V_G = 0$ V$_P$ C_1 is open	$V_{IN} = 1.405$ V$_P$ $V_G = 0$ V$_P$ C_1 is open	$V_{IN} = 1.400$ V$_P$ $V_G = 0$ V$_P$ C_1 is open
18	P18-26	$V_{OUT} = 14.0$ mV$_P \approx V_{IN}$ R_2 is open	$V_{OUT} = 13.9$ mV$_P \approx V_{IN}$ R_2 is open	$V_{OUT} = 14.0$ mV$_P \approx V_{IN}$ R_2 is open
	P18-27	$R_1 = 999.999$ GΩ R_1 is open	R_1 = -r- R_1 is open	R_1 = -r- R_1 is open
	P18-28	$V_{OUT} = -11.1$ V$_{PP}$ $V_{IN} = 2.8$ V$_{PP}$ $A_V = -3.96$ No fault	$V_{OUT} = -11.105$ V$_{PP}$ $V_{IN} = 2.827$ V$_{PP}$ $A_V = -3.93$ No fault	$V_{OUT} = -11.106$ V$_{PP}$ $V_{IN} = 2.827$ V$_{PP}$ $A_V = -3.93$ No fault
	P18-29	$V_{OUT} = 0.0$ V$_{PP}$ $V_{IN} = 14.1$ V$_{PP} = 7.1$ V$_P$ The op-amp is faulty	$V_{OUT} = 0.000$ V$_{PP}$ $V_{IN} = 14.069$ V$_{PP} = 7.035$ V$_P$ The op-amp is faulty	$V_{OUT} = 0.0$ V$_{PP}$ $V_{IN} = 14.128$ V$_{PP} = 7.061$ V$_P$ The op-amp is faulty
	P18-30	$V_{OUT} = 0.0$ V$_{PP}$ $V_{IN} = 1.6$ V$_{PP} = 786$ mV$_P$ C is open	$V_{OUT} = 0.000$ V$_{PP}$ $V_{IN} = 1.572$ V$_{PP} = 786$ mV$_P$ C is open	$V_{OUT} = 0.000$ V$_{PP}$ $V_{IN} = 1.572$ V$_{PP} = 786$ mV$_P$ C is open
19	P19-29	$R_2 = 999.999$ GΩ R_2 is open	R_2 = -r- R_2 is open	R_2 = -r- R_2 is open
	P19-30	$V_{IN} = 2.432$ V_{DC} $V_{OUT} = 2.432$ V_{DC} Op-amp is open	$V_{IN} = 2.432$ V_{DC} $V_{OUT} = 2.432$ V_{DC} Op-amp is open	$V_{IN} = 2.432$ V_{DC} $V_{OUT} = 2.432$ V_{DC} Op-amp is open
	P19-31	$V_{OUT} = 1.7$ V in 262.0 μs before leading edge $V_{OUT} = -1.7$ V in 108.0 μs after leading edge No fault	$V_{OUT} = 1.678$ V in 267.9 μs before leading edge $V_{OUT} = -1.660$ V in 106.4 μs after leading edge No fault	$V_{OUT} = 1.665$ V in 261.3 μs before leading edge $V_{OUT} = -1.664$ V in 105.5 μs after leading edge No fault

	P19-32	V_{IN} is a 1 kHz 5V square wave $V(-) = 0$ V C_1 is open	V_{IN} is a 1 kHz 5V square wave $V(-) = 358.5$ pV_{PP} C_1 is open	V_{IN} is a 1 kHz 5V square wave $V(-) = 1.409$ pV_{PP} C_1 is open
20	P20-32	$R_G = 47.619$ Ω R_G is leaky	$R_G = 47.619$ Ω R_G is leaky	$R_G = 47.619$ Ω R_G is leaky
	P20-33	$V_{D1} = 2.566$ V_{RMS} $V_{D2} = 4.753$ pV_{RMS} D_2 shorted	$V_{D1} = 2.565$ V_{RMS} $V_{D2} = 4.752$ pV_{RMS} D_2 shorted	$V_{D1} = 2.565$ V_{RMS} $V_{D2} = 4.752$ pV_{RMS} D_2 shorted
	P20-34	$V_D = 0$ V_{PP} Diode is shorted	$V_D = 0$ V_{PP} Diode is shorted	$V_D = 0$ V_{PP} Diode is shorted
	P20-35	$V_D = 5.997$ V_{DC} Zener diode is open	$V_D = 5.997$ V_{DC} Zener diode is open	$V_D = 5.997$ V_{DC} Zener diode is open
	P20-36	$V_{R1} = 11.881$ V_{DC} $V_{R2} = 0.119$ V_{DC} R_4 is open	$V_{R1} = 11.881$ V_{DC} $V_{R2} = 0.119$ V_{DC} R_4 is open	$V_{R1} = 11.881$ V_{DC} $V_{R2} = 0.119$ V_{DC} R_4 is open

PART FOUR

Special Topics

A CIRCUIT BREADBOARDING AND MEASUREMENTS

Breadboarding a Circuit

The term *breadboarding* refers to the process of installing components on a circuit board and interconnecting them to form a specified circuit. One common type of circuit board used for constructing circuits in the laboratory is shown in Figure A-1. It consists of rows of small sockets into which component leads and jumper wires are inserted.

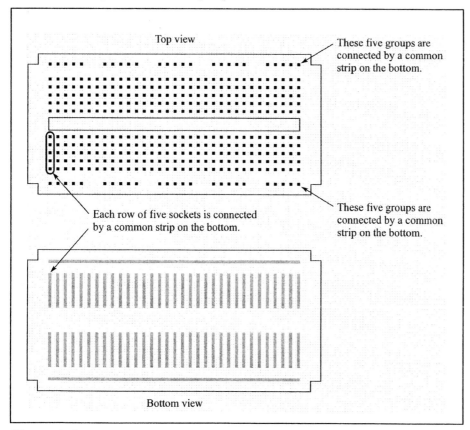

Figure A-1
A typical circuit board used for breadboarding.

In this particular configuration, all five sockets in each row are connected together and are effectively one electrical point as shown in the bottom view. All the sockets arranged on the outer edges of the board are typically connected together as shown. These two strips of sockets are normally used to distribute the supply voltages and ground to the circuit.

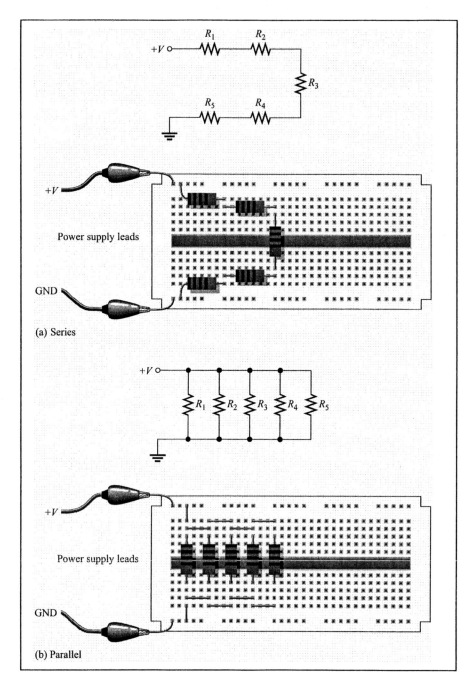

Figure A-2
Examples of breadboarding a circuit.

As examples of breadboarding a circuit, Figure A-2 shows how both simple series and parallel resistive circuits might be connected on the circuit board.

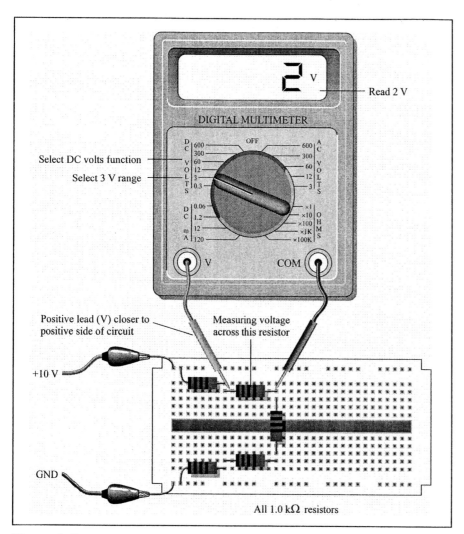

Figure A-3
Example of measuring voltage in a circuit.

Voltage Measurement

To measure voltage in a circuit using a multimeter, the following general steps should be taken:

1.   Insert the red (positive) meter lead into the connector labeled for *voltage* (V) on the meter and insert the black meter lead into the connector labeled *common* (COM).

2.   Set the function switch to the *volts* position (select either dc or ac).

3.   Set the range switch (the range switch and function switch are often the same) to the lowest setting that is higher than the voltage you expect to measure.

4.   Select the two points in the circuit between which you want to measure the voltage.

5.   Place the red meter lead on the point closest to the positive side of the circuit and the black lead on the point closest to the negative or ground side of the circuit as shown in Figure A-3.

6.   Read the voltage.

Current Measurement

To measure current in a circuit using a multimeter, the following general steps are taken:

1. Insert the red (positive) meter lead into the connector labeled for *current* (A or mA) on the meter and insert the black meter lead into the connector labeled *common* (COM).

2. Set the function switch to the *amps* position (select either dc or ac).

3. Set the range switch to the lowest setting that is higher than the current you expect to measure.

4. Select the point in the circuit at which you want to measure the current.

5. Turn off the power and break the circuit at the selected point by simply lifting a component lead or one end of a jumper wire from the socket. This permits the ammeter to be placed in series with the current path.

6. Insert the ammeter in the break by connecting the red lead to the point closest to the positive side of the circuit and the black lead to the point closest to the negative or ground side of the circuit as shown in Figure A-4.

7. Turn the power back on and read the current.

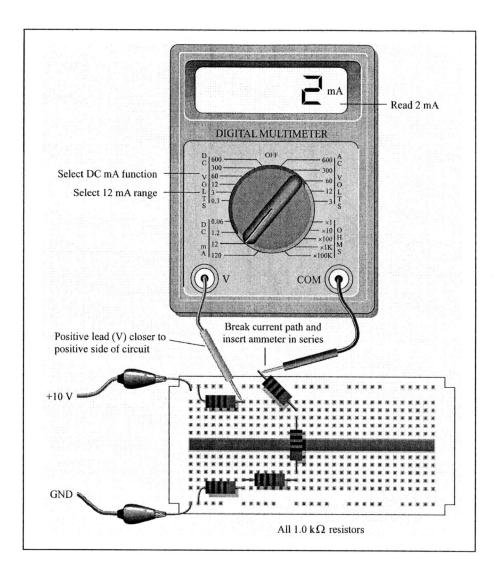

Read 2 mA

DIGITAL MULTIMETER

Select DC mA function

Select 12 mA range

Positive lead (V) closer to positive side of circuit

Break current path and insert ammeter in series

+10 V

GND

All 1.0 kΩ resistors

Figure A-4
Example of measuring current in a circuit.

Resistance Measurement

To measure resistance in a circuit using a multimeter, the following general steps are taken:

1. Insert one meter lead into the connector labeled for *ohms* (Ω) on the meter and the other lead into the connector labeled *common* (COM). Zero the ohmmeter if necessary.

2. Set the function switch to the *ohms* (Ω) position.

3. Select an appropriate multiplier setting ($\times1$, $\times10$, etc.).

4. Disconnect power from the circuit.

5. Remove the resistor to be measured or lift one lead so that it is disconnected from the rest of the circuit. If you wish to measure total resistance, none of the components has to be removed.

6. Connect the ohmmeter leads across the selected resistor as shown if Figure A-5. Polarity does not matter.

7. Read the resistance and reconnect the resistor and the power.

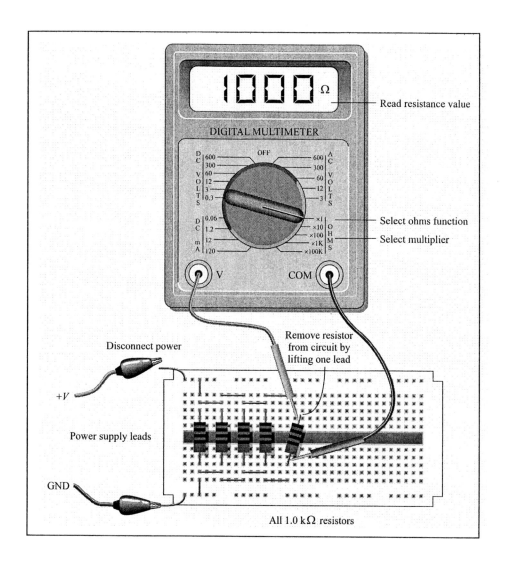

Figure A-5
Example of measuring resistance in a circuit.

DELTA-WYE (Δ-TO-Y) AND WYE-DELTA (Y-TO-Δ) NETWORK CONVERSIONS

A resistive delta (Δ) network has the form shown in Figure B-1(a). A wye (Y) network is shown in Figure B-1(b). Notice that letter subscripts are used to designate resistors in the delta network and that numerical subscripts are used to designate resistors in the wye.

Figure B-1
Delta and wye networks.

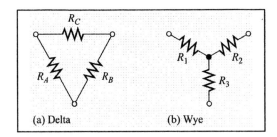

(a) Delta   (b) Wye

       Conversion between these two forms of circuits is sometimes helpful in areas such as bridge analysis and three-phase power systems. In this section, the conversion formulas and rules for remembering them are given.

Δ-to-Y Conversion

It is convenient to think of the wye positioned within the delta, as shown in Figure B-2. To convert from delta to wye, we need R_1, R_2, and R_3 in terms of R_A, R_B, and R_C. The conversion rule is as follows:

> *Each resistor in the wye is equal to the product of the resistors in two adjacent delta branches, divided by the sum of all three delta resistors.*

Figure B-2
"Y within Δ" aid for conversion formulas.

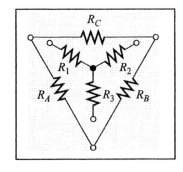

In Figure B-2, R_A and R_C are "adjacent" to R_1:

$$R_1 = \frac{R_A R_C}{R_A + R_B + R_C} \tag{1}$$

Also, R_B and R_C are "adjacent" to R_2:

$$R_2 = \frac{R_B R_C}{R_A + R_B + R_C} \tag{2}$$

and R_A and R_B are "adjacent" to R_3:

$$R_3 = \frac{R_A R_B}{R_A + R_B + R_C} \tag{3}$$

Y-to-Δ Conversion

To convert from wye to delta, we need R_A, R_B, and R_C in terms of R_1, R_2, and R_3. The conversion rule is as follows:

Each resistor in the delta is equal to the sum of all possible products of wye resistors taken two at a time, divided by the opposite wye resistor.

In Figure B-2, R_2 is "opposite " to R_A:

$$R_A = \frac{R_1 R_2 + R_1 R_3 + R_2 R_3}{R_2}$$

(4)

Also, R_1 is "opposite" to R_B:

$$R_B = \frac{R_1 R_2 + R_1 R_3 + R_2 R_3}{R_1}$$

(5)

and R_3 is "opposite" to R_C:

$$R_C = \frac{R_1 R_2 + R_1 R_3 + R_2 R_3}{R_3}$$

(6)

The following two examples illustrate conversion between these two forms of circuits.

Example 1

Convert the delta network in Figure B-3 to a wye network.

Figure B-3

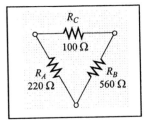

Solution Use Equations (1), (2), and (3):

$$R_1 = \frac{R_A R_C}{R_A + R_B + R_C} = \frac{(220\ \Omega)(100\ \Omega)}{220\ \Omega + 560\ \Omega + 100\ \Omega} = 25\ \Omega$$

$$R_2 = \frac{R_B R_C}{R_A + R_B + R_C} = \frac{(560\ \Omega)(100\ \Omega)}{880\ \Omega} = 63.6\ \Omega$$

$$R_3 = \frac{R_A R_B}{R_A + R_B + R_C} = \frac{(220\ \Omega)(560\ \Omega)}{880\ \Omega} = 140\ \Omega$$

The resulting wye network is shown in Figure B-4.

Figure B-4

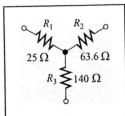

Example 2

Convert the wye network in Figure B-5 to a delta network.

Figure B-5

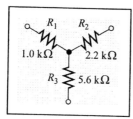

Solution Use Equations (4), (5), and (6):

$$R_A = \frac{R_1 R_2 + R_1 R_3 + R_2 R_3}{R_2}$$

$$= \frac{(1.0 \text{ k}\Omega)(2.2 \text{ k}\Omega) + (1.0 \text{ k}\Omega)(5.6 \text{ k}\Omega) + (2.2 \text{ k}\Omega)(5.6 \text{ k}\Omega)}{2.2 \text{ k}\Omega} = 9.15 \text{ k}\Omega$$

$$R_B = \frac{R_1 R_2 + R_1 R_3 + R_2 R_3}{R_1}$$

$$= \frac{(1.0 \text{ k}\Omega)(2.2 \text{ k}\Omega) + (1.0 \text{ k}\Omega)(5.6 \text{ k}\Omega) + (2.2 \text{ k}\Omega)(5.6 \text{ k}\Omega)}{1.0 \text{ k}\Omega} = 20.1 \text{ k}\Omega$$

$$R_C = \frac{R_1 R_2 + R_1 R_3 + R_2 R_3}{R_3}$$

$$= \frac{(1.0 \text{ k}\Omega)(2.2 \text{ k}\Omega) + (1.0 \text{ k}\Omega)(5.6 \text{ k}\Omega) + (2.2 \text{ k}\Omega)(5.6 \text{ k}\Omega)}{5.6 \text{ k}\Omega} = 3.59 \text{ k}\Omega$$

The resulting delta network is shown in Figure B-6.

Figure B-6

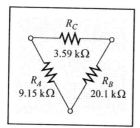

Application of Δ-to-Y Conversion to the Simplification of a Bridge Circuits

In Chapter 6 of the textbook, you saw how Thevenin's theorem can be used to simplify a bridge circuit. Now you will see how Δ-to-Y conversion can be used for conversion of a bridge circuit to a series parallel form for easier analysis.

Figure B-7 illustrates how the delta (Δ) formed by R_A, R_B, and R_C can be converted to a wye (Y), thus, creating an equivalent series-parallel circuit. Equations (1), (2), and (3) are used in this conversion.

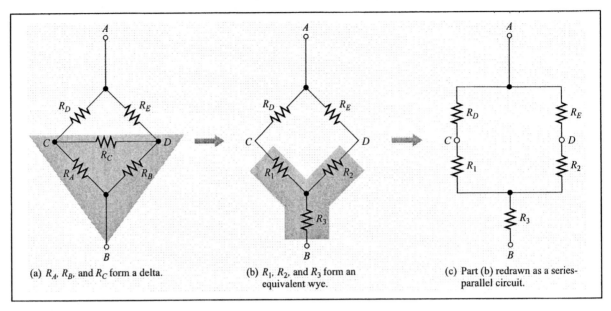

(a) R_A, R_B, and R_C form a delta.

(b) R_1, R_2, and R_3 form an equivalent wye.

(c) Part (b) redrawn as a series-parallel circuit.

Figure B-7
Conversion of a bridge circuit to a series-parallel configuration.

In a bridge circuit, the load is connected across points C and D. In Figure B-7(a), R_C represents the load resistor. When voltage is applied across points A and B, the voltage from C to D (V_{CD}) can be determined using the equivalent series-parallel circuit in Figure B-7(c) as follows. The total resistance from point A to point B is

$$R_T = \frac{(R_1 + R_D)(R_2 + R_E)}{(R_1 + R_D) + (R_2 + R_E)} + R_3$$

Then

$$I_T = \frac{V_{AB}}{R_T}$$

The resistance of the parallel portion of the circuit in Figure B-7(c) is

$$R_{T(p)} = \frac{(R_1 + R_D)(R_2 + R_E)}{(R_1 + R_D) + (R_2 + R_E)}$$

The current through the left branch is

$$I_{AC} = \left(\frac{R_{T(p)}}{R_1 + R_D} \right) I_T$$

The current through the right branch is

$$I_{AD} = \left(\frac{R_{T(p)}}{R_2 + R_E} \right) I_T$$

260

The voltage at point C with respect to point A is

$$V_{CA} = V_A - I_{AC}R_D$$

The voltage at point D with respect to point A is

$$V_{DA} = V_A - I_{AD}R_E$$

The voltage from point C to point D is

$$V_{CD} = V_{CA} - V_{DA} = (V_A - I_{AC}R_D) - (V_A - I_{AD}R_E)$$
$$= I_{AD}R_E - I_{AC}R_D$$

V_{CD} is the voltage across the load (R_C) in the bridge circuit of Figure B-7(a). The current through the load can be found by Ohm's law:

$$I_C = \frac{V_{CD}}{R_C}$$

Example 3

Determine the load voltage and the load current in the bridge circuit in Figure B-8. Notice that the resistors are labeled for convenient conversion using the previous formulas. R_C is the load resistor.

Figure B-8

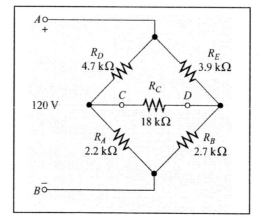

Solution First convert the delta formed by R_A, R_B, and R_C to a wye:

$$R_1 = \frac{R_A R_C}{R_A + R_B + R_C} = \frac{(2.2\ k\Omega)(18\ k\Omega)}{2.2\ k\Omega + 2.7\ k\Omega + 18\ k\Omega} = 1.73\ k\Omega$$

$$R_2 = \frac{R_B R_C}{R_A + R_B + R_C} = \frac{(2.7\ k\Omega)(18\ k\Omega)}{22.9\ k\Omega} = 2.12\ k\Omega$$

$$R_3 = \frac{R_A R_B}{R_A + R_B + R_C} = \frac{(2.2\ k\Omega)(2.7\ k\Omega)}{22.9\ k\Omega} = 259\ \Omega$$

261

The resulting equivalent series-parallel circuit is shown in Figure B-9.

Figure B-9

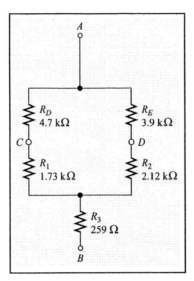

Now determine R_T and the branch currents in Figure B-9.

$$R_T = \frac{(R_1 + R_D)(R_2 + R_E)}{(R_1 + R_D) + (R_2 + R_E)} + R_3 = \frac{(6.43 \text{ k}\Omega)(6.02 \text{ k}\Omega)}{6.43 \text{ k}\Omega + 6.02 \text{ k}\Omega} + 259 \,\Omega = 3.37 \text{ k}\Omega$$

$$I_T = \frac{V_{AB}}{R_T} = \frac{120 \text{ V}}{3.37 \text{ k}\Omega} = 35.6 \text{ mA}$$

The total resistance of the parallel part of the circuit, $R_{T(p)}$, is 3.11 kΩ.

$$I_{AC} = \left(\frac{R_{T(p)}}{R_1 + R_D}\right)I_T = \left(\frac{3.11 \text{ k}\Omega}{1.73 \text{ k}\Omega + 4.7 \text{ k}\Omega}\right)35.6 \text{ mA} = 17.2 \text{ mA}$$

$$I_{AD} = \left(\frac{R_{T(p)}}{R_2 + R_E}\right)I_T = \left(\frac{3.11 \text{ k}\Omega}{2.12 \text{ k}\Omega + 3.9 \text{ k}\Omega}\right)35.6 \text{ mA} = 18.4 \text{ mA}$$

The voltage across the load is

$$\begin{aligned}
V_{CD} &= I_{AD}R_E - I_{AC}R_D \\
&= (18.4 \text{ mA})(3.9 \text{ k}\Omega) - (17.2 \text{ mA})(4.7 \text{ k}\Omega) \\
&= 71.8 \text{ V} - 80.8 \text{ V} = -9 \text{ V}
\end{aligned}$$

The load current

$$I_C = \frac{V_{CD}}{R_C} = \frac{-9 \text{ V}}{18 \text{ k}\Omega} = -500 \,\mu\text{A}$$

PART FIVE

Test Item File
to accompany

Electronics Fundamentals, Seventh Edition
by Floyd

Contents

Chapter 1   Quantities and Units

True or False

1) 0.0047 amps can be expressed in metric units as 47 μA.

2) 0.00015 can be expressed in powers of ten as 1.5×10^{-4}.

3) The symbol μ is an abbreviation for 10^{-6} or *micro*.

4) Scientific notation is the most widely used form of technical notation in electronics.

5) Engineering notation is typically used in the expression of extremely large and small quantities in the electronics field.

6) In engineering notation, 82,500 is expressed as 8.25×10^3.

7) In engineering notation 0.0047 is expressed as 4.7×10^{-3}.

Multiple Choice

8) The electrical symbol for inductance is _____.
   A) C   B) I   C) V   D) L

9) The symbol for electrical charge is _____.
   A) Q   B) C   C) V   D) I

10) The value 1.2×10^{-6} can be expressed as _____.
   A) 0.00012   B) 1.2 m or milli   C) 1.2 μ or micro   D) 1.2 M or Meg

11) If your calculator displays 3.45607×10^6, the equivalent metric value is _____.
   A) 3.456 micro   B) 3.456 Mega   C) 34.56 Mega   D) 3.456 kilo

12) The metric value 16 mA can be expressed as _____.
   A) 16×10^{-6} A   B) 16×10^3 A   C) 16×10^{-3} A   D) 16×10^0 A

13) To enter 0.00000056 into your calculator, use the entry _____.
   A) 56 –06   B) 5.6 –08   C) 56 –08   D) 00056 –05

14) Determine the correct calculation.

    A) $5600 \times (9.6 \times 10^{-7}) = 5.376$ milli   B) 4.7 m $\div 1.24 = .379$ m

    C) 89.4 k $\times 1.2$ m $= 1.072$ km   D) $5.6 \div 17$ m $= 32.9$ m

15) The correct expression for 8.54×10^{-5} is _____.

    A) 854 pico   B) 85.4 milli   C) 85.4 micro   D) 85.4 kilo

16) If you are trying to enter the number 16,000 into your calculator, the correct entry is _____.

    A) 1.6 02   B) 1.6 03   C) 1.6 05   D) 1.6 04

17) Express 7.5×10^{-4} in milli, basic units, and micro.

    A) 7.5 milli, 0.075, 75000 micro   B) 75 milli, 0.075, 7500 micro

    C) 75 milli, 0.0075, 750 micro   D) 0.75 milli, 0.00075, 750 micro

18) Express these two calculator displays in correct metric units:
    5.6 –07   2.2 05

    A) 56 micro, 22 kilo   B) 0.56 micro, 0.022 Meg

    C) 0.56 micro, 220 kilo   D) 56 micro, 220 kilo

19) The electrical symbol for voltage is _____.

    A) I   B) V   C) C   D) R

20) If your calculator displays **3.5 –06**, the equivalent metric value is _____.

    A) 35 milli   B) 35 micro   C) 3.5 Meg   D) 3.5 micro   E) 3.5 pico

21) Express 5.6×10^{-2} in milli, basic units, and micro.

    A) 5.6 milli, 0.056, 56000 micro   B) 56 milli, 0.056, 56000 micro

    C) 560 milli, 5.600, 5600 micro   D) 5600 milli, 56, 560

22) The difference between scientific and engineering notation is _____.

    A) powers of ten representation

    B) single vs multiple digits before decimal point

    C) groupings of multiple of three digits

    D) all of these

23) Mega is what relation to kilo?

    A) 10 times   B) 100 times

    C) 1000 times   D) 1,000,000 times

24) Pico is what relation to micro?

    A) 1/10th   B) 1/100th   C) 1/1,000th   D) 1/1,000,000th

25) Convert 0.00047 microfarads (μF) to the equivalent picofarads (pF).

    A) 0.47 pF   B) 4.7 pF   C) 47 pF   D) 470 pF

26) Add 21 mA and 8000 μA and express the result in milliamperes.

    A) 21.8 mA   B) 218 mA   C) 29 mA   D) 290 mA

27) Multiply 3 mA by 1000 μA and express the result in microamperes.

    A) 3 μA B) 30 μA C) 300 μA D) 3000 μA

28) 500 mA is equal to _____.

    A) 0.5 Amps   B) 500,000 μA

    C) 0.0005 kA   D) all of the above

29) The metric prefix μ (micro) is normally associated with _____ measurements.

    A) small   B) extremely small

    C) large   D) extremely large

30) 0.6 kV is equal to _____.

    A) 60 V   B) 6 V   C) 0.6 V   D) 600 V

31) 86,000 expressed in scientific notation equals _____.

    A) 8.6×10^3 B) 8.6×10^4 C) 860×10^2 D) 8.6×10^{-4}

1) FALSE
   Diff: 2
2) TRUE
   Diff: 2
3) TRUE
   Diff: 1
4) FALSE
   Diff: 1
5) TRUE
   Diff: 1
6) FALSE
   Diff: 2
7) TRUE
   Diff: 2
8) D
   Diff: 1
9) A
   Diff: 1
10) C
    Diff: 2
11) C
    Diff: 2
12) C
    Diff: 2
13) C
    Diff: 1
14) A
    Diff: 3
15) C
    Diff: 2
16) D
    Diff: 2
17) D
    Diff: 2
18) C
    Diff: 2
19) B
    Diff: 1
20) D
    Diff: 2
21) B
    Diff: 2
22) D
    Diff: 1

23) C
    Diff: 1
24) D
    Diff: 1
25) D
    Diff: 2
26) C
    Diff: 2
27) A
    Diff: 2
28) D
    Diff: 2
29) B
    Diff: 1
30) D
    Diff: 2
31) B
    Diff: 2

Chapter 2 Voltage, Current, and Resistance

True or False

1) The movement of free electrons through a conductor is called *current*.

2) Electrons attract each other.

3) A resistor color coded with yellow, violet and orange bands has a value of 4.7 kΩ.

4) A *SPST* switch is used to control one circuit.

5) To measure the current through a resistor, place the ammeter so the current must pass through the meter.

6) The *ohm* is the basic unit of resistance.

7) A resistor color-coded with brown, black and orange bands has a value of 10,000 Ω.

8) A *Normally Open Push Button* switch can carry current when not pushed.

9) Electrons have a positive charge.

10) *Resistance* is the opposition to the flow of current.

11) An element with a relatively large amount of electrons in the valence ring is considered to be a good conductor.

12) Electromotive force is measured in volts.

13) The Nickel–Metal Hydride battery is an example of a secondary battery.

14) A generator converts electrical energy into mechanical energy.

15) For electrical current to flow in a circuit voltage must be applied to that circuit.

Multiple Choice

16) A _____ is a material that has many free electrons.

   A) conductor

   B) insulator

   C) semiconductor

   D) poor conductor

17) An insulator is a material with _____.

   A) some free electrons

   B) very many free electrons

   C) very few free electrons

   D) all free electrons

18) A resistor with orange, orange, red and gold bands has a value and tolerance of _____.

   A) 3.3 kΩ ±10%   B) 3.3 kΩ ±5%   C) 33 kΩ ±5%   D) 33 kΩ ±10%

19) If a resistor is color coded with red, red, orange and silver bands, the resistance equals _____, the lower tolerance limit equals _____, and the upper tolerance limit equals _____.

   A) 22 kΩ, 17.6 kΩ, 26.4 kΩ

   B) 22 kΩ, 20.9 kΩ, 23.1 kΩ

   C) 22 kΩ, 19.8 kΩ, 24.2 kΩ

   D) 22 kΩ, 21.5 kΩ, 22.4 kΩ

20) The opposition to the flow of current is called _____.

   A) voltage   B) current   C) capacitance   D) resistance

21) If the current in a circuit equals 0 A, it is likely that the _____.

   A) voltage is too high

   B) resistance is too low

   C) circuit has a short

   D) circuit is open

22) If the measured circuit current is zero, it is likely that the _____.

   A) circuit has a short

   B) voltage is turned off

   C) resistance is very low

   D) circuit voltage is very high

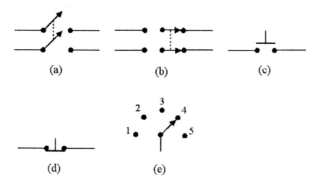

Figure 2–1

23) Identify the *Normally Open Push Button* switch in Figure 2–1.

    A) graph (a)   B) graph (b)   C) graph (c)   D) graph (d)   E) graph (e)

24) Identify the *DPST* switch in Figure 2–1.

    A) graph (a)   B) graph (b)   C) graph (c)   D) graph (d)   E) graph (e)

25) Identify the *Rotary* switch in Figure 2–1.

    A) graph (a)   B) graph (b)   C) graph (c)   D) graph (d)   E) graph (e)

26) Which switch in Figure 2–1 could be used to simultaneously open and close two circuits?

    A) graph (a)   B) graph (b)   C) graph (c)   D) graph (d)   E) graph (e)

27) Identify the *Normally Closed Push Button* switch in Figure 2–1.

    A) graph (a)   B) graph (b)   C) graph (c)   D) graph (d)   E) graph (e)

28) Which switch in Figure 2–1 is usually used to control a doorbell?

    A) graph (a)   B) graph (b)   C) graph (c)   D) graph (d)   E) graph (e)

29) The *Rotary* switch in Figure 2–1 is most likely to be used as _____.

    A) an old manual TV channel selector.

    B) a selector for different voltages in a power supply.

    C) a range selector switch in an analog voltmeter.

    D) all of the above

30) Identify the *DPDT* switch in Figure 2–1.

    A) graph (a)   B) graph (b)   C) graph (c)   D) graph (d)   E) graph (e)

31) Which switch in Figure 2-1 could be used to control a light and a fan at the same time?

    A) graph (a)   B) graph (b)   C) graph (c)   D) graph (d)   E) graph (e)

32) Which switch in Figure 2-1 could be used to switch two inputs to different output positions?

    A) graph (a)   B) graph (b)   C) graph (c)   D) graph (d)   E) graph (e)

33) Which switch in Figure 2-1 could be used to open a circuit momentarily?

    A) graph (a)   B) graph (b)   C) graph (c)   D) graph (d)   E) graph (e)

34) What do you call a diagram that shows the electrical connections of a circuit's components?

    A) a pictorial diagram   B) a block diagram

    C) a schematic diagram   D) an electrical diagram

35) To measure a circuit's source voltage, the voltmeter must _____.

    A) be placed in series in the circuit

    B) have the red lead towards the negative side of the source

    C) have the black lead towards the positive side of the source

    D) be placed across the source

36) A source, a path, and a load _____.

    A) make up a basic circuit

    B) can only be an open circuit

    C) will allow current to flow if the switch is open

    D) do not make up a complete circuit

37) Voltage is _____.

    A) the opposition to the flow of current

    B) the movement of free electrons

    C) the force that exists between charged particles

    D) the force that causes water to flow

38) Which unit of charge contains 6.25×10^{18} electrons?

    A) an ampere   B) a joule   C) a volt   D) a coulomb

39) A conductor is a material that has _____.

    A) few free electrons   B) a positive charge

    C) many free electrons   D) a structure similar to semiconductors

40) If a resistor equals 1.2 Ω ±5%, its color code is _____.

    A) brown, black, red, gold   B) brown, red, silver, gold

    C) brown, black, gold, silver   D) brown, red, gold, gold

41) Every electrical circuit must contain _____.

    A) a source, a load and a resistor   B) a battery, a resistor and a capacitor

    C) a source, a load and a path   D) a battery, a path and a switch

42) In order to measure the current in a circuit, an ammeter must _____.

    A) be placed across the load

    B) be placed so the current must pass through the meter

    C) be placed across the source

    D) all of these

43) A resistor with yellow, violet, orange and silver bands equals _____.

    A) 47 MΩ ±10%   B) 47 kΩ ±5%   C) 47 kΩ ±10%   D) 4.7 kΩ ±10%

44) A resistor with yellow, violet, orange, and gold bands equals _____.

    A) 47 MΩ ±10%   B) 47 kΩ ±5%   C) 47 kΩ ±10%   D) 4.7 kΩ ±10%

45) If a resistor is color coded with orange, orange, orange and silver bands, the resistance equals _____, the lower tolerance limit equals _____ and the upper tolerance limit equals _____.

    A) 33 kΩ, 32,670 Ω, 33,330 Ω B) 33 kΩ, 31,350 Ω, 34,650 Ω

    C) 33 kΩ, 29,700 Ω, 36,300 Ω D) 33 kΩ, 26,400 Ω, 39,600 Ω

46) A 100 kΩ ±10% resistor is color coded _____.

    A) black, brown, yellow, silver   B) brown, green, black, gold

    C) brown, black, yellow, gold   D) brown, black, yellow, silver

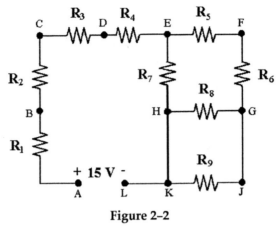

Figure 2-2

47) In Figure 2-2, if you place a voltmeter's red lead on point E and its black lead on point H, you will be measuring _____.

    A) V$_{R4}$ B) V$_{R7}$ C) V$_{R5}$ D) V$_{R6}$

48) To measure the current that flows through R$_6$ in Figure 2-2, the circuit must be opened and the ammeter placed at point _____.

    A) E   B) F   C) G   D) H

49) In Figure 2-2, the voltage V$_{GH}$ is the same as _____.

    A) V$_{R5}$ B) V$_{R6}$ C) V$_{R7}$ D) V$_{R8}$

50) In Figure 2-2, the voltage V$_{FG}$ is the same as _____.

    A) V$_{R6}$ B) V$_{R7}$ C) V$_{R8}$ D) V$_{R9}$

51) In Figure 2-2, a voltmeter placed across points C and D will measure _____.

    A) V$_{R1}$ B) V$_{R2}$ C) V$_{R3}$ D) V$_{R4}$

52) In Figure 2-2, the voltage V$_{CE}$ is the same as _____.

    A) V$_{R5}$ B) V$_{R3}$ + V$_{R4}$ C) V$_{R4}$ + V$_{R5}$ D) V$_{R6}$

53) An analog meter has _____.

    A) a digital readout

    B) a needle and a scale to indicate the value

    C) no moving parts

    D) a high degree of accuracy

54) An ohmmeter should _____.

    A) be connected across a circuit with the power on

    B) be inserted into the circuit so the current flows through it

    C) be placed across the resistor after the resistor has been disconnected from the circuit

    D) have the polarity carefully checked before its use

55) Most DMMs will measure _____ _____ and _____.

    A) frequency, voltage, current   B) voltage, current, capacitance

    C) voltage, frequency, resistance   D) voltage, current, resistance

56) On a resistor with five bands of color code, the fifth band may represent that:

    A) the resistor is a precision resistor.   B) the tolerance in percentage of value.

    C) the reliability in percentage of failure.   D) all of these.

57) On a resistor with four bands of color code, the fourth band represents:

    A) the voltage rating.   B) the wattage rating.

    C) the multiplier value.   D) the tolerance percentage.

58) On a resistor with numbers and letters, the position of the letter in the sequence represents:

    A) the numerical total.   B) the tolerance.

    C) the decimal point.   D) the resistance value.

59) Interpret the following mixed numbers and letters 4R7 on a resistor to the correct resistance of:

    A) 4.7 ohms.   B) 47 ohms.   C) 4.7 Kilohms.   D) 4.7 Megohms.

60) Interpret the following mixed numbers and letters 3M3 on a resistor to the correct resistance of:

    A) 3.3 Kilohms.   B) 33 Kilohms.   C) 330 Kilohms.   D) 3300 Kilohms.

61) Potentiometers and rheostats differ in that:

    A) potentiometers are used to vary voltages, while rheostats vary currents.

    B) potentiometers utilize three terminals, while rheostats usually use only two terminals.

    C) potentiometers utilize linear and nonlinear tapers, while rheostats utilize usually only linear tapers.

    D) all of these.

62) The most popular type of resistors are:

    A) carbon film.   B) metal film.

    C) carbon–composition.   D) wirewound.

63) In the American Wire Gauge sizes, as the numerical value of AWG goes higher, the cross sectional area of the wire:

    A) decreases.   B) halves.   C) increases.   D) doubles.

64) The basic difference between a fuse and a circuit breaker is that:

    A) a fuse is faster.   B) a fuse is reusable.

    C) a circuit breaker is reusable.   D) a circuit breaker is more reliable.

65) Which type of resistor is used for high power applications?

    A) film   B) carbon composition

    C) surface mount   D) wire wound

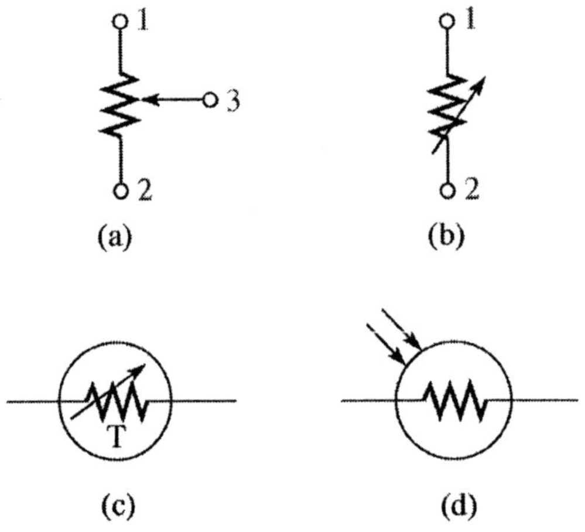

(a)   (b)

(c)   (d)

Figure 2–3

66) What does the schematic symbol (b) represent in Figure 2–3?

    A) rheostat   B) potentiometer

    C) thermistor   D) photoconductive cell

67) Which of the following is not a type of variable resistor?

    A) thermistor   B) potentiometer

    C) photoconductive cell   D) All are types of variable resistors.

68) The voltage measured directly across an open switch in a circuit will be:

A) 0 V.

B) full applied voltage.

C) half of applied voltage.

D) unpredictable.

69) What is the key difference when taking voltage measurements with an analog meter versus a digital meter?

A) where the negative lead is placed

B) adjustment of the scale

C) proper choice of the scale on the display

D) safety procedure in taking the measurement

1) TRUE
   Diff: 1
2) FALSE
   Diff: 1
3) FALSE
   Diff: 2
4) TRUE
   Diff: 1
5) TRUE
   Diff: 2
6) TRUE
   Diff: 1
7) TRUE
   Diff: 2
8) FALSE
   Diff: 1
9) FALSE
   Diff: 1
10) TRUE
    Diff: 1
11) FALSE
    Diff: 1
12) TRUE
    Diff: 1
13) TRUE
    Diff: 1
14) FALSE
    Diff: 1
15) TRUE
    Diff: 1
16) A
    Diff: 1
17) C
    Diff: 1
18) B
    Diff: 2
19) C
    Diff: 2
20) D
    Diff: 1
21) D
    Diff: 3
22) B
    Diff: 3

23) C
    Diff: 2
24) A
    Diff: 2
25) E
    Diff: 2
26) A
    Diff: 2
27) D
    Diff: 2
28) C
    Diff: 2
29) D
    Diff: 2
30) B
    Diff: 2
31) A
    Diff: 2
32) B
    Diff: 2
33) D
    Diff: 2
34) C
    Diff: 1
35) D
    Diff: 2
36) A
    Diff: 1
37) C
    Diff: 1
38) D
    Diff: 1
39) C
    Diff: 1
40) D
    Diff: 2
41) C
    Diff: 1
42) B
    Diff: 2
43) C
    Diff: 2
44) B
    Diff: 2

45) C
    Diff: 2
46) D
    Diff: 2
47) B
    Diff: 2
48) B
    Diff: 2
49) D
    Diff: 2
50) A
    Diff: 2
51) C
    Diff: 2
52) B
    Diff: 2
53) B
    Diff: 1
54) C
    Diff: 2
55) D
    Diff: 1
56) D
    Diff: 1
57) D
    Diff: 1
58) C
    Diff: 1
59) A
    Diff: 2
60) D
    Diff: 1
61) D
    Diff: 2
62) C
    Diff: 1
63) A
    Diff: 1
64) C
    Diff: 1
65) D
    Diff: 1
66) A
    Diff: 2

67) D
    Diff: 1
68) B
    Diff: 3
69) C
    Diff: 2

Chapter 3   Ohm's Law, Energy, and Power

True or False

1) If the current is constant, voltage and resistance are directly proportional.

2) If a circuit's supply voltage is 15 V and its resistance is 4700 Ω, its current is 3.19 mA.

3) If a 1 kΩ resistor has 32 mA flowing through it, it dissipates 1.024 W.

4) If a circuit's resistance increases, its current decreases.

5) If a 47 kΩ resistor carries 5 mA, it's safe to use a 1 W resistor.

6) If a circuit's supply voltage is 20 V and its resistance is 3300 Ω, its current is 6.06 mA.

7) If a 2.5 kΩ resistor carries 45 mA, it is dissipating 5.0625 W.

8) If a circuit's resistance decreases, its current also decreases.

9) If a 56 kΩ resistor carries 10 mA, it is safe to use a 10 W resistor.

10) If a 12 kΩ resistor carries 12 mA, the resistor drops 1 V.

11) If the voltage applied to a circuit doubles, then power dissipation doubles.

12) Power rating for a resistor is mainly based on the physical size.

13) An electronic power supply with a rated current capacity of 500 mA can adequately illuminate a 10 V @ 5 W lamp.

14) When taking current measurements, it is extremely important not to accidentally place the meter across the voltage source.

Multiple Choice

15) Voltage and current are _____.

    A) directly proportional   B) inversely proportional

    C) unrelated   D) quantities that add

16) If the voltage across a circuit increases, _____.

    A) the current decreases   B) the resistance increases

    C) the resistance decreases   D) the current increases

17) According to Ohm's Law, if voltage were to decrease while resistance remained the same, current would

    A) increase   B) decrease

    C) remain the same   D) no way to determine

18) According to Ohm's Law, if voltage were to increase while resistance remained the same, current would

    A) increase   B) decrease

    C) remain the same   D) no way to determine

19) According to Ohm's Law, if resistance were to decrease while voltage remained the same, current would

    A) increase   B) decrease

    C) remain the same   D) no way to determine

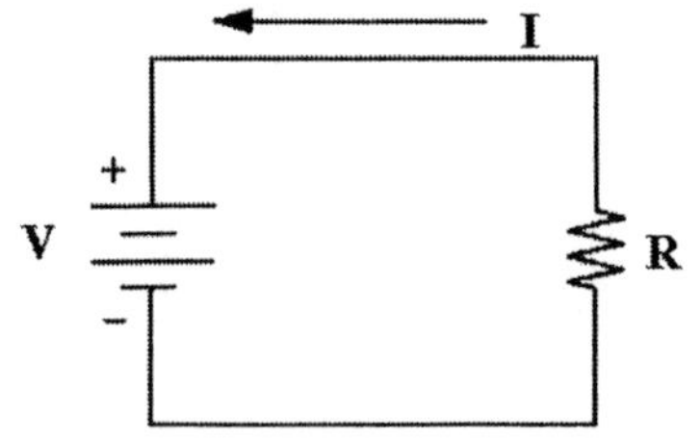

Figure 3–1

20) If $V = 25$ V and $R = 50$ kΩ in Figure 3–1, the current equals _____.

    A) 50 mA   B) 5 mA   C) 0.5 mA   D) 2 mA

21) If $I = 64$ mA and $R = 470$ Ω in Figure 3–1, the voltage equals _____.

    A) 30.08 V   B) 3.008 V   C) 73.43 V   D) 7.343 V

22) If V = 72 V and I = 12 mA in Figure 3-1, the resistance equals _____.

    A) 0.166 Ω B) 6 kΩ C) 864 Ω D) 47 kΩ

23) If V = 12 V and a 12 kΩ resistor shorts in Figure 3-1, the current is _____.

    A) 1 mA   B) 10 mA

    C) 0 A   D) extremely high

24) If the resistor opens in Figure 3-1, the following circuit conditions would exist.

    A) no power dissipation   B) no current flow

    C) resistor would read infinite resistance   D) all of the above

25) If V=12V and a 12kΩ resistor were to open in Figure 3-1, the current is _____.

    A) 1 mA   B) 10 mA

    C) 0 A   D) extremely high

26) If the voltage is suddenly switched off in Figure 3-1, _____.

    A) the current will suddenly drop to 0 A

    B) the current will gradually decrease to 0 A

    C) the current will first increase and then decrease to 0 A

    D) there is no way to predict the current

27) If V = 100 V and I = 1 mA in Figure 3-1, the power dissipated by the resistor equals _____.

    A) 10 W   B) 1 W   C) 100 mW   D) 10 mW

28) If I = 32 mA and R = 469 Ω in Figure 3-1, the voltage equals _____.

    A) 12 V   B) 15 V   C) 19 V   D) 22 V

29) If voltage is 12 V and the resistance is color-coded brown-black-orange in Figure 3-1, what are the minimum and maximum possible currents?

    A) $I_{MINIMUM}$ = 1.2 mA, $I_{MAXIMUM}$ = 1.4 mA

    B) $I_{MINIMUM}$ = 1 mA, $I_{MAXIMUM}$ = 1.6 mA

    C) $I_{MINIMUM}$ = 0.8 mA, $I_{MAXIMUM}$ = 1.2 mA

    D) $I_{MINIMUM}$ = 1 mA, $I_{MAXIMUM}$ = 1.5 mA

30) If the resistor opens in Figure 3–1, the _____.

    A) power dissipation increases   B) circuit current drops to 0 A

    C) source voltage decreases to 0 V   D) resistance decreases

31) If I = 64 mA and R = 47 Ω in Figure 3–1, the voltage equals _____.

    A) 30.08 V   B) 3.008 V   C) 73.43 V   D) 7.343 V

32) If V = 85 V and I = 15 mA in Figure 3–1, the resistance equals _____.

    A) 1.275 Ω   B) 52.3 Ω   C) 5.667 kΩ   D) 566 Ω

33) If V = 50 V and I = 37 mA in Figure 3–1, _____ is dissipated by the resistor.

    A) 1.85 W   B) 1.35 W   C) 0.185 m W   D) 135 m W

34) If V = 50 V and R = 25 kΩ in Figure 3–1, the current equals _____.

    A) 50 mA   B) 5 mA   C) 0.5 mA   D) 2 mA

35) If I = 45 mA and R = 40 kΩ in Figure 3–1, the voltage equals _____.

    A) 1.125 V   B) 1800 V   C) 18 V   D) 1.8 V

36) If a 10 kΩ resistor dissipates 0.5 W in Figure 3–1, then the supply voltage equals _____.

    A) 5000 V   B) 70.7 V   C) 7.07 m V   D) 50 V

37) If the voltage is 15 V and resistance is color coded red–red–brown–silver in Figure 3–1, what are the maximum and minimum possible current?

    A) $I_{MINIMUM}$ = 71.8 mA, $I_{MAXIMUM}$ = 64.9 mA

    B) $I_{MINIMUM}$ = 75.8 mA, $I_{MAXIMUM}$ = 62.0 mA

    C) $I_{MINIMUM}$ = 85.2 mA, $I_{MAXIMUM}$ = 56.8 mA

    D) none of these

38) If V = 60 V and R = 47 kΩ in Figure 3–1, the current equals _____.

    A) 1.28 mA   B) 12.8 mA   C) 128 mA   D) 0.128 mA

39) If a 1/2 W resistor is used in the circuit in Figure 3-1, the current value _____.

    A) is over 12 mA

    B) is less than 12 mA

    C) depends upon the voltage applied

    D) depends upon the circuit's voltage and resistance

40) If the voltage were suddenly switched on in Figure 3-1, _____.

    A) the current would gradually decrease

    B) the current would be zero

    C) the current would flow

    D) the current would gradually decrease and then increase

41) If I = 27 mA and R = 4.7 Ω in Figure 3-1, the voltage equals _____.

    A) 127 mV   B) 5.74 V   C) 174 mV   D) 7.8 V

42) If a resistor that is color-coded yellow-violet-orange-gold is placed across a 15 V source, the resistance and wattage rating could be _____.

    A) 4.7 kΩ 1/8 W   B) 47 kΩ 1/4 W

    C) 4700 Ω 1/4 W   D) 0.47 M Ω 1/4 W

43) A 220 Ω 1/2 W resistor has burned open, so you look in your parts box to find a replacement. Which one of the following resistors could you use to repair the circuit?

    A) 2200 Ω 1/2 W   B) 220 Ω 1/4 W   C) 220 Ω 1/8 W   D) 220 Ω 1 W

44) What is the resistance of a 100 W bulb when it is operating in a circuit with a supply of 120 V?

    A) 56 Ω   B) 2.14 Ω   C) 144 Ω   D) 560 Ω

45) If a resistor is rated at 1/2 W, it _____.

    A) can safely dissipate 1/2 W of power

    B) always dissipates 1/2 W

    C) always provides 1/2 W of power

    D) can only dissipate more than 1/2 W of power

46) Which is the correct formula for Ohm's Law?

    A) V = I ÷ R   B) R = V × I   C) I = V ÷ R   D) P = V × I

47) If a resistor that is color-coded yellow–violet–brown–gold is connected to a 12 V source, then what is the current flow?

    A) 24.3 mA   B) 25.5 mA   C) 26.9 mA   D) 255 mA

48) Resistance and current are _____.

    A) directly proportional   B) inversely proportional

    C) not related   D) similar to voltage

49) Which of the following terms is **not** a resistor rating?

    A) resistor value in ohms   B) resistor tolerance

    C) current   D) power rating

50) A 250 µA current flowing through a 4.7 kΩ resistor produces a _____ voltage drop.

    A) 53.2 V   B) 1.175 mV   C) 18.8 V   D) 1.175 V

51) If a resistance of 2.2 MΩ is connected across a 1 kV source, current equals about _____.

    A) 2.2 mA   B) 0.455 mA   C) 45.5 µA   D) 0.455 A

52) If a 330 Ω resistor dissipates 2 W, its voltage drop equals _____.

    A) 2.57 V   B) 660 V   C) 6.6 V   D) 25.7 V

53) The power rating of a resistor that must dissipate up to 1.1 W should be _____.

    A) 0.25 W   B) 1 W   C) 2 W   D) 5 W

54) What is the resistance of a 150 W bulb when it is operating in a circuit with a supply of 125 V?

    A) 75 Ω   B) 104 Ω   C) 9375 Ω   D) 2.14 Ω

55) Which is the correct formula for finding power?

    A) $P = V \times I$ B) $P = I^2 \times R$ C) $P = V^2 \div R$ D) all of these

56) If a resistor that is color-coded red–red–brown–silver is connected to a 15 V source, what is the maximum current that can flow?

    A) 75.8 mA   B) 62 mA   C) 68.2 mA   D) 71.9 mA

57) If a resistor that is color coded yellow–violet–red is placed across a 25 V source voltage, what value resistor and wattage rating could be used?

A) 47000 Ω, 1/4 W

B) 4700 Ω, 1/8 W

C) 470 Ω, 1/2 W

D) 4700 Ω, 1/4 W

58) Using Watt's law and substituting power can be calculated as _____.

A) $P = V^2/R$ B) $P = I^2R$ C) $P = VI$ D) all of these

59) Power as it is used in electric circuits can be best defined as:

A) the rate motion is exerted over time.

B) the rate current flows over time.

C) the rate voltage is applied over time.

D) the rate energy is used over time.

60) The symbol for a certain amount of energy used over time is _____.

A) P   B) W   C) I   D) V

61) A kilowatt–hour is best defined as:

A) a kilo divided by 1 watt–hour.

B) 1,000 watts divided by 1 hour.

C) a kilo multiplied by 1 watt–hour.

D) 1,000 watts multiplied by 1 hour.

62) The average cost for a kilowatt–hour of electric power in the United States is:

A) 0.1 cent.   B) 1 cent.   C) 10 cents.   D) 50 cents.

63) The ampere–hour rating of a battery is defined as the:

A) number of amperes supplied in 1 hour.

B) number of amperes supplied over the number of hours at a given current.

C) number of hours per amperes supplied.

D) all of these.

64) The current flow for a given circuit has doubled, therefore the _____ has been halved.

A) voltage   B) current   C) power   D) resistance

65) The voltage of a power supply drops to 0 V when connected to a lamp circuit. What is a possible problem?

A) the lamp is open

B) the lamp is shorted

C) the lamp requires more current than the power supply can deliver

D) both B and C

66) Which is the most unlikely resistor failure?

A) opening

B) shorting

C) resistance change

D) All are common failures.

67) In the operation of electrical circuits, which, in most cases, is an unwanted by-product?

A) light

B) mechanical motion

C) heat

D) both B and C

68) Typically, which is the first type of measurement taken in a known defective circuit?

A) resistance

B) current

C) voltage

D) power

1) TRUE
   Diff: 1
2) TRUE
   Diff: 2
3) TRUE
   Diff: 2
4) TRUE
   Diff: 1
5) FALSE
   Diff: 2
6) TRUE
   Diff: 2
7) TRUE
   Diff: 2
8) FALSE
   Diff: 1
9) TRUE
   Diff: 2
10) FALSE
   Diff: 2
11) TRUE
   Diff: 2
12) TRUE
   Diff: 1
13) TRUE
   Diff: 3
14) TRUE
   Diff: 1
15) A
   Diff: 1
16) D
   Diff: 1
17) B
   Diff: 2
18) A
   Diff: 2
19) A
   Diff: 2
20) C
   Diff: 2
21) A
   Diff: 2
22) B
   Diff: 2

23) D
   Diff: 2
24) D
   Diff: 2
25) C
   Diff: 2
26) A
   Diff: 2
27) C
   Diff: 2
28) B
   Diff: 2
29) D
   Diff: 2
30) B
   Diff: 3
31) B
   Diff: 2
32) C
   Diff: 2
33) A
   Diff: 2
34) D
   Diff: 2
35) B
   Diff: 2
36) B
   Diff: 2
37) B
   Diff: 2
38) A
   Diff: 2
39) D
   Diff: 2
40) C
   Diff: 1
41) A
   Diff: 2
42) B
   Diff: 2
43) D
   Diff: 1
44) C
   Diff: 2

45) A
   Diff: 1
46) C
   Diff: 1
47) B
   Diff: 2
48) B
   Diff: 1
49) C
   Diff: 1
50) D
   Diff: 2
51) B
   Diff: 2
52) D
   Diff: 2
53) C
   Diff: 2
54) B
   Diff: 2
55) D
   Diff: 1
56) A
   Diff: 2
57) D
   Diff: 2
58) D
   Diff: 1
59) D
   Diff: 1
60) B
   Diff: 1
61) D
   Diff: 1
62) C
   Diff: 1
63) B
   Diff: 1
64) D
   Diff: 2
65) D
   Diff: 3
66) B
   Diff: 2

67) C
   Diff: 1
68) C
   Diff: 2

Chapter 4 Series Circuits

True or False

1) In a series circuit, the current is the same at every point in the circuit.

2) *Kirchhoff's Voltage Law* states that the algebraic sum of all the voltages around a closed path is zero.

3) The total power dissipated in a series circuit equals the sum of the individual powers.

4) If 6.8 kΩ, 1.2 kΩ and 5.6 kΩ resistors are wired in series, the total resistance is 13.6 kΩ.

5) If a resistor is dissipating 1/4 W, it can supply 1/4 W to the load.

6) If 4.7 kΩ, 2.2 kΩ and 1.2 kΩ resistors are wired in series, the total resistance is 8.7 kΩ.

7) Total power dissipated in a series circuit equals source voltage multiplied by current.

8) If a resistor is rated at 1/2 W, it can safely dissipate 0.325 W.

9) According to *Kirchhoff's Voltage Law*, the sum of the individual voltage drops in a series circuit equals the source voltage.

10) If a 1/4 W resistor and a 1/2 W resistor are wired in series, they can safely dissipate 3/4 W.

11) A series circuit has multiple current paths.

12) Calculating current for a series resistor circuit can be accomplished with a measured voltage across one of the resistors divided by that resistor's value.

13) Voltage sources in series increase both voltage and current capacity.

14) Three 2 V cells in series with one in series–opposing would yield 2 V.

Multiple Choice

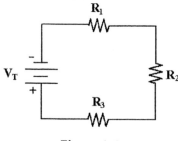

Figure 4–1

15) What is the total resistance in Figure 4–1 if $R_1 = 10$ kΩ, $R_2 = 10$ kΩ and $R_3 = 15$ kΩ?

    A) 25 kΩ B) 35 kΩ C) 0 kΩ D) infinite Ω

16) Calculate the current in Figure 4–1 if $V_{R1} = 16$ V, $R_1 = 10$ kΩ, $R_2 = 10$ kΩ and $R_3 = 15$ kΩ.

    A) 3.2 mA   B) 1.6 mA   C) 0 A   D) 12 mA

17) Calculate V_{R2} and V_{R3} in Figure 4–1 if $V_{R1} = 16$ V, $R_1 = 10$ kΩ, $R_2 = 10$ kΩ and $R_3 = 15$ kΩ.

    A) $V_{R2} = 16$ V, $V_{R3} = 12$ V   B) $V_{R2} = 16$ V, $V_{R3} = 24$ V

    C) $V_{R2} = 16$ V, $V_{R3} = 16$ V   D) $V_{R2} = 24$ V, $V_{R3} = 12$ V

18) Calculate P_{R2} in Figure 4–1 if $V_{R1} = 16$ V, $R_1 = 10$ kΩ, $R_2 = 10$ kΩ and $R_3 = 15$ kΩ.

    A) 25.6 mW   B) 2.56 mW   C) 0.256 mW   D) 0.0256 mW

19) Calculate V_T in Figure 4–1 if $V_{R1} = 16$ V, $R_1 = 10$ kΩ, $R_2 = 10$ kΩ and $R_3 = 15$ kΩ.

    A) 16 V   B) 24 V   C) 56 V   D) 112 V

20) $V_{R1} = 16$ V, $R_5 = 10$ kΩ, $R_2 = 10$ kΩ and $R_3 = 15$ kΩ in Figure 4–1. If R_2 opens, then R_T is

    _____.

    A) 25 kΩ B) 10 kΩ C) 0 Ω D) infinite Ω

21) If R_2 opens in Figure 4–1, the total power dissipated _____.

    A) increases to maximum   B) decreases to zero

    C) remains the same   D) will depend upon the source voltage

22) Calculate P_T in Figure 4-1 if $V_T = 100$ V and all three resistors are each 47 kΩ.

A) 70.9 mW   B) 23.6 mW   C) 22 W   D) 709 mW

23) Calculate V_{R3} in Figure 4-1 if $V_T = 50$ V, $V_{R1} = 19.7$ V and $V_{R2} = 2.7$ V.

A) 30.3 V   B) 47.3 V   C) 22.4 V   D) 27.6 V

24) How much voltage is dropped across R_2 and R_3 in Figure 4-1 if $R_1 = 4.7$ kΩ, $V_{R1} = 10$ V, $R_2 = 4.7$ kΩ and $R_3 = 4.7$ kΩ?

A) $V_{R2} = 10$ V, $V_{R3} = 10$ V   B) $V_{R2} = 4.7$ V, $V_{R3} = 10$ V

C) $V_{R2} = 10$ V, $V_{R3} = 4.7$ V   D) $V_{R2} = 14.7$ V, $V_{R3} = 14.7$ V

25) Calculate I_T in Figure 4-1 if $R_1 = 4.7$ kΩ, $V_{R1} = 10$ V, $R_2 = 4.7$ kΩ and $R_3 = 4.7$ kΩ.

A) 1 mA   B) 2.13 mA   C) 4.26 mA   D) 6 mA

26) Calculate V_T in Figure 4-1 if $R_1 = 4.7$ kΩ, $V_{R1} = 10$ V, $R_2 = 4.7$ kΩ and $R_3 = 4.7$ kΩ.

A) 4.7 V   B) 10 V   C) 14.7 V   D) 30 V

27) If R_2 shorts in Figure 4-1, the total circuit power _____.

A) increases   B) decreases

C) remains the same   D) depends upon the source voltage

28) $R_1 = 4.7$ kΩ, $R_2 = 4.7$ kΩ and $R_3 = 4.7$ kΩ in Figure 4-1. What is R_T if R_2 shorts?

A) 0 Ω   B) 4.7 kΩ   C) 9.4 kΩ   D) infinite Ω

29) What is the total supply voltage if 16 V and 12 V sources are wired in series opposing?

A) 28 V   B) 16 V   C) 12 V   D) 4 V

30) If 12 V and −19 V sources are connected so their total voltage is −7 V, they are _____.

A) series aiding   B) series opposing

C) in parallel   D) connected dangerously

31) Based upon electron current flow, the polarity on the side of the resistor where current enters is _____. The polarity on the side of the resistor where current exits is _____.

A) positive, positive   B) negative, negative

C) negative, positive   D) positive, negative

32) When 50 V is applied to four series resistors, 100 μA flows. If R_1 = 12 kΩ, R_2 = 47 kΩ and R_3 = 56 kΩ, what is the value of R_4?

A) 38.5 kΩ   B) 3.85 kΩ   C) 385 kΩ   D) 3.85 MΩ

33) If R_1 = 12 kΩ and R_2 = 5 kΩ and they are wired in series across a 20 V source, what is V_{R1} and V_{R2}?

A) V_{R1} = 5.88 V, V_{R2} = 14.12 V   B) V_{R1} = 14.12 V, V_{R2} = 5.88 V

C) V_{R1} = 10 V, V_{R2} = 10 V   D) V_{R1} = 0 V, V_{R2} = 20 V

34) Four resistors are connected in series across an 18 V source. Three resistors drop 0 V and one resistor drops 18 V. What's the trouble?

A) Two of the resistors are shorted.

B) The three resistors are open.

C) One resistor is open.

D) There is no trouble; these voltages are normal.

35) If 12 V and 17 V sources are wired in series aiding, what is the total supply voltage?

A) 5 V   B) 12 V   C) 29 V   D) 17 V

36) Two 100 kΩ resistors are wired in series across a 20 V source. How much voltage does each resistor drop?

A) 20 V   B) 10 V   C) 100 mA   D) 100 kΩ

37) A 22 kΩ and 12 kΩ resistor are connected across a 68 V source. How is the voltage divided?

A) 44 V and 24 V   B) 34 V and 34 V   C) 22 V and 12 V   D) 68 V and 68 V

38) A 500 kΩ potentiometer is connected across a 5 V source. If the voltage from the wiper to the lower end of the potentiometer is 1.2 V, what is the resistance of that lower part?

A) 380 kΩ   B) 120 kΩ   C) 500 kΩ   D) 0 Ω

39) –1.2 V, +5 V and +6 V batteries are connected in series. The total voltage is _____.

A) 12.2 V   B) 9.8 V   C) 1.2 V   D) 1.3 V

40) If a 100 Ω, 220 Ω, and 330 Ω resistor are connected in series, total resistance equals _____.

A) less than 100 Ω   B) the average of the three values

C) 650 Ω   D) 1650 Ω

41) If a 68 Ω, 33 Ω, 100 Ω and 47 Ω resistor are connected in series across a 9 V battery, the current equals _____.

    A) 36.29 mA   B) 27.56 A   C) 22.32 mA   D) 326.6 mA

42) If each of the six resistors in a series circuit drops 5 V, the source voltage _____.

    A) equals 5 V   B) equals 30 V

    C) depends on the resistor values   D) depends on the current

43) If a 4.7 kΩ, 5.6 kΩ and 10 kΩ resistor are in series, which resistor drops the most voltage?

    A) the 4.7 kΩ resistor

    B) the 5.6 kΩ resistor

    C) the 10 kΩ resistor

    D) That can't be determined from the given information.

44) If five equal resistors dissipate a total of 10 W in a series circuit, how much power does each resistor dissipate?

    A) 10 W   B) 50 W   C) 5 W   D) 2 W

45) If 18 V and 6 V sources are connected in series opposing, what is the total voltage?

    A) 2 V   B) 6 V   C) 18 V   D) 12 V

46) If –12 V and –6 V are connected so they equal –18 V, these sources are _____.

    A) series aiding   B) series opposing

    C) in parallel   D) connected dangerously

47) If three 2.2 kΩ resistors are connected in series across a 50 V source, P_T equals _____.

    A) 52.08 mW   B) 104.2 mW   C) 379 mW   D) 402 mW

48) Three resistors are connected in series across a 60 V source. If $V_{R1} = 19$ V and $V_{R2} = 14.3$ V, then what is the voltage drop across R3?

    A) 26.7 V   B) 19 V   C) 14.3 V   D) 45.7 V

49) If 5 V and 16 V power supplies are connected in series aiding, what is the total voltage?

    A) 21 V   B) 16 V   C) 24 V   D) 80 V

50) Two resistors are in series across a 12 V source. If each resistor equals 470 kΩ, what is the voltage across each resistor?

    A) 3 V   B) 6 V   C) 9 V   D) 12 V

51) If a 10 kΩ and 5 kΩ resistor are connected in series across a 12 V source, the voltage across the 10 kΩ resistor is _____ and the voltage across the 5 kΩ resistor is _____.

    A) 8 V, 4 V   B) 4 V, 8 V   C) 8 V, 8 V   D) 4 V, 4 V

52) Four series resistors are connected across a 30 V source and carry 0.125 mA. If $R_1 = 10$ kΩ, $R_2 = 33$ kΩ and $R_3 = 47$ kΩ, what is the value of R_4?

    A) 150 Ω   B) 1.5 kΩ   C) 15 kΩ   D) 150 kΩ

53) The voltage drop across any resistor or combination of resistors in a series circuit equals:

    A) the applied voltage across the resistor (A).

    B) the ratio of the resistance values times the source voltage.

    C) the product of the circuit current times the resistance value.

    D) all of these.

54) A 50 kΩ potentiometer is connected across a 15 V source. If the voltage from the wiper to the lower end of the potentiometer is 3.2 V, what is the resistance of that lower part?

    A) 10.67 kΩ   B) 39.3 kΩ   C) 50 kΩ   D) 0 Ω

55) One of the most popular applications of a potentiometer is as an adjustable voltage divider also known as a:

    A) voltage control.   B) current control.

    C) volume control.   D) divider control.

56) In a series circuit, total power P_T is calculated as:

    A) $P_1 + P_2 + P_3$ + etc.   B) $1/P_1 + 1/P_2 + 1/P_3$ + etc.

    C) $P_1 \div P_2 \div P_3 \div$ etc.   D) $P_1 \times P_2 \times P_3 \times$ etc.

57) In a series circuit, the largest amount of power is dissipated by:

    A) the first resistor.

    B) the smallest resistor.

    C) the largest resistor.

    D) any resistor, since the current is the same throughout the circuit.

58) Circuit ground or chassis ground can be thought of as a:

    A) common point.   B) reference point.

    C) neutral connection point.   D) all of these

59) An open in a series circuit results in:

    A) no current flow.

    B) no power dissipation.

    C) source voltage appearing across the open.

    D) all of these.

60) A short in a series circuit results in:

    A) decreased or reduced current flow.   B) increased or maximum current flow.

    C) decreased power consumption.   D) increased circuit resistance.

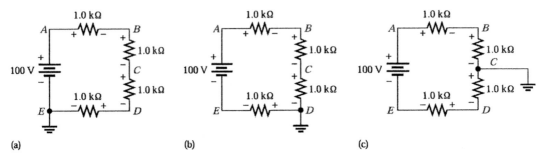

Figure 4–2

61) Refer to Figure 4–2. Voltage B to ground is less than normal. What could be the cause of failure?

    A) open between B and C   B) short between E and D

    C) open between C and D   D) short between A and B

62) Refer to Figure 4–2. Voltage from C to ground is 100 V. What is the probable cause of failure?

    A) open between A and B   B) short between A and B

    C) open between E and D   D) voltage reading is normal

63) Refer to Figure 4–2. The resistor between points E and D looks charred. What most likely would cause this?

    A) short between A and B   B) open A and the power supply

    C) short between A and D   D) Any of these could cause this problem.

64) What type of resistor could be used as variable voltage–divider?

    A) rheostat

                                             B) thermistor

    C) potentiometer

                                             D) any one of the above

65) What is the easiest, most practical measurement performed during troubleshooting?

    A) resistance   B) current   C) voltage   D) power

1) TRUE
Diff: 1

2) TRUE
Diff: 2

3) TRUE
Diff: 1

4) TRUE
Diff: 1

5) FALSE
Diff: 2

6) FALSE
Diff: 1

7) TRUE
Diff: 2

8) TRUE
Diff: 1

9) TRUE
Diff: 1

10) FALSE
Diff: 1

11) FALSE
Diff: 1

12) TRUE
Diff: 2

13) FALSE
Diff: 1

14) TRUE
Diff: 2

15) B
Diff: 1

16) B
Diff: 2

17) B
Diff: 2

18) A
Diff: 2

19) C
Diff: 2

20) D
Diff: 3

21) B
Diff: 3

22) A
Diff: 2

23) D
Diff: 2

24) A
Diff: 2

25) B
Diff: 2

26) D
Diff: 2

27) A
Diff: 3

28) C
Diff: 3

29) D
Diff: 2

30) B
Diff: 2

31) C
Diff: 2

32) C
Diff: 2

33) B
Diff: 2

34) C
Diff: 3

35) C
Diff: 2

36) B
Diff: 2

37) A
Diff: 2

38) B
Diff: 3

39) B
Diff: 2

40) C
Diff: 1

41) A
Diff: 2

42) B
Diff: 1

43) C
Diff: 2

44) D
Diff: 1

45) D
Diff: 2

46) A
Diff: 2

47) C
Diff: 2

48) A
Diff: 2

49) A
Diff: 2

50) B
Diff: 2

51) A
Diff: 2

52) D
Diff: 2

53) D
Diff: 1

54) A
Diff: 2

55) C
Diff: 1

56) A
Diff: 1

57) C
Diff: 1

58) D
Diff: 1

59) D
Diff: 2

60) B
Diff: 2

61) B
Diff: 3

62) C
Diff: 3

63) C
Diff: 3

64) C
Diff: 2

65) C
Diff: 1

Chapter 5   Parallel Circuits

True or False

1) If three equal resistors are connected in parallel across 12 V, each resistor drops 4 V.

2) The total resistance of four resistors in parallel is always less than the smallest resistance.

3) If $I_{R1} = 0.065$ mA and $I_{R2} = 0.098$ mA in a two branch parallel circuit, $I_T = 0.163$ mA.

4) If one branch of a parallel circuit opens, the total resistance decreases.

5) The total power dissipated by a parallel circuit can be found by adding the individual powers.

6) Kirchhoff's Current Law states that the sum of the currents into a junction must equal the sum of the currents out of that junction.

7) The total resistance of three parallel resistors equals the sum of the individual resistor values.

8) If $I_{R1} = 75$ mA and $I_{R2} = 12.7$ mA in a two branch parallel circuit, $I_T = 85.7$ mA.

9) If one branch of a parallel circuit shorts, the total resistance decreases.

10) $P_{R1} = 0.25$ W and $P_{R2} = 1.2$ W in a parallel circuit. The total power dissipated is 1.25 W.

11) Measurement of total current is accomplished with the ammeter in series with the source voltage.

12) A parallel circuit can be easily identified because only one end of each component is connected to each other.

13) Accurate troubleshooting of a parallel circuit cannot be performed with a voltmeter.

14) Total power for a parallel circuit can be determined by the same method as a series circuit.

Multiple Choice

15) If a 5.5 kΩ, 22 kΩ and 500 Ω resistor are connected in parallel, what is R_T?

A) 28.1 kΩ   B) 27.6 kΩ   C) 449 Ω   D) 330 Ω

16) If a 500 Ω, 1200 Ω and 10 kΩ resistor are connected in parallel across a 25 V source, how much current flows through the 1200 Ω resistor?

A) 20.83 mA   B) 50 mA   C) 2.5 mA   D) 2.4 mA

17) If a 2.2 kΩ resistor and a 3.3 kΩ resistor are connected in parallel, R_T equals _____.

A) 2.2 kΩ   B) 3.3 kΩ

C) greater than 2.2 kΩ   D) less than 2.2 kΩ

18) In a three-resistor parallel circuit, R_1 = 0.22 MΩ and R_2 = 1 MΩ. If R_T = 0.1166 MΩ, then what is the value of R3?

A) 1.34 M Ω   B) 0.33 M Ω   C) 0.134 M Ω   D) 13,400 Ω

19) If a 1 MΩ resistor, 0.47 MΩ resistor and 0.5 MΩ resistor are connected in parallel across an 18 V source, what is the total current if the 1 MΩ resistor opens?

A) 74.3 μA   B) 74.3 mA   C) 92.3 μA   D) 92.3 mA

20) If twelve 1.5 MΩ resistors are connected in parallel across 50 V, R_T equals _____.

A) 1.5 M Ω   B) 1.25 MΩ   C) 1 MΩ   D) 0.125 MΩ

21) I_T equals 0.1 mA in a 3-branch parallel circuit. If I_1 = 0.022 mA and I_2 = 0.007 mA, I3 = ?

A) 0.029 mA   B) 0.071 mA   C) 0.142 mA   D) 0.213 mA

22) If one resistor opens in a parallel circuit, the total circuit resistance _____ and the total circuit current _____.

A) decreases, increases   B) increases, increases

C) decreases, decreases   D) increases, decreases

23) If three 22 kΩ resistors are connected in parallel across a 10 V source, P_T equals _____.

A) 4.5 m W   B) 13.6 m W   C) 18.1 m W   D) 22.6 m W

24) If one resistor shorts in a parallel circuit, the total current _____.

A) equals 0 A

B) increases

C) decreases

D) decreases momentarily, then returns to the original value

25) If four 100 W lamps are connected in parallel across a 120 V source, what is the total current?

A) 3.33 A   B) 833 mA   C) 33.3 A   D) 8.33 A

26) If you measure a lower than normal total current in a parallel circuit, _____.

A) a resistor shorted   B) the power supply is off

C) all of the resistors are opened   D) a resistor opened

27) A formula that applies to a two-branch parallel circuit is _____.

A) $R_T = R_1 + R_2$ B) $V_T = V_{R1} + V_{R2}$

C) $I_T = I_{R1} + I_{R2}$ D) $R_T = V_1 \div R_2$

28) The current through any branch of a parallel circuit _____.

A) depends on the power rating of the resistor

B) only depends on the circuit voltage

C) is directly proportional to the branch resistance

D) is inversely proportional to the branch resistance

29) If you want to measure a load voltage with a DVM, connect the meter _____.

A) in series with the load   B) across the source

C) in parallel with the load   D) in series with the source

30) The total resistance of a three-branch parallel circuit is 76.92 Ω. If $R_1 = 100\ \Omega$ and $R_2 = 500\ \Omega$, what is the value of R_3?

A) 140 Ω

B) 1000 Ω

C) 1850 Ω

D) More information is needed to calculate R_3.

31) A two–branch parallel circuit contains these values: $R_1 = 1200\ \Omega$, $I_T = 0.005$ mA, $I_2 = 0.003$ mA. What is the value of V_{R1}?

A) 6 m V B) 18 m V C) 3.6 m V D) 2.4 m V

32) As additional branch resistors are connected in a parallel circuit, _____.

A) I_T decreases and R_T increases B) I_T decreases and R_T decreases

C) I_T increases and R_T decreases D) I_T increases and R_T increases

33) If a 4.7 kΩ resistor, a 3.3 kΩ resistor and a 5.43 kΩ resistor are connected in parallel across a 50 V source, what is the current through the 5.43 kΩ resistor?

A) 10.64 mA B) 15.15 mA C) 9.21 mA D) 4.72 mA

34) $R_T = 330\ \Omega$ and $R_1 = 470\ \Omega$ in a two–branch parallel circuit. What is the value of R_2?

A) 770 Ω B) 1108 Ω C) 194 Ω D) 110 Ω

35) If a 330 Ω resistor, 270 Ω resistor and 68 Ω resistor are connected in parallel, what is the approximate value for R_T?

A) 668 Ω B) 47 Ω C) 68 Ω D) 22 Ω

36) If 5 A and 3 A enter a junction from two separate paths, how much current flows out of the junction?

A) 2 A B) 3 A

C) 8 A D) the larger of the two

37) Each branch in a four–branch parallel circuit carries 10 mA. If one of the branches opens, then the current in each of the other three branches equals _____.

A) 13.33 mA B) 10 mA C) 0 A D) 30 mA

38) If there is 100 mA of current flowing into a three–branch parallel circuit and two of the branch currents are 40 mA and 20 mA, the third branch current is _____.

A) 60 mA B) 20 mA C) 160 mA D) 40 mA

39) If the power dissipation in each of four parallel branches is 1 W, P_T equals _____.

A) 1 W B) 4 W C) 0.25 W D) 0 W

40) If a 2.2 kΩ resistor, 10 kΩ resistor and 1.2 kΩ resistor are connected in parallel, the total resistance equals _____.

    A) 721 Ω   B) 13.4 kΩ   C) 2.27 kΩ   D) 1.2 kΩ

41) If a 470 Ω resistor, 680 Ω resistor and 830 Ω resistor are connected in parallel, the total resistance equals _____.

    A) 1980 Ω   B) 1510 Ω   C) 1150 Ω   D) 208 Ω

42) If a 4.7 kΩ resistor and 2.2 kΩ resistor are connected in parallel, the total resistance is

_____.

    A) 2200 Ω   B) 4700 Ω

    C) greater than 2200 Ω   D) less than 2200 Ω

43) In a three–branch parallel circuit, $R_1 = 1.2$ MΩ, $R_2 = 1$ MΩ and $R_T = 0.5$ MΩ. Calculate R_3.

    A) 6 MΩ   B) 1.7 MΩ   C) 2 MΩ   D) 7.7 MΩ

44) A 5.2 MΩ resistor, 1.2 MΩ resistor and 1 MΩ resistor are connected in parallel across a 15 V source. What is the total current if the 1.2 MΩ resistor opens?

    A) 2.88 μA   B) 17.88 μA   C) 12.5 μA   D) 2.41 μA

45) If eight 47 kΩ resistors are connected in parallel across a 25 V source, R_T equals _____.

    A) 376 kΩ   B) 6.71 kΩ   C) 5.875 kΩ   D) 4.7 kΩ

46) A three–branch parallel circuit carries a total current of 1.2 mA. If $I_1 = 0.2$ mA and $I_2 = 0.7$ mA, then what is the value of I_3?

    A) 2.4 mA   B) 0.3 mA   C) 7.2 mA   D) 8.7 mA

47) If three 4.7 kΩ resistors are connected in parallel across a 12 V source, what is the value of P_T?

    A) 91.9 mW   B) 14.1 mW   C) 1.41 W   D) 141 mW

48) If one resistor opens in a parallel circuit, the total current _____.

    A) increases   B) decreases

    C) remains unchanged   D) varies wildly

49) If three 75 W lamps are connected in parallel across a 125 V source, I_T equals _____.

    A) 18 mA   B) 180 mA   C) 1.8 A   D) 18 A

50) If the total current equals 0 A in a four–branch parallel circuit, the trouble is that _____.

    A) one of the resistors has shorted   B) the power supply is off

    C) three of the resistors have opened   D) one resistor has opened

51) The power dissipated by any branch of a parallel circuit _____.

    A) depends on the power rating of the resistor

    B) only depends on the circuit voltage

    C) only depends on the total current

    D) depends on the voltage and value of the resistor

52) To measure the current through one branch of a parallel circuit, the meter is connected _____.

    A) in series with the branch resistor   B) across the source

    C) in parallel with the branch resistor   D) in series with the source

53) If the $R_T = 6.8$ kΩ and $R_1 = 10$ kΩ in a two–branch parallel circuit, what is the value of R_2?

    A) 16.8 kΩ   B) 3.2 kΩ   C) 21.25 kΩ   D) 12 kΩ

54) As resistors are disconnected from a parallel circuit, _____.

    A) I_T decreases and R_T increases   B) I_T decreases and R_T decreases

    C) I_T increases and R_T decreases   D) I_T increases and R_T increases

55) The most popular application for a parallel circuit in electronics is as a:

    A) voltage divider.   B) current divider.

    C) resistance divider.   D) power divider.

56) In a parallel circuit, total power P_T is calculated as:

    A) $P_1 + P_2 + P_3$ + etc.   B) $1/P_1 + 1/P_2 + 1/P_3$ + etc.

    C) $P_1 \div P_2 \div P_3 \div$ etc.   D) $P_1 \times P_2 \times P_3 \times$ etc.

57) In a parallel circuit, the largest amount of power is dissipated by:

    A) the first resistor.

    B) the smallest resistor.

    C) the largest resistor.

    D) any resistor, since the voltage is the same across each of the branch circuits.

58) An open in one branch of a parallel circuit results in:

    A) increased circuit resistance.   B) decreased or reduced current flow.

    C) decreased power consumption.   D) all of these.

59) A short in one branch of a parallel circuit results in:

    A) increased circuit resistance.

    B) increased current flow.

    C) decreased power consumption.

    D) increased voltage drops in the remaining branches.

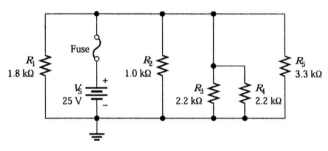

Figure 5–1

60) Refer to Figure 5–1. The voltage across R2 is 0 V. What is most likely the problem?

    A) R2 open   B) R1 open

    C) fuse open   D) none of the above

61) Refer to Figure 5–1. To accurately measure the total current for this circuit, how must the ammeter be connected?

    A) between the negative terminal and the supply and ground

    B) between R1 and the fuse

    C) between the positive terminal and the fuse

    D) either A or C

62) Refer to Figure 5–1. The total current for this circuit is measured and the ammeter reads 57.8 mA. What is the problem, if any?

    A) R2 open   B) R1 open

    C) R3 open   D) This is normal.

63) Refer to Figure 5–1. The fuse in this circuit is rated at 100 mA. Would the fuse blow if an additional 1 kΩ were placed in parallel with R5?

    A) yes

    B) no

    C) Fuse has nothing to do with this part of the circuit.

64) Refer to Figure 5–1. What is the power dissipation of R3?

    A) 284.09 mW   B) 11.36 mW   C) 25 mW   D) 568.18 mW

1) FALSE
   Diff: 1
2) TRUE
   Diff: 1
3) TRUE
   Diff: 2
4) FALSE
   Diff: 3
5) TRUE
   Diff: 1
6) TRUE
   Diff: 1
7) FALSE
   Diff: 1
8) FALSE
   Diff: 2
9) TRUE
   Diff: 1
10) FALSE
    Diff: 2
11) TRUE
    Diff: 2
12) FALSE
    Diff: 1
13) TRUE
    Diff: 1
14) TRUE
    Diff: 1
15) C
    Diff: 2
16) A
    Diff: 2
17) D
    Diff: 2
18) B
    Diff: 2
19) A
    Diff: 2
20) D
    Diff: 2
21) B
    Diff: 2
22) D
    Diff: 3

23) B
    Diff: 2
24) B
    Diff: 3
25) A
    Diff: 2
26) D
    Diff: 3
27) C
    Diff: 1
28) D
    Diff: 1
29) C
    Diff: 2
30) B
    Diff: 2
31) D
    Diff: 2
32) C
    Diff: 2
33) C
    Diff: 2
34) B
    Diff: 2
35) B
    Diff: 2
36) C
    Diff: 2
37) B
    Diff: 3
38) D
    Diff: 2
39) B
    Diff: 2
40) A
    Diff: 2
41) D
    Diff: 2
42) D
    Diff: 2
43) A
    Diff: 2
44) B
    Diff: 3

45) C
    Diff: 2
46) B
    Diff: 2
47) A
    Diff: 2
48) B
    Diff: 2
49) C
    Diff: 2
50) B
    Diff: 3
51) D
    Diff: 2
52) A
    Diff: 2
53) C
    Diff: 2
54) A
    Diff: 2
55) B
    Diff: 1
56) A
    Diff: 1
57) B
    Diff: 1
58) D
    Diff: 3
59) B
    Diff: 3
60) C
    Diff: 3
61) D
    Diff: 2
62) C
    Diff: 3
63) B
    Diff: 3
64) A
    Diff: 2

Chapter 6 Series–Parallel Circuits

True or False

1) If two resistors are in parallel, they drop the same voltage.

2) A *combination* circuit consists of resistors in both series and parallel.

3) No problems could occur if a 10 V source and a 20 V source were connected in parallel.

4) A loaded voltage divider is a *combination* circuit.

5) Two or more resistors connected in series form a circuit known as a *voltage divider*.

6) If two resistors are in parallel, they carry the same current.

7) A voltmeter, when connected across a component, can be viewed as being a resistor in series with that component.

8) A bridge circuit's resistances must all be of the same value to be in a balanced condition.

9) Thevinizing a circuit creates an equivalent series circuit.

10) Maximum power is achieved when the load resistance is approximately two times the source resistance.

11) The voltage across any open in a series–parallel circuit will be the source voltage.

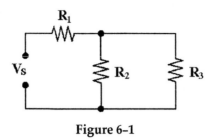

Figure 6–1

12) R_2 is in parallel with R_3 in Figure 6–1.

13) R_1 is in series with R_3 in Figure 6–1.

14) R_1 is in series with the parallel combination R_2 and R_3 in Figure 6–1.

15) R_1 is in series with the series combination R_2 and R_3 in Figure 6–1.

Multiple Choice

16) In Figure 6–1, R_2 is connected in _____.

    A) series with R_1 B) series with R_3

    C) parallel with R_1 D) parallel with R_3

17) If R_3 opens in Figure 6–1, V_{R1} _____.

    A) increases   B) decreases

    C) remains the same   D) decreases to zero

18) If V_s = 20 V, R_1 = 10 kΩ, R_2 = 50 kΩ and R_3 = 15 kΩ in Figure 6–1, P_{R2} equals _____.

    A) 2.29 mW   B) 7.64 mW   C) 8.63 mW   D) 18.6 mW

19) In Figure 6–1, R_1 is connected in _____.

    A) series with R_2

    B) series with R_3

    C) parallel with R_2

    D) parallel with R_3

    E) none of the above

20) If $R_1 = 4.7$ kΩ, $R_2 = 3.3$ kΩ and $R_3 = 1$ kΩ in Figure 6-1, the total resistance equals _____.

    A) 5700 Ω   B) 5467 Ω   C) 4125 Ω   D) 660 Ω

21) If $R_1 = 4.7$ kΩ, $R_2 = 3.3$ kΩ, $R_3 = 1$ kΩ and $V_s = 50$ V in Figure 6-1, I_T equals _____.

    A) 8.8 mA   B) 9.15 mA   C) 12.1 mA   D) 75.7 mA

22) If $R_1 = 10$ kΩ, $R_2 = 15$ kΩ and $R_3 = 50$ kΩ in Figure 6-1, R_T equals _____.

    A) 21.5 kΩ   B) 11.5 kΩ   C) 10 kΩ   D) 9.5 kΩ

23) If $V_s = 25$ V, $R_1 = 10$ kΩ, $R_2 = 15$ kΩ and $R_3 = 50$ kΩ in Figure 6-1, I_T equals _____.

    A) 2.17 mA   B) 2.5 mA   C) 1.58 mA   D) 1.16 mA

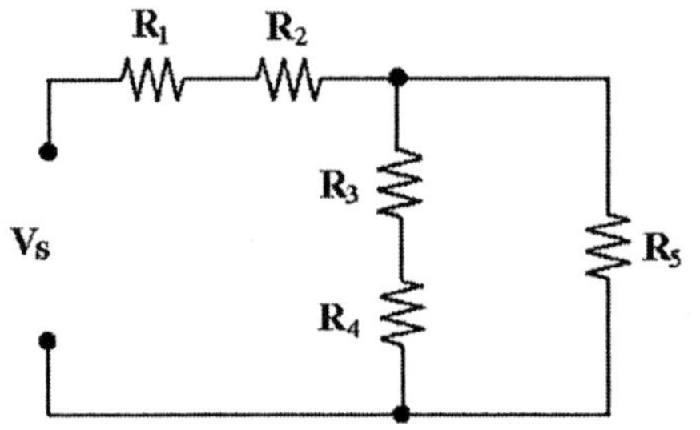

Figure 6-2

24) If R_3 shorts in Figure 6-2, V_{R5} _____.

    A) increases   B) decreases   C) remains the same

25) If all of the resistors in Figure 6-2 are 4.7 kΩ, what is the value of R_T?

    A) 12.53 kΩ   B) 18.8 kΩ   C) 9.4 kΩ   D) 4.7 kΩ

26) In Figure 6-2, R_3 and R_4 are connected in _____.

    A) series with each other and R_5 B) series with each other and R_1 and R_2

    C) series with each other   D) parallel with R_1 and R_2

27) If $R_1 = 50$ kΩ, $R_2 = 10$ kΩ, $R_3 = 10$ kΩ, $R_4 = 50$ kΩ and $R_5 = 10$ kΩ in Figure 6-2, what is the value of R_T?

    A) 8.57 kΩ   B) 130 kΩ   C) 68.57 kΩ   D) 85.7 kΩ

28) If all resistors equal 4.7 kΩ and V_s equals 20 V in Figure 6-2, what is the value of I_{R3}?

    A) 12.53 mA   B) 0.53 mA   C) 11.99 mA   D) 1.06 mA

29) If R2 opens in Figure 6-2, V_R3 _____.

    A) increases   B) decreases

    C) remains the same   D) causes the fuse to blow

30) If R4 shorts in Figure 6-2, V_R5 _____.

    A) increases   B) decreases

    C) remains the same   D) decreases to zero

31) If R1 shorts in Figure 6-2, V_R4 _____.

    A) increases   B) decreases

    C) remains the same   D) equals V_R2

32) In Figure 6-2, R3 and R4 are connected in _____.

    A) series with each other and in parallel with R5

    B) parallel with each other

    C) series with R2

    D) series with R5

33) If every resistor in Figure 6-2 equals 2.2 kΩ, what is the value of R_T?

    A) 5.87 kΩ   B) 5.5 kΩ   C) 4.4 kΩ   D) 2.2 kΩ

34) If V_S = 15 V and every resistor equals 2.2 kΩ in Figure 6-2, what is the value of I_R4?

    A) 2.55 mA   B) 5.11 mA   C) 0.85 mA   D) 0.42 mA

35) In Figure 6-2 if R1 = 10 kΩ, R2 = 4.7 kΩ, R3 = 4.7 kΩ, R4 = 10 kΩ and R5 = 4.7 kΩ, R_T = ?

    A) 6.1 kΩ   B) 18.3 kΩ   C) 24.7 kΩ   D) 0 Ω

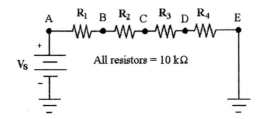

Figure 6–3

36) What is the resistance between points B and E in Figure 6–3?

    A) 10 kΩ   B) 20 kΩ   C) 30 kΩ   D) 40 kΩ

37) If $V_{R4} = 10$ V in Figure 6–3, what is the value of V_{AD}?

    A) 10 V   B) 20 V   C) 30 V   D) 40 V

38) If $V_S = 22$ V in Figure 6–3, what is the is the value of V_{DB}?

    A) 5.5 V   B) –22 V   C) 11 V   D) –11 V

39) If $V_S = 12$ V in Figure 6–3, what is the value of V_{EB} if R3 shorts?

    A) –3 V   B) –8 V   C) 6 V   D) 8 V

40) If a 10 kΩ resistor is placed in parallel with R4 in Figure 6–3, how will V_{R4} change?

    A) V_{R4} will increase.   B) V_{R4} will decrease.

    C) V_{R4} will remain the same.   D) V_{R4} will change to 4 volts.

41) What is the resistance between points A and D in Figure 6–3?

    A) 10 kΩ   B) 20 kΩ   C) 30 kΩ   D) 40 kΩ

42) If $V_{R1} = 15$ V in Figure 6–3, what is the value of V_{BD}?

    A) 60 V   B) –30 V   C) 30 V   D) –60 V

43) If $V_S = 50$ V in Figure 6–3, what is the value of V_{CA}?

    A) 5 V   B) 25 V   C) –5 V   D) –25 V

44) If $V_S = 40$ V and R3 opens in Figure 6–3, what is the value of V_{R3}?

    A) 0 V   B) 10 V   C) 20 V   D) 30 V   E) 40 V

45) If a fifth 10 kΩ resistor is connected in series in Figure 6–3, how does V_{R4} change?

    A) V_{R4} increases.   B) V_{R4} decreases.

    C) V_{R4} remains the same.   D) V_{R4} increases to 10 V.

46) If the current is 12 mA in Figure 6–3, what is the value of V_{EB}?

    A) 360 V   B) –360 V   C) –240 V   D) 240 V

47) If the current is 1.2 mA in Figure 6–3, what is the value of P_T?

    A) 0.576 mW   B) 5.76 mW   C) 57.6 mW   D) 576 mW

48) If V_{R3} = 17 V in Figure 6–3, what is the value of P_1?

    A) 1.7 mW   B) 28.9 mW   C) 2.89 W   D) 17 mW

49) If four parallel 10 kΩ resistors are connected in series with a single 20 kΩ resistor and one of the parallel resistors opens, how does the voltage across the other parallel resistors change?

    A) It increases.   B) It decreases.   C) It remains the same.

50) Two series 1 kΩ resistors are connected in parallel with a 2.2 kΩ resistor. If the voltage across one of the 1 kΩ resistors is 6 V, what is the voltage across the 2.2 kΩ resistor?

    A) 6 V   B) 3 V   C) 12 V   D) 13.2 V

51) The parallel combination of a 330 Ω resistor and a 470 Ω resistor is connected in series with the parallel combination of four 1 kΩ resistors. If a 100 V source is connected across the circuit, then which resistor carries the most current?

    A) 1 kΩ   B) 330 Ω   C) 470 Ω

52) The parallel combination of a 330 Ω resistor and a 470 Ω resistor is connected in series with the parallel combination of four 1 kΩ resistors. If a 100 V source is connected across the circuit, then which resistor drops the most voltage?

    A) 1 kΩ   B) 330 Ω   C) 470 Ω

53) If a voltage divider consists of two 10 kΩ resistors, which one of these load resistors will change the output voltage the most?

    A) 1 MΩ   B) 20 kΩ   C) 100 kΩ   D) 10 kΩ

54) In a two-source circuit, one source alone produces 10 mA through a branch. If the other source alone produces 8 mA in the opposite direction through the same branch, what is the total current through the branch?

A) 10 mA   B) 8 mA   C) 18 mA   D) 2 mA

55) If four parallel 10 kΩ resistors are in series with a single 20 kΩ resistor and one of the parallel resistors shorts, the voltage across the other parallel resistors _____.

A) increases   B) decreases   C) remains the same

56) Power in a series–parallel resistor circuit is dissipated as:

A) voltage loss.   B) current flow.
C) resistance change.   D) heat.

57) In solving series–parallel circuits using Ohm's law, first solve for:

A) IT.   B) RT.
C) ET.   D) any of these, it doesn't matter.

58) In solving series–parallel circuits using Ohm's law, first solve for:

A) the series resistance.   B) the parallel resistance.
C) the series current.   D) the parallel current.

59) In solving series–parallel circuits, the last and easiest to solve for is:

A) ET.   B) IT.   C) RT.   D) PT.

60) One Ohm's law formula $P_T = P_1 + P_2 +$ etc. can be used to solve for total power in:

A) series circuits.   B) parallel circuits.
C) series–parallel circuits.   D) all of these.

61) In the series portion of series–parallel circuits, the total resistance is:

A) less than any one resistance.   B) greater than the largest resistance.
C) less than the largest resistance.   D) equal to the largest resistance.

62) In the parallel portion of series–parallel circuits, the total resistance is:

A) less than any one resistance.   B) greater than the largest resistance.
C) less than the smallest resistance.   D) equal to the smallest resistance.

63) The Wheatstone bridge circuit is widely used to measure:

    A) exact voltages.   B) accurate currents.

    C) precise resistances.   D) all of these.

64) The difference between a balanced and an unbalanced Wheatstone bridge is measured by:

    A) an ohmmeter.   B) an ammeter.

    C) a voltmeter.   D) a galvanometer.

65) Thevenin's theorem provides a method for:

    A) building complex series–parallel circuits.

    B) simplifying complex series–parallel circuits.

    C) designing complex series–parallel circuits.

    D) all of these.

66) According to the maximum power transfer theorem, maximum power is delivered to any load when the load resistance is:

    A) less than one–half of the source resistance.

    B) larger than source resistance.

    C) at least twice or more than the source resistance.

    D) exactly equal to the source resistance.

67) The super position theorem provides a method for:

    A) building complex series–parallel circuits.

    B) analyzing complex series–parallel circuits.

    C) designing complex series–parallel circuits.

    D) all of these.

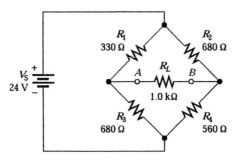

Figure 6–4

68) Refer to Figure 6–4. What approximate R1 resistor value would it take to balance this bridge circuit?

A) 680 Ω   B) 330 Ω   C) 560 Ω   D) 825 Ω

69) Refer to Figure 6–4. With circuit balanced there is:

A) maximum current flow through the load.

B) no current through the load.

C) no current flow through the total circuit.

D) Cannot be determined without detailed analysis.

70) Refer to Figure 6–4. If R1 is changed to 500 Ω, the Thevenin resistance and voltage would be:

A) 595 and 3 V.   B) 595 and 807 mV.

C) 1 k and 3 V.   D) 1 k and 807 mV.

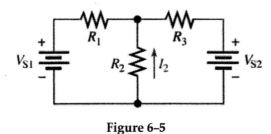

Figure 6–5

71) Refer to Figure 6–5. Determine the amount of current flow through R2 with the following component parameters. V_{S1} = 10 V, V_{S2} = 3 V, R_1 = 2 k, R_2 = 3 k, and R_3 = 700

A) 0 A   B) 5.3 mA   C) 3.6 mA   D) 1 mA

72) Refer to Figure 6–5. If all of the resistors of this circuit are 5 kΩ and V_{S1} and V_{S2} are 10 V but opposing polarities, what would be the current flow through R_2?

A) 1.33 mA   B) 13.33 mA   C) 2.66 mA   D) 0 A

1) TRUE
   Diff: 1
2) TRUE
   Diff: 1
3) FALSE
   Diff: 2
4) TRUE
   Diff: 1
5) TRUE
   Diff: 2
6) FALSE
   Diff: 1
7) FALSE
   Diff: 1
8) FALSE
   Diff: 2
9) TRUE
   Diff: 1
10) FALSE
    Diff: 1
11) FALSE
    Diff: 2
12) TRUE
    Diff: 1
13) FALSE
    Diff: 1
14) TRUE
    Diff: 1
15) FALSE
    Diff: 1
16) D
    Diff: 1
17) B
    Diff: 3
18) A
    Diff: 2
19) E
    Diff: 2
20) B
    Diff: 2
21) B
    Diff: 2
22) A
    Diff: 1

23) D
    Diff: 2
24) B
    Diff: 3
25) A
    Diff: 2
26) C
    Diff: 1
27) C
    Diff: 2
28) B
    Diff: 3
29) B
    Diff: 3
30) B
    Diff: 3
31) A
    Diff: 3
32) A
    Diff: 2
33) A
    Diff: 2
34) C
    Diff: 2
35) B
    Diff: 2
36) C
    Diff: 1
37) C
    Diff: 2
38) D
    Diff: 2
39) B
    Diff: 3
40) B
    Diff: 2
41) C
    Diff: 2
42) C
    Diff: 2
43) D
    Diff: 2
44) E
    Diff: 3

45) B
    Diff: 2
46) B
    Diff: 2
47) C
    Diff: 2
48) B
    Diff: 2
49) A
    Diff: 2
50) C
    Diff: 2
51) B
    Diff: 2
52) A
    Diff: 2
53) D
    Diff: 3
54) D
    Diff: 2
55) B
    Diff: 3
56) D
    Diff: 2
57) B
    Diff: 1
58) B
    Diff: 1
59) D
    Diff: 1
60) D
    Diff: 1
61) B
    Diff: 1
62) C
    Diff: 1
63) C
    Diff: 1
64) D
    Diff: 1
65) B
    Diff: 1
66) D
    Diff: 1

67) B
    Diff: 1
68) C
    Diff: 2
69) B
    Diff: 2
70) A
    Diff: 3
71) C
    Diff: 3
72) D
    Diff: 3

Chapter 7 Magnetism and Electromagnetism

True or False

1) A permanent magnet will retain its magnetism for a long period of time.

2) Unlike magnetic poles repulse one another.

3) *Magnetic flux* is another name for a *magnetic field.*

4) A conductor with no current through it will still have a magnetic field around it.

5) Aluminum, brass, and iron make good magnets.

6) Two north magnetic poles attract one another.

7) A magnetic field around a conductor is a good indication that current is flowing.

8) A *strong* magnetic field around a conductor indicates a *small* current flowing through the conductor.

9) The opposition to being magnetized is called *permeability.*

10) Soft iron, copper, and silver make good magnets.

11) Flux lines are concentrated at the center of a magnet.

12) The left–hand rule can be used to determine the amount of magnetomotive force.

13) The speed of movement of the coil of a generator affects the direction of current produced.

14) A solenoid converts electrical energy into mechanical energy

15) A DC generator produces a smooth DC voltage output.

Multiple Choice

16) A solenoid consists of _____.

   A) two plates separated by an insulator   B) a burglar alarm relay

   C) a coil of wire wound around a core   D) a permanent magnet

17) A coil of wire with current flowing through it is called a(n) _____.

   A) capacitor   B) north pole   C) south pole   D) electromagnet

18) If two north magnetic poles are brought close to each other, _____.

   A) a force of attraction pulls them together   B) an electromagnet is created

   C) a force of repulsion pushes them apart   D) a current is induced

19) How does the magnetic field change around a conducting wire if the current increases?

   A) The field grows stronger.

   B) The field grows weaker.

   C) There is no magnetic field around a conducting wire.

   D) It is impossible to predict.

20) Permeability is _____.

   A) the shielding effect of a material

   B) the ease of a material to be magnetized

   C) the opposition to being magnetized

   D) the ability of a magnetic material to conduct a current

21) Which one of the statements below does NOT apply to the voltage induced into a wire when it is moved through a magnetic field?

   A) It depends on the strength of the magnetic field.

   B) It depends on the current flowing in the wire.

   C) It depends on the speed of wire motion.

   D) It depends on the length of moving wire in the field.

22) Unlike magnetic poles _____ and like poles _____.

   A) repel, repel   B) repel, attract   C) attract, attract   D) attract, repel

23) According to the *left-hand rule* for the magnetic field around a conductor, what points in the direction of current flow?

    A) fingers   B) meter   C) thumb   D) index finger

24) In which one of the following applications is electromagnetism used?

    A) tape recorders   B) loudspeakers   C) relays   D) all of these

25) If the cross-sectional area of a magnetic field decreases, the flux density _____.

    A) increases   B) decreases   C) remains the same

26) If a basic one-loop, dc generator rotates at 60 revolutions each second, how many times each second does its dc output voltage reach a peak value?

    A) 0   B) 60   C) 120   D) 240

27) A _____ is a type of electromagnetic device that has a movable iron core called a *plunger*.

    A) relay   B) speaker   C) solenoid   D) analog meter

28) If a relay picks up and makes a contact but does not stay picked up, what's the trouble?

    A) The magnetic field is too strong.

    B) The magnetic field is too weak.

    C) The relay coil is open.

    D) There is no trouble. The relay is operating normally.

29) If a tape recorder's output voltage increases and decreases when you shake the recorder, a possible problem might be _____.

    A) an open circuit in the speaker

    B) a loose circular magnet around the speaker's voice coil

    C) too high a source voltage

    D) an open capacitor

30) If the contacts fail to open when a relay is de-energized, what is the trouble?

    A) There is too little current in the relay coil.

    B) Dirt is causing the relay armature to stick.

    C) The return spring tension is too large.

    D) There is no trouble. The relay is operating normally.

31) How will two permanent bar magnets react if they are brought close to each other?

    A) They will attract if their north poles are together.

    B) They will attract if their south poles are together.

    C) They will repel if the north and south poles are together.

    D) They will attract if the north and south poles are together.

32) The quantity of lines of force per unit of area is known as _____.

    A) magnetic flux   B) flux density   C) ampere–turns   D) permeability

33) The voltage produced by a magnetic field cutting through a conductor depends on the _____.

    A) direction of motion   B) speed of motion

    C) length of the conductor   D) all of the above

34) The polarity of an induced voltage depends on the _____.

    A) time that the conductor remains stationary in a magnetic field

    B) length of a conductor in a magnetic field

    C) direction of motion of a conductor in a magnetic field

    D) amount of current flowing

35) The magnetic term that is equivalent to *voltage* is _____.

    A) reluctance   B) flux density

    C) magnetomotive force   D) current

36) The permeability of air is _____.

    A) 1   B) 7   C) 19.2   D) 22

37) The magnetic field around an electromagnet is produced by _____.

    A) the conductor's permeability   B) a permanent magnet

    C) the laminated iron core   D) a current flowing through the winding

38) A *weber* is a unit of _____.

    A) magnetic flux   B) magnetomotive force

    C) reluctance   D) permeability

39) A *tesla* is a unit of _____.

    A) magnetic flux density   B) magnetomotive force

    C) reluctance   D) permeability

40) The term *reluctance* in magnetic circuits is like the term _____ in electrical circuits.

    A) current   B) voltage   C) resistance   D) capacitance

41) Soft iron has a high _____.

    A) mmf   B) permeability   C) resistance   D) reactance

42) Magnetic lines that are close to each other are said to have a high _____.

    A) reluctance   B) inductance   C) flux density   D) current

43) Reversing the current through an electromagnet _____ the magnetic field.

    A) increases   B) decreases   C) collapses   D) reverses

44) An *ampere–turn* is a unit of _____.

    A) magnetomotive force (mmf)   B) permeability

    C) resistance   D) reactance

45) If the number of turns of wire on an electromagnet increases, the magnetomotive force *mmf* _____.

    A) increases   B) decreases   C) remains the same

46) The amount of voltage that is induced in a conductor depends on the _____.

    A) length of time a conductor remains stationary in the magnetic field

    B) length of the conductor in the magnetic field

    C) direction of motion of the conductor in the magnetic field

    D) direction of the current flowing

47) Increasing the speed at which a magnet moves through a coil of wire causes the induced voltage to _____.

    A) increase   B) decrease   C) remain the same

48) If more turns of wire are added to a coil and then that coil is moved through a magnetic field, the voltage produced will _____.

A) be more than the original coil

B) be less than the original coil

C) be the same as the original coil

49) The _____ electromagnet cannot be further magnetized.

A) capacitive   B) saturated   C) open   D) shorted

50) An iron core electromagnet has a higher _____ than an air core electromagnet.

A) permeability   B) resistance   C) reactance   D) current

51) Applying an ac voltage to an electromagnet's coil will produce a _____.

A) steady magnet field   B) north magnetic field

C) south magnetic field   D) changing magnetic field

52) If some turns of wire are removed from an electromagnet, the magnetic field will _____.

A) be more than the original electromagnet

B) be less than the original electromagnet

C) be the same as the original electromagnet

53) Like magnetic poles _____.

A) attract each other   B) repel each other

C) have no effect on each other   D) have the same current through them

54) A simple electric doorbell probably uses _____ to ring the bell.

A) transistor   B) a *DPDT* switch

C) an electromagnet   D) a permanent magnet

55) A relay is a device that _____.

A) uses an electromagnet to open and close contacts

B) isolates the actuating signal from the control signal

C) has a coil to actuate some contacts that control other circuits

D) all of these

56) The principal difference between a solenoid and a relay is that:

   A) solenoids do mechanical work, relays do electrical work.

   B) solenoids do electrical work, relays do mechanical work.

   C) relays relay electricity, solenoids do not.

   D) relays use magnets, solenoids do not.

57) The movable part of the solenoid is the:

   A) magnetic field.   B) electromagnetic coil.

   C) the plunger.   D) all of these.

58) The movable part of the relay is the:

   A) magnetic field.   B) electromagnetic coil.

   C) the armature.   D) all of these.

59) Hysteresis is a characteristic of magnetic materials wherein a change in magnetization:

   A) occurs before the application of a magnetizing force.

   B) occurs after the application of a magnetic force.

   C) occurs exactly with the application of a magnetic force.

   D) varies according to the current flow.

60) Electromagnetic induction is best defined as the process by which a voltage is produced in a conductor when there is:

   A) motion between the magnetic poles.

   B) motion between the conductor and the magnetic field.

   C) motion around the magnetic fields.

   D) energy produced by the rotating coils.

61) Induced voltage resulting from electromagnetic induction is proportional to:

   A) the rate at which the conductor and magnetic fields move relative to each other.

   B) the number of turns of wire in the coil.

   C) the angle at which the conductor cuts the magnetic field.

   D) all of these.

62) Faraday's law states that the voltage induced across a coil of wire is proportional to these two factors.

    A) the size of the coil and the rate of change of the magnetic flux

    B) the number of turns in the coil and the rate of change of the magnetic flux

    C) the size of the magnets and the rate of change of the magnetic flux

    D) the diameter of the conductor and the rate of change of the magnetic flux

63) Faraday's law and Lenz's law are related in that they deal with:

    A) varying magnetic field.   B) an induced voltage.

    C) a resulting current flow.   D) all of these.

64) The flux line direction and the conductor direction of movement affect:

    A) voltage polarity.   B) current flow direction.

    C) amount of voltage.   D) both A and B.

65) The purpose of a commutator in a dc generator is to:

    A) maximize the current generated.   B) provide filtration.

    C) keep current flowing in one direction.   D) concentrate flux density.

66) The direction of motor torque is determined by what factors?

    A) amount of voltage applied and resistance of the windings

    B) polarity of voltage applied and the polarity of the surrounding magnetic field

    C) can rotate either way based on what the position of the coil is

    D) none of the above

67) For a high current switching application where it is not practical to route heavy wiring to the switch location which device would be used?

    A) solenoid   B) generator   C) relay   D) electromagnet

68) If a higher voltage is needed from a generator, what must be done?

    A) Decrease the number of coils.

    B) Increase the distance between the coil and magnetic field.

    C) Turn the coil faster.

    D) both B and C.

1) TRUE
   Diff: 1
2) FALSE
   Diff: 1
3) TRUE
   Diff: 1
4) FALSE
   Diff: 1
5) FALSE
   Diff: 1
6) FALSE
   Diff: 1
7) TRUE
   Diff: 1
8) FALSE
   Diff: 1
9) FALSE
   Diff: 1
10) FALSE
    Diff: 1
11) FALSE
    Diff: 1
12) FALSE
    Diff: 1
13) FALSE
    Diff: 1
14) TRUE
    Diff: 1
15) FALSE
    Diff: 1
16) C
    Diff: 1
17) D
    Diff: 1
18) C
    Diff: 1
19) A
    Diff: 1
20) B
    Diff: 1
21) B
    Diff: 2
22) D
    Diff: 1

23) C
    Diff: 1
24) D
    Diff: 1
25) A
    Diff: 1
26) C
    Diff: 2
27) C
    Diff: 1
28) B
    Diff: 1
29) B
    Diff: 1
30) B
    Diff: 3
31) D
    Diff: 1
32) B
    Diff: 1
33) D
    Diff: 1
34) C
    Diff: 1
35) C
    Diff: 1
36) A
    Diff: 1
37) D
    Diff: 1
38) A
    Diff: 1
39) A
    Diff: 1
40) C
    Diff: 1
41) B
    Diff: 1
42) C
    Diff: 1
43) D
    Diff: 1
44) A
    Diff: 1

45) A
    Diff: 1
46) B
    Diff: 1
47) A
    Diff: 1
48) A
    Diff: 1
49) B
    Diff: 1
50) A
    Diff: 1
51) D
    Diff: 1
52) B
    Diff: 1
53) B
    Diff: 1
54) C
    Diff: 1
55) D
    Diff: 1
56) A
    Diff: 1
57) C
    Diff: 1
58) C
    Diff: 1
59) B
    Diff: 1
60) B
    Diff: 1
61) D
    Diff: 1
62) B
    Diff: 1
63) D
    Diff: 1
64) C
    Diff: 1
65) C
    Diff: 1
66) B
    Diff: 2

67) C
    Diff: 1
68) C
    Diff: 2

Chapter 8   Introduction to Alternating Current and Voltage

True or False

1) A sine wave's frequency equals the reciprocal of its period.

2) The higher a sine wave's frequency, the shorter its period.

3) A sine wave's peak value is smaller than its RMS value.

4) An ac current is inversely proportional to an ac voltage.

5) One complete sine wave contains 360°.

6) *RMS* is another name for *peak*.

7) 7.07 VPP is approximately equal to 2.5 VRMS.

8) The term *RMS* stands for "root-mean-square."

9) The period of a 5 Hz wave form is 200 ms.

10) Commercial line voltages are usually square waves at a frequency of 60 Hz.

11) Current flows both ways simultaneously in an AC circuit.

12) Only frequency increases with the speed of an AC generator.

13) 20 Vrms of alternating current will illuminate a given lamp at the same intensity as 20 V of direct current.

14) Rise time, fall time, and duty cycle are all terms associated with sine wave measurement.

15) Kirchhoff's voltage law can be used with resistive ac circuits.

Multiple Choice

16) The *RMS* value of a sine wave means _____.

   A) the same as Ipp × R

   B) the *root mean square* value

   C) the heating effect of an ac generator of the same voltage

   D) the same as Ip × R

17) What is the instantaneous voltage at 42° on a 230 Vp sine wave?

   A) 76.09 V   B) 115 V   C) 149 V   D) 153.9 V

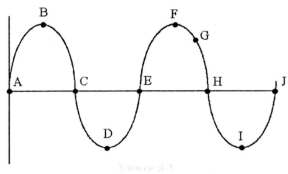

Figure 8–1

18) Which one of the following represents the value at point G in Figure 8–1?

   A) the period   B) the RMS voltage

   C) the peak voltage   D) the frequency

19) which of the following can be measured from points B to F in Figure 8–1?

   A) the frequency   B) the angle

   C) the period   D) the peak–to–peak voltage

20) Vpp is measured between points _____ in Figure 8–1.

   A) A and B   B) G and I   C) C and H   D) D and F

21) Which point in Figure 8–1 is 180° away from point E?

   A) A   B) B   C) C   D) D

22) In Figure 8–1, the time from point C to E is called _____.

   A) an alternation   B) the period   C) a cycle   D) peak voltage

23) In Figure 8-1, which of the following can be measured from point E to point F?

   A) the RMS voltage

   B) the peak voltage

   C) the peak to peak voltage

   D) one cycle of voltage

24) In Figure 8-1, if the time from point A to H is 60 µs the frequency is _____.

   A) 25 kHz

   B) 16.67 kHz

   C) 50 kHz

   D) More information is required to calculate the frequency.

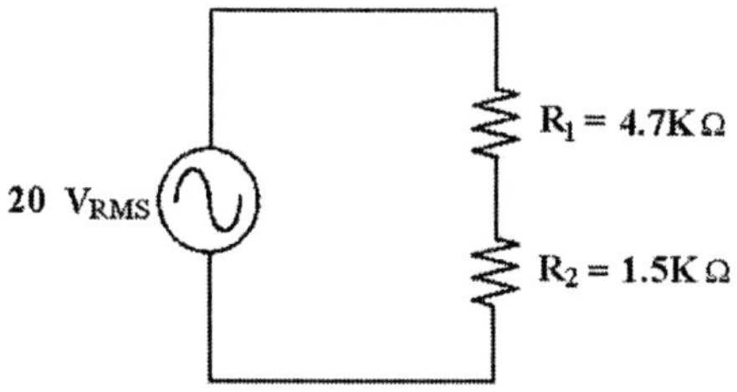

Figure 8-2

25) Calculate V_{R2} in Figure 8-2.

   A) 6.84 V_{PP} B) 13.15 V_P C) 6.84 V_P D) 4.83 V_P

26) What is the approximate peak input voltage to the circuit in Figure 8-2?

   A) 28.28 V_P B) 14.14 V_P C) 20 V_P D) 10 V_P

27) Calculate V_{R1} in Figure 8-2.

   A) 21.44 V_P B) 6.84 V_P C) 13.15 V_P D) 13.68 V_P

28) In Figure 8-2, what is the instantaneous voltage across R_1 at an angle of 22°?

   A) 8.03 V   B) 11.96 V   C) 2.56 V   D) 20.25 V

29) V_{R2} _____ if R_1 opens in Figure 8-2.

   A) increases   B) decreases   C) remains the same

30) Find R_T in Figure 8-2.

   A) 1.13 kΩ   B) 4.7 kΩ   C) 4.77 kΩ   D) 6.2 kΩ

31) Find P_{R1} in Figure 8-2.

    A) 97.84 mW   B) 195.69 mW   C) 48.91 mW   D) 0 W

32) If R_7 shorts in Figure 8-2, V_{R2} _____.

    A) increases   B) decreases   C) remains the same

33) In Figure 8-2, what is the instantaneous voltage across R_1 at 122°?

    A) 18.19 V   B) 5.8 V   C) 11.15 V   D) 11.6 V

34) Calculate I_T in Figure 8-2.

    A) 4.55 mAPP   B) 3.22 mAPP   C) 9.12 mAPP   D) 6.44 mAPP

35) If you measure about 56 VPP across the source in Figure 8-2, what is the trouble?

    A) R_1 is open.

    B) R_2 is open.

    C) Both R_1 and R_2 are open.

    D) There is no trouble. 56 VPP is a normal measurement for the source voltage.

    E) any of these

36) Calculate the total power dissipation in the circuit in Figure 8-2.

    A) 64.5 mW   B) 45.6 mW   C) 9.12 mW   D) 182 mW

37) In Figure 8-2, if you look at V_{R1} with an oscilloscope and you find no trace, a possible trouble might be that _____.

    A) R_1 is open   B) R_2 is shorted

    C) R_2 is open   D) the resistance of R_2 has changed

38) What is the instantaneous voltage at 284° on a 22 VPP sine wave?

    A) 10.67 V   B) 0.33 V   C) –10.67 V   D) –2.66 V

39) If a rectangular wave's pulse width is 50 μS and its frequency is 4 kHz, its duty cycle is

    _____.

    A) 80%   B) 20%   C) 1.25%   D) 98.75%

40) The time required by a 10 V square wave to change from 1 V to 9 V is known as the _____.

    A) fall time   B) period   C) pulse width   D) rise time

41) What is the approximate instantaneous voltage at 37° on a 169 VP sine wave?

    A) 135 V   B) 119 V   C) 239 V   D) 102 V

42) A 60 Hz sine wave completes _____ cycles every 10 seconds.

    A) 6   B) 10   C) 1/16   D) 600

43) A 10 VP sine wave is equal to _____.

    A) 20 VPP   B) 5 VPP

    C) 100 VPP   D) none of the above

44) A sine wave's instantaneous voltage is 0 V at _____ degrees.

    A) 0   B) 180   C) 360   D) all of these

45) If a 10 kΩ resistor carries 5 mARMS of current, its voltage drop equals _____.

    A) 70.7 VRMS   B) 7.07 VRMS   C) 5 VRMS   D) 50 VRMS

46) In a two–resistor series circuit V_{R1} = 6.5 VRMS and V_{R2} = 3.2 VRMS. The source voltage is _____.

    A) 9.7 VP   B) 9.19 VP   C) 13.72 VP   D) 4.53 VP

47) A formula for VRMS is _____.

    A) 0.707 × VPP   B) 0.707 × VP   C) 2 × VP   D) 2.8 × VP

48) What is the instantaneous voltage at 17° on a 169 VP sine wave?

    A) 49.4 V   B) 98.8 V   C) 161 V   D) 80.5 V

49) A 12 VP sine wave equals _____.

    A) 24 VPP   B) 8.48 VRMS   C) 7.64 VAVG   D) all of these

50) An oscilloscope's volts/division switch is set on 50 mV/cm. If the vertical deflection of the oscilloscope's trace is 1.6 cm, what voltage is being measured?

    A) 80 mV   B) 50 mV   C) 1.6 mV   D) 0.008 V

51) An oscilloscope's seconds/division switch is set on 20 ms/cm. If a sine wave measures 4 cm horizontally, what frequency is being measured?

A) 50 Hz

B) 25 Hz

C) 12.5 Hz

D) More information is needed.

52) An oscilloscope's seconds/division switch is set on 20 μs/cm. If the trace is 7.5 cm long, what is the period?

A) 1.5 μs

B) 5 μs

C) 150 μs

D) 0.0015 s

53) When an accurate oscilloscope measurement is needed, _____.

A) the trace can be any size

B) the trace should be large and you should look straight at the trace

C) no particular care is required

D) the trace need only be large

54) If the period of a square wave is 22 ms, what is its frequency?

A) 45.45 kHz

B) 45.45 Hz

C) 22 Hz

D) 22 kHz

55) The symbol for the period of a wave form is:

A) P.

B) T.

C) W.

D) F.

56) The period of most AC waveforms is measured in units of:

A) cycles.

B) revolutions.

C) seconds.

D) alternations.

57) The time (T) and the frequency (f) of an AC waveform are related as:

A) complimentary proportional.

B) directly proportional.

C) inversely proportional.

D) universally proportional.

58) Superimposed DC and AC voltages mean the two voltages are combined:

A) in series aiding or opposing.

B) in parallel aiding or opposing.

C) in series–parallel aiding or opposing.

D) all of these

59) The AC sine wave varies from zero to its maximum value in accordance with:

A) a geometric progression.

B) an algebraic function.

C) a trigonometric relationship.

D) a mathematical formula.

60) A square wave is a unique form of the rectangular pulse wave in that:

   A) the positive and negative halves are equal.

   B) the wave is symmetrical.

   C) the duty cycle is 50%.

   D) all of these

61) The average value of a rectangular pulse wave is calculated as:

   A) Vaug = 0.637 Vp.   B) Vaug = Vbaseline + Vp.

   C) Vaug = Vbaseline + (duty cycle) × Vp.   D) Vaug = 1.57 Vp.

62) The formula to convert degrees to radians is:

   A) degrees $= \left[\dfrac{180°}{\pi \text{ rad}}\right] \times$ radians.

   B) radians $= \left[\dfrac{\pi \text{ rad}}{180°}\right] \times$ degrees.

   C) $180° = \pi$ radians.

   D) all of these.

63) The value of a AC sine wave at any instant can be represented by:

   A) a graph of the voltage or current vs. the angular measurement.

   B) a phasor whose angle and magnitude are representative of the AC signal.

   C) the formula $V_i = V_p \times \sin \theta$.

   D) all of these.

64) The square wave is made up of:

   A) just the fundamental frequency.

   B) the fundamental frequency and all the odd harmonics.

   C) the fundamental frequency and all the even harmonics.

   D) the fundamental frequency and both the odd and even harmonics.

65) The largest numerical value in the measurement of alternating current is:

   A) peak.   B) peak to peak.   C) rms.   D) average.

66) Troubleshooting an AC circuit can be performed with which of the following tools?

   A) oscilloscope   B) analog voltmeter

   C) digital multimeter   D) any of the above

67) Superimposing an AC voltage of 3.54 Vrms with a DC source of 10 V results in a waveform that:

A) peaks at 13.54 V.   B) peaks at 15 V.

C) peaks at 20 V.   D) both B and C

68) While troubleshooting a circuit the voltage seems to be zero; what if any adjustment should be checked on the oscilloscope?

A) time division setting   B) trigger level

C) AC/GND/DC switch   D) focus setting

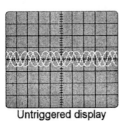

Untriggered display

Figure 8-3

69) This display in Figure 8-3 illustrates maladjustment of which control on the oscilloscope?

A) volts/div   B) coupling   C) intensity   D) trigger level

1) TRUE
   Diff: 1
2) TRUE
   Diff: 1
3) FALSE
   Diff: 1
4) FALSE
   Diff: 1
5) TRUE
   Diff: 1
6) FALSE
   Diff: 1
7) TRUE
   Diff: 2
8) TRUE
   Diff: 1
9) TRUE
   Diff: 2
10) FALSE
    Diff: 1
11) FALSE
    Diff: 1
12) FALSE
    Diff: 1
13) TRUE
    Diff: 1
14) FALSE
    Diff: 1
15) TRUE
    Diff: 1
16) B
    Diff: 1
17) D
    Diff: 2
18) B
    Diff: 1
19) C
    Diff: 1
20) D
    Diff: 1
21) C
    Diff: 1
22) A
    Diff: 1

23) B
    Diff: 1
24) A
    Diff: 2
25) C
    Diff: 2
26) A
    Diff: 2
27) A
    Diff: 2
28) A
    Diff: 2
29) B
    Diff: 3
30) D
    Diff: 2
31) C
    Diff: 2
32) B
    Diff: 3
33) A
    Diff: 2
34) C
    Diff: 2
35) E
    Diff: 3
36) A
    Diff: 2
37) C
    Diff: 3
38) C
    Diff: 2
39) B
    Diff: 2
40) D
    Diff: 1
41) D
    Diff: 2
42) D
    Diff: 2
43) A
    Diff: 2
44) D
    Diff: 1

45) D
    Diff: 2
46) C
    Diff: 2
47) B
    Diff: 1
48) A
    Diff: 2
49) C
    Diff: 2
50) A
    Diff: 2
51) C
    Diff: 2
52) C
    Diff: 2
53) B
    Diff: 1
54) B
    Diff: 2
55) B
    Diff: 1
56) C
    Diff: 1
57) C
    Diff: 1
58) A
    Diff: 1
59) C
    Diff: 1
60) D
    Diff: 1
61) C
    Diff: 1
62) B
    Diff: 1
63) D
    Diff: 1
64) B
    Diff: 1
65) B
    Diff: 1
66) D
    Diff: 1

67) B
    Diff: 2
68) C
    Diff: 1
69) D
    Diff: 2

Chapter 9   Capacitors

True or False

1) *Capacitance* is the ability to store voltage.

2) A capacitor blocks dc and passes ac.

3) When two capacitors are connected in parallel across a dc source, the smaller capacitor drops the larger voltage.

4) If the distance between the plates of a capacitor increases, the capacitance decreases.

5) A capacitor can fully charge in one *time constant*.

6) *Capacitance* is a capacitor's ability to store resistance.

7) When two capacitors are connected in series across a dc source, the smallest capacitor drops the largest voltage.

8) A capacitor will fully charge in about five time constants.

9) To find the total capacitance of two capacitors in parallel, you must combine them using a similar procedure as resistors in parallel.

10) If the plate area of a capacitor decreases, the capacitance decreases.

11) The voltage rating of a capacitor indicates the voltage it will charge up to.

12) Electrolytic capacitors are ideal for alternating current applications.

13) Efficient filtering is directly related to RC time constant.

14) Leakage through a capacitor is undesirable.

Multiple Choice

15) What is the capacitance of a capacitor that drops 50 V and stores 0.500 µC of charge?

    A) 0.1 µF   B) 1 µF   C) 0.001 µF   D) 0.01 µF

16) How much charge is stored in a 0.022 µF capacitor that drops 22 V?

    A) 0.0484 µC   B) 4.84 µC   C) 0.484 µC   D) 48.4 µC

17) If the dc working voltage of a capacitor is 100 V, the dielectric must withstand _____.

    A) 100 V_{DC} B) 75 V_{RMS} C) 220 V_{PP} D) 85 V_{RMS}

18) If a 0.05 µF and 0.1 µF capacitor are connected in parallel across a 20 V source, the total capacitance equals _____ and each capacitor drops _____.

    A) 0.15 µF, 10 V   B) 0.05 µF, 15 V   C) 0.10 µF, 20 V   D) 0.15 µF, 20 V

19) If a 0.022 µF, 0.022 µF and 0.05 µF capacitor are connected in series across a 25 V source, the voltage drop across the largest capacitor equals _____.

    A) 10.24 V   B) 11.76 V   C) 4.5 V   D) 17.5 V

20) What is one time constant of a 4.7 µF capacitor in series with a 22 kΩ resistor?

    A) 0.103 ms   B) 1.03 ms   C) 10.3 ms   D) 103 ms

21) How long will it take a 0.047 µF capacitor to fully charge through a 100 kΩ resistor?

    A) 2.35 s   B) 0.235 ms   C) 23.5 ms   D) 235 ms

22) How long will it take a 1 µF capacitor to completely discharge through a 47 kΩ resistor?

    A) 47 s   B) 235 s   C) 47 ms   D) 235 ms

23) If a 1 µF capacitor and a 10 kΩ resistor are connected in series across 20 V_{DC}, approximately how much voltage will the capacitor drop after charging for just one time constant?

    A) 17 V   B) 12.06 V   C) 10.99 V   D) 12.6 V

24) If a 4.7 µF capacitor and a 10 kΩ resistor are connected in series across 25 V_{DC}, approximately how much voltage will the resistor drop after charging for just one time constant?

    A) 9.2 V   B) 23.75 V   C) 21.63 V   D) 15.8 V

25) If a 4.7 µF capacitor operates at 10 kHz, X_C equals _____.

    A) 338.8 Ω   B) 294 µΩ   C) 3.38 Ω   D) infinite Ω

26) At what frequency is a 2000 pF capacitor operating if its reactance is 745 Ω?

    A) 106.8 kHz   B) 10.14 kHz   C) 1.014 kHz   D) 1014 Hz

27) If a 22 μF capacitor is connected to a 15 V 400 Hz source, its current equals _____.

    A) 55 mA   B) 18.1 mA   C) 829 mA   D) 1.81 A

28) If a 0.1 μF, 0.1 μF and 0.05 μF capacitor are connected in series across a 75 V source, the voltage drop across the smallest capacitor equals _____.

    A) 18.75 V   B) 50 V   C) 37.5 V   D) 100 V

29) How long will it take to completely charge a 0.047 μF capacitor through a 1 MΩ resistor?

    A) 0.047 s   B) 0.029 s   C) 0.235 s   D) 0.47 s

30) If a 0.1 μF capacitor and a 2.2 kΩ resistor are connected in series across 30 V$_{DC}$, how much voltage will the capacitor drop after charging for just one time constant?

    A) 29.4 V   B) 28.5 V   C) 25.9 V   D) 18.9 V

31) If the frequency applied to a capacitor increases, the capacitive reactance _____.

    A) increases   B) decreases

    C) remains the same   D) varies up and down

32) A capacitor that transfers an ac signal from one stage to another is called a _____ capacitor.

    A) bypass   B) filter   C) coupling   D) transfer

33) If a 1 μF, 2.2 μF and 0.05 μF capacitor are connected in series, C$_T$ is less than _____.

    A) 1 μF   B) 2.2 μF   C) 0.05 μF   D) 0.001 μF

34) If four 0.022 μF capacitors are connected in parallel, C$_T$ equals _____.

    A) 0.022 μF   B) 0.088 μF   C) 0.044 μF   D) 0.049 μF

35) If an uncharged capacitor, a resistor, a switch and a 12 V battery are connected in series, what is the voltage across the capacitor at the instant the switch is closed?

    A) 12 V   B) 6 V   C) 24 V   D) 0 V

36) If an uncharged capacitor, a resistor, a switch and a 12 V battery are connected in series, what is the voltage across the capacitor after it is fully charged?

    A) 12 V   B) 6 V   C) 24 V   D) –6 V

37) If an uncharged capacitor, a resistor, a switch and a 12 V battery are connected in series, at approximately what time will the capacitor reach full charge?

   A) R × C

   B) 5 × R × C

   C) 12 × R × C

   D) The time cannot be predicted.

38) What is the capacitance that stores 1.175 µC of charge and drops 25 V?

   A) 0.047 µF   B) 0.47 µF   C) 4.7 µF   D) 47 µF

39) How much charge is stored in a 0.47 µF capacitor that drops 18 V?

   A) 846 µC   B) 84.6 µC   C) 8.46 µC   D) 0.846 µC

40) What is the minimum dc working voltage rating for a capacitor that must drop 120 V RMS?

   A) 120 V   B) 169.7 V   C) 84.8 V   D) 339 V

41) If a 0.047 µF, 0.047 µF and 0.47 µF capacitor are connected in series across a 25 V source, the total capacitance equals _____ and each 0.047 µF capacitor drops _____.

   A) 0.022 µF, 11.9 V   B) 0.022 µF, 25 V

   C) 0.564 µF, 1.2 V   D) 0.564 µF, 11.9 V

42) If a 22 µF and 100 µF capacitor are connected in parallel across a 15 V source, the total capacitance equals _____ and the 22 µF capacitor drops _____.

   A) 18 µF, 15 V   B) 18 µF, 5.2 V   C) 122 µF, 15 V   D) 1220 µF, 30 V

43) What is one time constant of a 47 µF capacitor in series with a 120 kΩ resistor?

   A) 0.564 ms   B) 564 ms   C) 5.64 s   D) 54.6 s

44) How long will it take for a 22 µF capacitor to completely charge through a 47 kΩ resistor?

   A) 1.034 s   B) 2.068 s   C) 8.272 s   D) 5.17 s

45) How long will it take for a 22 µF capacitor to completely discharge through a 4.7 kΩ resistor?

   A) 0.827 s   B) 0.517 s   C) 0.207 s   D) 0.103 s

46) How much voltage is dropped across a 150 µF capacitor after 3.33 seconds if it is charged by a 50 V source through a 22 KΩ resistor?

   A) 31.7 V   B) 43.25 V   C) 47.5 V   D) 49 V

47) If a 0.047 µF capacitor operates at 220 kHz, X_C equals _____.

    A) 15.4 kΩ   B) 1.54 kΩ   C) 154 Ω   D) 15.4 Ω

48) At what frequency is a 0.001 µF capacitor operating if its reactance is 45 kΩ?

    A) 3.54 kHz   B) 35.4 kHz   C) 354 kHz   D) 3.54 MHz

49) If a 47 µF capacitor is connected to a 20 V, 400 Hz source, the current is _____.

    A) 425 A   B) 2.36 A   C) 8.51 A   D) 0.851 A

50) When connecting a large electrolytic capacitor to a circuit with a 100 V_{DC} source, place the negative end of the capacitor _____.

    A) towards the positive side of the source

    B) towards the negative side of the source

    C) in either position; the polarity is not important

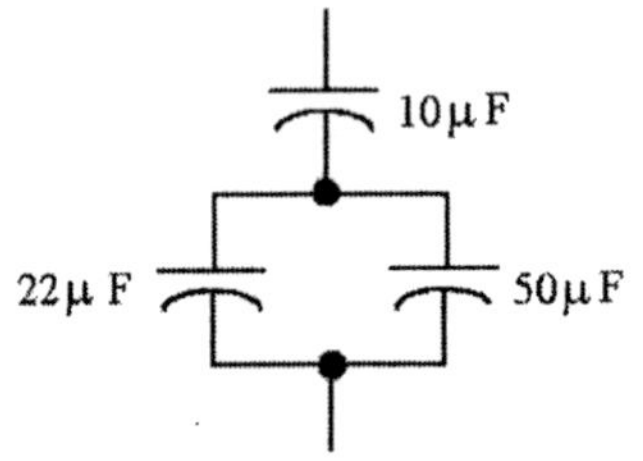

10 µF

22 µF   50 µF

Figure 9–1

51) What is C_T in Figure 9–1?

    A) 82 µF   B) 8.78 µF   C) 25.2 µF   D) 70.1 µF

52) Electrolytic capacitors differ from many other capacitors in construction in that they are:

    A) smaller.   B) larger.   C) polarized.   D) sensitized.

53) Electrolytic capacitors must be connected into a circuit such that:

    A) positive lead to positive voltage; negative lead to negative voltage.

    B) voltage rating marked is not exceeded.

    C) reversal of polarity does not happen.

    D) all of these.

54) When capacitors are connected in series, their total capacitance act like:

    A) resistance connected in series.   B) resistance connected in parallel.

    C) resistance connected in series–parallel.   D) all of these.

55) When capacitors are connected in parallel, their total capacitance act like:

    A) resistance connected in series.   B) resistance connected in parallel.

    C) resistance connected in series–parallel.   D) all of these.

56) The time constant of a capacitor is:

    A) the time required to charge to 63% or discharge to 37%.

    B) directly proportional to the capacitance in the circuit.

    C) directly proportional to the resistance in the circuit.

    D) all of these.

57) The time constant for a capacitor for each time period is:

    A) 63% of the increase in value.   B) 37% of the decrease in value.

    C) a constant factor.   D) all of these.

58) Reactive power (P_r) in a capacitor is defined as the rate at which a capacitor stores or returns energy and is measured in:

    A) volts per time constant.   B) current per time constant.

    C) volt-ampere reactive.   D) watts reactive.

59) In a capacitive AC circuit, the phase relationship between the voltage and the current is such that the:

    A) current is leading the voltage.

    B) voltage is leading the current.

    C) current is 180 degrees out of phase with voltage.

    D) voltage is 360 degrees out of phase with current.

60) A common use for electrolytic capacitors found in power supplies is _____.

    A) decoupling   B) blocking DC   C) passing AC   D) filtering

61) A test instrument designed to be used for the testing of capacitors is the _____.

    A) digital multimeter   B) analog multimeter

    C) LCR Meter   D) oscilloscope

62) A commonplace use for capacitors in electronics is to:

    A) pass AC voltages.   B) pass DC voltages.

    C) block AC voltages.   D) block DC voltages.

63) Upon checking the voltage output of a power supply with an oscilloscope, you notice an unusually large amount of ripple. What could possibly be the problem?

A) shorted filter capacitor

B) shorted load

C) open filter capacitor

D) either B or C

64) With three capacitors in series, the current lags the voltage by:

A) 270 degrees.

B) 90 degrees.

C) 30 degrees.

D) none of the above.

65) A 65 Vrms signal is applied to a 10 F capacitor. What is the total peak current?

A) 6.5 A

B) 6.5 kA

C) 153 mA

D) not enough information

66) What is the small amount of power lost in a capacitive circuit due to the internal resistance of the capacitors?

A) reactive power

B) instantaneous power

C) true power

D) ideal power

67) The removal of high frequency transient voltages with a capacitor is called:

A) decoupling.

B) coupling.

C) bypassing.

D) ac blocking.

1) FALSE
   Diff: 1
2) TRUE
   Diff: 1
3) FALSE
   Diff: 1
4) TRUE
   Diff: 1
5) FALSE
   Diff: 1
6) FALSE
   Diff: 1
7) TRUE
   Diff: 1
8) TRUE
   Diff: 1
9) FALSE
   Diff: 1
10) TRUE
   Diff: 1
11) FALSE
   Diff: 1
12) FALSE
   Diff: 1
13) TRUE
   Diff: 1
14) TRUE
   Diff: 1
15) D
   Diff: 2
16) C
   Diff: 2
17) A
   Diff: 2
18) D
   Diff: 2
19) C
   Diff: 2
20) D
   Diff: 2
21) C
   Diff: 2
22) D
   Diff: 2

23) D
   Diff: 2
24) A
   Diff: 2
25) C
   Diff: 2
26) A
   Diff: 2
27) C
   Diff: 2
28) C
   Diff: 2
29) C
   Diff: 2
30) D
   Diff: 2
31) B
   Diff: 2
32) C
   Diff: 2
33) C
   Diff: 2
34) B
   Diff: 2
35) D
   Diff: 2
36) A
   Diff: 2
37) B
   Diff: 2
38) A
   Diff: 2
39) C
   Diff: 2
40) B
   Diff: 2
41) A
   Diff: 2
42) C
   Diff: 2
43) C
   Diff: 2
44) D
   Diff: 2

45) B
   Diff: 2
46) A
   Diff: 2
47) D
   Diff: 2
48) A
   Diff: 2
49) B
   Diff: 2
50) B
   Diff: 2
51) B
   Diff: 2
52) C
   Diff: 1
53) D
   Diff: 1
54) B
   Diff: 1
55) A
   Diff: 1
56) D
   Diff: 1
57) D
   Diff: 1
58) C
   Diff: 1
59) A
   Diff: 1
60) D
   Diff: 2
61) C
   Diff: 2
62) D
   Diff: 1
63) D
   Diff: 3
64) D
   Diff: 2
65) D
   Diff: 1
66) C
   Diff: 1

67) A
   Diff: 1

Chapter 10 RC Circuits

True or False

1) The total current in an RC circuit always leads the source voltage.

2) The phasor combination of V_R and V_C in an RC series circuit equals the source voltage.

3) An RC circuit can be used as a filter to eliminate selected frequencies.

4) As the frequency applied to an RC circuit is decreased, the phase angle decreases.

5) As the frequency applied to an RC circuit varies, both X_C and resistance vary.

6) The total current in an RC circuit always lags the source voltage.

7) The phasor combination of X_C and R is called Z.

8) As the frequency applied to an RC circuit increases, the impedance decreases.

9) The phase angle of an RC circuit varies inversely with frequency.

10) When the frequency applied to an RC circuit varies, the value of X_C varies.

11) Power factor values close to 0 denotes an RC circuit with mostly true power.

12) A VA rating is more relevant when judging the current delivery capacity for a given signal source.

13) A leaky capacitor can be equated as a capacitor with a resistor being placed in series with it.

14) A high pass filter will cause some phase shifting of the signal.

Multiple Choice

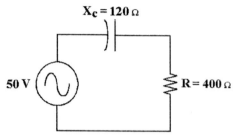

Figure 10-1

15) If the frequency equals 60 Hz in Figure 10-1, what is the value of capacitance?

    A) 22 μF   B) 44 μF   C) 66 μF   D) 88 μF

16) What is the circuit's impedance in Figure 10-1?

    A) 120 Ω   B) 280 Ω   C) 418 Ω   D) 520 Ω

17) What is the true power in Figure 10-1?

    A) 916 mW   B) 5.72 mW   C) 5.72 W   D) 275 mW

18) If the operating frequency increases in Figure 10-1, how does the current change?

    A) It increases.   B) It remains the same.

    C) It decreases.   D) It decreases to zero.

19) If the operating frequency increases in Figure 10-1, how does the phase angle change?

    A) It increases.   B) It remains the name.

    C) It decreases.   D) It changes to another quadrant.

20) If the operating frequency increases in Figure 10-1, how does the resistor value change?

    A) It increases.   B) It remains the same.

    C) It decreases.   D) It opens.

21) If the frequency is 400 Hz in Figure 10-1, what is the value of capacitance?

    A) 3.3 μF   B) 6.6 μF   C) 8.8 μF   D) 10 μF

22) If the source voltage is changed to 100 V in Figure 10-1, find the true power.

    A) 22.9 W   B) 22.9 mW   C) 3.66 W   D) 11 W

23) If the operating frequency decreases in Figure 10–1, how does the current change?

    A) It increases.   B) It remains the same.

    C) It decreases.   D) It decreases to zero.

24) If the operating frequency decreases in Figure 10–1, how does the phase angle change?

    A) It increases.   B) It remains the same.

    C) It decreases.   D) It changes to another quadrant.

25) If the operating frequency decreases in Figure 10–1, how does the capacitance value change?

    A) It increases.   B) It remains the same.

    C) It decreases.   D) It decreases to zero.

26) If the operating frequency decreases in Figure 10–1, how does the resistance value change?

    A) It increases.   B) It remains the same.

    C) It decreases.   D) It opens.

27) If the resistor changes to 2.2 kΩ in Figure 10–1, how does the total current change?

    A) It increases.   B) It remains the same.

    C) It decreases.   D) It decreases to zero.

28) Calculate the voltage drop across the capacitor in Figure 10–1.

    A) 11.53 V   B) 4.82 V   C) 3.69 V   D) 2.10 V

29) Calculate the apparent power in Figure 10–1.

    A) 1.70 VA   B) 5.66 VA   C) 5.91 VA   D) 14.37 VA

30) If the frequency increases in Figure 10–1, the phase angle _____ and the impedance _____.

    A) decreases, increases   B) decreases, decreases

    C) increases, decreases   D) increases, increases

31) If the frequency decreases in Figure 10–1, the phase angle _____ and the impedance _____.

    A) decreases, increases   B) decreases, decreases

    C) increases, decreases   D) increases, increases

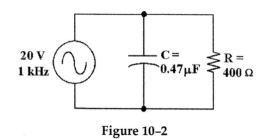

Figure 10–2

32) If the resistor value increases in Figure 10-2, then how does the total current change?

A) It increases.   B) It remains the same.

C) It decreases.   D) It decreases to zero.

33) How much voltage does the resistor drop in Figure 10-2?

A) 10 V   B) 20 V   C) 59 mV   D) 19.94 V

34) What change would increase the power factor in Figure 10-2?

A) Increasing the value of the source voltage

B) Increasing the value of the resistor

C) Increasing the value of the capacitor

D) Decreasing the value of the capacitor

35) Which statement describes the relationship of I_C and I_R in Figure 10-2?

A) They are in phase.   B) I_C leads I_R.

C) I_C lags I_R.   D) They are 180° out of phase.

36) How much voltage does the capacitor drop in Figure 10-2?

A) 10 V   B) 20 V   C) 59 mV   D) 19.94 V

37) What change would decrease the power factor in Figure 10-2?

A) increasing the value of Vs   B) increasing the value of the resistor

C) increasing the value of the capacitor D) decreasing the value of the capacitor

38) Calculate the total impedance in Figure 10-2.

A) 1000 Ω   B) 880 Ω   C) 258 Ω   D) 62 Ω

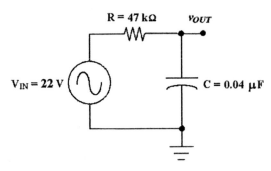

R = 47 kΩ v_{OUT}

V_{IN} = 22 V

C = 0.04 μF

Figure 10–3

39) The circuit in Figure 10–3 is known as a _____.
  A) high-pass filter   B) band-pass filter
  C) low-pass filter   D) parallel RC circuit

40) What is the cutoff frequency in Figure 10–3?
  A) 85 Hz   B) 118 Hz   C) 995 Hz   D) 1012 Hz

41) What is the output voltage at the cutoff frequency in Figure 10–3?
  A) 6.446 V   B) 31.12 V   C) 15.554 V   D) 22 V

42) If the output were taken across the resistor in Figure 10–3, the circuit would be known as a
  _____.
  A) low-pass filter   B) high-pass filter
  C) band-pass filter   D) band–notch filter

43) If the circuit in Figure 10–3 has an output voltage that's too high at the cutoff frequency,
  _____.
  A) the resistor has opened   B) the capacitor has shorted
  C) the resistor has shorted   D) the capacitor has become leaky

44) If the resistor is changed to 100 kΩ in Figure 10–3, what is the new cutoff frequency?
  A) 39.8 Hz   B) 79.6 Hz   C) 159.2 Hz   D) 318 Hz

45) If the resistance is reduced to 4 kΩ in Figure 10–3, the cutoff frequency equals _____.
  A) 6250 Hz   B) 99 Hz   C) 480 Hz   D) 995 Hz

46) If the resistor changes to 2.2 kΩ in Figure 10–3, the new cutoff frequency equals _____.
  A) 1.81 kHz   B) 1.18 kHz   C) 995 Hz   D) 1.01 kHz

47) If the input voltage increases to 50 V in Figure 10–3, what is the output voltage at the cutoff frequency?

    A) 70.7 V   B) 35.35 V   C) 17.675 V   D) 8.84 V

48) What is the circuit fault in Figure 10–3 if the output voltage equals 0 V at the cutoff frequency?

    A) The capacitor has opened.   B) The capacitor has shorted.

    C) The resistor has shorted.   D) The capacitor has become leaky.

49) If there is 10 V_{RMS} across the resistor and 10 V_{RMS} across the capacitor in a series RC circuit, then the source voltage equals _____.

    A) 20 V_{RMS} B) 14.14 V_{RMS} C) 28.28 V_{RMS} D) 10 V_{RMS}

50) If there is 1 A_{RMS} through the resistor and 1 A_{RMS} through the capacitor in a parallel RC circuit, then the total current equals _____.

    A) 1 A_{RMS} B) 2 A_{RMS} C) 2.28 A_{RMS} D) 1.414 A_{RMS}

51) A power factor of 1 indicates that the circuit phase angle is _____.

    A) 90°   B) 45°   C) 180°   D) 0°

52) If the true power is 100 W and the reactive power is 100 VAR, the apparent power is _____.

    A) 200 VA   B) 100 VA   C) 141.4 VA   D) 141.4 W

53) If the bandwidth of a low–pass filter is 0 to 1 kHz, the cutoff frequency is _____.

    A) 0 Hz   B) 500 Hz   C) 2 kHz   D) 1 kHz

54) When an AC voltage is supplied to an RC circuit, the AC's current and amplitude will be:

    A) similar in waveform.   B) leading the voltage.

    C) varying in the same manner.   D) all of these.

55) When the AC voltage and AC current through an RC circuit are varying in the same manner but slightly different in time, the signals are said to be:

    A) offset in time.   B) out of sync.   C) out of phase.   D) all of these.

56) In an RC circuit, the capacitive reactance is:

    A) inversely proportional to the capitance.

    B) inversely proportional to the frequency.

    C) decreases as the frequency increases.

    D) all of these.

57) Power in an RC circuit can be measured as:

    A) true power (P_{true}).   B) reactive power (P_r).

    C) apparent power (P_a).   D) all of these.

58) In a series RC circuit, as the phase angle between the applied voltage and the total current increases, this is the same as:

    A) power factor increasing.   B) power factor decreasing.

    C) true power decreasing.   D) apparent power decreasing.

59) An RC lag network is similar to a:

    A) low pass filter.   B) high pass filter.

    C) band pass filter.   D) stop pass filter.

60) An RC high pass filter takes its output across:

    A) the series capacitor.   B) the parallel capacitor.

    C) the series resistor.   D) the parallel resistor.

61) In an RC filter circuit, the cutoff frequency is defined as the frequency at which:

    A) the output voltage drops to 33% of maximum.

    B) the output voltage drops to 66% of maximum.

    C) the output voltage drops to 70% of maximum.

    D) the output voltage is cutoff, with minimum or zero output.

62) Simple RC circuits can be viewed as what type of filter?

    A) low pass   B) high pass   C) active   D) passive

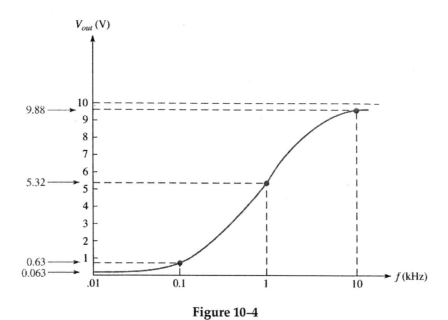

V_{out} (V)

9.88

5.32

0.63
0.063

.01   0.1   1   10 f (kHz)

Figure 10–4

63) This frequency response curve in Figure 10–4 represents what type of filter?

    A) low pass   B) high pass   C) band pass   D) band stop

64) The output voltage of an RC high pass filter at a designated frequency is low. What is a possible problem?

    A) open resistor   B) shorted capacitor

    C) function generator misadjusted   D) not enough information

65) Which of these troubleshooting procedures should be performed first?

    A) Take random measurements around point of failure.

    B) Analyze the problem and decide where to best start.

    C) Check test equipment connections.

    D) Slap the device firmly to dislodge foreign objects.

66) It has been determined that the phase shift of a given parallel RC circuit is lower than predicted. Which of the following most likely has caused this?

    A) Resistance has decreased.

    B) The function generator frequency control has been accidentally moved to a lower frequency.

    C) The capacitance has decreased.

    D) could be A or C

1) TRUE
   Diff: 1
2) TRUE
   Diff: 1
3) TRUE
   Diff: 1
4) FALSE
   Diff: 1
5) FALSE
   Diff: 1
6) FALSE
   Diff: 1
7) TRUE
   Diff: 1
8) TRUE
   Diff: 1
9) TRUE
   Diff: 1
10) TRUE
   Diff: 1
11) FALSE
   Diff: 1
12) TRUE
   Diff: 1
13) FALSE
   Diff: 1
14) TRUE
   Diff: 1
15) A
   Diff: 2
16) C
   Diff: 2
17) C
   Diff: 2
18) A
   Diff: 2
19) C
   Diff: 2
20) B
   Diff: 1
21) A
   Diff: 2
22) A
   Diff: 2

23) C
   Diff: 1
24) A
   Diff: 1
25) B
   Diff: 1
26) B
   Diff: 1
27) C
   Diff: 1
28) D
   Diff: 2
29) C
   Diff: 2
30) B
   Diff: 1
31) D
   Diff: 1
32) C
   Diff: 1
33) B
   Diff: 2
34) D
   Diff: 1
35) B
   Diff: 1
36) B
   Diff: 2
37) C
   Diff: 1
38) C
   Diff: 2
39) C
   Diff: 1
40) A
   Diff: 2
41) C
   Diff: 2
42) B
   Diff: 1
43) D
   Diff: 1
44) A
   Diff: 2

45) D
   Diff: 2
46) A
   Diff: 2
47) B
   Diff: 2
48) B
   Diff: 3
49) B
   Diff: 2
50) D
   Diff: 2
51) D
   Diff: 1
52) C
   Diff: 2
53) D
   Diff: 2
54) D
   Diff: 1
55) D
   Diff: 1
56) D
   Diff: 1
57) D
   Diff: 1
58) B
   Diff: 1
59) A
   Diff: 1
60) C
   Diff: 1
61) C
   Diff: 1
62) D
   Diff: 1
63) B
   Diff: 1
64) C
   Diff: 3
65) B
   Diff: 1
66) D
   Diff: 3

Chapter 11 Inductors

True or False

1) The total inductance of two parallel inductors equals the sum of their inductance values.

2) The energy stored in an inductor's electromagnetic field is produced by the inductor's current.

3) An inductor passes direct current and opposes alternating current.

4) Inductive reactance decreases as frequency increases.

5) The voltage leads the current in an inductive circuit.

6) The energy stored in an inductor's electromagnetic field is produced by the resistance of the inductor's winding.

7) The voltage and current are in phase in an inductive circuit.

8) Inductors in series or parallel combine just like resistors in series or parallel.

9) When a DC voltage is first applied to an inductor, the initial circuit current is zero.

10) If an inductor is placed in an ac circuit, the ac voltage across the inductor leads the ac current through it.

11) True power for an inductor is measured in VAR rather than watts.

12) The quality factor for an inductor becomes more apparent at higher frequencies.

13) An inductor is placed in series with the load for power supply filtration.

14) An iron-core inductor in low frequency applications.

Multiple Choice

15) What is the total inductance if a 50 mH inductor is connected in series with a 15 mH inductor?

   A) 11.5 mH   B) 15 mH   C) 50 mH   D) 65 mH

16) What is the maximum current in a 12 mH inductor if it is connected in series with a 10 kΩ resistor and a 15 VDC source?

   A) 1.2 mA   B) 1.5 mA   C) 2.2 mA   D) 6.32 mA

17) If an inductor has an ac current flowing through it, the magnetic field is _____.

   A) steady   B) constantly changing
   C) moving from south to north   D) collapsed

18) Do iron-core inductors or air-core inductors generally have the larger inductance?

   A) air core

   B) neither; iron-core inductors and air-core inductors have the same inductance

   C) iron core

   D) There is no way to tell.

19) If a 50 mH inductor operates at 22 kHz, X_L equals _____.

   A) 6908 Ω   B) 500 Ω   C) 113 Ω   D) 1100 Ω

20) In an inductive circuit, the _____ lags the _____.

   A) voltage, resistance   B) current, voltage
   C) current, resistance   D) voltage, reactance

21) If a 27 m H inductor has a reactance of 5.5 kΩ, the frequency equals _____.

   A) 932 Hz   B) 324 Hz   C) 3.24 kHz   D) 32.4 kHz

22) What is one time constant for a 10 mH inductor connected in series with a 47 kΩ resistor?

   A) 0.213 μS   B) 470 S   C) 213 μS   D) 470 mS

23) How many time constants will it take to completely collapse an inductor's magnetic field?

   A) 1   B) 3   C) 4   D) 5

24) What is the inductive reactance of a 0.2 mH inductor operating at 1 kHz?

   A) 1.256 kΩ   B) 125.6 kΩ   C) 1.256 Ω   D) 125.6 Ω

25) What is the inductive reactance of an inductor that drops 12 V$_{RMS}$ and carries 50 mA$_{RMS}$?

    A) 6 Ω   B) 60 Ω   C) 600 Ω   D) 240 Ω

26) What is the inductance of a 20 mH inductor connected in parallel with a 50 mH inductor?

    A) 20 mH   B) 50 mH   C) 70 mH   D) 14.29 mH

27) Connecting a _____ inductor in _____ with a 100 m H inductor produces a 65 m H inductance.

    A) 185.7 mH, series   B) 185.7 mH, parallel

    C) 35 mH, parallel   D) 35 mH, series

28) If an inductor carries 100 mA$_{DC}$ of current when connected across a 30 V$_{DC}$ source, then what is its resistance?

    A) 0 Ω   B) 60 Ω   C) 300 Ω   D) 30 Ω

29) If two 2.5 mH inductors are connected in series with a 4.7 kΩ resistor and the source voltage is 100 V$_{DC}$, what is the circuit's current?

    A) 21.3 mA   B) 63.2 mA   C) 1.1 mA   D) 7.9 mA

30) What is the inductive reactance of a 150 mH inductor operating at 10 kHz?

    A) 1500 Ω   B) 6280 Ω   C) 8450 Ω   D) 9420 Ω

31) What is the time constant for a 50 mH inductor and 5 kΩ resistor connected in series?

    A) 10 μs   B) 100 s   C) 250 s   D) 10 ms

32) What is the total inductance of a 40 mH inductor and a 24 mH inductor connected in parallel?

    A) 64 mH   B) 32 mH   C) 15 mH   D) 150 mH

33) An 0.05 μH inductance is larger than a _____.

    A) 0.0000005 H inductance   B) 0.000005 H inductance

    C) 0.000000008 H inductance   D) 0.00005 H inductance

34) A 0.33 mH inductance is smaller than a _____.

    A) 33 pH inductance   B) 330 pH inductance

    C) 0.05 mH inductance   D) 0.0005 H inductance

35) What is the total inductance of four 10 mH inductors connected in series?

    A) 40 mH   B) 2.5 mH   C) 40,000 μH   D) 250 mH

36) If a 1 mH, 3.3 mH, and 0.1 mH inductor are connected in parallel, L_T equals _____.

    A) 4.4 mH   B) greater than 3.3 mH

    C) less than 0.1 mH   D) 5.3 mH

37) If an inductor, resistor and switch are connected in series to a 12 V battery, what is the inductor's voltage at the instant that the switch is closed?

    A) 0 V   B) 12 V   C) 6 V   D) 4 V

38) If two inductors are connected in a series AC circuit, which inductor drops more voltage?

    A) the larger inductance   B) the smaller inductance

    C) It depends upon the frequency.   D) It depends upon the source voltage.

39) What is the total inductance of a 14 mH, 22 mH and 45 mH inductor connected in series?

    A) 81 μH   B) 7.2 mH   C) 81 mH   D) 20 mH

40) If a 50 mH inductor is in series with a 50 kΩ resistor across a 50 V_{DC} source, what is the maximum current that will flow in the circuit?

    A) 1 μA   B) 100 μA   C) 1 mA   D) 10 mA

41) If a 25 mH inductor drops 50 V while operating at 400 Hz, what is X_L?

    A) 62.8 Ω   B) 628 Ω   C) 6.28 kΩ   D) 62.8 kΩ

42) If a 15 μH inductor has a 2.2 KΩ reactance, the frequency equals _____.

    A) 23.4 kHz   B) 23.4 MHz   C) 4.28 MHz   D) 4.28 kHz

43) How many time constants will it take to completely build a magnetic field around an inductor?

    A) 1   B) 2   C) 3   D) 4   E) 5

44) What is the reactance of a 100 μH inductor operating at 100 kHz?

    A) 62.8 kΩ   B) 62.8 Ω   C) 6.28 Ω   D) infinite Ω

45) What is the reactance of an inductor that carries 1.25 mA_P and drops 25 V_P at 100 Hz?

    A) 31.25 Ω   B) 15.7 kΩ   C) 3.125 kΩ   D) 20 kΩ

46) What is the total inductance of a 25 mH inductor connected in parallel with a 100 mH inductor?

    A) 20 mH

                                   B) 125 mH

    C) more than 125 mH

                                   D) less than 20 mH

47) Connecting a _____ inductor in _____ with a 70 mH inductor produces a 100 mH inductance.

    A) 233 mH, series

                                   B) 233 mH, parallel

    C) 30 mH, parallel

                                   D) 30 mH, series

48) If an inductor carries 150 mA$_{DC}$ of current when connected across a 65 V$_{DC}$ source, what is its resistance?

    A) 433 Ω   B) 26.7 Ω   C) 65 Ω   D) 30 Ω

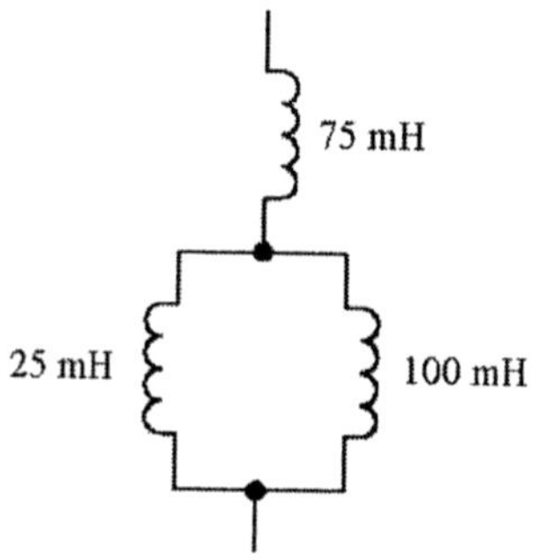

Figure 11–1

49) How much current flows in the circuit in Figure 11–1 if connected to a 12 V$_{PP}$, 2 kHz source?

    A) 10.05 mAp-p   B) 4.77 mAp-p   C) 60.48 mAp-p   D) 126.32 mAp-p

50) What is the total inductance in Figure 11–1?

    A) 225 mH   B) 95 mH   C) 15.8 mH   D) 12.7 mH

51) Inductors _____.

    A) pass direct current

                                     B) block direct current

    C) have high reactance to direct current

                                     D) have a high resistance to direct current

52) Which type of inductor core material is likely to produce the least inductance?

    A) iron   B) ferrite   C) air

53) When inductors are connected in series, their total inductance acts like:

    A) resistance connected in series.   B) resistance connected in parallel.

    C) resistance connected in series-parallel.   D) all of these.

54) When inductors are connected in parallel, their total inductance acts like:

    A) resistance connected in series.   B) resistance connected in parallel.

    C) resistance connected in series-parallel.   D) all of these.

55) The time constant of an inductor is:

    A) the time required to increase to 63% or to decrease to 37%.

    B) directly proportional to the inductance in the circuit.

    C) inversely proportional to the resistance in the circuit.

    D) all of these.

56) The time constant for an inductor for each time period is:

    A) 63% of the increase in value.   B) 37% of the decrease in value.

    C) a constant factor.   D) all of these.

57) Reactive power (P_r) in an inductor is defined as the rate at which an inductor stores or returns energy and is measured in:

    A) volts per time constant.   B) current per time constant.

    C) volt-ampere reactive.   D) watts reactive.

58) In an inductive AC circuit, the phase relationship between the voltage and the current is such that the:

    A) current is lagging the voltage.

    B) voltage is lagging the current.

    C) current is 180 degrees out of phase with voltage.

    D) voltage is 360 degrees out of phase with voltage.

59) The most commonplace use for inductors in electronics:

    A) pass AC voltages.   B) pass DC voltages.

    C) block AC voltages.   D) block DC voltages.

60) The quality factor of a coil or inductor is calculated by:

A) $QL = 2\pi\ fL$.

B) $QL = 2\pi\ fL/RW$.

C) $QL = \dfrac{1}{2\pi\ fL}$

D) $QL = \dfrac{L}{R}$

61) Stray capacitance for a coil becomes a problem:

A) with low frequencies.

B) with high frequencies.

C) at resonant frequencies.

D) with ac circuits.

62) The ripple voltage as measured at the output of a power supply has increased. Which of the following could be the problem?

A) partial shorting of the windings of the filtering coil

B) load resistance has dropped

C) resistance of the coil has decreased

D) either A or B

63) It has been determined that the source of audible noise for a radio has traced to the power supply voltage. How can an inductor be configured to eliminate this noise?

A) An inductor will not affect the noise.

B) Connect the inductor in parallel with the radio.

C) Connect the inductor in series with the radio power wire.

D) both B and C

64) Determination of an inductor's value can be had by what method(s)?

A) Apply a signal of a known frequency and voltage, then use Ohm's law and the inductive reactance formula.

B) Use an inductance meter.

C) Connect the inductor in series with a known value of resistance, apply a square wave of a known voltage value, then use the time constant formula.

D) any of the above

1) FALSE
   Diff: 1
2) TRUE
   Diff: 1
3) TRUE
   Diff: 1
4) FALSE
   Diff: 1
5) TRUE
   Diff: 1
6) FALSE
   Diff: 1
7) FALSE
   Diff: 1
8) TRUE
   Diff: 1
9) TRUE
   Diff: 1
10) TRUE
    Diff: 1
11) FALSE
    Diff: 1
12) FALSE
    Diff: 1
13) TRUE
    Diff: 1
14) TRUE
    Diff: 1
15) D
    Diff: 2
16) B
    Diff: 2
17) B
    Diff: 1
18) C
    Diff: 1
19) A
    Diff: 2
20) B
    Diff: 1
21) D
    Diff: 2
22) A
    Diff: 2

23) D
    Diff: 1
24) C
    Diff: 2
25) D
    Diff: 2
26) D
    Diff: 2
27) B
    Diff: 2
28) C
    Diff: 2
29) A
    Diff: 2
30) D
    Diff: 2
31) A
    Diff: 2
32) C
    Diff: 2
33) C
    Diff: 2
34) D
    Diff: 2
35) A
    Diff: 2
36) C
    Diff: 2
37) B
    Diff: 2
38) A
    Diff: 1
39) C
    Diff: 2
40) C
    Diff: 2
41) A
    Diff: 2
42) B
    Diff: 2
43) E
    Diff: 1
44) B
    Diff: 2

45) D
    Diff: 2
46) A
    Diff: 2
47) D
    Diff: 2
48) A
    Diff: 2
49) A
    Diff: 2
50) B
    Diff: 2
51) A
    Diff: 1
52) C
    Diff: 1
53) A
    Diff: 1
54) B
    Diff: 1
55) D
    Diff: 1
56) D
    Diff: 1
57) C
    Diff: 1
58) A
    Diff: 1
59) C
    Diff: 1
60) B
    Diff: 1
61) B
    Diff: 1
62) D
    Diff: 3
63) C
    Diff: 3
64) D
    Diff: 3

Chapter 12 RL Circuits

True or False

1) The source voltage always leads the total current in an RL circuit.

2) A low-pass filter passes high frequencies and blocks other frequencies.

3) The impedance of an RL series circuit varies inversely with the frequency.

4) If the resistance decreases in an RL filter circuit, the cutoff frequency increases.

5) The impedance of a series RL circuit is found by adding the values of X_L and R.

6) The source voltage always lags the total current in an RL circuit.

7) A high-pass filter passes high frequencies and blocks low frequencies.

8) If the frequency increases in an RL circuit, the impedance decreases.

9) If the inductance increases in an RL filter circuit, the cutoff frequency increases.

10) The impedance of a series RL circuit is found by adding the values of X_L and R using a phasor diagram.

11) Power dissipated by the resistor in an RL circuit can be increased with the addition of a capacitor in parallel.

12) The output at the cutoff frequency of a low pass RL filter is 0 V.

13) An ohmmeter can be used to accurately test the impedance of an RL circuit.

14) The overall phase angle of a parallel circuit with a resistance of 20 Ω and an inductive reactance of 25 kΩ would be nearly 90 degrees.

Multiple Choice

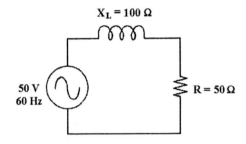

$X_L = 100 \, \Omega$

50 V
60 Hz

$R = 50 \, \Omega$

Figure 12–1

15) If the frequency is 60 Hz in Figure 12–1, what is the inductance?

    A) 265 mH   B) 3.768 H   C) 26.5 mH   D) 3.768 mH

16) What is the impedance in Figure 12–1?

    A) 104 Ω B) 112 Ω C) 1120 Ω D) 1040 Ω

17) Calculate the true power in Figure 12–1.

    A) 1 W   B) 400 mW   C) 4 W   D) 10 W

18) If the frequency increases in Figure 12–1, the current _____.

    A) increases   B) decreases

    C) remains the same   D) decreases to zero

19) If the frequency increases in Figure 12–1, the phase angle _____.

    A) increases   B) decreases

    C) remains the same   D) changes to another quadrant

20) If the frequency increases in Figure 12–1, inductance _____.

    A) increases   B) decreases

    C) remains the same   D) decreases to zero

21) What is the voltage across the inductor in Figure 12–1?

    A) 0.4 V   B) 0.894 V   C) 4.47 V   D) 44.6 V

22) If the frequency decreases in Figure 12–1, the phase angle _____ and the current _____.

    A) increases, increases   B) decreases, decreases

    C) increases, decreases   D) decreases, increases

23) What is the apparent power in Figure 12–1?

    A) 0.4 VA   B) 0.8 VA   C) 8.94 VA   D) 22.27 VA

24) If the frequency increases in Figure 12–1, the phase angle _____ and the impedance _____.

    A) decreases, increases   B) decreases, decreases

    C) increases, decreases   D) increases, increases

25) What is the cutoff frequency in Figure 12–1?

    A) 25 Hz   B) 63 Hz   C) 83 Hz   D) 408 Hz

26) If the frequency is 400 Hz in Figure 12–1, what is the inductance?

    A) 39.8 mH   B) 39.8 H   C) 25.12 mH   D) 25.12 H

27) What is the phase angle in Figure 12–1?

    A) 54.3   B) 63.4   C) 71.2   D) 86.3

28) If the source voltage changes to 100 V in Figure 12–1, the true power is _____.

    A) 40 mW   B) 4 W   C) 16 W   D) 40 W

29) If the operating frequency decreases in Figure 12–1, the current _____.

    A) increases   B) decreases

    C) remains the same   D) decreases to zero

30) If the operating frequency decreases in Figure 12–1, the phase angle _____.

    A) increases   B) decreases

    C) remains the same   D) changes to another quadrant

31) If the operating frequency decreases in Figure 12–1, the inductance _____.

    A) increases   B) decreases

    C) remains the same   D) decreases to zero

32) If the frequency increases in Figure 12–1, the phase angle _____ and the current _____.

    A) increases, increases   B) decreases, decreases

    C) increases, decreases   D) decreases, increases

33) If the frequency decreases in Figure 12-1, the phase angle _____ and the impedance _____.

A) decreases, increases

B) decreases, decreases

C) increases, decreases

D) increases, increases

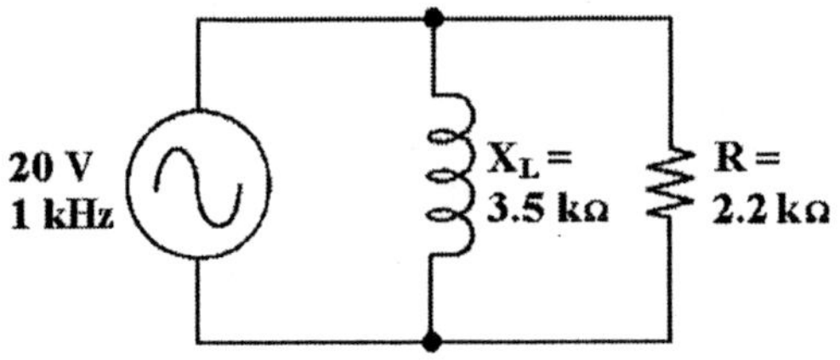

Figure 12-2

34) If the resistance increases in Figure 12-2, the total current _____.

A) increases

B) decreases

C) remains the same

D) decreases to zero

35) What change would increase the power factor in Figure 12-2?

A) increasing the source voltage

B) decreasing the source voltage

C) decreasing the value of the resistor

D) increasing the value of the resistor

36) Which statement describes the relationship of I_L and I_R in Figure 12-2?

A) They are in phase.

B) I_L leads I_R.

C) I_L lags I_R.

D) They are 180° out of phase.

37) What is the total impedance in Figure 12-2?

A) 1.074 kΩ   B) 9.09 kΩ   C) 5.71 kΩ   D) 1.86 kΩ

38) If the resistor decreases in Figure 12-2, the total current _____.

A) increases

B) decreases

C) remains the same

D) decreases to zero

39) What change would decrease the power factor in Figure 12-2?

A) Increase the source voltage.

B) Decrease the source voltage.

C) Decrease the value of the resistor.

D) Increase the value of the resistor.

40) If the resistance increased to 10 kΩ in Figure 12-2, the total impedance is _____.

A) 3.304 kΩ   B) 6.607 kΩ   C) 13.21 kΩ   D) infinite Ω

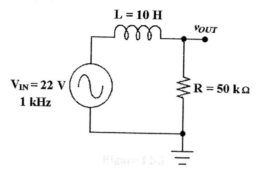

Figure 12-3

41) The circuit in Figure 12-3 is known as a _____ filter.

    A) low-pass   B) high-pass   C) band-pass   D) notch

42) What is the cutoff frequency in Figure 12-3?

    A) 637 Hz   B) 796 Hz   C) 637 kHz   D) 7.96 kHz

43) What is the phase angle in Figure 12-3, at the cutoff frequency?

    A) 44.9   B) 49.9   C) 51.4   D) 54.3

44) If some of the turns of the inductor in Figure 12-3 have shorted, how will the circuit change?

    A) The cutoff frequency will increase.

    B) The cutoff frequency will decrease.

    C) The output voltage at the cutoff frequency will increase.

    D) The output voltage at the cutoff frequency will decrease.

45) If the output is taken across the inductor in Figure 12-3, the circuit is known as a _____.

    A) low-pass filter   B) high-pass filter

    C) band-pass filter   D) notch filter

46) What is V_{OUT} at the cutoff frequency in Figure 12-3?

    A) 12.9 V   B) 15.5 V   C) 14.4 V   D) 15.1 V

47) What effect will an open inductor have on the circuit in Figure 12-3?

    A) The cutoff frequency will increase.

    B) The current will drop to zero.

    C) The output voltage at the cutoff frequency will increase.

    D) The output voltage at the cutoff frequency will decrease.

48) If V_R is 10 V and V_L is 10 V in a series RL circuit, the source voltage equals _____.

A) 14.14 V   B) 28.28 V   C) 10 V   D) 20 V

49) If the resistive current is 2 A and the inductive current is 2 A in a parallel RL circuit, total current is _____.

A) 4 A T   B) 5.656 A   C) 2 A   D) 2.828 A

50) If a load is purely inductive and the reactive power is 10 VAR, the apparent power is _____.

A) 10 VA   B) 14.14 VA   C) 1.144 VA   D) 3.16 VA

51) If the true power is 10 W and the reactive power is 10 VAR, the apparent power is _____.

A) 5 VAT   B) 20 VA   C) 14.14 VA   D) 100 VA

52) If a low-pass R_L filter's cutoff frequency is 20 kHz, its bandwidth is _____.

A) 0 – 20 kHz   B) 0 – 40 kHz   C) 0 Hz   D) unknown

53) If a high-pass R_L filter's cutoff frequency is 55 kHz, its bandwidth is _____.

A) 55 kHz   B) 110 kHz   C) 0 kHz   D) unknown

54) When an AC voltage is supplied to an RL circuit, the AC's current and amplitude will be:

A) similar in waveform.   B) lagging the voltage.

C) varying in the same manner.   D) all of these.

55) When the AC voltage and AC current through an RL circuit are varying in the same manner but slightly different in time, the signals are said to be:

A) offset in time.   B) out of sync.   C) out of phase.   D) all of these.

56) In a RL circuit, the inductive reactance is:

A) directly proportional to the inductance.   B) directly proportional to the frequency.

C) increases as the frequency increases.   D) all of these.

57) Power in an RL circuit can be measured as:

A) true power (P_{true}).   B) reactive power (P_r).

C) apparent power (P_a).   D) all of these.

58) In a series RL circuit, as the phase angle between the applied voltage and the total current increases, this is the same as:

A) power factor increasing.

B) power factor decreasing.

C) true power decreasing.

D) apparent power decreasing.

59) An RL lag network is similar to a:

A) low pass filter.

B) high pass filter.

C) band pass filter.

D) stop pass filter.

60) An RL high pass filter takes its output across:

A) the series inductor.

B) the parallel inductor.

C) the series resistor.

D) the parallel resistor.

61) In an RL filter circuit, the cutoff frequency is defined as the frequency at which:

A) the output voltage drops to 33% of maximum.

B) the output voltage drops to 66% of maximum.

C) the output voltage drops to 70% of maximum.

D) the output voltage is cutoff, with minimum or zero output.

62) A measured voltage of 0 V across the resistor in a parallel RL circuit would indicate:

A) an open in the resistor.

B) an short in the inductor.

C) a blown fuse.

D) either A or B.

63) The voltage measured across the inductor in a series RL has dropped significantly from normal. What could possibly be the problem?

A) partial shorting of the windings of the inductor

B) The resistor has gone up in value.

C) The resistor has gone down in value.

D) either A or B

64) It is suspected that a high pass filter's cutoff frequency has changed. What pieces of test equipment could be used to check it out?

A) voltmeter and a sine wave generator

B) an oscilloscope and a square wave generator

C) either A or B

D) none of the above

65) After having troubleshot a series RL circuit, you check the resistance of the inductor and it is around 40 ohms. What conclusion does this bring you to?

    A) Since the inductor's voltage was nearly zero, you are sure the windings have shorted.

    B) Since the inductor's voltage was nearly zero, the inductor is probably okay, so the resistor must be open.

    C) Since the inductor's voltage was nearly zero, the inductor is probably okay so the resistor must be shorted.

    D) not enough information

66) Which of the following is typically most important of the three types of power in terms of work being done?

    A) reactive   B) apparent   C) true   D) inductive

1) TRUE
   Diff: 1
2) FALSE
   Diff: 1
3) FALSE
   Diff: 1
4) FALSE
   Diff: 1
5) FALSE
   Diff: 1
6) FALSE
   Diff: 1
7) TRUE
   Diff: 1
8) FALSE
   Diff: 1
9) TRUE
   Diff: 1
10) TRUE
    Diff: 1
11) TRUE
    Diff: 1
12) FALSE
    Diff: 1
13) FALSE
    Diff: 1
14) FALSE
    Diff: 1
15) A
    Diff: 2
16) B
    Diff: 2
17) D
    Diff: 2
18) B
    Diff: 1
19) A
    Diff: 1
20) C
    Diff: 1
21) D
    Diff: 2
22) D
    Diff: 1

23) D
    Diff: 2
24) D
    Diff: 1
25) C
    Diff: 2
26) A
    Diff: 2
27) B
    Diff: 2
28) D
    Diff: 2
29) A
    Diff: 1
30) B
    Diff: 1
31) C
    Diff: 1
32) C
    Diff: 1
33) B
    Diff: 1
34) B
    Diff: 1
35) C
    Diff: 1
36) C
    Diff: 1
37) D
    Diff: 2
38) A
    Diff: 1
39) D
    Diff: 1
40) A
    Diff: 2
41) A
    Diff: 1
42) B
    Diff: 2
43) A
    Diff: 2
44) A
    Diff: 3

45) B
    Diff: 1
46) B
    Diff: 2
47) B
    Diff: 3
48) A
    Diff: 2
49) D
    Diff: 2
50) A
    Diff: 2
51) C
    Diff: 2
52) A
    Diff: 2
53) D
    Diff: 2
54) D
    Diff: 1
55) D
    Diff: 1
56) D
    Diff: 1
57) D
    Diff: 1
58) B
    Diff: 2
59) A
    Diff: 1
60) A
    Diff: 1
61) C
    Diff: 1
62) C
    Diff: 3
63) D
    Diff: 3
64) A
    Diff: 3
65) B
    Diff: 3
66) C
    Diff: 1

Chapter 13 RLC Circuits and Resonance

True or False

1) The total impedance equals the resistance of a resonant series RLC circuit.

2) At resonance, a parallel RLC circuit is capacitive.

3) At resonance, X_C equals X_L.

4) In a resonant circuit, as Q increases the bandwidth decreases.

5) In a series resonant circuit, the impedance is minimum and the current is maximum.

6) In a parallel resonant circuit, the impedance is minimum and the line current is maximum.

7) At resonance, a parallel RLC circuit is inductive.

8) At resonance, the impedance of a series RLC circuit equals its resistance.

9) At resonance, a series RLC circuit has maximum current.

10) A resonant RLC circuit is said to be very selective if its Q is very low.

11) A highly selective filter has a very wide bandwidth.

12) The true power of an RLC circuit depends on the value of resistance.

13) A series RLC circuit can be configured for band-pass or band-stop filtering purposes.

14) The capacitor's resistive effects are significant when considering the Q of an RLC circuit.

15) Current leads in a series RLC circuit with more capacitive reactance than inductive reactance.

Multiple Choice

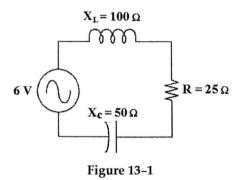

$X_L = 100 \, \Omega$

$6 \, V$

$X_C = 50 \, \Omega$

$R = 25 \, \Omega$

Figure 13–1

16) Find the voltage across the capacitor in Figure 13–1.

    A) 5.37 V   B) 0.633 V   C) 10.7 V   D) –4.9 V

17) To operate the circuit in Figure 13–1 at resonance, _____ the resistance and _____ the frequency.

    A) increase, increase   B) decrease, decrease

    C) don't change, increase   D) don't change, decrease

18) If frequency increases in Figure 13–1, the impedance _____ and the current _____.

    A) decreases, decreases   B) decreases, increases

    C) increases, increases   D) increases, decreases

19) If the resistance increases in Figure 13–1, the impedance _____.

    A) increases   B) decreases

    C) remains the same   D) becomes zero

20) As the frequency approaches the resonant frequency in Figure 13–1, the V_R _____.

    A) increases   B) decreases

    C) remains the same   D) becomes increasingly unstable

21) If the frequency decreases in Figure 13–1, the impedance _____ and the phase angle _____.

    A) increases, increases   B) increases, decreases

    C) decreases, decreases   D) decreases, increases

22) To operate the circuit in Figure 13–1 below the resonant frequency, _____ the resistance and _____ the frequency.

    A) increase, increase   B) decrease, decrease

    C) do not change, increase   D) do not change, decrease

23) If the frequency decreases in Figure 13–1, the impedance _____ and the current _____.

    A) decreases, decreases   B) decreases, increases

    C) increases, increases   D) increases, decreases

24) If the resistance decreases in Figure 13–1, the impedance _____.

    A) increases   B) decreases

    C) remains the same   D) becomes zero

25) If a resonant circuit has a low Q, it _____.

    A) has a narrow pass–band   B) tunes sharply

    C) has a wide pass–band   D) has a small voltage across the capacitor

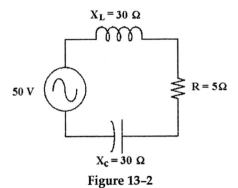

$X_L = 30 \ \Omega$

$R = 5 \Omega$

50 V

$X_c = 30 \ \Omega$

Figure 13–2

26) If the resistance increases in Figure 13–2, the bandwidth _____.

    A) increases   B) remains the same

    C) decreases   D) varies

27) If the capacitor opens in Figure 13–2, the current _____.

    A) increases because of the inductor

    B) remains the same

    C) decreases to zero

    D) continues to flow, but the circuit would not be resonant

28) At resonance, the current in Figure 13–2 is _____.

    A) 10 A   B) 10 mA   C) 1.66 4   D) 1.66 mA

29) If the resistance decreases in Figure 13–2, the bandwidth _____.

    A) increases   B) remains the same

    C) decreases   D) varies

30) If the resistor shorts in Figure 13–2, the current _____.

    A) increases

    B) does not change

    C) decreases

    D) continues, but the circuit would not be resonant

31) If the current is 0 A in Figure 13–2, maybe _____.

    A) the inductor is shorted

    B) the capacitor is shorted

    C) the resistor is open

    D) the resistor has changed values to 100 Ω

32) What is the resonant frequency of a tank circuit with a 50 mH inductor and $C = 256$ pF capacitor?

    A) 44.5 Hz   B) 44.5 kHz   C) 445 kHz   D) 4.45 kHz

33) What is the bandwidth of a resonant circuit if its resonant frequency is 14.2 MHz, the capacitive reactance is 3.5 kΩ and the coil's resistance is 8 ohm?

    A) 28.4 kHz   B) 2285 Hz   C) 14.2 MHz   D) 32.5 kHz

34) What is the tank current in a parallel resonant circuit if its impedance is 0.22 MΩ, Q is 100 and $V_S = 50$ V?

    A) 0.0227 mA   B) 0.227 mA   C) 2.27 mA   D) 22.7 mA

35) What is the V_{OUT}/V_{IN} ratio (expressed in dB) of an RLC series resonant circuit if the resonant frequency is 14 MHz, the source voltage is 12 V and the inductor drops 300 V?

    A) 25 dB   B) 13.98 dB   C) 27.96 dB   D) 42.91 dB

36) What is the power at f_1 and f_2 in a resonant circuit that delivers 120 W?

    A) 84.84 W

    B) 84.84 W at f_1 and 60 W at f_2

    C) 60 W

    D) 17 W at both frequencies

37) If an LC tank circuit is operating below resonance, the circuit is _____ in nature.

    A) resistive   B) capacitive   C) inductive   D) positive

38) If a tuned tank circuit has a very narrow bandwidth, its Q is probably _____.

    A) very low   B) very high   C) about 10   D) below 10

39) In a parallel resonant RLC circuit, the impedance is _____ and the total current is _____.

    A) maximum. maximum

    B) maximum, minimum

    C) minimum, minimum

    D) minimum, maximum

40) The resonant frequency of a tank circuit with a 0.150 mH inductor and 300 pF capacitor is _____.

    A) 1.65 MHz   B) 751 kHz   C) 347 kHz   D) 6.05 MHz

41) If the resonant frequency is 1 MHz and Q = 50, f_1 = _____ and f_2 = _____.

    A) 0.98 MHz, 1.01 0 Hz

    B) 0.99 MHz, 1.01 MHz

    C) 0.99 MHz, 1.02 8 Hz

    D) 0.98 MHz, 1.02 0 Hz

42) What is the resonant impedance of a series RLC circuit with a 15 mH inductor, 0.015 μF capacitor and 80 Ω resistor?

    A) 15 kΩ B) 80 Ω C) 30 Ω D) 0 Ω

43) What is the source voltage in a series resonant circuit if V_C = 150 V, V_L = 150 V and V_R = 50 V?

    A) 150 V   B) 300 V   C) 50 V   D) 350 V

44) Replacing the inductor in a series resonant band–pass filter with one having a lower Q value causes the bandwidth to _____.

    A) increase

    B) decrease

    C) remain the same

    D) be more selective

45) In an ideal parallel resonant circuit, the total current into the L and C branches is _____.

    A) maximum   B) low   C) high   D) zero

46) The total reactance of a series RLC circuit at resonance is _____.

    A) zero

    C) infinity

    B) equal to the resistance

    D) capacitive

47) A resonant circuit with a high Q _____.

    A) has a very wide pass–band

    C) has no pass–band

    B) tunes sharply

    D) has a small voltage across the capacitor

48) What is the resonant frequency of a tank circuit with a 150 mH inductor and a 300 pF capacitor?

    A) 23.7 Hz   B) 23.7 kHz   C) 237 kHz   D) 2.37 MHz

49) What is the bandwidth of the resonant circuit if the resonant frequency is 1.42 MHz, the capacitive reactance is 3.5 kΩ and the coil's resistance is 8 ohm?

    A) 3.245 kHz   B) 2285 Hz   C) 1.42 8 Hz   D) 32.5 kHz

50) What is the lower cut off frequency in an RLC resonant circuit if the inductive reactance is 1.2 kΩ, the resonant frequency is 22 kHz and the resistance is 60 Ω?

    A) 21.45 kHz   B) 21.82 kHz   C) 20.9 kHz   D) 21.7 kHz

51) What is the tank current in a parallel resonant circuit if its impedance is 0.22 MΩ, the Q is 100 and the source voltage is 100 V?

    A) 0.04545 mA   B) 0.4545 mA   C) 4.545 mA   D) 45.45 mA

52) What is the ratio of V_{OUT}/V_{IN} (expressed in dB) in an RLC series resonant circuit if the resonant frequency is 14 MHz, the source voltage is 18 V and the inductor drops 300 V?

    A) 28 dB   B) 13.98 dB   C) 24.43 dB   D) 42.91 dB

53) What is the power at f_1 and f_2 in a resonant circuit that delivers 750 W?

    A) 375 W at both frequencies

    C) 750 W at both frequencies

    B) 375 W at f_1 and 750 W at f_2

    D) 17 W at both frequencies

54) If a tank circuit is operating above resonance, it is _____ in nature.

    A) resistive   B) capacitive   C) inductive   D) positive

55) If a tuned tank circuit has a very wide bandwidth, its Q might be _____.

    A) very low   B) very high   C) about 10   D) about 100

56) In a series AC circuit at resonance, the capacitive reactance (X_C) and the inductive reactance (X_L):

A) are minimum.

B) are moderate.

C) cancel each other.

D) add to each other.

57) In a series AC circuit at resonance:

A) the impedance Z is at minimum.

B) X_C equals X_L and they cancel.

C) the impedance is mostly resistive.

D) all of these.

58) In a series AC circuit just below the resonant frequency, the impedance is:

A) at minimum.

B) more inductive.

C) more capacitive.

D) at maximum.

59) In a series AC circuit just above the resonant frequency, the impedance is:

A) at minimum.

B) more inductive.

C) more capacitive.

D) at maximum.

60) In a parallel AC circuit, the capacitive reactance (X_C) and the inductive reactance (X_L):

A) are minimum.

B) are moderate.

C) equal and oppose current flow.

D) add to each to cancel current flow.

61) In a parallel AC just below the resonant frequency, the impedance is:

A) at minimum.

B) more inductive.

C) more capacitive.

D) at maximum.

62) In a parallel AC circuit just above the resonant frequency, the impedance is:

A) at minimum.

B) more inductive.

C) more capacitive.

D) at maximum.

63) Between the lower and upper critical frequencies of a band–pass filter:

A) the frequencies pass a maximum level.

B) the frequencies pass a minimum level.

C) the frequencies pass at 70% to their maximum levels.

D) the frequencies pass at 30% to their maximum levels.

64) The output voltage of a circuit at 70.7% of its maximum level measured in dB is:

    A) 3 dB.   B) –3 dB.   C) 7 dB.   D) –7 db.

65) Why does a resistive load increase the bandwidth of a given band-pass filter?

    A) The resistance increases the quality of the circuit.

    B) The resistance decreases the quality of the circuit.

    C) A resistive load actually decreases the bandwidth.

    D) not enough information

66) Which statement best describes the phase angle of a parallel RLC circuit at resonance?

    A) With a net reactance at maximum the phase angle is zero.

    B) With a net reactance at minimum the phase angle is zero.

    C) Total current flow is minimum.

    D) either A or C

67) For the tuning circuit of a radio frequency receiver, the filter:

    A) need not be highly selective.   B) bandwidth should be narrow.

    C) high Q components are not necessary.   D) any of the above

68) When tuning across the resonant frequency of a band-pass filter, which of the following is true?

    A) The voltage across the filter should be minimum at resonance.

    B) The voltage across the filter should be maximum at resonance.

    C) The output voltage across the load is minimum.

    D) Current flow through the load is minimum.

69) The selectivity of a given band-pass filter has degraded significantly, yet the f_r is within tolerance. Which of the following could have caused this?

    A) The inductance has increased.   B) The capacitance has increased.

    C) The load has opened.   D) none of the above

1) TRUE
   Diff: 1
2) FALSE
   Diff: 1
3) TRUE
   Diff: 1
4) TRUE
   Diff: 1
5) TRUE
   Diff: 1
6) FALSE
   Diff: 1
7) FALSE
   Diff: 1
8) TRUE
   Diff: 1
9) TRUE
   Diff: 1
10) FALSE
    Diff: 1
11) FALSE
    Diff: 1
12) TRUE
    Diff: 1
13) TRUE
    Diff: 1
14) FALSE
    Diff: 1
15) TRUE
    Diff: 1
16) A
    Diff: 2
17) D
    Diff: 2
18) D
    Diff: 2
19) A
    Diff: 1
20) A
    Diff: 1
21) C
    Diff: 2
22) D
    Diff: 2

23) B
    Diff: 2
24) B
    Diff: 1
25) C
    Diff: 1
26) A
    Diff: 1
27) C
    Diff: 3
28) A
    Diff: 2
29) C
    Diff: 1
30) A
    Diff: 1
31) C
    Diff: 3
32) B
    Diff: 2
33) D
    Diff: 2
34) B
    Diff: 2
35) C
    Diff: 2
36) C
    Diff: 2
37) C
    Diff: 1
38) B
    Diff: 1
39) B
    Diff: 2
40) B
    Diff: 2
41) B
    Diff: 2
42) B
    Diff: 2
43) C
    Diff: 2
44) A
    Diff: 2

45) D
    Diff: 1
46) A
    Diff: 1
47) B
    Diff: 1
48) B
    Diff: 2
49) A
    Diff: 2
50) A
    Diff: 2
51) B
    Diff: 2
52) C
    Diff: 2
53) A
    Diff: 2
54) B
    Diff: 1
55) A
    Diff: 1
56) C
    Diff: 1
57) D
    Diff: 1
58) B
    Diff: 1
59) C
    Diff: 1
60) C
    Diff: 1
61) C
    Diff: 1
62) B
    Diff: 1
63) C
    Diff: 1
64) B
    Diff: 1
65) B
    Diff: 3
66) D
    Diff: 3

67) B
    Diff: 2
68) A
    Diff: 2
69) D
    Diff: 3

Chapter 14 Transformers

True or False

1) Only the number of turns in the primary and secondary of a transformer determines the actual secondary voltage.

2) A transformer can be used as an impedance matching device.

3) A step-down transformer could have a primary–secondary turns ratio of 4:1.

4) Transformer cores are made from laminated iron to reduce losses.

5) The efficiency of all transformers is very low.

6) A transformer with a turns ratio of 1:1 is often used to isolate a load from a source.

7) A transformer with a turns ratio of 1:7 is a step down transformer.

8) If a dc voltage is input to a transformer's primary, then an ac voltage is induced in its secondary.

9) An ideal transformer has no power loss.

10) A typical transformer fault would be an open winding.

11) The primary to secondary resistance should be relatively low.

12) Autotransformers cannot be used for isolation purposes since there is only one winding.

13) An ideal 10:1 transformer with 20 VA of power has less than 2 VA on the output.

14) A core material is not always necessary for proper operation of a transformer.

15) The impedance matching characteristic for a transformer is needed for a situation where maximum power transfer to the load is desired.

Multiple Choice

16) The *hysteresis loss* in a transformer is _____.

    A) caused by current flowing in the core

    B) caused by rapid reversal of the magnetic field

    C) caused by the resistance of the wire

    D) another name for *flux leakage loss*

17) *Eddy current loss* in a transformer is _____.

    A) due to current flowing in the core

    B) caused by rapid reversal of the magnetic field

    C) caused by the resistance of the wire

    D) another name for *flux leakage loss*

18) The phrase "Maximum power is delivered to the load when the load resistance equals the source resistance" is a definition of _____.

    A) Lenz's Law   B) Ohm's Law

    C) the maximum power transfer theorem   D) Kirchhoff's Law

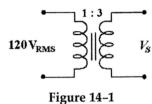

Figure 14–1

19) What is the secondary voltage in Figure 14–1 if the turns ratio is 1:3?

    A) 40 V$_{RMS}$ B) 80 V$_{RMS}$ C) 240 V$_{RMS}$ D) 360 V$_{RMS}$

20) What is the secondary voltage in Figure 14–1 if the turns ratio is 7:1?

    A) 17.14 V$_{RMS}$ B) 840 V$_{RMS}$ C) 8.59 V$_{RMS}$ D) 420 V$_{RMS}$

21) What is the secondary current in Figure 14–1 with a 100 Ω load resistor and 3:1 turns ratio?

    A) 33 mA$_{RMS}$ B) 40 mA$_{RMS}$ C) 330 mA$_{RMS}$ D) 400 mA$_{RMS}$

22) What is the primary current in Figure 14–1 if the turns ratio equals 1:3 and I$_S$ equals 240 mA?

    A) 60 mA   B) 120 mA   C) 720 mA   D) 1.2 A

23) What is the reflected resistance seen by the primary in Figure 14-1 if the turns ratio is 3:1 and I_S is 240 mA?

    A) 167 Ω   B) 500 Ω   C) 1500 Ω   D) 9000 Ω

24) What is the secondary voltage in Figure 14-1 if the turns ratio is 4.5:1?

    A) 540 V   B) 26.67 V   C) 5.92 V   D) 4.72 V

25) What is the secondary current in Figure 14-1 with a 50 Ω load resistor and 4:1 turns ratio?

    A) 1.66 A   B) 600 mA   C) 9.6 A   D) 4.8 A

26) What is the primary current in Figure 14-1 if I_S = 40 mA and the turns ratio equals 4:1 ?

    A) 160 mA   B) 40 mA   C) 10 mA   D) 4 mA

27) What is the reflected resistance seen by the primary in Figure 14-1 if the turns ratio is 4:1 and I_S is 40 mA?

    A) 4 kΩ   B) 8 kΩ   C) 12 kΩ   D) 16 kΩ

28) In Figure 14-1, if there are five times more turns in the primary than in the secondary, then what is the secondary voltage?

    A) 600 V   B) 120 V   C) 24 V   D) 12 V

29) What is the secondary voltage in Figure 14-1 if the turns ratio is 9:1?

    A) 13.3 V   B) 26.6 V   C) 53.2 V   D) 106 V

30) In Figure 14-1, if the primary to secondary turns ratio is changed to 4:1 and a 1 kΩ load resistor is in the secondary, the secondary current equals _____.

    A) 480 mA   B) 240 mA   C) 120 mA   D) 30 mA

31) In Figure 14-1, the primary to secondary turns ratio is 1:3 and the secondary current equals 120 mA. What is the primary current?

    A) 360 mA

    B) 40 mA

    C) 180 mA

    D) cannot compute because the voltage is not given

32) In Figure 14-1, the primary secondary turns ratio is changed to 2.5:1 and the secondary current equals 100 mA. What is the reflected resistance seen by the primary?

    A) 1.2 kΩ   B) 2.5 kΩ   C) 3 kΩ   D) 5 kΩ

33) In Figure 14-1, if the primary to secondary turns ratio is 7.5:1, the output voltage equals
_____.

    A) 32 V_{RMS} B) 16 V_{RMS} C) 9 V_{RMS} D) 900 V_{RMS}

34) In Figure 14-1, if a load resistor of 75 Ω is placed in the secondary circuit, what is the secondary current?

    A) 533 mA   B) 5.33 A   C) 4.8 A   D) 16 A

35) In Figure 14-1, if the secondary current is 50 mA, the primary current is _____.

    A) 50 mA   B) 150 mA   C) 48.7 mA   D) 300 mA

36) In Figure 14-1, if the secondary current is 50 mA, the reflected resistance seen by the primary equals _____.

    A) 800 Ω   B) 2.4 kΩ   C) 7.2 kΩ   D) 14.4 kΩ

37) In Figure 14-1, if the primary to secondary turns ratio is 9:1 and a 1 kΩ load resistor is placed in the secondary, the reflected resistance seen by the primary equals _____.

    A) 111 Ω   B) 1 kΩ   C) 81 kΩ   D) 162 kΩ

38) If 10 W of power are applied to the primary of an ideal transformer with a turns ratio of 1:5, the power delivered to the secondary load is _____.

    A) 50 W   B) 0.5 W   C) 0 W   D) 10 W

39) When a 1 kΩ load resistor is connected across the secondary winding of a transformer with a turns ratio of 1:2, the source "sees" a reflected load of _____.

    A) 250 Ω   B) 2 kΩ   C) 4 kΩ   D) 1 kΩ

40) When a 1 kΩ load resistor is connected across the secondary winding of a transformer with a turns ratio of 2:1, the source "sees" a reflected load of _____.

    A) 1 kΩ   B) 2 kΩ   C) 4 kΩ   D) 500 Ω

41) The turns ratio required to match a 50 Ω source to a 200 Ω load is _____.

    A) 4:1   B) 2:1   C) 1:4   D) 1:2

42) If a 12 V battery is connected across the primary of a transformer with a turns ratio of 1:4, then the secondary voltage is _____.

    A) 0 V   B) 12 V   C) 48 V T   D) 3 V

43) What is the problem if a power transformer is delivering a low output voltage even though the primary voltage is correct?

    A) an open secondary   B) a shorted primary

    C) an open primary   D) a partially shorted secondary

44) A matching transformer's primary needs _____ more turns than its secondary to match a 600 Ω audio signal distribution line to an 8 Ω speaker.

    A) 8.66   B) 75   C) 0.013   D) 0.115

45) To couple two circuits together with no change in either voltage or current, use _____.

    A) a step–up transformer   B) an isolation transformer

    C) a step–down transformer   D) a power transformer

46) Transformers _____.

    A) convert a lower current into a higher current

    B) convert a higher voltage into a lower voltage

    C) match the impedance of a source to the impedance of a load

    D) all of these

47) Which winding will have the lowest measured resistance in a transformer with four secondary windings?

    A) the 550 V secondary   B) the 6.3 V secondary

    C) the 12 V secondary   D) the 5 V secondary

48) What is the likeliest way to fix a center–tapped transformer which outputs unequal voltages on each half of the secondary?

    A) Add some turns to the half with the lower voltage winding.

    B) Remove some turns from the half with the higher voltage winding.

    C) Replace the transformer.

    D) Do not concern yourself; the customer will probably not notice the problem.

49) A step–up transformer will increase _____ and decrease _____.

    A) voltage, impedance   B) current, impedance

    C) voltage, power   D) power, current

50) When the turns ratio of a transformer is 1:10 and the primary AC voltage in 6 V, then the secondary voltage is _____.

    A) 60 V   B) 0.6 V   C) 6 V   D) 36 V

51) Although the input voltage to the transformer's primary is correct, the transformer is outputting zero volts. A probable trouble is _____.

    A) a partially shorted secondary   B) an open primary

    C) a shorted primary   D) a partially shorted primary

52) To match a 600 Ω audio load to a 4 Ω speaker system, the primary of the impedance matching transformer must have _____ more turns than the secondary.

    A) 12.24

    B) 150

    C) 3.06

    D) The primary should have less turns than the secondary.

53) A step–up transformer will increase _____ and decrease _____.

    A) current, impedance   B) voltage, impedance

    C) impedance, current   D) current, voltage

54) The small dot placed on schematics of transformers indicates:

    A) the polarity of the voltages.   B) the phase of the voltages.

    C) the direction of the winding.   D) all of these.

55) For a transformer to operate properly, it must:

    A) be connected to a load.

    B) be supplied with the proper AC signal.

    C) work within its voltage, current and power ratings.

    D) all of these.

56) The turns ratio of a transformer (n) is defined as:

    A) the number of turns in the primary multiplied by the number of turns in the secondary.

    B) the number of turns in the primary divided by the number of turns in the secondary.

    C) the number of turns in the secondary multiplied by the number of turns in the primary.

    D) the number of turns in the secondary divided by the number of turns in the primary.

57) The relationship for the voltage ratio (V_{sec}/V_{pri}) in a transformer is:

    A) less than the turns ratio (N_{sec}/N_{pri}).   B) more than the turns ratio (N_{sec}/N_{pri}).

    C) the same as the turns ratio (N_{sec}/N_{pri}).   D) opposite to the turns ratio (N_{sec}/N_{pri}).

58) The relationship for the current ration (I_{sec}/I_{pri}) in a transformer is:

   A) less than the turns ration (N_{sec}/N_{pri}).

   B) more than the turns ration (N_{sec}/N_{pri}).

   C) the same as the turns ration (N_{sec}/N_{pri}).

   D) opposite to the turns ratio (N_{sec}/N_{pri}).

59) The relationship for the impedance matching ratio (R_L/R_{pri}) in a transformer is:

   A) equal to the turns ratio (N_{sec}/N_{pri}).

   B) opposite to the turns ratio (N_{sec}/N_{pri}).

   C) equal to the turns ratio (N_{sec}/N_{pri}) squared.

   D) opposite to the turns ratio (N_{sec}/N_{pri}) squared.

60) The reflected load in a transformer is defined as actual load as it appears to the source and results from:

   A) the voltage ratio.   B) the current ratio.

   C) the power ratio.   D) the turns ratio.

61) An autotransformer differs from most transformers in that:

   A) primary and secondary windings are the same.

   B) source voltage flows through on the windings.

   C) it does not isolate the primary voltage from the secondary voltage.

   D) all of these.

62) A center tap transformer has a connection at the midpoint of the secondary winding resulting in:

   A) two equal magnitude secondary voltages.

   B) two 180 degree out of phase secondary voltages.

   C) secondary voltages half that of a non–center tapped transformer with the same turns ratio.

   D) all of these.

63) The measured voltage on the secondary of a given transformer is 0 V. Which of the following could have caused this?

   A) open primary   B) open secondary

   C) shorted load   D) any of the above

64) How can the windings ratio be safely determined for an unmarked transformer?

A) The turns ratio is the same as the ratio of primary resistance to secondary resistance ratio.

B) Standardized wire color codes indicate windings ratio.

C) Apply known low voltage ac to the primary and measure the secondary output. The ratio of the voltages is the same as the windings ratio.

D) either A or C

65) 36 V of dc is applied to a windings ratio of 1:2. What is the secondary voltage?

A) 72 V

B) something slightly less than 72 V since transformers do have some loss

C) 144 V

D) none of the above

66) What type transformer most likely has a 1:1 turns ratio?

A) impedance matching   B) isolation

C) power   D) center tapped

67) An air core transformer would most likely be used for:

A) radio frequencies.   B) isolation.

C) audio frequencies   D) impedance matching

1) FALSE
   Diff: 1
2) TRUE
   Diff: 1
3) TRUE
   Diff: 1
4) TRUE
   Diff: 1
5) FALSE
   Diff: 1
6) TRUE
   Diff: 1
7) FALSE
   Diff: 1
8) FALSE
   Diff: 1
9) TRUE
   Diff: 1
10) TRUE
    Diff: 1
11) FALSE
    Diff: 1
12) TRUE
    Diff: 1
13) FALSE
    Diff: 2
14) TRUE
    Diff: 1
15) TRUE
    Diff: 1
16) B
    Diff: 1
17) A
    Diff: 1
18) C
    Diff: 1
19) D
    Diff: 2
20) A
    Diff: 2
21) D
    Diff: 2
22) C
    Diff: 2

23) C
    Diff: 2
24) B
    Diff: 2
25) B
    Diff: 2
26) C
    Diff: 2
27) C
    Diff: 2
28) C
    Diff: 2
29) A
    Diff: 2
30) D
    Diff: 2
31) A
    Diff: 2
32) C
    Diff: 2
33) B
    Diff: 2
34) C
    Diff: 2
35) B
    Diff: 2
36) A
    Diff: 2
37) C
    Diff: 2
38) D
    Diff: 2
39) A
    Diff: 2
40) C
    Diff: 2
41) D
    Diff: 2
42) A
    Diff: 2
43) D
    Diff: 3
44) A
    Diff: 2

45) B
    Diff: 2
46) D
    Diff: 1
47) D
    Diff: 2
48) C
    Diff: 3
49) A
    Diff: 1
50) A
    Diff: 2
51) B
    Diff: 3
52) A
    Diff: 2
53) C
    Diff: 1
54) D
    Diff: 1
55) D
    Diff: 1
56) D
    Diff: 1
57) C
    Diff: 1
58) D
    Diff: 1
59) C
    Diff: 1
60) D
    Diff: 1
61) D
    Diff: 1
62) D
    Diff: 1
63) D
    Diff: 3
64) C
    Diff: 3
65) D
    Diff: 2
66) B
    Diff: 2

67) A
    Diff: 2

Chapter 15 Time Response of Reactive Circuits

True or False

1) In an RC integrating circuit, the output is taken across the capacitor.

2) When the input pulse width to an RC integrator is much less than 5τ, the output approaches the shape of the input.

3) In an RL integrating circuit, the output is taken across the inductor.

4) It takes a capacitor 5 time constants to nearly reach full charge.

5) The output of an RC differentiating circuit is taken across the resistor.

6) An RC integrating circuit is a basic high-pass filter with a pulse applied to it.

7) The output of an RC integrator is the capacitor's voltage drop.

8) An RL integrator is a basic RL low-pass filter with a pulse applied to it.

9) In an RC integrator, as the time constant gets longer, the maximum capacitor voltage gets smaller.

10) The output from an RL integrator can look exactly the same as the output from an RC integrator.

11) Since voltage is constant during the peak of a pulse input, the output of an LC integrator is constant during this time as well.

12) The output of an RC differentiator with an open capacitor will look like the input.

13) LC and RC integrators, with respect to input and output, perform exactly the same.

14) An open inductor in an RL diffrentiator will cause the output to resemble the input.

15) The output of a differentiator circuit will reach the same maximum and minimum levels as the input as long as the time constant of the circuit is less than the width of the input pulse.

Multiple Choice

16) What is one time constant in an integrating circuit if a 47 kΩ resistor is in series with a 0.01 μF capacitor?

    A) 0.047 ms   B) 0.047 μs   C) 0.47 ms   D) 0.47 s

17) What is one time constant in an integrating circuit if a 10 kΩ resistor is in series with a 470 μF capacitor?

    A) 0.047 μs   B) 0.47 μs   C) 0.47 ms   D) 4.7 s

18) How long will it take a 22 μF capacitor to completely charge through a 1.2 MΩ resistor?

    A) 13.2 s   B) 132 s   C) 0.264 s   D) 2.64 s

19) How long will it take a 0.047 μF capacitor to completely discharge through a 10 kΩ resistor?

    A) 5 s   B) 0.47 ms   C) 2.35 ms   D) 0.18 ms

20) What is V_C at the end of the input pulse to an RC integrator if the input pulse is 15 V and the pulse width equals one time constant?

    A) 14.7 V   B) 14.25 V   C) 12.975 V   D) 9.48 V

21) What is V_C at the end of the input pulse to an RC integrator if the resistance is 5 kΩ, the capacitance is 0.47 μF and the input is a 15 V, 4.7 ms pulse?

    A) 9.48 V   B) 12.975 V   C) 14.25 V   D) 14.7 V

22) If the input pulse to an RC differentiator is very short compared to the circuit's time constant, the differentiator's output is _____.

    A) zero volts

    B) a square wave very similar to the input voltage

    C) a dc value of about half the peak input voltage

    D) a dc voltage equal to the peak input voltage

23) The output from an RL differentiator is taken across the _____.

    A) resistor   B) resistor and inductor

    C) inductor   D) source

24) To charge a 100 μF capacitor in 15 seconds, use a _____ resistor.

    A) 15 kΩ   B) 30 kΩ   C) 25 kΩ   D) 35 kΩ

25) What is output voltage at the end of the input pulse to an RL integrator if the resistance is 22 k Ω, the inductor is 2 H and the input is a 12 V, 0.0909 ms pulse?

A) 7.58 V   B) 10.38 V   C) 11.4 V   D) 11.76 V

26) What is the output voltage at the end of the input pulse to an RL integrator if the resistance is 1.2 kΩ, the inductor is 200 mH and the input is a 5 V, 1.2 ms pulse?

A) 3.16 V   B) 4.532 V   C) 4.75 V   D) 5 V

27) What is output voltage at the end of the input pulse to an RC integrator if the resistance is 10 k Ω, the capacitance is 100 µF and the input is a 50 V, 10 s pulse?

A) 31.6 V   B) 43.25 V   C) 47.5 V   D) 50 V

28) How does the RC differentiator output look when 5τ is much less than the pulse width?

A) positive spikes   B) positive and negative spikes

C) negative spikes   D) square waves

29) What is the output voltage at the end of the input pulse to an RL integrator if the resistance is 1 kΩ, the inductor is 1 H and the input is a 22 V, 2 ms pulse?

A) 13.9 V   B) 19.03 V   C) 20.9 V   D) 21.56 V

30) RC and RL integrators provide the same output when the inputs are _____.

A) different

B) the same

C) the outputs are never the same

31) What is one time constant in an integrating circuit if a 4.7 kΩ resistor is in series with a 0.005 µF capacitor?

A) 0.0235 ms   B) 2.35 ms   C) 235 ms   D) 0.00235 ms

32) What is V_C at the end of the input pulse to an RC integrator if the input pulse is 12 V and the pulse width equals one time constant?

A) 4.41 V   B) 12 V   C) 7.58 V   D) 0 V

33) What is V_C at the end of the input pulse to an RC integrator if the resistance is 22 k Ω, the capacitance is 0.05 µF and the input is a 12 V, 2.2 ms pulse?

A) 10.38 V   B) 12 V   C) 7.58 V   D) 4.42 V

34) If an RC integrator uses a 47 μF capacitor, a 12 kΩ resistor and a square wave input with a frequency of 200 kHz, its approximate output is _____.

    A) a square wave with a frequency of 100 kHz

    B) 0 V

    C) a square wave with a frequency of 200 kHz

    D) a near dc voltage of about half the peak square wave voltage

35) What is the output voltage from an RL integrator that uses a 10 mH inductor, a 10 Ω resistor and a 16 V, 1 ms input pulse?

    A) 10.11 V   B) 13.84 V   C) 15.2 V   D) 16.32 V

36) The capacitor of an RC integrator charges to _____ if the input is a 10 V pulse with a pulse width equal to one time constant.

    A) 10 V   B) 5 V   C) 6.3 V   D) 3.7 VC

37) The capacitor of an RC integrator charges to _____ if the input is a 10 V pulse with a pulse width equal to six time constants.

    A) 10 V   B) 5 V   C) 6.3 V   D) 3.7 V

38) The output from an RC integrator resembles the input if _____.

    A) τ is much larger that the pulse width   B) τ is equal to the pulse width

    C) τ is less than the pulse width   D) τ is much less than the pulse width

39) The output from an RC differentiator resembles the input if _____.

    A) τ is much larger that the pulse width   B) τ is equal to the pulse width

    C) τ is less than the pulse width   D) τ is much less than the pulse width

40) If RC and RL differentiators with equal time constants receive the same pulse, _____.

    A) the RC has the widest output pulse

    B) the RL has the most narrow spikes on the output

    C) one outputs an increasing exponential while the other outputs a decreasing exponential

    D) you can't tell the difference by observing the output wave forms

41) What is the time constant in an RC integrating circuit if a 22 kΩ resistor is in series with a 0.02 μF capacitor?

    A) 0.044 ms   B) 0.044 μs   C) 0.44 ms   D) 0.44 s

42) What is the time constant in an RC integrating circuit if a 10 kΩ resistor is in series with a 220 μF capacitor?

    A) 2.2 ms   B) 22 ms   C) 0.22 ms   D) 2.2 s

43) How long will it take to completely charge a 0.22 μF capacitor through a 5.2 MΩ resistor?

    A) 5.72 s   B) 1.144 s   C) 2.288 s   D) 4.576 s

44) How long will it take to completely discharge a 0.47 μF capacitor through a 10 kΩ resistor?

    A) 2.35 s   B) 0.47 ms   C) 23.5 ms   D) 0.18 ms

45) The capacitor of an RC integrator charges to _____ if the input is a 30 V pulse with a pulse width equal to one time constant.

    A) 18.96 V   B) 25.95 V   C) 28.5 V   D) 29.4 V

46) What is V_C at the end of the input pulse to an RC integrator if the resistance is 5 kΩ, the capacitance is 47 μF and the input is a 15 V, 470 ms pulse?

    A) 9.48 V   B) 12.975 V   C) 14.25 V   D) 14.7 V

47) If the input pulse to an RC differentiator is very short compared to the circuit's time constant, then the differentiator's output is _____.

    A) zero volts

    B) a square wave very similar to the input voltage

    C) a dc value of about half the peak input voltage

    D) a dc voltage equal to the peak input voltage

48) The output of an RL integrator is taken across the _____.

    A) resistor   B) resistor and inductor

    C) inductor   D) source

49) To completely charge a 500 μF capacitor in 15 seconds, use a _____ resistor.

    A) 6 kΩ   B) 12 kΩ   C) 18 kΩ   D) 24 kΩ

50) What is the output voltage from an RL integrator that uses a 200 mH inductor, a 22 kΩ resistor and a 12 V, 9.09 μs input pulse?

    A) 7.58 V   B) 10.38 V   C) 11.4 V   D) 11.76 V

51) What is the output voltage from an RL integrator that uses a 400 mH inductor, a 5 kΩ resistor and a 5 V, 1.2 ms input pulse?

    A) 3.16 V   B) 4.532 V   C) 4.75 V   D) 5 V

52) What is the output voltage at the end of the input pulse to an RC integrator if the resistance is 12 kΩ, the capacitance is 10 μF and the input is a 50 V, 1 s pulse?

    A) 31.6 V   B) 43.25 V   C) 47.5 V   D) 50 V

53) How does the RC differentiator output look when 5τ is much longer than the pulse width?

    A) positive spikes   B) positive and negative spikes

    C) negative spikes   D) square waves

54) What is the output voltage from an RL integrator that uses a 2 H inductor, a 10 kΩ resistor and a 32 V, 0.4 ms input pulse?

    A) 13.9 V   B) 19.03 V   C) 27.67 V   D) 21.56 V

55) If a square wave input produces 0 V output from an RC integrator, _____.

    A) the capacitor is open   B) the resistor is shorted

    C) the capacitor is leaky   D) the resistor is open

56) RC integrators can be used in timing circuits to set a specified time delay if the output is coupled to:

    A) a voltage generating circuit.   B) a current sensitive circuit.

    C) a voltage threshold sensitive circuit.   D) a power threshold sensitive circuit.

57) RC integrators can be used to convert a repetitive pulse waveform to a constant dc voltage equal to the average voltage of the waveform if:

    A) τ is very small compared to t_W.   B) τ is equal to t_W.

    C) τ is five times t_W.   D) τ is very large compared to t_W.

58) Pulse width (t_W) is defined as:

    A) the time interval between identical points on the pulse.

    B) the time interval between opposite points on the pulse.

    C) the time interval between changes in the pulse.

    D) all of these.

59) In RC and RL integrators and differentiators, transient time is equal to the:

    A) pulse width.
    B) pulse width times five.
    C) time constant.
    D) time constant times five.

60) RC and RL integrators produce an output voltage that equals the:

    A) mathematical sum.
    B) mathematical difference.
    C) mathematical product.
    D) mathematical average.

61) RC and RL differentiators produce an output voltage that closely approximates the:

    A) mathematical sum.
    B) mathematical average.
    C) mathematical difference.
    D) mathematical rate of change process.

62) A pulse-waveform to DC convertor makes use of an integrator:

    A) with a time constant shorter than the width of the input pulse.

    B) with a time constant much wider than the width of the input pulse.

    C) with an extremely large time constant.

    D) either B or C

63) A timing circuit makes use of which of the following?

    A) RC integrator
    B) RL differentiator
    C) RL integrator
    D) either A or C

64) A given circuit using an RC integrator to turn on after 20 seconds now takes now takes much longer to turn on. What is the most probable cause?

    A) The resistor has decreased in value.
    B) The resistor has opened.
    C) The capacitor has increased in value.
    D) The capacitor has decreased in value.

65) A given circuit using an RC integrator to turn on after 20 seconds now takes has been taking much longer to turn on. Now it entirely fails to turn on. What is the problem?

    A) The resistor has decreased in value.
    B) The resistor has opened.
    C) The capacitor has increased in value.
    D) The capacitor has decreased in value.

66) Polarity of the output of an RL differentiator is determined by:

    A) the placement of the inductor.
    B) the polarity of the incoming pulse.
    C) the time constant of the RL circuit.
    D) an external clipping circuit.

1) TRUE
Diff: 1

2) FALSE
Diff: 1

3) FALSE
Diff: 1

4) TRUE
Diff: 1

5) TRUE
Diff: 1

6) FALSE
Diff: 1

7) TRUE
Diff: 1

8) TRUE
Diff: 1

9) TRUE
Diff: 1

10) TRUE
Diff: 1

11) FALSE
Diff: 1

12) FALSE
Diff: 2

13) TRUE
Diff: 1

14) TRUE
Diff: 1

15) TRUE
Diff: 1

16) C
Diff: 2

17) D
Diff: 2

18) B
Diff: 2

19) C
Diff: 2

20) D
Diff: 2

21) B
Diff: 2

22) B
Diff: 2

23) C
Diff: 2

24) B
Diff: 2

25) A
Diff: 2

26) D
Diff: 2

27) D
Diff: 2

28) B
Diff: 1

29) B
Diff: 2

30) B
Diff: 1

31) A
Diff: 2

32) C
Diff: 2

33) A
Diff: 2

34) D
Diff: 2

35) A
Diff: 2

36) C
Diff: 2

37) A
Diff: 2

38) D
Diff: 1

39) A
Diff: 1

40) D
Diff: 1

41) C
Diff: 2

42) D
Diff: 2

43) A
Diff: 2

44) C
Diff: 2

45) A
Diff: 2

46) B
Diff: 2

47) B
Diff: 1

48) A
Diff: 1

49) A
Diff: 2

50) A
Diff: 2

51) D
Diff: 2

52) D
Diff: 2

53) D
Diff: 1

54) C
Diff: 2

55) D
Diff: 3

56) C
Diff: 1

57) D
Diff: 1

58) B
Diff: 1

59) D
Diff: 1

60) D
Diff: 1

61) D
Diff: 1

62) D
Diff: 2

63) A
Diff: 3

64) C
Diff: 3

65) B
Diff: 3

66) D
Diff: 1

Chapter 16 Diodes and Applications

True or False

1) Most diodes are made from a semiconductor material called silicon.

2) Adding impurities to semiconductor materials is called *doping*.

3) A forward–biased silicon diode normally drops about 16 V.

4) Reverse breakdown usually occurs when a diode is forward biased by about 0.7 V.

5) A forward–biased germanium diode normally drops about 0.3 V.

6) Most diodes are made from a semiconductor material called germanium.

7) A forward–biased silicon diode normally drops about 0.7 V.

8) The movement of free electrons is called *electron current*.

9) A common name for a PN junction is the *transistor*.

10) The ripple frequency of a half–wave rectifier equals the supply frequency.

11) A half–wave rectifier uses four diodes as rectifiers.

12) Diode clampers cut off voltage above or below specified levels.

13) A zener diode is used as a constant voltage regulator.

14) Ripple voltage is caused by the charging and discharging of the diodes.

15) To *rectify* is to convert dc to pulsating ac.

16) Zener diodes can conduct very large currents.

17) Varactor diodes are used as voltage–variable capacitors.

18) LEDs will emit light if a reverse voltage is applied to them.

19) Photodiodes will conduct more as the light intensity upon them increases.

Multiple Choice

20) Current flow through a diode is normally caused by _____.

    A) forward voltage across the diode

    B) a reverse voltage across the diode

    C) depletion layer breakdown

    D) thermally produced electron–hole pairs

21) If you measure the voltage across a diode and it measures 0.3 V, the diode is probably made of _____ and is _____ biased.

    A) silicon, forward   B) germanium, forward

    C) silicon, reverse   D) germanium, reverse

22) You test a diode with an ohmmeter. The two readings indicate a very low value of resistance. The diode is probably _____.

    A) open   B) shorted

    C) normal   D) conducting heavily

23) A forward biased silicon diode is in series with a 12 kΩ resistor. The source voltage is 5 V. The voltage across the diode is _____ and the voltage across the resistor is _____.

    A) 0.3 V, 4.7 V   B) 4.3 V, 0.7 V   C) 4.7 V, 0.3 V   D) 0.7 V, 4.3 V

24) If the cathode voltage of a forward biased silicon diode is 4.5 V, what is the anode voltage?

    A) 0.7 V   B) –0.7 V   C) 5.2 V   D) –5.2 V

25) To forward bias a silicon diode with –1.6 V on the anode, you must apply a voltage of _____ on the cathode.

    A) –0.9 V   B) 0.9 V   C) –2.3 V   D) 2.3 V

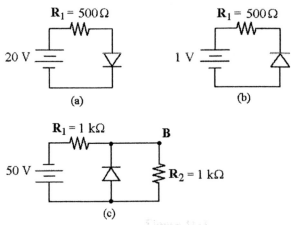

$R_1 = 500\,\Omega$

$R_1 = 500\,\Omega$

20 V

1 V

(a)

(b)

$R_1 = 1\ k\Omega$

B

50 V

$R_2 = 1\ k\Omega$

(c)

Figure 16–1

26) If the diode is silicon, what is the voltage across the resistor in Figure 16–1(a)?

A) 20 V   B) 19.3 V   C) 0 V   D) 0.7 V

27) What is the voltage across the silicon diode in Figure 16–1(b)?

A) –0.7 V   B) 0.7 V   C) 0.3 V   D) 1.0 V

28) If the polarity of the silicon diode is reversed in Figure 16–1(c), V_{R2} is _____.

A) 0.7 V   B) 49.3 V   C) 0 V   D) 25 V

29) What is the current through R_1 in Figure 16–1(c) if the diode is germanium?

A) 49.7 mA   B) 49.3 mA   C) 0 A   D) 25 mA

30) If the diode is made of silicon in Figure 16–1(b), what is the current?

A) 10 mA   B) 8.6 mA   C) 9.4 mA   D) 0 A

31) What is the current through R_2 in Figure 16–1(c) if the diode is silicon?

A) 0.7 mA   B) 25 mA   C) 0 A   D) 0.3 mA

32) What is the voltage across R_1 in Figure 16–1(c) if the diode is silicon?

A) 50 V   B) 25 V   C) 49.3 V   D) 49.7 V

33) What is the voltage across the resistor in Figure 16–1(a) if the diode is germanium?

A) 20 V   B) 19.7 V   C) 0 V   D) 0.7 V

34) If the diode opens in Figure 16–1(b), the voltage across the diode is _____.

    A) 0 V   B) 0.7 V   C) 1 V   D) 4.3 V

35) If the polarity of the source voltage is reversed in Figure 16–1(c), V_{R2} is _____.

    A) 0.7 V   B) 49.3 V   C) 0 V   D) 25 V

36) What is the current through R_1 in Figure 16–1(c) if the diode is silicon?

    A) 49.7 mA   B) 49.3 mA   C) 0 A   D) 25 mA

37) What is the current in Figure 16–1(b) if the diode is made of silicon and the polarity of the source voltage is reversed?

    A) 10 mA   B) 5 mA   C) 0.6 mA   D) 0 A

38) If an ohmmeter check of a diode indicates a high resistance in one direction and low resistance in the other, the diode is probably _____.

    A) open   B) shorted   C) good   D) bad

39) If you measure 17 V across a diode, it is probably _____.

    A) forward biased   B) in heavy conduction

    C) reverse biased   D) shorted

40) If the "+" lead on an ohmmeter is connected to a diode's anode and the "–" lead on the ohmmeter is connected to the diode's cathode, the measured resistance is normally _____.

    A) very high   B) very low   C) 0 Ω   D) 140 kΩ

41) If the measured resistance of a diode is high in both directions, the diode is probably _____.

    A) shorted   B) forward biased

    C) open   D) reverse biased

42) The PN junction is found in _____.

    A) semiconductor diodes   B) transistors

    C) all semiconductor materials   D) both A and B

43) A DC voltage that sets the operating conditions of a semiconductor device is called the _____.

    A) bias   B) depletion voltage

    C) battery   D) barrier potential

44) In a semiconductor diode, the two bias conditions are _____.

    A) positive and negative   B) blocking and non–blocking

    C) open and closed   D) forward and reverse

45) When a diode is forward biased it is _____.

    A) blocking current

    B) conducting current

    C) similar to an open switch

    D) similar to a closed switch

    E) both B and D

46) When the positive lead of an ohmmeter is connected to the cathode of a diode and the negative lead is connected to the anode, the meter reads _____.

    A) a very low resistance

    B) an infinitely high resistance

    C) a high resistance initially, decreasing to about 100 Ω

    D) a gradually increasing resistance

47) Current through a diode is blocked by _____.

    A) forward voltage across the diode

    B) reverse voltage across the diode

    C) depletion layer breakdown

    D) thermally produced electron–hole pairs

48) If you measure 0.7 V across a diode, the diode is probably made of _____ and is _____ biased.

    A) silicon, forward   B) germanium, forward

    C) silicon, reverse   D) germanium, reverse

49) If the measured resistance of a diode is very low in both directions, the diode is probably _____.

    A) open   B) shorted

    C) normal   D) conducting heavily

50) If a forward biased silicon diode is in series with a 22 kΩ resistor and a 10 V source, the voltage across the diode is _____ and the voltage across the resistor is _____.

    A) 0.3 V, 9.7 V   B) 9.3 V, 0.7 V   C) 9.7 V, 0.3 V   D) 0.7 V, 9.3 V

51) If the cathode voltage of a forward-biased silicon diode equals 6.5 V, the anode voltage equals
_____.

    A) 0.7 V   B) –0.7 V   C) 7.2 V   D) –7.2 V

52) To forward bias a silicon diode with a –71.6 V anode voltage, apply a _____ cathode
voltage.

    A) +72.3 V   B) –72.3 V   C) +70.9 V   D) –70.9 V

53) The arrowhead in the schematic symbol for a diode represents:

    A) the anode.   B) the cathode.

    C) the semiconductor lead.   D) all of these.

54) Applying the reverse breakdown voltage to a diode will _____.

    A) cause it to act like a switch   B) usually damage the diode

    C) cause it to act like a capacitor   D) never do any harm

55) Materials whose molecules arrange themselves into a crystal structure are bound together by:

    A) sharing valence electrons.   B) full valence shells.

    C) covalent bonding.   D) all of these.

56) Doping a semiconductor material with pentavalent impurities results in:

    A) P-type material.   B) N-type material.

    C) P-N type material.   D) N-P type material.

57) In a P-N diode, the region near the P-N junction is called:

    A) the neutral region.   B) the recombination region.

    C) the depletion region.   D) the diffusion region.

58) The forward bias on a P-N diode to make the diode conduct must be greater than the:

    A) reverse bias.   B) barrier potential.

    C) volence bond.   D) conduction bond.

59) Reverse breakdown current is carried by:

    A) trualent impurity atoms.   B) pentavalent impurity atoms.

    C) majority carrier.   D) minority carriers.

60) If a half-wave rectifier outputs 58 Vp, the diode's PIV should be more than _____.

    A) 116 V   B) 58 V   C) 29 V   D) 15 V

61) If a full-wave rectifier outputs 38 Vp, its average output equals _____.

    A) 24.19 V   B) 19.26 V   C) 76.67 V   D) 38 V

62) A full-wave rectifier requires _____.

    A) four diodes and a center-tapped transformer

    B) two diodes and a transformer with a single secondary

    C) two diodes and a center-tapped transformer

    D) a high voltage to operate it

63) The ripple voltage from a power supply _____.

    A) is very high   B) is zero

    C) is about 1 V   D) varies with load

64) If the diode in a half-wave rectifier shorts, the _____.

    A) output ripple would be very small

    B) output voltage would not change

    C) output voltage would equal the transformer secondary voltage

    D) output voltage would be zero

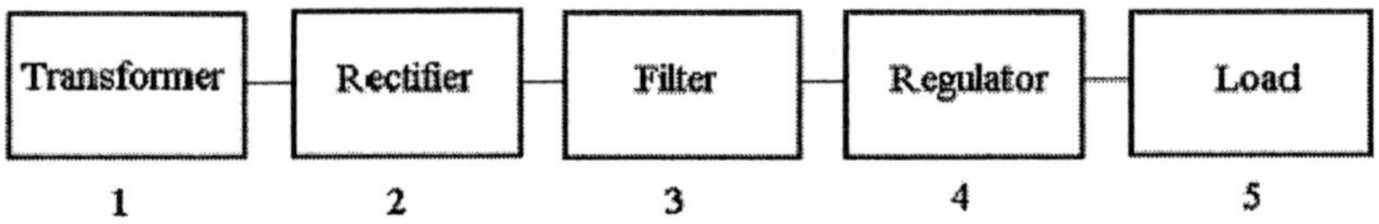

Transformer	Rectifier	Filter	Regulator	Load
1	2	3	4	5

Figure 16-2

65) Which block in Figure 16-2 changes ac to pulsating dc?

    A) 1   B) 2   C) 3   D) 4

66) Which block in Figure 16-2 will change the amplitude of the ac voltage?

    A) 1   B) 2   C) 3   D) 4

67) Which block conditions in Figure 16-2 will keep the output voltage nearly constant under varying load?

    A) 1   B) 2   C) 3   D) 4

68) Which block will smooth out the pulsating dc in Figure 16-2?

    A) 1   B) 2   C) 3   D) 4

69) If the filter capacitor opens in Figure 16-2, _____.

    A) the output dc will be very low   B) the ripple voltage increases

    C) the diodes would open   D) a loud hum will be heard

70) The purpose of Block 4 in Figure 16-2 is to _____.

    A) adjust the output voltage to the correct ac value

    B) keep the dc output voltage constant as the load changes

    C) make sure that the fuse will not blow

    D) maintain a constant output current when the load current changes

71) If the filter capacitor becomes leaky in Figure 16-2, _____.

    A) the output dc will be very low   B) the ripple voltage will increase

    C) the diodes would open   D) a loud hum will be heard

72) The output of Block 2 in Figure 16-2 is:

    A) a pulsating AC voltage.   B) a pulsating DC voltage.

    C) a steady DC voltage.   D) a steady DC current.

73) If a diode in a half-wave rectifier opens in Figure 16-2, _____.

    A) the output dc voltage decreases and the ripple voltage increases

    B) the output dc voltage increases and the ripple frequency decreases

    C) the output dc voltage increases and the ripple voltage decreases

    D) the output dc voltage decreases and the ripple voltage decreases

74) If the load current decreases in a simple zener regulator, the _____.

    A) current through the series resistor decreases

    B) voltage across the series resistor decreases

    C) zener current decreases

    D) zener current increases

75) A full-wave bridge rectifier requires _____.

   A) a center-tapped transformer

   B) four diodes and a transformer with a single secondary

   C) two diodes and a transformer with a single secondary

   D) a high voltage to operate it

76) If a diode in a full-wave rectifier opens, _____.

   A) the dc output voltage will decrease and the ripple voltage will decrease

   B) the dc output voltage will increase and the ripple frequency will decrease

   C) the dc output voltage will increase and the ripple voltage will decrease

   D) the dc output voltage will decrease and the ripple frequency will decrease

77) If the load current increases in a simple zener regulator, the _____.

   A) total current increases

   B) current through the series resistor increases

   C) voltage across the series resistor decreases

   D) zener current decreases

78) If the source voltage increases in a simple zener regulator, _____.

   A) the load current increases

   B) the voltage across the zener increases

   C) the voltage across the series resistor decreases

   D) the zener current increases

79) If a 60 Hz sine wave is input to a half-wave rectifier, its output frequency is _____.

   A) 30 Hz   B) 60 Hz   C) 120 Hz   D) 0 Hz

80) If a 75 Vp sine wave is applied to a half-wave rectifier, the diode's peak inverse voltage is
   _____.

   A) 75 V   B) 150 V   C) 37.5 V   D) 0 V

81) If a 60 Hz sine wave is input to a full-wave rectifier, its output frequency is _____.

   A) 30 Hz   B) 60 Hz   C) 120 Hz   D) 0 Hz

82) Zener diodes are widely used as _____.

    A) current limiters   B) power distributors

    C) voltage regulators   D) variable resistors

83) The small variation in the output voltage of a dc power supply is called _____.

    A) average voltage   B) ac to dc conversion

    C) residual voltage   D) ripple voltage

84) A full-wave rectifier uses _____ diode(s) and its output frequency is _____ the input frequency.

    A) two, twice   B) two, equal to   C) one, twice   D) one, equal to

85) If a half-wave rectifier outputs 36 V_P, the PIV of the diode should be more than _____.

    A) 116 V   B) 36 V   C) 29 V   D) 15 V

86) If a full-wave rectifier outputs 36 V_P, the average output is _____.

    A) 22.9 V   B) 19 V   C) 76 V   D) 38 V

87) A full-wave rectifier uses _____ diodes and a transformer with a _____.

    A) four, center tap   B) two, single secondary

    C) two, center tap   D) one, single secondary

88) The ripple voltage from a power supply is _____.

    A) zero   B) very high

    C) about 1 V   D) dependent upon the load

89) If the diode in a half-wave rectifier opens, _____.

    A) the output ripple would be very small

    B) the output voltage would not change

    C) the output voltage would equal the transformer secondary voltage

    D) the output voltage would be zero

90) If the load current increases in a simple zener regulator, the _____.

    A) total current decreases

    B) current through the series resistor decreases

    C) zener current decreases

    D) zener current increases

91) If a diode shorts in a full−wave rectifier, _____.

    A) the output dc voltage will increase

    B) the output dc voltage will decrease and possibly damage the power supply

    C) no change would occur in the output

    D) the output current would increase

92) If an aircraft full−wave, dc power supply operates from a 400 Hz sine wave, the ripple frequency is _____.

    A) 60 Hz   B) 120 Hz   C) 400 Hz   D) 800 Hz

93) The formula for line regulation is:

    A) $\dfrac{\Delta V_{IN}}{\Delta V_{OUT}} \times 100\%$.   B) $\dfrac{\Delta V_{OUT}}{\Delta V_{IN}} \times 100\%$.

    C) $\dfrac{\Delta V_{NL}}{\Delta V_{FL}} \times 100\%$.   D) $\dfrac{\Delta V_{FL}}{\Delta V_{NL}} \times 100\%$.

94) The formula for load regulation is:

    A) $\left[\dfrac{V_{NL}-V_{FL}}{V_{FL}}\right] \times 100\%$.   B) $\left[\dfrac{V_{FL}-V_{NL}}{V_{FL}}\right] \times 100\%$

    C) $\left[\dfrac{V_{FL}-V_{NL}}{V_{NL}}\right] \times 100\%$ D) $\left[\dfrac{V_{NL}-V_{FL}}{V_{NL}}\right] \times 100\%$

95) In the simplest sense, a zener diode is really a:

    A) voltage regulator.   B) current regulator.

    C) reference voltage.   D) reference current.

96) To operate as a voltage regulator, a zener diode requires a:

    A) transformer.   B) silicon diode.

    C) series resistor.   D) series capacitor.

97) To generate light, an LED requires:

    A) avalanche breakdown.   B) zener breakdown.

    C) forward DC bias.   D) reverse DC bias.

98) To detect light, a photodiode requires:

    A) avalanche breakdown.   B) zener breakdown.

    C) forward bias.   D) reverse bias.

1) TRUE
Diff: 1
2) TRUE
Diff: 1
3) FALSE
Diff: 1
4) FALSE
Diff: 1
5) TRUE
Diff: 1
6) FALSE
Diff: 1
7) TRUE
Diff: 1
8) TRUE
Diff: 1
9) FALSE
Diff: 1
10) TRUE
Diff: 1
11) FALSE
Diff: 1
12) FALSE
Diff: 1
13) TRUE
Diff: 1
14) FALSE
Diff: 1
15) FALSE
Diff: 1
16) FALSE
Diff: 1
17) TRUE
Diff: 1
18) FALSE
Diff: 1
19) TRUE
Diff: 1
20) A
Diff: 1
21) B
Diff: 2
22) B
Diff: 3

23) D
Diff: 2
24) C
Diff: 2
25) C
Diff: 2
26) B
Diff: 2
27) D
Diff: 2
28) D
Diff: 2
29) A
Diff: 2
30) D
Diff: 2
31) A
Diff: 2
32) C
Diff: 2
33) B
Diff: 2
34) C
Diff: 2
35) D
Diff: 2
36) B
Diff: 2
37) C
Diff: 2
38) C
Diff: 3
39) C
Diff: 3
40) B
Diff: 2
41) C
Diff: 3
42) D
Diff: 1
43) A
Diff: 1
44) D
Diff: 1

45) E
Diff: 1
46) B
Diff: 2
47) B
Diff: 1
48) A
Diff: 1
49) B
Diff: 2
50) D
Diff: 2
51) C
Diff: 2
52) B
Diff: 2
53) A
Diff: 1
54) B
Diff: 1
55) D
Diff: 1
56) B
Diff: 1
57) C
Diff: 1
58) B
Diff: 1
59) D
Diff: 1
60) B
Diff: 2
61) A
Diff: 2
62) C
Diff: 1
63) D
Diff: 1
64) C
Diff: 3
65) B
Diff: 2
66) A
Diff: 2

67) D
Diff: 2
68) C
Diff: 2
69) B
Diff: 3
70) B
Diff: 2
71) B
Diff: 3
72) B
Diff: 2
73) D
Diff: 3
74) D
Diff: 2
75) B
Diff: 1
76) D
Diff: 3
77) D
Diff: 2
78) D
Diff: 2
79) B
Diff: 2
80) A
Diff: 2
81) C
Diff: 2
82) C
Diff: 1
83) D
Diff: 1
84) A
Diff: 1
85) B
Diff: 2
86) A
Diff: 2
87) C
Diff: 1
88) D
Diff: 1

89) D
   Diff: 3
90) C
   Diff: 2
91) B
   Diff: 3
92) D
   Diff: 2
93) B
   Diff: 2
94) A
   Diff: 2
95) C
   Diff: 1
96) C
   Diff: 1
97) C
   Diff: 1
98) D
   Diff: 1

Chapter 17 Transistors and Applications

True or False

1) The two types of BJTs are the NPN and PNP.

2) A BJT has three elements: emitter, gate, and collector.

3) The gate current in a JFET is normally zero.

4) A depletion–type MOSFET can operate with a positive or negative value of V_{GS}.

5) A transistor can be used as an electronic switch.

6) The two types of BJTs are the PNP and the P–channel.

7) An N–channel JFET has three elements: source, gate, and drain.

8) An enhancement–type MOSFET can operate with a positive value of V_{GS}.

9) To correctly bias a BJT, reverse–bias the base–emitter junction and forward–bias the base–collector junction.

10) Two types of FETs are the JFET and the MOSFET.

11) The general characteristics of a common–emitter amplifier are low voltage gain, low current gain and very high power gain.

12) The overall voltage gain of a multistage amplifier is the product of the individual stage gains.

13) A current gain of almost one is a characteristic of a common–base amplifier.

14) Voltage gain can be found by $A_V = V_{IN} \div V_{OUT}$

15) An amplifier that provides its own input is called an oscillator.

16) The general characteristics of a common–emitter amplifier are high voltage gain, high current gain and no phase reversal between the input and output voltages.

17) The voltage gain of several amplifiers in series is found by adding the individual stage voltage gains.

18) A common–collector amplifier has a high input impedance compared to a common –emitter amplifier.

19) If a common–emitter amplifier measures the same voltage on the collector as V_{CC}, the amplifier is operating in saturation.

20) Class C amplifiers are used primarily at radio frequencies.

Multiple Choice

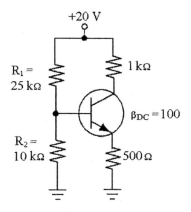

+20 V

$R_1 = 25\ k\Omega$

$1\ k\Omega$

$\beta_{DC} = 100$

$R_2 = 10\ k\Omega$

$500\ \Omega$

Figure 17–1

21) Find V_{BE} in Figure 17–1.

    A) 5.71 V   B) 0.7 V   C) 5 V   D) 15 V

22) If $V_C = 20$ V in Figure 17–1, which statement describes a possible trouble?

    A) The power is off.   B) The amplifier is cut off.

    C) The amplifier is saturated.   D) This is normal.

23) If the base–emitter junction opened in Figure 17–1, V_E equals _____.

    A) 5 V   B) 20 V   C) 0 V   D) 10 V

24) If the BJT's collector opened internally in Figure 17–1, V_{RC} equals _____.

    A) 20 V   B) 0 V   C) 10 V   D) V_{BE}

25) Find V_{CE} in Figure 17–1.

    A) 11.4 V   B) 5 V   C) 6.4 V   D) 16.4 V

26) Which voltage might indicate that the amplifier in Figure 17–1 is cut off?

    A) $V_C = 20$ V   B) $V_E = 20$ V   C) $V_{CE} = 0$ V   D) $V_{BE} = 0.7$ V

27) If V_{CC} equals 15 V in Figure 17–1, V_{BE} equals _____.

    A) 4.71 V   B) 0.7 V   C) 5 V   D) 15 V

28) If the collector-to-emitter voltage is about 0 V in Figure 17–1, the possible trouble is _____.

    A) the transistor is open   B) the amplifier is cut off

    C) the amplifier is saturated   D) this is a normal condition

29) If the emitter resistor opened in Figure 17–1, V_B equals _____.

    A) 5.71 V   B) 0 V   C) 0.7 V   D) 20 V

30) If R_1 opens in Figure 17–1, V_C equals _____.

    A) 0 V   B) 0.7 V   C) 10 V   D) 20 V

31) If R_2 opens in Figure 17–1, I_C _____.

    A) increases   B) decreases

    C) remains the same   D) decreases to zero

32) If V_C equals V_E in Figure 17–1, the _____.

    A) power is off   B) emitter has opened

    C) emitter is shorted to the collector   D) transistor is cutoff

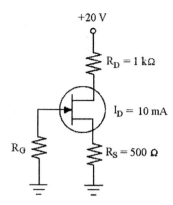

Figure 17–2

33) The amplifier in Figure 17–2 uses a _____ and the gate current is _____.

   A) BJT, 0 A   B) TRIAC, 10 mA   C) JFET, 0 A   D) JFET, 5 mA

34) Find V_G in Figure 17–2.

   A) 5 V   B) 10 V   C) 15 V   D) 0 V

35) The device in Figure 17–2 is a _____.

   A) P–channel MOSFET   B) NPN type BJT

   C) N–channel JFET   D) depletion type MOSFET

36) Find V_{GS} in Figure 17–2.

   A) 5 V   B) –5 V   C) –10 V   D) 10 V

37) If I_D = 20 mA in Figure 17–2, V_G equals _____.

   A) 5 V   B) 10 V   C) 15 V   D) 0 V

38) If I_D = 15 mA in Figure 17–2, V_{GS} equals _____.

   A) 0 V   B) –7.5 V   C) 15 V   D) 25 V

39) The amplifier in circuit Figure 17–2 uses a _____ and V_D equals _____.

   A) BJT, 10 V   B) JFET, 0 V   C) JFET, 10 V   D) TRIAC, 5 V

40) In all FETs, the drain current equals the _____ current.

   A) collector   B) emitter   C) gate   D) source

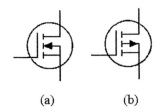

(a)   (b)

Figure 17-3

41) The symbol in Figure 17-3(b) represents the _____.

    A) N-channel depletion-type JFET

    B) P-channel enhancement-type MOSFET

    C) N-channel enhancement-type MOSFET

    D) N-channel enhancement-type JFET

42) The symbol in Figure 17-3(a) represents the _____.

    A) N-channel depletion-type JFET

    B) P-channel enhancement-type MOSFET

    C) N-channel enhancement-type MOSFET

    D) N-channel enhancement-type JFET

43) When a BJT amplifier is saturated, V_{CE} is about _____ and I_C is _____.

    A) zero, maximum   B) zero, minimum

    C) V_{CC}, minimum   D) 25 V, 10 mA

44) If a BJT amplifier is operated as a switch that is off, this operating condition is known as _____.

    A) saturation   B) V_P

    C) cutoff   D) thermal runaway

45) For normal operation of a NPN transistor, the base must be _____.

    A) disconnected   B) negative with respect to the emitter

    C) positive with respect to the emitter   D) positive with respect to the collector

46) Beta (β) is the ratio of _____.

    A) collector current to emitter current   B) collector current to base current

    C) emitter current to base current   D) output voltage to input voltage

47) If a transistor's beta equals 30 and I_B equals 1 mA, I_C equals _____.

    A) 0.33 mA   B) 1 mA   C) 30 mA   D) unknown

48) If the base current increases, _____.

    A) the collector current increases and the emitter current decreases

    B) the collector current decreases and the emitter current decreases

    C) the collector current increases and the emitter current does not change

    D) the collector current increases and the emitter current increases

49) When a negative gate–to–source voltage is applied to an N–channel MOSFET, it operates _____.

    A) in the cutoff state   B) in the saturated state

    C) in the enhancement mode   D) in the depletion mode

50) In all N–channel FET's, the current into the source equals the current leaving the _____.

    A) collector   B) emitter   C) drain   D) source

51) To analyze the operation of a BJT in an amplifier circuit, use characteristic curves of:

    A) emitter current versus emitter to collector voltage.

    B) base current versus collector to emitter voltage.

    C) collector current versus emitter to collector voltage.

    D) collector current versus collector to emitter voltage.

52) In using BJT characteristic curves, the intersection of the load line with a specific base current curve is called:

    A) intersection point.   B) nudpoint.

    C) Q point.   D) base point.

53) In using BJT characteristic curves, the straight line drawn between the cutoff and the saturation points is called:

    A) cutoff line.   B) saturation line.

    C) load line.   D) operating line.

54) On transistor spec sheet, the key difference between β_{DC} and α_{DC} is that:

    A) β_{DC} represents I_E/I_C; α_{DC} represents I_C/I_E.

    B) β_{DC} represents I_C/I_B; α_{DC} represents I_B/I_C.

    C) β_{DC} represents I_C/I_E; α_{DC} represents I_C/I_B.

    D) β_{DC} represents I_E/I_C; α_{DC} represents I_B/I_C.

55) Although BJT transistors are current operated devices, a key characteristic is the signal voltage gain as an amplifier specified as:

    A) $A_V \cong R_C/R_B$ B) $A_V \cong R_C/R_E$.   C) $A_V \cong R_E/R_C$ D) $A_V \cong R_B/R_E$.

56) To recognize transistor packages and identify the terminals, look for:

    A) the protruding tab.   B) the flat side.

    C) the imprinted dot.   D) all of these.

57) The Class B amplifier conducts for _____ of the input cycle.

    A) a small portion   B) $180°$

    C) $360°$ D) only $10°$

58) Which one of these amplifiers has very low input resistance and very high output resistance?

    A) common–emitter   B) common–collector

    C) common–base   D) common–gate

59) Which one of these characteristics is found in a common–collector amplifier?

    A) a low input resistance   B) a very high power gain

    C) a current gain of one   D) a high input resistance

60) What is the total voltage gain of a three–stage amplifier that has stage gains of 22, 112, and 8?

    A) 142   B) 1,420   C) 19,712   D) 197,120

61) What type of amplifier normally has a voltage gain of one?

    A) common–drain   B) common–emitter

    C) common–source   D) common–base

62) Which one of these amplifiers does NOT have the output in phase with the input?

    A) common–drain   B) common–source

    C) common–collector   D) common–base

63) Crossover distortion occurs in a _____ amplifier when the amplifier is biased at _____.

    A) common–emitter, saturation   B) push–pull, saturation

    C) push–pull, cutoff   D) common–source, cutoff

64) Which one of these amplifiers has high input resistance and low output resistance?

    A) common–emitter   B) common–collector

    C) common–base   D) common–gate

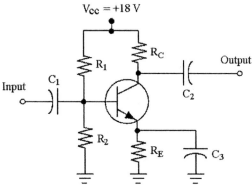

Figure 17–4

65) Which voltage might allow the circuit in Figure 17–4 to operate with minimum distortion?

    A) $V_{BC} = 0$ V   B) $V_{CE} = 0.15$ V   C) $V_C = 18$ V   D) $V_{BE} = 0.7$ V

66) Which voltage would indicate that the amplifier in Figure 17–4 is operating in saturation?

    A) $V_{BE} = 9$ V   B) $V_{CE} = 0.15$ V   C) $V_C = 18$ V   D) $V_{BE} = 0.7$ V

67) If C_3 opens in Figure 17–4, _____.

    A) the dc emitter voltage decreases   B) the voltage gain increases

    C) the dc emitter voltage increases   D) the voltage gain decreases

68) If R_1 opens in Figure 17–4, V_C equals _____.

    A) 9 V   B) 0 V   C) 18 V   D) V_E

69) If the collector opens in Figure 17–4, the output voltage _____.

    A) increases   B) decreases to zero

    C) remains the same   D) varies with temperature

70) Which voltage would enable the circuit in Figure 17–4 to operate with little distortion?

   A) $V_{BC} = 0$ V   B) $V_{CE} = 9$ V   C) $V_C = 18$ V   D) $V_{BE} = 7$ V

71) Which voltage would indicate that the amplifier in Figure 17–4 is operating in cutoff?

   A) $V_{BC} = 9$ V   B) $V_{CE} = 9$ V   C) $V_C = 18$ V   D) $V_{BE} = 7$ V

72) If the base–emitter junction opens in Figure 17–4, V_C _____.

   A) increases to V_{CC} B) decreases to 0 volts

   C) decreases to V_E D) does not change

73) If R_1 shorts in Figure 17-4, V_C _____.

   A) increases to V_{CC} B) decreases to 0 V

   C) decreases to V_E D) does not change

74) If the BJT's collector opens internally in Figure 17–4, V_B _____.

   A) increases   B) decreases

   C) remains the same   D) drops almost to zero

75) If R_E opens in Figure 17–4, V_E _____.

   A) increases   B) decreases

   C) remains the same   D) drops almost to zero

76) If the BJT's emitter internally shorted to its collector in Figure 17–4, V_{CE} _____.

   A) increases   B) decreases

   C) remains the same   D) drops almost to zero

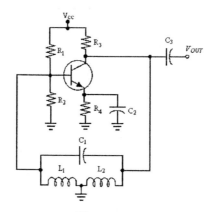

Figure 17-5

77) The circuit in Figure 17-5 is a _____ oscillator and uses _____ feedback.

    A) Colpitts, positive   B) Hartley, positive

    C) Clapp, negative   D) Colpitts, negative

78) The circuit in Figure 17-5 is known as a _____ oscillator because it has a _____ coil.

    A) Colpitts, dual   B) Clapp, dual   C) Hartley, dual   D) crystal, dual

79) In Figure 17-5, L_1, L_2 and C_1 form a _____ that provides _____ feedback to the amplifier.

    A) tank circuit, positive   B) tank circuit, negative

    C) feedback network, negative   D) tank circuit, out-of-phase

80) If C_1 opens in Figure 17-5, the circuit will probably _____.

    A) continue to operate normally   B) decrease its oscillating frequency

    C) increase its oscillating frequency   D) stop oscillating entirely

81) If the value of C_1 increases in Figure 17-5, the circuit _____.

    A) operates at a higher frequency   B) operates at a lower frequency

    C) operates at dc   D) does not change at all

82) A Clapp oscillator is similar to a Colpitts oscillator EXCEPT that _____.

    A) the feedback is negative

    B) there is an additional series capacitor in the tank

    C) the feedback network is an RC circuit

    D) no coupling capacitor is used

83) A Class _____ amplifier is very efficient. It is useful mainly at _____ frequencies.

A) B, audio   B) C, audio   C) A, radio   D) C, radio

84) The output signal of a CE amplifier is always _____.

A) in-phase with the input signal   B) out-of-phase with the input signal

C) larger than the input signal   D) equal to the input signal

85) The largest theoretical voltage gain obtainable with a CC amplifier is _____.

A) 100   B) 10

C) 1   D) dependent on β

86) One advantage of the Darlington pair is _____.

A) increased overall voltage gain   B) less cost

C) decreasing the input impedance   D) increased overall beta

87) In a class A amplifier, the output signal is _____.

A) distorted   B) clipped

C) the same shape as the input   D) smaller in amplitude than the input

88) Oscillators operate on the principle of _____.

A) signal feed-through   B) positive feedback

C) negative feedback   D) attenuation

89) A class C amplifier conducts during _____ of the input cycle.

A) a small portion   B) 180°

C) 360°   D) only 50%

90) Which one of these amplifiers has a very high power gain?

A) common-emitter   B) common-collector

C) common-base   D) common-gate

91) Which one of these characteristics is found in a common-base amplifier?

A) a very low output resistance   B) a very high power gain

C) a current gain of one   D) a high input resistance

92) What is the total voltage gain of a three-stage amplifier that has stage gains of 17, 142, and 4?

    A) 163   B) 2414   C) 9656   D) 28,968

93) What type of amplifier normally has a current gain of one?

    A) common-drain   B) common-emitter

    C) common-source   D) common-base

94) Which of the following amplifiers has phase inversion?

    A) common-drain   B) common-emitter

    C) common-collector   D) common-base

95) A crystal oscillator uses a crystal to determine the _____.

    A) dc output   B) amount of positive feedback

    C) output frequency   D) amount of negative feedback

96) A crystal oscillator usually has a very high _____.

    A) V   B) I   C) Q   D) BW

97) Amplifiers are electronic circuits that accept an AC input signal and produce an output signal that represents a:

    A) voltage gain.   B) current gain.   C) power gain.   D) all of these.

98) The terms common-base, common-emitter and common-collector mean that:

    A) one of the leads is a common reference to the other two leads.

    B) one of the leads is a common input signal point.

    C) one of the leads is a common DC bias point.

    D) all of these.

99) The most popular and widely used transistor amplifier configuration is the:

    A) common-base.   B) common-emitter.

    C) common-collector.   D) common-drain.

100) The classification of transistor amplifiers by classes: A, B, C, is based on:

    A) voltage flow.   B) current flow.

    C) signal voltages.   D) bias voltages.

101) The most accurate signal reproduction in transistor amplifiers is provided by:

    A) class A   B) class B   C) class C   D) class AB

102) Oscillators are amplifiers that produce a repetitive waveform and that utilize:

    A) negative feedback.   B) degenerative feedback.

    C) positive feedback.   D) both negative and positive feedback.

103) Positive feedback is defined as feeding back a portion of the output to the input such that:

    A) the two are in phase.   B) there is no net phase shift.

    C) it reinforces the signal at the input.   D) all of these.

1) TRUE
   Diff: 1
2) FALSE
   Diff: 1
3) TRUE
   Diff: 1
4) TRUE
   Diff: 1
5) TRUE
   Diff: 1
6) FALSE
   Diff: 1
7) TRUE
   Diff: 1
8) TRUE
   Diff: 1
9) FALSE
   Diff: 1
10) TRUE
    Diff: 1
11) FALSE
    Diff: 1
12) TRUE
    Diff: 1
13) TRUE
    Diff: 1
14) FALSE
    Diff: 1
15) TRUE
    Diff: 1
16) FALSE
    Diff: 1
17) FALSE
    Diff: 1
18) TRUE
    Diff: 1
19) FALSE
    Diff: 1
20) TRUE
    Diff: 1
21) B
    Diff: 1
22) B
    Diff: 3

23) C
    Diff: 2
24) B
    Diff: 2
25) B
    Diff: 2
26) A
    Diff: 2
27) B
    Diff: 2
28) C
    Diff: 3
29) A
    Diff: 2
30) D
    Diff: 3
31) A
    Diff: 3
32) C
    Diff: 3
33) C
    Diff: 2
34) D
    Diff: 2
35) C
    Diff: 1
36) B
    Diff: 2
37) D
    Diff: 2
38) B
    Diff: 2
39) C
    Diff: 2
40) D
    Diff: 1
41) B
    Diff: 1
42) C
    Diff: 1
43) A
    Diff: 2
44) C
    Diff: 2

45) C
    Diff: 2
46) B
    Diff: 1
47) C
    Diff: 2
48) D
    Diff: 2
49) D
    Diff: 1
50) C
    Diff: 1
51) D
    Diff: 1
52) C
    Diff: 1
53) C
    Diff: 1
54) C
    Diff: 1
55) B
    Diff: 1
56) D
    Diff: 1
57) B
    Diff: 1
58) C
    Diff: 1
59) D
    Diff: 1
60) C
    Diff: 2
61) A
    Diff: 1
62) B
    Diff: 1
63) C
    Diff: 1
64) B
    Diff: 1
65) D
    Diff: 2
66) B
    Diff: 2

67) D
    Diff: 3
68) C
    Diff: 3
69) B
    Diff: 3
70) B
    Diff: 2
71) C
    Diff: 3
72) A
    Diff: 3
73) B
    Diff: 3
74) C
    Diff: 3
75) A
    Diff: 3
76) D
    Diff: 3
77) B
    Diff: 1
78) C
    Diff: 1
79) A
    Diff: 1
80) D
    Diff: 3
81) B
    Diff: 3
82) B
    Diff: 1
83) D
    Diff: 1
84) B
    Diff: 1
85) C
    Diff: 1
86) D
    Diff: 1
87) C
    Diff: 1
88) C
    Diff: 1

89) A
   Diff: 1
90) A
   Diff: 1
91) C
   Diff: 1
92) C
   Diff: 2
93) D
   Diff: 1
94) B
   Diff: 1
95) C
   Diff: 1
96) C
   Diff: 1
97) D
   Diff: 1
98) D
   Diff: 1
99) B
   Diff: 1
100) B
   Diff: 1
101) A
   Diff: 1
102) C
   Diff: 1
103) D
   Diff: 1

Chapter 18 The Operational Amplifier

True or False

1) The ideal amplifier has infinite gain, infinite input impedance, and zero output impedance.

2) The slew rate of an op-amp is determined by the frequency response of the internal amplifiers.

3) An op-amp with a low CMRR easily rejects noise signals that appear at both inputs.

4) A voltage-follower op-amp has a voltage gain greater than one.

5) The open-loop voltage gain of an op-amp is very large.

6) Practical op-amps come reasonably close to the requirements for an ideal amplifier.

7) Differential amplifiers provide high voltage gain and low common-mode rejection.

8) An op-amp's CMRR is usually expressed in dB.

9) An op-amp's input offset voltage, V_{OS}, is the differential input voltage required to make the differential output voltage zero.

10) A typical value of input bias current for an op-amp is around 80 nA.

Multiple Choice

11) Which one of these op-amp terminals provides an output that is in-phase with the input?
    A) V_{CC} B) non-inverting   C) inverting   D) offset null

12) Which of these amplifiers provide a variable input resistance and a variable gain?
    A) a voltage-follower amp   B) an open-loop amp
    C) a non-inverting amp   D) an inverting amp with potentiometer

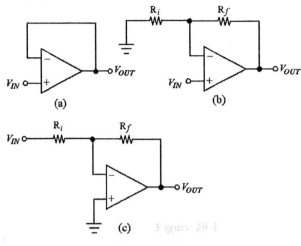

Figure 18-1

13) What is the voltage gain of the amplifier in Figure 18-1(a)?

 A) 100,000   B) 1000   C) 10   D) 1

14) Identify the open-loop amplifier in Figure 18-1.

 A) Figure 18-1(a) B) Figure 18-1(b) C) Figure 18-1(c) D) none of these

15) Identify the non-inverting amplifier in Figure 18-1.

 A) Figure 18-1(a) B) Figure 18-1(b) C) Figure 18-1(c) D) none of these

16) If R_i = 4.7 kΩ and R_f = 0.18 MΩ in Figure 18-1(c), the voltage gain equals _____.

 A) 38.3   B) 39.3   C) 1   D) infinite

17) Which of the amplifiers in Figure 18-1 would be used as a buffer amplifier?

 A) Figure 20-1(a) B) Figure 20-1(b) C) Figure 20-1(c) D) none of these

18) If R_f = 0.5 MΩ and R_i = 10 kΩ in Figure 18-1(b), the voltage gain equals _____.

 A) 50   B) 51   C) 5   D) 6

19) If R_f = 1.2 MΩ and A_V = 120 in Figure 18-1(c), R_i equals _____.

 A) 120 Ω   B) 10 kΩ   C) 1 kΩ   D) 100 kΩ

20) What trouble in the amplifier in Figure 18-1(c) could cause the voltage gain to drop to 1?

 A) R_i is open   B) the power is off

 C) R_f is open   D) V_{OUT} is grounded

21) V_{RF} equals _____ in Figure 18–1(c).

    A) V_{CC} B) V_{RI} C) V_{OUT} D) V_{IN}

22) The circuit in Figure 18–1(c) is known as the _____.

    A) non–inverting amplifier   B) open–loop amplifier

    C) inverting amplifier   D) voltage follower amplifier

23) If $R_f = 470$ kΩ and $R_i = 5$ kΩ in Figure 18–1(b), the voltage gain equals _____.

    A) 1.01   B) 470   C) 95   D) 94

24) If $R_f = 150$ kΩ and $R_i = 10$ kΩ in Figure 18–1(c), the voltage gain equals _____.

    A) 0.066   B) 1   C) 15   D) 16

25) The circuit in Figure 18–1(a) is used as a(n) _____.

    A) high gain amplifier   B) inverting amplifier

    C) buffer amplifier   D) oscillator

26) If $R_f = 100$ kΩ and $R_i = 6.8$ kΩ in Figure 18–1(c), the voltage gain equals _____.

    A) 15.7   B) 14.7   C) 1   D) infinite

27) If $R_f = 150$ kΩ and $R_i = 2.2$ kΩ in Figure 18–1(c), the voltage gain equals _____.

    A) 68.2   B) 69.2   C) 1   D) infinite

28) If $R_f = 333$ kΩ and $R_i = 22$ kΩ in Figure 18–1(b), the voltage gain equals _____.

    A) 15   B) 16   C) 15.1   D) 16.1

29) If $R_f = 1.2$ MΩ and $R_i = 47$ kΩ in Figure 18–1(b), the voltage gain equals _____.

    A) 25.5   B) 26.5   C) 25   D) 26

30) If $R_f = 100$ kΩ and $A_V = 833$ in Figure 18–1(c), R_i equals _____.

    A) 120 Ω B) 10 kΩ C) 1 kΩ D) 100 kΩ

31) What trouble in the amplifier in Figure 18–1(c) could cause the output voltage to clip severely?

    A) The power is off.

    B) The input signal is too large.

    C) The amplifier's gain is too low.

    D) The input signal is too small for the amplifier to respond.

32) What trouble in the amplifier in Figure 18–1(b) could cause the voltage between the inverting and non–inverting inputs to nearly equal 0 V?

    A) R_f is open.   B) R_i is open.

    C) The power is off.   D) There is no problem; 0 V is normal.

33) The input impedance of the amplifier in Figure 18–1(b) is _____.

    A) very low   B) very high.   C) about 10 kΩ

34) If $R_f = 5\ k\Omega$ and $R_i = 10\ k\Omega$ in Figure 18–1(c), the voltage gain equals _____.

    A) –5   B) 0   C) –0.5   D) –2

35) A CMRR of 35,000 equals a decibel CMRR of _____.

    A) 88 dB   B) 35000 dB   C) 91 dB   D) –91 dB

36) To build an amplifier with a 5 K Ω input impedance and a voltage gain of 40, use the _____ amplifier, $R_i =$ _____, $R_f =$ _____.

    A) non–inverting, 5 kΩ, 40 kΩ   B) inverting, 5 kΩ, 2 kΩ

    C) non–inverting, 40 kΩ, 200 kΩ   D) inverting, 5 kΩ, 200 kΩ

37) One characteristic of a noninverting amplifier is a _____.

    A) voltage gain of one

    B) very low input impedance

    C) high output impedance

    D) voltage gain slightly more than an inverting amplifier with the same values

38) Which one of these devices produces amplifiers with characteristics close to those of an ideal amplifier?

    A) JFET   B) MOSFET   C) Op–amp   D) BJT

39) A typical op–amp has _____ input impedance and _____ output impedance.

    A) high, high   B) low, high   C) low, low   D) high, low

40) If an op-amp's output increases 8 V every 12 μs in response to a step input voltage, the slew rate equals _____.

    A) 0.667 V/μs   B) 1.5 V/μs   C) 96 V/μs   D) 0.75 V/μs

41) If $R_i = 1$ kΩ, $R_f = 100$ kΩ and $V_{OUT} = 5$ V in a noninverting op-amp, V_{RI} equals _____.

    A) 50 mV   B) 49.5 mV   C) 495 mV   D) 500 mV

42) If $R_i = 1$ kΩ, $R_f = 100$ kΩ and $V_{OUT} = 5$ V in a noninverting op-amp, A_{CL} equals _____.

    A) 0.0099   B) 1   C) 99   D) 101

43) One characteristic of a voltage follower is its _____.

    A) large voltage gain   B) phase inversion

    C) high output impedance   D) non-inversion

44) If $R_i = 2.2$ kΩ, $R_f = 220$ kΩ and $A_{OL} = 25,000$ in an inverting op-amp, A_{CL} equals _____.

    A) –100   B) –0.01   C) 100   D) –250

45) Which of these amplifiers provides a high input resistance and a variable gain?

    A) voltage-follower amp

    B) open-loop amp

    C) inverting amp

    D) non-inverting amp with a potentiometer as R_f.

46) A CMRR of 90,000 equals a decibel CMRR of _____.

    A) 99 dB   B) 90,000 dB   C) 91 dB   D) –99 dB

47) To build an amplifier with a 10 K Ω input impedance and a voltage gain of 41, use the _____ amplifier, $R_i = $ _____, $R_f = $ _____.

    A) non-inverting, 10 kΩ, 410 kΩ   B) inverting, 10 kΩ, 410 kΩ

    C) non-inverting, 40 kΩ, 200 kΩ   D) inverting, 10 kΩ, 200 kΩ

48) To use an op-amp as a buffer, use the _____.

    A) inverting amplifier   B) non-inverting amplifier

    C) voltage follower amplifier   D) differential amplifier

49) Which one of these characteristics do an op-amp and a MOSFET have in common?

A) high current gain

B) high voltage gain

C) high CMRR

D) high input impedance

50) If an op-amp's output increases 6 V every 18 μs in response to a step input voltage, the slew rate equals _____.

A) 3 V/μs

B) 0.33 V/μs

C) 33 V/μs

D) 0.99 V/μs

51) A diff-amp with 1 input grounded and the signal voltage applied only to the other input is called:

A) grounded input.

B) single input.

C) single ended.

D) single output.

52) A diff-amp with two out-of-phase signal voltages applied to the two inputs is called:

A) phase inverter input.

B) phase inverter output.

C) differential input.

D) differential output.

53) A diff-amp with two identical signal voltage applied to the two inputs is called:

A) same phase input.

B) same signal input.

C) common mode input.

D) common mode output.

54) A practical differential amplifier provides:

A) very small common mode gain < 1.

B) very high differential voltage gain > 1000.

C) very high input impedance.

D) all of these.

55) A CMRR of 10,000 means that the op-amp provides that:

A) the differential input is amplified highly.

B) the common mode input is greatly reduced.

C) $Av_{(d)}/Acm = 10,000$.

D) all of these.

56) The principal operating characteristic of the voltage follower configuration is:

A) non-inverting output.

B) voltage gain of unity.

C) very high input impedance.

D) very low output impedance.

57) If you know an op-amp's open-loop gain only, you can determine the closed-loop gain of:

    A) an inverting op-amp.   B) an non-inverting op-amp.

    C) a voltage follower op-amp.   D) all of these.

58) The feedback attenuation of a voltage follower op-amp is:

    A) < 1.   B) > 1.   C) = 1.   D) R_f/R_i.

59) The op-amp configuration with the highest possible input impedance is:

    A) inverting op-amp.   B) non-inverting op-amp.

    C) differential op-amp.   D) voltage-follower op-amp.

1) TRUE
   Diff: 1
2) TRUE
   Diff: 1
3) FALSE
   Diff: 1
4) FALSE
   Diff: 1
5) TRUE
   Diff: 1
6) TRUE
   Diff: 1
7) FALSE
   Diff: 1
8) TRUE
   Diff: 1
9) TRUE
   Diff: 1
10) TRUE
   Diff: 1
11) B
   Diff: 1
12) D
   Diff: 1
13) D
   Diff: 2
14) D
   Diff: 1
15) B
   Diff: 1
16) A
   Diff: 2
17) A
   Diff: 1
18) B
   Diff: 2
19) B
   Diff: 2
20) B
   Diff: 3
21) C
   Diff: 1
22) C
   Diff: 1

23) C
   Diff: 2
24) C
   Diff: 2
25) C
   Diff: 1
26) B
   Diff: 2
27) A
   Diff: 2
28) D
   Diff: 2
29) B
   Diff: 2
30) A
   Diff: 2
31) B
   Diff: 3
32) D
   Diff: 3
33) B
   Diff: 1
34) C
   Diff: 2
35) C
   Diff: 2
36) D
   Diff: 2
37) D
   Diff: 1
38) C
   Diff: 1
39) D
   Diff: 1
40) A
   Diff: 2
41) B
   Diff: 2
42) D
   Diff: 2
43) D
   Diff: 1
44) A
   Diff: 2

45) D
   Diff: 1
46) A
   Diff: 2
47) B
   Diff: 2
48) C
   Diff: 1
49) D
   Diff: 1
50) B
   Diff: 2
51) C
   Diff: 2
52) C
   Diff: 2
53) C
   Diff: 2
54) D
   Diff: 1
55) D
   Diff: 1
56) B
   Diff: 1
57) C
   Diff: 1
58) C
   Diff: 1
59) D
   Diff: 1

Chapter 19 Basic Op–Amp Circuits

True or False

1) The terminals on a three-terminal regulator are input voltage, output voltage and ground.

2) A series-pass transistor is used in a voltage regulator.

3) A Wien-bridge oscillator produces an excellent quality square wave.

4) Butterworth filters are characterized by a linear response in the pass band.

5) Op-amp comparators are often used as zero-level detectors.

6) An op-amp comparator can be used to determine when an input voltage crosses a certain reference voltage.

7) An op-amp summing amplifier has no limitations on the number of inputs it can handle.

8) An op-amp integrator will produce a linear increasing output voltage for a constant negative input voltage until cutoff is reached.

9) Hartley, Colpitts, and Clapp oscillators can use op–amps.

10) A second-order Butterworth filter rolls-off at 40 dB/decade.

Multiple Choice

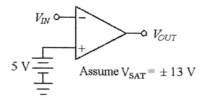

V_{IN}

V_{OUT}

5 V

Assume $V_{SAT} = \pm 13$ V

Figure 19-1

11) If V_{IN} equals 4 V in Figure 19-1, V_{OUT} equals _____.

   A) 1 V   B) –1 V   C) 13 V   D) –13 V

12) If V_{IN} equals 8 V in Figure 19-1, V_{OUT} equals _____.

   A) 1 V   B) –1 V   C) 13 V   D) –13 V

13) If $V_{IN} = -3$ V in Figure 19–1, V_{OUT} equals _____ .

    A) 1 V   B) –1 V   C) 13 V   D) –13 V

14) If $V_{IN} = 4.2$ V in Figure 19–1, V_{OUT} equals _____ .

    A) 0.8 V   B) –0.8 V   C) 13 V   D) –13 V

15) If $V_{IN} = 8.3$ V in Figure 19–1, V_{OUT} equals _____ .

    A) 3.3 V   B) –3.3 V   C) 13 V   D) –13 V

16) If $V_{IN} = -2$ V in Figure 19–1, V_{OUT} equals _____ .

    A) 3 V   B) –3 V   C) 13 V   D) –13 V

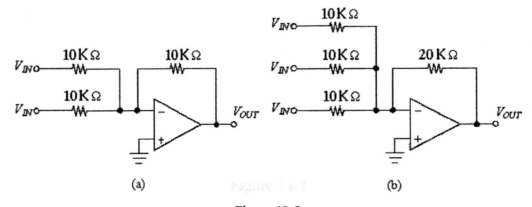

(a)   (b)

Figure 19–2

17) If the inputs are 8.4 V and 1.2 V in Figure 19–2(a), the output voltage equals _____ .

    A) 9.6 V   B) 10.08 V   C) –9.6 V   D) 7.2 V

18) If the inputs are 4.1 V, –0.7 V and 3.1 V in Figure 19–2(b), the output voltage equals _____ .

    A) –13 V   B) 13 V   C) 6.5 V   D) –6.5 V

19) What change causes the circuit in Figure 19–2(b) to output the average of the three input voltages?

    A) Change the feedback resistor to 10 kΩ.   B) Change the input resistors to 3.3 kΩ.

    C) Change to a different type of op–amp.   D) Change the feedback resistor to 3.3 kΩ.

20) If the inputs are –7.1 V and 12 V in Figure 19–2(a), what is the output voltage?

    A) –4.9 V   B) 4.9 V   C) 19.1 V   D) –19.1 V

21) If the two input voltages are 9.2 V and 0.7 V in Figure 19–2(a), what is the output voltage?

    A) 9.9 V   B) –9.9 V   C) 8.5 V   D) –8.5 V

22) If the inputs are 1.2 V, –0.5 V and 2.4 V in Figure 19–2(b), what is the output voltage?

    A) –6.2 V   B) 13 V   C) 6.2 V   D) –4.1 V

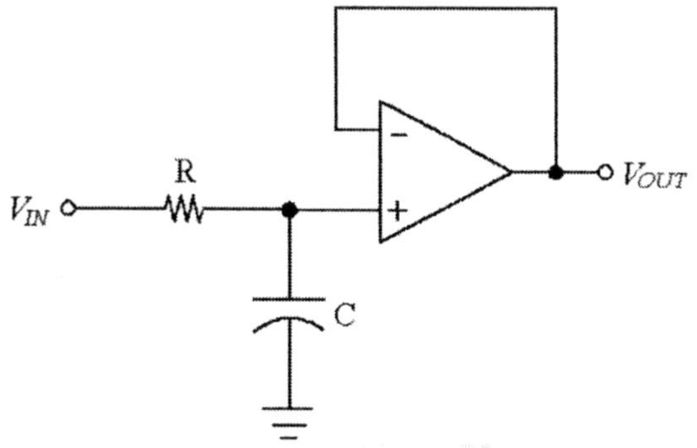

Figure 19–3

23) If $R = 47$ kΩ and $C = 0.02$ μF in Figure 19–3, f_{CO} equals _____.

    A) 169 Hz   B) 16.9 Hz   C) 51.9 Hz   D) 5.19 Hz

24) If V_{IN} equals 22 V in Figure 19–3, V_{OUT} at the f_{CO} equals _____.

    A) 31.1 V   B) 15.55 V   C) 7.79 V   D) 0

25) In Figure 19–3, what will change the circuit into a high–pass filter?

    A) increasing the value of the resistor

    B) decreasing the value of the capacitor

    C) placing the capacitor in the feedback loop

    D) switching the positions of the resistor and capacitor

26) If $R = 1.5$ kΩ and $C = 256$ pF in Figure 19–3, the F_{CO} equals _____.

    A) 41.5 kHz   B) 415 kHz   C) 257 Hz   D) 25.7 Hz

27) If $R = 22$ kΩ and $C = 0.05$ μF in Figure 19–3, f_{CO} equals _____.

    A) 1.45 kHz   B) 145 Hz   C) 4.8 Hz   D) 48 Hz

28) If $R = 56$ kΩ and $C = 0.05$ μF in Figure 19–3, f_{CO} equals _____.

    A) 57 Hz   B) 570 Mz   C) 3.0 Hz   D) 300 Hz

29) If V_{IN}= 70 Vp in Figure 19–3, the output voltage at f_{CO} equals _____.

A) 44.2 Vp   B) 49.5 Vp   C) 13 Vp   D) 0 Vp

30) If R = 1.2 kΩ and C = 0.005 μF in Figure 19–3, the f_{CO} equals _____.

A) 2.65 kHz   B) 26.5 kHz   C) 65 Hz   D) 650 Hz

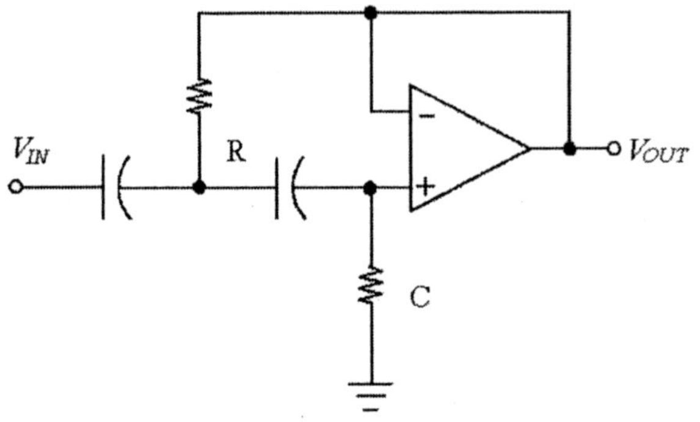

Figure 19–4

31) The prime characteristic of the filter in Figure 19–4 is _____.

A) it has the largest response of any filter type

B) it has a flat response curve in the pass band

C) it only works in a high–pass configuration

D) nothing special

32) If 22 V in the pass–band is input to the circuit in Figure 19–4, what is the output voltage at f_{CO}?

A) 15.5 V   B) 31.1 V   C) 7.75 V   D) 8.92 V

33) If 22 V in the pass–band is input to the circuit in Figure 19–4, what is the output voltage at a frequency that is 1 decade higher?

A) 15.5 V   B) 31.1 V   C) 7.75 V   D) 22 V

34) In Figure 19–4, if the frequency is decreased from the pass band to 1 decade below f_{CO}, the output voltage drops _____.

A) 3 dB   B) 6 dB   C) 20 dB   D) 43 dB

35) The circuit in Figure 19-4 is known as the _____ and it rolls off at a rate of _____.

   A) Butterworth high-pass filter, -40 dB/decade

   B) Butterworth low-pass filter, -40 dB/decade

   C) Butterworth high-pass filter, -20 dB/decade

   D) Butterworth low-pass filter, -20 dB/decade

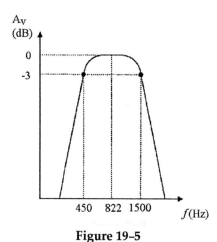

Figure 19-5

36) The frequency response curve in Figure 19-5 represents the output from the _____, and the bandwidth is _____.

   A) band-reject filter, 1050 kHz

   B) band-pass filter, 678 Hz

   C) band-pass filter, 1050 Hz

   D) two-pole high-pass filter, 1050 Hz

37) If V_{OUT} equals 12 V at 822 Hz in Figure 19-5, the output voltage equals _____ at 450 Hz.

   A) 8.484 V   B) 4.242 V   C) 2.121 V   D) 1.061 V

38) The curve in Figure 19-5 is from a _____ and its lower cutoff frequency equals _____.

   A) band-reject filter, 450 kHz

   B) band-pass filter, 822 Hz

   C) band-pass filter, 450 Hz

   D) two-pole high-pass filter, 1500 Hz

39) If the output voltage is 6 V at 1500 Hz in Figure 19-5, what is the output voltage at 822 Hz?

   A) 8.48 V   B) 4.24 V   C) 2.12 V   D) 1.06 V

40) If the output voltage is 27.4 V at 822 Hz in Figure 19-5, what is the output voltage at 1.5 kHz?

   A) 27.4 V   B) 19.37 V   C) 13.7 V   D) 6.85 V

41) A three-terminal voltage regulator _____.

    A) comes in a variety of voltage and current ratings

    B) is very durable

    C) is available in both positive and negative voltage ratings

    D) all of the above

42) A series–pass voltage regulator has _____.

    A) an error amplifier   B) a load

    C) a shunt regulator   D) all of these

43) Short-circuit or overload protection is an integral part of _____.

    A) most three-terminal regulators   B) most TRIACs

    C) most op-amps   D) most JFETs

44) If an inverting amplifier has a capacitor in the feedback loop, the circuit is known as the _____. When a square wave input is applied, the output is a _____ wave.

    A) differentiator, triangle   B) integrator, square

    C) integrator, triangle   D) open loop, triangle

45) The purpose of a comparator is to _____.

    A) amplify an input voltage

    B) detect the occurrence of a changing input voltage

    C) produce a change in output when an input voltage equals a reference voltage

    D) maintain a constant output when the dc input voltage changes

46) If all four input resistors to a summing amplifier are 2.2 kΩ, the feedback resistor is 2.2 kΩ and all four input voltages are –2 V, the output voltage equals _____.

    A) 2 V   B) 10 V   C) 2.2 V   D) 8 V

47) If all four input resistors to a summing amplifier are 2.2 kΩ and the feedback resistor is 2.2 kΩ, then the gain equals _____.

    A) 1   B) 2.2   C) 4   D) unknown

48) In a scaling adder, the _____.

   A) input resistors are all the same value

   B) input resistors are all different values

   C) input resistors have values depending on the assigned weight of each input

   D) ratio R_F/R_{IN} must be the same for each input

49) The input frequency of a single-pole, low-pass active filter increases from 1.5 kHz to 150 kHz. If the critical frequency is 1.5 kHz, the gain decreases by _____.

   A) 3 dB   B) 20 dB   C) 40 dB   D) 60 dB

50) The output of an op-amp differentiator depends on the values of _____ and _____.

   A) R_{IN}, C_F B) R_{IN}, R_F C) C_{IN}, C_F D) C_{IN}, R_F

51) In an inverting input op-amp integrator supplied with a square wave pulse or a step, the output is a:

   A) sine wave.   B) opposite phase square wave.

   C) same phase ramp.   D) opposite phase ramp.

52) In an inverting input op-amp, differentiator supplied with a ramp or triangular wave, the output is a:

   A) sine wave.   B) same phase square wave.

   C) opposite phase square wave.   D) opposite phase ramp.

53) In a Wein-bridge op-amp oscillator, the output is a repetitive:

   A) sine wave.   B) square wave.

   C) triangular wave.   D) all of these.

54) Using op-amps in a triangular wave oscillator results in a:

   A) square wave output.   B) triangular wave output.

   C) function generator output.   D) all of these.

55) In a voltage-controlled oscillator (VCO), the output signal frequency is dependent on:

   A) the value of a resistor.

   B) the value of a capacitor.

   C) the value of a resistor-capacitor combination.

   D) the value of an applied voltage.

56) The basic op-amp square oscillator is actually a:

    A) Wein-bridge oscillator.

    B) sine wave oscillator.

    C) resistor-capacitor (RC) time constant oscillator.

    D) all of these.

57) In a filter circuit, the terminology single pole means:

    A) one fixed contact.   B) one movable contact.

    C) one single RC circuit.   D) two cascaded RC circuits.

58) Each pole in a filter circuit causes the output voltage to roll off or drop at a rate of:

    A) 3 dB per decade or octave.   B) 6dB per decade or octave.

    C) 10 dB per decade or octave.   D) 20 dB per decade or octave.

59) At the cutoff frequency of a filter circuit, the output voltage is:

    A) – 3 dB.   B) – 10 dB.   C) = 20 dB.   D) – 40 dB.

60) In a series voltage regulator, the four circuit blocks are:

    A) control element, reference voltage, error detector, current limiter.

    B) control element, reference voltage, error detector, sampling circuit.

    C) reference voltage, series load, reference voltage, current limiter.

    D) error detector, reference voltage, series regulator, sampling circuit.

61) A series and a shunt regulator are differentiated by the circuit placement of a:

    A) series resistor versus parallel resistor.

    B) series transistor versus parallel transistor.

    C) series reference voltage versus parallel reference voltage.

    D) none of these.

1) TRUE	23) D	45) C
Diff: 1	Diff: 2	Diff: 1
2) TRUE	24) B	46) D
Diff: 1	Diff: 2	Diff: 2
3) FALSE	25) D	47) A
Diff: 1	Diff: 3	Diff: 2
4) TRUE	26) C	48) C
Diff: 1	Diff: 2	Diff: 1
5) TRUE	27) C	49) C
Diff: 1	Diff: 2	Diff: 2
6) TRUE	28) C	50) D
Diff: 1	Diff: 2	Diff: 1
7) TRUE	29) B	51) D
Diff: 1	Diff: 2	Diff: 1
8) FALSE	30) C	52) C
Diff: 1	Diff: 2	Diff: 1
9) TRUE	31) B	53) A
Diff: 1	Diff: 1	Diff: 1
10) TRUE	32) A	54) D
Diff: 1	Diff: 2	Diff: 1
11) C	33) D	55) D
Diff: 2	Diff: 2	Diff: 1
12) D	34) D	56) C
Diff: 2	Diff: 2	Diff: 1
13) C	35) A	57) C
Diff: 2	Diff: 1	Diff: 1
14) C	36) C	58) C
Diff: 2	Diff: 2	Diff: 1
15) D	37) A	59) A
Diff: 2	Diff: 2	Diff: 1
16) C	38) C	60) B
Diff: 2	Diff: 2	Diff: 1
17) C	39) A	61) C
Diff: 2	Diff: 2	Diff: 1
18) A	40) B	
Diff: 2	Diff: 2	
19) D	41) D	
Diff: 2	Diff: 1	
20) A	42) A	
Diff: 2	Diff: 1	
21) B	43) A	
Diff: 2	Diff: 1	
22) A	44) C	
Diff: 2	Diff: 1	

Chapter 20 Special-Purpose Op-Amp Circuits

True or False

1) A basic instrumentation amplifier has three op-amps.

2) One of the key characteristics of an instrumentation amplifier is its low input impedance.

3) The voltage gain of an instrumentation amplifier is set with an external resistor.

4) A basic isolation amplifier has two electrically isolated sections.

5) Most isolation amplifiers use transformer coupling for isolation.

6) OTA stands for operational transistor amplifier.

7) A voltage-to-current converter has a JFET in the feedback loop.

8) The diode clamper circuit output is an ac signal that has a dc reference point of the peak voltage of the ac.

9) The main purpose of an instrumentation amplifier is to amplify common mode voltage.

10) The OTA is a voltage-to-current amplifier.

11) An active clamping circuit negates the opposite polarity 0.7 V peak by using two diodes in series.

12) A voltage limiter that limits both positive and negative peaks uses two zener diodes connected anode to cathode.

13) Active limiting and clamping employs an amplifier circuit.

14) A peak detector's output continually changes based on the input.

15) A voltage-to-current converter works by controlling current proportional to the input voltage.

Multiple Choice

16) The OTA has a _____ input impedance and a _____ CMRR.

    A) high, low   B) low, high   C) high, high   D) low, low

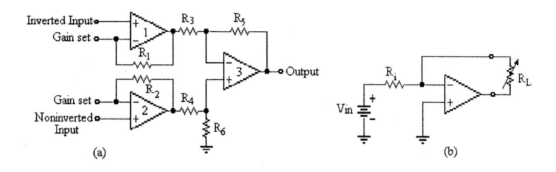

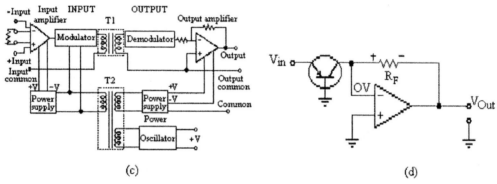

Figure 20–1

17) Refer to Figure 20–1. Which of these circuits is known as an antilog amplifier?

    A) (a)   B) (b)   C) (c)   D) (d)

18) Refer to Figure 20–1. Which of these circuits is known as a constant–current source?

    A) (a)   B) (b)   C) (c)   D) (d)

19) Refer to Figure 20–1. Which of these circuits is known as an isolation amplifier?

    A) (a)   B) (b)   C) (c)   D) (d)

20) Refer to Figure 20–1. Which of these circuits is known as an instrumentation amplifier?

    A) (a)   B) (b)   C) (c)   D) (d)

21) Refer to Figure 20-1 (a). If $R_1 = R_2 = 30\ k\Omega$ and the closed loop gain is 450, the value of the external gain–setting resistor R_G is:

A) 133.64 kΩ. B) 133.64 Ω.

C) 13.364 Ω. D) none of the above.

22) Refer to Figure 20-1 (a). If $R_1 = R_2 = 28\ k\Omega$ and $R_G = 100\Omega$, the A_{cl} would be:

A) 5.51 B) 55.1 C) 551 D) 550

23) Refer to Figure 20-1 (b). If $V_{in} = 5$ V and $R_{in} = 22\ k\Omega$, the current thru the load R_L would be:

A) 227.27 mA. B) 227 μA. C) 22.72 mA. D) 227.27 μA.

24) Refer to Figure 20-1 (d). If $V_{in} = 200$ mV, $R_F = 52$ k, and $I_{EBO} = 50$ nA, the V_{out} would be:

A) 77.5 V. B) 7.75 mV. C) 7.75 V. D) 775 mV.

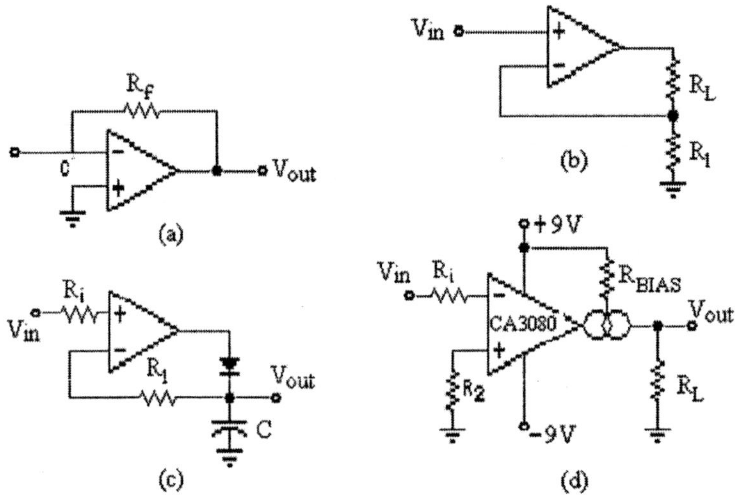

Figure 20-2

25) Refer to Figure 20-2. Which of these circuits is known as a voltage–to–current converter?

A) (a) B) (b) C) (c) D) (d)

26) Refer to Figure 20-2. Which of these circuits is known as a current–to–voltage converter?

A) (a) B) (b) C) (c) D) (d)

27) Refer to Figure 20-2. Which of these circuits contains an OTA?

A) (a) B) (b) C) (c) D) (d)

28) Refer to Figure 20-2. Which of these circuits is known as a peak detector?

A) (a)   B) (b)   C) (c)   D) (d)

29) Refer to Figure 20-2 (b). If $R_L = 20$ k, $R_1 = 1.2$ k, and $V_{in} = 2.5$ V, the load current I_L would be:

A) 20.83 mA.   B) 2.083 mA.   C) 2.083 A.   D) 208.3 A.

30) Refer to Figure 20-2 (d). If $g_m = 25$ mS and $R_L = 25$ kΩ, the voltage gain would be:

A) 625

B) 62.5

C) 6.25

D) not enough information.

31) The input signal for an instrumentation amplifier usually comes from:

A) an inverting amplifier.

B) a transducer.

C) a differential amplifier.

D) a wheatstone bridge.

32) In the classic three op-amp instrumentation amplifier, the differential voltage gain is usually produced by the:

A) first stage.

B) second stage.

C) mismatched resistors.

D) output op amp.

33) An instrumentation amplifier has a high:

A) output impedance.

B) power gain.

C) CMRR.

D) supply voltage.

34) An input transducer converts:

A) voltage to current.

B) current to voltage.

C) an electrical quantity to a nonelectrical quantity.

D) a nonelectrical quantity to an electrical quantity.

35) In some respects an isolation amplifier is nothing more than an elaborate:

A) op amp.

B) instrumentation amplifier.

C) rectifier and filter.

D) both A and B

36) The primary function of the oscillator in an isolation amplifier is to:

A) convert dc to high frequency ac.

B) convert dc to low frequency ac.

C) rectify high frequency ac to dc.

D) produce dual polarity dc voltages for the input to the demodulator.

37) The voltage gain of an OTA can be calculated using the formula:

A) $A_V = R_f/R_i$

B) $A_V = g_m R_L$

C) $A_V = (R_f/R_i) + 1$

D) $A_V = 2 R_f/R_i$

38) If an operational transconductance amplifier (OTA) is used as a nonlinear mixer and an audio signal is mixed with an RF signal, the output will be a(n) _____ signal.

A) square wave

B) triangular wave

C) frequency modulated (FM)

D) amplitude modulated (AM)

39) When using an OTA in a Schmitt-trigger configuration, the trigger points are controlled by:

A) the I_{OUT}.   B) the I_{BIAS}.   C) the V_{OUT}.   D) both A and B.

40) An active limiter includes an op-amp which:

A) allows a reference level to be set.

B) increases the output voltage.

C) keeps the circuit from oscillating.

D) works better under loaded conditions.

41) Two zener diodes are used in a limiter circuit to:

A) better regulate a power supply.

B) reduce interelectrode capacitance at high frequencies.

C) limit both positive and negative peaks.

D) none of the above

42) A voltage-to-current converter is used in applications where it's necessary to have an output loadcurrent that is controlled by _____.

A) input voltage

B) input resistance

C) output resistance

D) input frequency

43) The output of a peak detector is always:

A) 70.7% of input.

B) equal to the max value of the peak level received since the last reset pulse.

C) equal to the min value of the peak level received since the last reset pulse.

D) none of the above.

44) An instrumentation amp with one open input:

A) may work correctly in a low noise environment.

B) will not work at all.

C) will allow common–mode noise to be present on the output.

D) both A and C

45) How many op–amps does the basic instrumentation amplifier consist of?

A) 2   B) 3   C) 4   D) 5

46) Which statement best describes the action of an OTA amplitude modulator?

A) The power supply bias adjusts the output level.

B) The variations of voltages applied to the current bias input adjusts the gain of the amplifier.

C) Variations of light intensity adjust the gain of the amplifier.

D) The OTA is versatile and can be configured to work in any of these ways.

47) Which op–amp circuit would be useful to switch to an "on" condition at a specified voltage?

A) instrumentation amp

B) operational transconductance amplifier configured as a Schmitt–trigger

C) isolation amplifier

D) voltage–to–current converter

48) Which statement best differentiates between limiter and clamper circuits?

A) A limiter limits the both peaks of the output of a given signal, while the clamper limits only one.

B) A limiter sets a dc reference voltage that the ac signal varies upon while the clamper limits the peak output.

C) A limiter sets the limit of the peak output of a given signal while the clamper establishes a dc reference level based on the peak output of the signal that the ac signal will vary from.

D) none of the above

1) TRUE
   Diff: 1
2) FALSE
   Diff: 1
3) TRUE
   Diff: 1
4) FALSE
   Diff: 1
5) TRUE
   Diff: 1
6) FALSE
   Diff: 1
7) FALSE
   Diff: 1
8) TRUE
   Diff: 1
9) FALSE
   Diff: 1
10) TRUE
    Diff: 1
11) FALSE
    Diff: 1
12) FALSE
    Diff: 1
13) TRUE
    Diff: 1
14) FALSE
    Diff: 1
15) TRUE
    Diff: 1
16) C
    Diff: 1
17) D
    Diff: 1
18) B
    Diff: 1
19) C
    Diff: 1
20) A
    Diff: 1
21) B
    Diff: 2
22) C
    Diff: 2

23) D
    Diff: 2
24) C
    Diff: 2
25) B
    Diff: 1
26) A
    Diff: 1
27) D
    Diff: 1
28) C
    Diff: 1
29) B
    Diff: 2
30) A
    Diff: 2
31) D
    Diff: 1
32) A
    Diff: 1
33) C
    Diff: 1
34) D
    Diff: 1
35) D
    Diff: 1
36) A
    Diff: 1
37) B
    Diff: 2
38) D
    Diff: 1
39) D
    Diff: 1
40) A
    Diff: 2
41) C
    Diff: 2
42) A
    Diff: 1
43) B
    Diff: 1
44) C
    Diff: 1

45) B
    Diff: 1
46) B
    Diff: 2
47) B
    Diff: 2
48) C
    Diff: 3

Chapter 21 Measurements, Conversion, and Control

True or False

1) The typical output for a normally operating thermocouple is in the range of 1 V to 10 V.

2) RTDs and Thermistors both operate on the same principle of resistive change with temperature

3) Strain gauges are used to detect minute changes in temperature.

4) Pressure sensors make use of an RTD for their operation.

5) Displacement transducers can be made using a variety of types of optical or electrical circuits.

6) The aperture time for a sample–and–hold circuit refers to the change in the voltage from the sampled value during the hold interval time.

7) Analog–to–Digital conversion takes a specific analog quantity and produces a unique binary number to represent that quantity.

8) A SCR is used mainly in the control of AC circuits.

9) A triac must be triggered for each alternation for proper operation.

10) Conversion of analog signals to digital signals is common in most controlled industrial processes.

Multiple Choice

11) Basic analog physical parameters such as angular position, temperature, pressure, strain, and flow rate can be measured by what devices?

    A) transmitters   B) transmissions   C) telemeters   D) transducers

12) The ac value that is equal to the same dc heating effect is usually called:

    A) average value.   B) peak value.   C) heat value.   D) rms value.

13) In order to find the square of voltage values:

   A) use a voltage follower.

   B) use an op amp with a linear multiplier in the feedback loop.

   C) use a linear multiplier with two inputs tied together.

   D) Any of the above will yield the same result.

14) Using a low-pass filter (single-pole) on the input of a voltage follower makes it a voltage-averager. Why?

   A) The first time constant of the capacitor is about 62%, or average value of the input.

   B) The RC filter is designed to do the mathematical averaging.

   C) The RC filter will pass only the dc component (average value).

   D) none of the above

15) In order to keep the output amplitude constant, rms-to-dc converters are used as what kind of circuit?

   A) PLL   B) positive feedback

   C) synthesizer   D) automatic gain control

16) Which of the following is not an internal function performed by an rms-to-dc convertor?

   A) squaring circuit   B) averaging circuit

   C) square root circuit   D) divide-by-two circuit

17) The type of transducer that is used for shaft angle measurement is a:

   A) tachometer.   B) anemometer.   C) digitizer.   D) synchro.

18) The primary difference between resolvers and synchros is:

   A) the angle between the stator windings.   B) the angle between the rotor windings.

   C) the induced voltage in the stator.   D) none of the above.

19) In order to convert analog signals into digital signals from the syncros and resolvers, the voltage must be formatted. What accomplishes this?

   A) resolver formatter   B) synchro formatter

   C) scott-t transformer   D) none of the above

20) How does a binary word represent angular position?

    A) each bit position is weighted as an angular measurement in degree

    B) one word divides 180 degrees into 26000 intervals

    C) binary is converted to a radian measure in octal

    D) any of the above

21) Which of the following is not a temperature sensor?

    A) triac   B) thermocouple

    C) thermistor   D) resistance temperature detector

22) What device is formed by adjoining two dissimilar metals?

    A) sequencer   B) pop–sensor

    C) thermocouple   D) none of the above

23) A cold–junction:

    A) opposes measured temperature.

    B) its value depends on ambient temperature.

    C) can have an unpredictable effect on the thermocouple effect.

    D) all of the above.

24) One method of providing an accurate thermocouple interface is:

    A) to use a reference thermocouple.

    B) to use a reference voltage in the feedback circuit.

    C) to use a swamping resistor.

    D) capacitive coupling.

25) Circuits that contain features such as common–mode rejection, isolation, gain, etc. are called:

    A) thermocouples.   B) interfaces.

    C) signal conditioners.   D) none of the above.

26) What device has the same function as a thermocouple but has a more linear output?

    A) capactive temperature detector   B) analog temperature device

    C) linear temperature device   D) resistance temperature detectors

27) What affects the accurate operation of a resistance bridge measuring temperature?

      A) length of wires going to the detector   B) ambient temperature

      C) input voltage   D) all of the above

28) Which of the following devices changes resistance inversely with the temperature?

      A) RTD   B) thermistor   C) thermocouple   D) triac

29) Which of the following is not a force-related parameter?

      A) strain   B) pressure   C) motion   D) velocity

30) The deformation of a material due to force acting on it is called:

      A) stress.   B) strain.   C) pressure.   D) compression.

31) A device that exhibits a change in resistance based on a change in pressure is called a:

      A) pressure transducer.   B) gauge transducer.

      C) psi gauge.   D) none of the above.

32) One common method of measuring flow rate of a fluid through a pipe is the:

      A) wein-bridge method.   B) twin-t method.

      C) differential pressure method.   D) hall effect.

33) What quantity indicates change in positions of a body or point?

      A) relative velocity   B) motion coefficient

      C) displacement   D) FIFO

34) The quantity usually measured using a spring-supported seismic mass is:

      A) acceleration.   B) velocity.   C) weight.   D) volume.

35) The device often used as an electronic switch in many applications is the:

      A) SCR.   B) diode.   C) SPDT.   D) SPST.

36) Which of the following components is not used as a temperature measurement device?

      A) triac

      B) thermocouple

      C) RTD

      D) All are used to measure temperature changes.

37) Displacement transducers make use of which of the following?

    A) magnetism   B) light

    C) capacitance   D) any of the above

38) Voltage storage in a sample and hold amplifier is accomplished by:

    A) the output buffer op-amp.   B) a JFET switch

    C) a holding capacitor.   D) a holding inductor.

39) Which of the following ADC circuits has the highest resolution?

    A) 4 bit   B) 16 bit

    C) one that has the highest aperture time   D) none of the above

40) Since the triac can be triggered to allow current to flow both directions, it can be used in:

    A) ac circuits.   B) dc circuits.

    C) phase control.   D) any of the above.

41) Sample and hold circuits:

    A) increase resolution.

    B) reduce quantization error.

    C) convert analog voltages to a binary number.

    D) all of the above.

42) Precise control of a triac to prevent high-frequency transients is called:

    A) pulse switch triggering.   B) microcontroller pulsing.

    C) negative feedback biasing.   D) zero-voltage switching.

1) FALSE
   Diff: 1
2) TRUE
   Diff: 1
3) FALSE
   Diff: 1
4) FALSE
   Diff: 1
5) TRUE
   Diff: 1
6) FALSE
   Diff: 1
7) TRUE
   Diff: 1
8) FALSE
   Diff: 1
9) TRUE
   Diff: 1
10) TRUE
    Diff: 1
11) A
    Diff: 1
12) D
    Diff: 1
13) C
    Diff: 2
14) C
    Diff: 2
15) D
    Diff: 1
16) D
    Diff: 1
17) D
    Diff: 1
18) A
    Diff: 1
19) C
    Diff: 2
20) A
    Diff: 2
21) A
    Diff: 1
22) C
    Diff: 1

23) D
    Diff: 1
24) A
    Diff: 1
25) C
    Diff: 1
26) D
    Diff: 2
27) A
    Diff: 1
28) B
    Diff: 1
29) D
    Diff: 1
30) B
    Diff: 1
31) A
    Diff: 1
32) C
    Diff: 1
33) C
    Diff: 2
34) A
    Diff: 1
35) A
    Diff: 1
36) A
    Diff: 2
37) D
    Diff: 2
38) C
    Diff: 1
39) B
    Diff: 2
40) D
    Diff: 1
41) D
    Diff: 1
42) D
    Diff: 1

PART SIX

Laboratory Solutions for

Experiments in Electronics Fundamentals and Electric Circuits Fundamentals

Seventh Edition

David Buchla

Table of Contents

Note: Answers for Application Assignments are found in Part Two of this manual.

Checkup 1

1. d
2. b
3. a
4. a
5. c
6. c
7. d
8. a
9. b
10. c

11. A VOM can measure voltage, resistance, and current.

12. Primary divisions are the major subdivisions of a meter scale, are indicated by larger marks and are usually numbered. Secondary divisions are subdivisions of primary marks and are typically unnumbered.

13. a) ohms   b) farads
    c) hertz   d) henries
    e) volts   f) joules

14. a) Ω b) F
    c) W   d) Hz
    e) C   f) A

15. a) 1.05×10^3 b) 5.75×10^{-2}
    c) 2.51×10^4 d) 8.90×10^{-4}
    e) 4.91×10^{-6} f) 1.35×10^{-4}

16. a) 5.20×10^3 b) 59.2×10^3
    c) 76.0×10^6 d) 1.90×10^{-3}
    e) 0.122×10^3 f) 5.09×10^{-12}

17. a) 1.24 μA   b) 7.5 kΩ
    c) 47 kHz   d) 33 nF
    e) 2.2 ps   f) 95 mH

18. a) 0.000 070 amps   b) 50 000 000 Hz
    c) 0.000 000 010 farads   d) 5000 milliwatts
    e) 0.022 volts   f) 0.0033 microfarads

19. a) 10.2×10^3 or 1.02×10^4 b) 91.9×10^3 or 9.19×10^4
    c) 32.5×10^{-3} or 3.25×10^{-2} d) 4.83×10^{-6}
    e) 291×10^{-6} or 2.91×10^{-4} f) 57.3×10^6 or 5.73×10^7

20. The independent variable.

21. The divisions are spaced equally and values assigned increase (to the right) by a fixed amount.

1.   c
2.   b
3.   b
4.   a
5.   c
6.   d
7.   b
8.   a
9.   a
10.   b

11.   To assure that the correct values were used and to have a record of the circuit "as built"

12.   Minimum value = 5.32 kΩ, maximum value = 5.88 kΩ

13.   A positive value of V_{AB} means that point A in the circuit is more positive than point B; the location of ground does not alter this fact.

14.   a)   9.1 kΩ +/−10%
      b)   5.6 MΩ +/−5%
      c)   10 Ω +/−5%
      d)   47 kΩ +/−10%
      e)   5.1 Ω +/−5%

15.   a)   yellow - violet - yellow - silver
      b)   brown - gray - brown - gold
      c)   yellow - orange - red - gold
      d)   brown - black - gold - sliver
      e)   red - violet - green - gold

16.   The terms "positive" and "negative" are relative terms when used with voltages as voltage is measured with respect to some reference point. By selecting a reference point that is higher than some voltage and lower than others, both positive and negative voltages can be measured. Similarly, if a voltage is positive when measured from A to B, then it must be negative when measured from B to A.

17.   a)   +22.6 V
      b)   −22.6 V
      c)   +18.9 V
      d)   −18.9 V
      e)   −3.7 V
      f)   +3.7 V

18.   Voltage

1. c
2. e
3. d
4. a
5. a
6. d
7. d
8. d
9. a
10. c

11. 5 V

12. a) The peak would shift to the left and have a higher maximum value. The maximum occurs when the variable resistance is equal to the fixed resistance.

    b) The graph would ideally be a hyperbola, with power approaching infinity for $R=0$ and approaching zero as R approached infinity. Note that the power still is maximum when the variable resistance is equal to the fixed resistance (namely zero).

13. a) 200 mA   b)   4 W

14. It must be in series. The positive terminal must be connected to the more positive point in the circuit.

15. a) 833 mA

    b) 2.5 W (assuming the same resistance)

1.   d
2.   b
3.   a
4.   d
5.   a
6.   b
7.   b
8.   b
9.   a
10.   c

11.   1.97 MΩ

12.   The battery connections are shown in C-4-1.

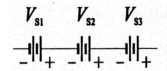

Figure C-4-1

13.   Place the leads of a voltmeter across the power supply. Then move the positive probe through the circuit, one component at a time, toward the ground probe and note when the meter reading drops to zero. The open is between the point where full voltage is read and the zero reading.

14.   a)   10.6 V
        b)   70.7 mA

15.   4.5%

16.   a)   26 Ω
        b)   8 Ω

17.   If all resistors were 20% larger, the current in the circuit would be reduced but the resistance ratios and voltage drops would have been the same.

1.   a
2.   d
3.   d
4.   a
5.   c
6.   a
7.   b
8.   d
9.   d
10.   b

11.   The total circuit conductance is increased because the addition of more resistors provided more current paths.

12.   In parallel circuits, the addition of branches does not affect the voltage drop or current in any other branch. If household wiring were done in series, a failure or an open in any path would affect all other loads in the circuit.

13.   a)   7 A
      b)   16.43 Ω
      c)   3.83 Ω

14. $I_{R1} = 208$ μA
      $I_{R2} = 142$ μA

15.   a)   50 mW
      b)   7.07 V

16. R_2 is most likely open. From Ohm's law the branch currents should be:
         $I_{R1} = 1.2$ mA, $I_{R2} = 800$ μA, and $I_{R3} = 545$ μA.
      The total current should be 2.55 mA. Since 800 μA is missing from the total, it is likely that the branch containing R_2 is open.

Checkup 6

1.   c
2.   b
3.   d
4.   a
5.   c
6.   a
7.   c
8.   c
9.   a
10.   d

11. $V_L = 1.89$ V
       $I_L = 126$ μA

12.   302 Ω

13.   Although the two methods are not fully independent, they serve as a check that computed answers are reasonable and illustrate that there is often more than one way to solve a problem.

14.   The replacement of a source with a jumper is only valid for sources that have very low internal resistance such as a power supply or battery.

15.   No. There are no series or parallel combinations in a loaded Wheatstone bridge; therefore, the methods of Experiment 10 cannot be applied to solving the circuit.

Checkup 7

1.   d
2.   d
3.   a
4.   b
5.   c
6.   b
7.   b
8.   a
9.   c
10.   a

11.   The connection to form a latching relay is shown in Figure C-7-1. One of the unused, normally-open contacts is wired in parallel with the switch as shown.

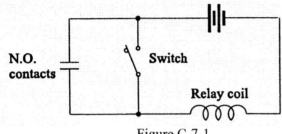

Figure C-7-1

12.   The release voltage of a relay is less than the pull-in voltage because of hysteresis. In the case of a relay, the current (and thus the voltage) required to produce a magnetic field strong enough to energize the relay is greater than that needed to maintain the field.

13.   a) $\left.\begin{array}{l} B_1 = 100\ \text{At} \\ B_2 = 100\ \text{At} \end{array}\right\}$ The field strengths (NI) of both coils are identical.

          b)   The flux intensities are the same if the lengths are the same.

14.   Faraday's law states that a changing magnetic field will induce a voltage across a coil. In a dc generator, a spinning magnet and fixed coil (sometimes a spinning coil and fixed magnet) are used to produce a changing magnetic flux through the coil that produces the observed voltage.

15.   a) $50 \times 10^{-3}\ \text{Wb/m}^2$
          b) $5 \times 10^{-6}\ \text{Wb}$

Checkup 8

1. a
2. b
3. a
4. a
5. b
6. a
7. c
8. c
9. d
10. b

11. a)   325 V_{pp}
    b)   16.7 ms

12. 8000

13. a)   40 V_p
    b)   35° (lagging)

14. The phasor drawing is shown in Figure C-8-1.

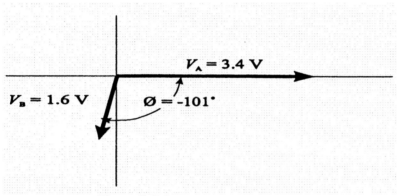

Figure C-8-1

15. The frequency is approximately 326 MHz.

16. a)   5.8 ns
    b)   approximately 9.9 ns (a 24% error)

17. A ×10 probe is normally provided with general purpose oscilloscopes because it provides a high impedance connection to the scope (less loading effect) and extends the frequency response (and rise time) of the scope over a ×1 probe.

Checkup 9

1. a
2. c
3. b
4. d
5. d
6. c
7. a
8. b
9. b
10. d

11. a) $0.032 \ \mu F$

    b) about $760 \ \mu s$

12. Connect an ohmmeter across the capacitor's terminals using a high resistance scale. If the capacitor can store and hold a charge, the resistance should increase as the capacitor charges toward a very high reading. When performing this test, the polarity of the meter should be observed.

13. The capacitive reactance is greater than $1.0 \ k\Omega$ (value of R_1).

14. Approximately $0.022 \ \mu F$

15. 220 pF, which is $0.00022 \ \mu F$

Checkup 10

1. b
2. d
3. a
4. a
5. a
6. a
7. b
8. c
9. a
10. a

11. In a series circuit, the current is common to all components, so it is logical to use it as the reference (although the generator voltage is sometimes preferred). In a parallel circuit, the generator voltage is common to all components; therefore, it is the logical choice as a reference.

12. a)   339 Hz
    b)   707 μA
    c)   7.07 V

13. The phasor diagram is shown in Figure C-10-1.

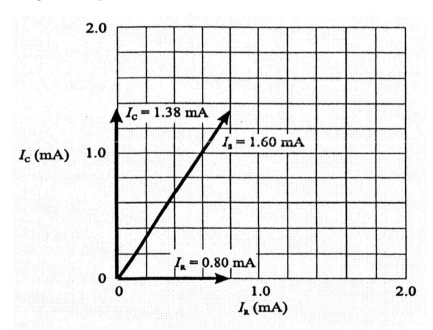

Figure C-10-1

14. No. The magnitude of the 1.0 kΩ resistors in relation to the impedance of the original circuit is large enough to seriously affect circuit measurements. The phase angle of the capacitive branch would change from −90° to −87.4° and the total impedance would change from 10.8 kΩ to 12.1 kΩ.

Checkup 11

1. b
2. d
3. a
4. d
5. a
6. d
7. a
8. c
9. c
10. c

11. Four factors affecting coil inductance are

    a) number of turns
    b) core material
    c) cross-sectional area
    d) coil length

12. A smaller inductor will work but stores less energy and will have a smaller time constant. The larger inductor is easier to observe.

13. In the *RC* circuit, source current leads source voltage, whereas in the *RL* circuit, source voltage leads source current. This is true for both series or parallel circuits.

14. a)   550 μH   b)   3.89 V

15. To observe the exponential response of the circuit, it is necessary to have a period of 10 time constants (five for the rise; five for the fall). The predicted time constant was 212 μs, so a period of 2.12 ms is the shortest period that should be selected. This puts an upper limit of about 471 Hz for the circuit with the component values given. The frequency could be increased slightly above the 300 Hz called for in the experiment.

16. $X_L = 19.0$ kΩ $L_1 = 30.3$ mH

Checkup 12

1. d
2. a
3. c
4. c
5. c
6. c
7. b
8. c
9. d
10. b

11. By making both signals appear to have the same amplitude, the phase shift can be measured along any horizontal line on the scope with minimal error. If this is not done, the only place that the phase shift can be measured accurately is in the exact center of both signals.

12. The generator supplies the total current to the circuit; the generator voltage is common to all components and is in phase with the current in the resistor. Therefore, the phase angle between the total current and the resistor current is the same as the phase angle between the generator current and generator voltage.

13. a) −63.4°
    b) The phasor diagram is shown in Figure C-12-1.

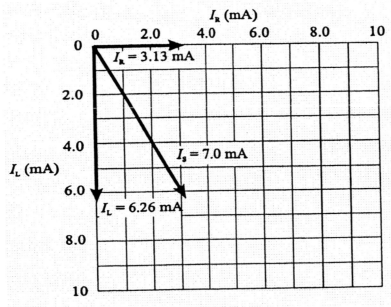

Figure C-12-1

14. a) 222 ∠ 12.9° Ω
    b) 45.1 ∠ 12.9° mA
    c) 3.38 V
    d) 28.6°

Checkup 13

1. a
2. c
3. a
4. c
5. c
6. c
7. a
8. b
9. a
10. b

11. a) 1.125 MHz
    b) 20 Ω
    c) 35.4

12. The parallel resistance will lower the Thevenin resistance of the generator, thus raising the Q of the circuit.

13. a) $C_{MIN} = 49.2$ pF, $C_{MAX} = 442.5$ pF
    b) At 535 kHz, $Q_L = 67.2$ At 1605 kHz, $Q_L = 201.6$
    c) At 535 kHz, $BW = 7.96$ kHz   At 1605 kHz, $BW = 7.96$ kHz

14. a) 550 Ω
    b) 22

Checkup 14

1. b
2. c
3. d
4. c
5. a
6. c
7. c
8. b
9. c
10. b

11. A power transformer is designed to operate at a specific frequency and can be optimized for this frequency. An impedance matching transformer must operate over a wide range of frequencies, and is therefore not as efficient.

12. a) 93%
    b) 164 mA
    c) 0.255

13. A tapped transformer has a continuous winding with multiple connections that provide a variety of turns ratios. A multiple winding transformer has two or more windings. With multiple windings, the leads from each winding are electrically isolated, whereas in a tapped transformer, electrical isolation is not provided by the common winding.

14. An isolation transformer is a special power transformer with a 1:1 ratio. It electrically isolates the ground in two different circuits and permits "floating" measurements to be made.

15. The fuse will need to carry up to 105 mA. A fuse with a slightly higher rating should be used. A 1/8 amp fuse is a good choice.

16. a) $P_L = 238$ mW
    b) $n = 0.4$

Checkup 15

1. c
2. c
3. c
4. a
5. b
6. d
7. d
8. a
9. a
10. d

11. Connect the inductor and a known resistor, R, in series with the square wave generator and measure the time constant. Find L from the formula $L = R\tau$ (where τ is the time constant).

12. a) The original time constant is 100 μs. To lengthen the time constant to 330 μs, the easiest change is to either increase R or increase C by a factor of 3.3. If R is selected, the value is 33 kΩ instead of 10 kΩ. If C is selected, the new value is 0.033 μF.

    b) For the required time constant, $L = 3.3$ H. See Figure C-15-1.

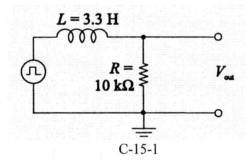

C-15-1

13. a) 56.4 μs
    b) 1.77 kHz
    c) See Figure C-15-2.

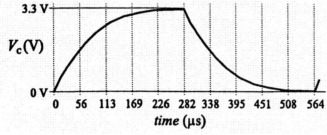

Figure C-15-2

471

1. d
2. d
3. a
4. a
5. a
6. c
7. c
8. c
9. b
10. c

11. Different ranges of an ohmmeter provide different current to the device whose resistance is being measured. Since the forward resistance of a diode varies as the amount of current changes, the resistance will depend on the range selected.

12. a) diode is shorted
    b) diode is open
    c) no fault
    d) power supply may be off or resistor is open

13. a) If all diodes are good, the ripple frequency from the bridge is twice the input ripple frequency. If any diode is open, the output ripple frequency will be the same as the input ripple frequency.

    b) The open diode will have the full ac secondary voltage across it.

14. a) 16.4 V (assuming 0.7 V diode drops)
    b) 3.5 mA

Checkup 17

1.   a
2.   a
3.   d
4.   b
5.   c
6.   a
7.   a
8.   d
9.   d
10.   c

11.   This is cutoff clipping. When the collector voltage rises, the current in the collector resistor drops. At the limit, the collector reaches V_{CC} and the transistor current is zero (cutoff).

12.   a)   7.36 V
       b)   5.96 V
       c)   Self-bias

13.   The input resistance of the BJT amplifier is approximately 4.8 kΩ (computed from re*$\beta \parallel R_1 \parallel R_2$) = (54 Ω*120 $\parallel$ 22 kΩ $\parallel$ 100 kΩ = 4.8 kΩ). The input resistance of the JFET amplifier is approximately 1 MΩ (the gate resistance).

14.   112 (loaded gain)

15.   7.8 (loaded gain)

16.   20 (to make the loop gain = 1).

1. b
2. a
3. c
4. b
5. b
6. d
7. d
8. a
9. c
10. d

11. Virtual ground refers to a point in a circuit which acts like a circuit ground in maintaining a voltage equal to ground reference but unlike ground does not sink current.

12. Open-loop gain does not involve negative feedback from the output to the input. Closed-loop gain uses negative feedback to establish the amplifier gain.

13. a) The ratio of R_f to R_i is 13:1.

    b) There are many reasonable answers. Possible values are $R_f = 47$ kΩ and $R_i = 3.6$ kΩ. The circuit with these values is shown in Figure C-18-1.

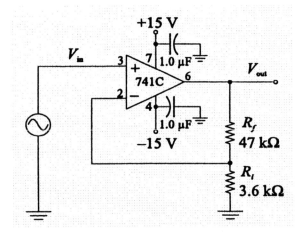

Figure C-18-1

14. a) +5.0 V
    b) 1.0 V
    c) 100 μA
    d) 100 μA
    e) +0.3 V The voltage across R_f (4.7 V) is subtracted from the voltage at the inverting input).

1.   c
2.   a
3.   a
4.   d
5.   c
6.   a
7.   b
8.   d
9.   b
10.   a

11.   The waveforms are shown in Figure C-19-1.

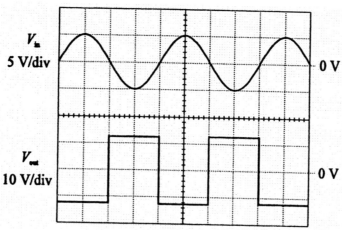

Figure C-19-1

12.   +5.0 V

13.   a) $A_{V1} = -37$ $A_{V2} = -17.9$

       b) $V_{out} = (-37 \times V_{in1}) + (-17.9 \times V_{in2})$

14.   a)   In an integrating circuit, the output is proportional to the area under the input signal. In a differentiating circuit, the output is proportional to the rate of change of the input signal.

       b)   A resistor and an inductor can be used for either circuit. *RL* circuits are not widely used because they are more expensive than *RC* circuits. In addition, inductors are large and, because of coil resistance, are not as close to ideal components as capacitors.

Checkup 20

1. b
2. a
3. a
4. c
5. c
6. d
7. d
8. c
9. a
10. b

11. R_7 balances the common-mode gain so as to cancel common-mode signals.

12. The differential gain will be 1 if R_G is open.

13. It charges to the peak voltage of the input signal.

14. The circuit will respond faster to changes in the input but the peak voltage will not remain on the capacitor as long.

15. The capacitor will be charged to the negative peak.

Checkup 21

1. c
2. a
3. b
4. c
5. c
6. d
7. b
8. c
9. d
10. c

11. Compensation refers to a circuit that produces a voltage to cancel the effect of an unwanted thermocouple voltage due to the reference junction.

12. The third wire allows the wire resistance to the thermocouple to be "split" into two separate arms of the bridge, thus canceling the effect of wire resistance.

13. 1) Reduce the anode voltage to a point that causes the anode current to drop below the holding current.
    2) Apply a voltage between the anode and cathode that opposes the conduction (commutation).

14. Turn it on at the zero-crossing of the ac.

Experiment 1: Metric Prefixes, Scientific Notation, and Graphing

Procedure:

Some possible responses are listed in Table 1-3.

Table 1-3

Instrument	Control	Metric Unit	Meaning
Oscilloscope	SEC/DIV	ms	10^{-3} s
Oscilloscope	SEC/DIV	µs	10^{-6} s
Function Gen	Range	kHz	10^3 Hz
DMM	Function	kΩ	10^3 Ω
Oscilloscope	V/DIV	mV	10^{-3} V

Table 1–4

Dimension	Length in Millimeters	Length in Meters
A	7.2 mm	7.2×10^{-3} m
B	15.4 mm	15.4×10^{-3} m
C	9.0 mm	9.0×10^{-3} m
D	31.3 mm	31.3×10^{-3} m
E	14.0 mm	14.0×10^{-3} m
F	6.0 mm	6.0×10^{-3} m
G	10.2 mm	10.2×10^{-3} m

Table 1-5

Number	Scientific Notation	Engineering Notation	Metric Value
0.0829 V	8.29×10^{-2} V	82.9×10^{-3} V	82.9 mV
48,000 Hz	4.8×10^4 Hz	48×10^3 Hz	48 kHz
2,200,000 Ω	2.2×10^6 Ω	2.2×10^6 Ω	2.2 MΩ
0.000 015 A	1.5×10^{-5} A	15×10^{-6} A	15 µA
7,500 W	7.5×10^3 W	7.5×10^3 W	7.5 kW
0.000 000 033 F	$3.3 \ 10^{-8}$ F	33×10^{-9} F	33 nF
270,000 Ω	2.7×10^5 Ω	270×10^3 Ω	270 kΩ
0.000 010 H	1.0×10^{-5} H	10×10^{-6} H	10 µH

Table 1–6

Metric Value	Engineering Notation
100 pF	100×10^{-12} F
12 kV	12×10^{3} V
85.0 μA	85.0×10^{-6} A
50 GHz	50×10^{9} Hz
33 kΩ	33×10^{3} Ω
250 mV	250×10^{-3} V
7.8 ns	7.8×10^{-9} s
2.0 MΩ	2.0×10^{6} Ω

Table 1–7

Metric Unit in Operand	Mathematical Operation	Metric Unit in Operand		Metric Unit in Result
milli	multiplied by	milli	=	micro
kilo	multiplied by	micro	=	**milli**
nano	multiplied by	kilo	=	**micro**
milli	multiplied by	mega	=	**kilo**
micro	divided by	nano	=	**kilo**
micro	divided by	pico	=	**mega**
pico	divided by	pico	=	**unit**
milli	divided by	mega	=	**nano**

Table 1–8 Inductance, L, of coils wound on identical iron cores (mH).

Length, l (cm)	Number of Turns , N (t)			
	100	200	300	400
2.5	3.9	16.1	35.8	64.0
5.5	1.7	7.5	16.1	29.3
8.0	1.2	5.1	11.4	19.8
12.0	0.8	3.3	7.5	13.1

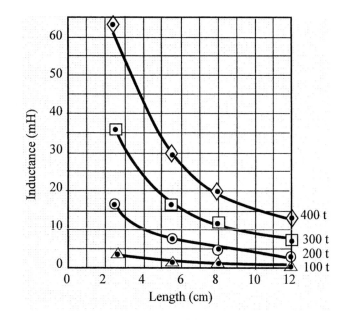

Plot 1-1

479

Evaluation and Review Questions:

1.   a)   kW   b)   mA
      c)   pF   d)   ns
      e)   MΩ   f)   μH

2.   a)   megawatt   b)   nanoampere
      c)   microjoule   d)   millivolt
      e)   kilohm   f)   gigahertz

3.   a) 3.2×10^{1}
      b) -1.1×10^{-6}
      c) 1.9×10^{-2}
      d) 5.0×10^{-2}

4.   a) -6.3×10^{5} b) 7.6×10^{6}
      c) 3.1×10^{9} d) -2.2×10^{-5}

5.   a) $-630 \times 10^{3} = -630 \text{ k}$ b) $7.6 \times 10^{6} = 7.6 \text{ M}$
      c) $3.1 \times 10^{9} = 3.1 \text{ G}$ d) $-22 \times 10^{-6} = -22 \text{ μ}$

6.   Steps in preparing a linear graph:
        1.   Choose a scale factor that enables all of the data to be plotted on the graph.
        2.   Number the major divisions along each axis.
        3.   Label each axis to indicate the quantity being measured and the measurement units.
        4.   Plot the data points with a small dot with a small circle around each point.
        5.   Draw a smooth line that represents the data trend.
        6.   Title the graph.

For Further Investigation:

The data from Table 1-8, plotted on log-log paper.

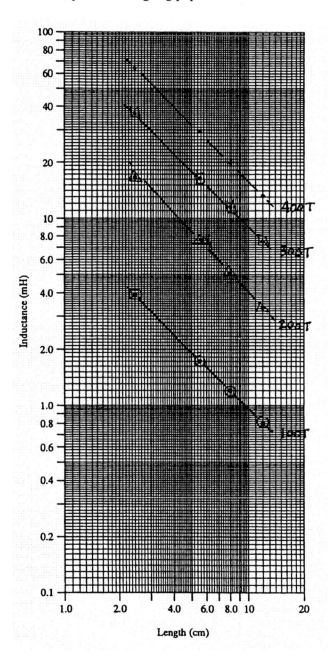

Experiment 2: Laboratory Meters and Power Supply

Procedure:

1. Each secondary division is worth 0.5 V. The meter reads 15.0 V.

2. Each secondary division is worth 5.0 V. The meter reads 150 V.

3. The voltmeter reads 25.5 V.

4. The ohmmeter reads 175 Ω. On the 12 V DC VOLTS scale, the reading is 2.4 V.

5. The ohmmeter reads 155 Ω. On the 30 V AC VOLTS scale, the reading is 21.9 V.

6, 7. Answers vary depending on particular power supply.

9. Reading on the power supply meter: 5.0 V. Reading on the DMM: 4.98 V.

10. Reading on the power supply meter: 12. V. Reading on the DMM: 12.0 V.

11. Reading on the power supply meter: 0 V. Reading on the DMM: 0.01 V.

Evaluation and Review Questions:

1. The precision of a typical 3 1/2 digit DMM is one part in 2000. The precision of a power supply meter depends on the type of meter but is typically one part in 100. This question can lead to a post-lab discussion of the difference between resolution and accuracy.

2. An autoranging meter automatically switches to the appropriate range to display the measured quantity.

3. A multiple scale is one with more than one range on the scale. A complex scale is used for more than one function on the same scale.

4. A linear scale has equally spaced divisions across the meter face; a nonlinear scale does not.

5. Each secondary mark has a value of 0.2. The meter reading is 3.2.

6. The three basic measurements are voltage, resistance, and current. Many DMMs have additional capabilities.

For Further Investigation:

Results will vary depending on equipment and meter used.

Experiment 3: Measurement of Resistance

Procedure:
> Answers for both tables depend on the particular resistors used. Note that the sum of the readings on Table 3-3 (column 3) is approximately constant.

Evaluation and Review Questions:

1. Answer depends on the potentiometer used. Normally, the resistance is a minimum between terminals 1 and 2 and maximum between terminals 2 and 3 when the shaft is rotated fully CW.

2. a) Answers vary.
    b) Check result with another meter or measure a known resistor with the meter in question.

3. a) brown - red - black - silver
    b) blue - gray - red - silver
    c) white - brown - brown - silver
    d) yellow - violet - green - silver
    e) brown - black - gold - silver

4. a) 22 Ω (5%)
    b) 750 Ω (10%)
    c) 510 Ω (5%)
    d) 9.1 Ω (5%)
    e) 820 kΩ (10%)

5. a) largest value = 28,350 Ω
    b) smallest value = 25,650 Ω

6. A rheostat is a two-terminal variable resistor used to control current in a circuit. A potentiometer is a three-terminal variable resistor with a wiper that slides along a fixed resistance. A potentiometer can be connected as a rheostat by leaving open one of the fixed terminals.

For Further Investigation:
> Although not as meaningful statistically as standard deviation, the average deviation is easy to find by computing the average value and finding the variation of each resistor from the average. Results vary but the student will observe that all (or nearly all) are within the deviation specified by the tolerance.

Procedure:

Table 4-2

	Measured Value
V_S	+10.0 V
V_{AB}	+1.64 V
V_{BC}	+3.38 V
V_{CD}	+4.98 V

Table 4-3

	Measured Voltage	Voltage Difference Calculation
V_A	+10.0 V	$V_{AB} = V_A - V_B =$ **+1.64 V**
V_B	+8.36 V	$V_{BC} = V_B - V_C =$ **+3.38 V**
V_C	+4.98 V	$V_{CD} = V_C - V_D =$ **+4.98 V**
V_D	0.0 V (ref)	

Table 4-4

	Measured Voltage	Voltage Difference Calculation
V_A	+5.02 V	$V_{AB} = V_A - V_B =$ **+1.64 V**
V_B	+3.38 V	$V_{BC} = V_B - V_C =$ **+3.38 V**
V_C	+0.0 V (ref)	$V_{CD} = V_C - V_D =$ **+4.98 V**
V_D	−4.98 V	

Table 4-5

	Measured Voltage	Voltage Difference Calculation
V_A	+1.64 V	$V_{AB} = V_A - V_B =$ **+1.64 V**
V_B	0.0 V (ref)	$V_{BC} = V_B - V_C =$ **+3.38 V**
V_C	−3.38 V	$V_{CD} = V_C - V_D =$ **+4.98 V**
V_D	−8.36 V	

Table 4-6

	Measured Voltage	Voltage Difference Calculation
V_A	0.0 V (ref)	$V_{AB} = V_A - V_B =$ **+1.64 V**
V_B	−1.64 V	$V_{BC} = V_B - V_C =$ **+3.38 V**
V_C	−5.02 V	$V_{CD} = V_C - V_D =$ **+4.98 V**
V_D	−10.0 V	

Evaluation and Review Questions:

1. The voltage difference calculations indicate that the voltage difference is independent of the ground reference point. Voltage is frequently defined with respect to ground (using a single subscript), but voltage difference is measured between the two points named by the subscripts.

2. Reference ground is the point in a circuit defined as 0 V. All other voltages in a circuit are referenced to this point.

3. -12 V

4. -70 V

5. $+8.3$ V

For Further Investigation:

The voltage difference calculations should be the same as the results in Tables 4-3 to 4-6.

Experiment 5: Ohm's Law

Procedure:

Table 5-2 (R_1) (0.996 kΩ)

$V_S =$	2.0 V	4.0 V	6.0 V	8.0 V	10.0 V
$I =$	2.0 mA	4.0 mA	6.0 mA	8.0 mA	10.0 mA

Table 5-3 (R_2) (1.52 kΩ)

$V_S =$	2.0 V	4.0 V	6.0 V	8.0 V	10.0 V
$I =$	1.3 mA	2.7 mA	4.0 mA	5.3 mA	6.7 mA

Table 5-4 (R_3) (2.20 kΩ)

$V_S =$	2.0 V	4.0 V	6.0 V	8.0 V	10.0 V
$I =$	0.9 mA	1.8 mA	2.7 mA	3.6 mA	4.5 mA

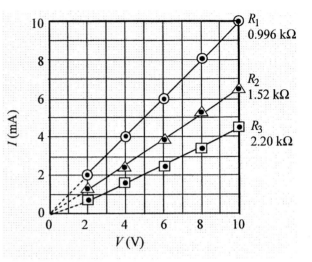

Plot 5-1

Evaluation and Review Questions:

1.   The slope represents the conductance of each resistor. For R_1, the slope is 1.0 mS; for R_2 the slope is 0.67 mS, for R_3 the slope is 0.45 mS.

2.   The slope is lower for larger resistors.

3.   a)   The current is doubled.
      b)   The current is doubled.

4.   2.0 kΩ

5.   0.5 A

For Further Investigation:

Measured data for a Jameco 120299 CdS cell is shown below and in plot 5-2. Room light was held constant for these measurements.

Table 5-5 (CdS Cell)

$V_S =$	2.0 V	4.0 V	6.0 V	8.0 V	10.0 V
$I =$	1.99 mA	3.97 mA	5.96 mA	8.03 mA	10.21 mA

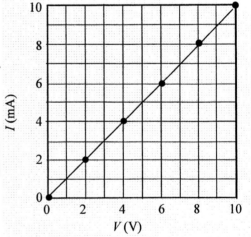

Plot 5-2

Procedure:

Table 6-1

Variable Resistance Setting (R_2)	$I_T = \dfrac{V_T}{R_T}$	V_1 (measured)	V_2 (measured)	Power in R_2: P_2
0.5 kΩ	3.75 mA	10.12 V	1.88 V	7.0 mW
1.0 kΩ	3.24 mA	8.76 V	3.24 V	10.5 mW
2.0 kΩ	2.55 mA	6.89 V	5.11 V	13.0 mW
3.0 kΩ	2.11 mA	5.68 V	6.32 V	13.3 mW
4.0 kΩ	1.79 mA	4.84 V	7.16 V	12.8 mW
5.0 kΩ	1.56 mA	4.21 V	7.79 V	12.1 mW
7.5 kΩ	1.17 mA	3.18 V	8.82 V	10.4 mW
10.0 kΩ	0.94 mA	2.55 V	9.45 V	8.9 mW

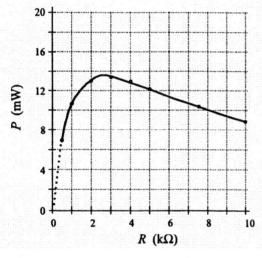

Plot 6-1

Evaluation and Review Questions:

1. The resistance of R_2 at the peak is 2.7 kΩ (matching load). The data should support the answer that it is approximately 3 kΩ.

2. The total current was decreasing.

3. Since R_1 is a fixed resistor the current in it will decrease as the resistance of R_2 increases. The power equation $P = I^2R$ shows that the power must also go down as R_2 increases. Student may also observe that the tabulated voltage drop across R_1 is lower as the resistance of R_2 increases indicating lower power in R_1.

4. a)   15 mA
    b)   337.5 mW
    c)   A 1/4 watt = 250 mW. A 1/4 watt resistor should not be used.

5. Size.

6. It is dissipated as heat.

For Further Investigation:
   See Plot 6-2 for current and voltage plots. The solid line represents the current; the dotted line represents the voltage. The current-voltage product is the same as Plot 6-1.

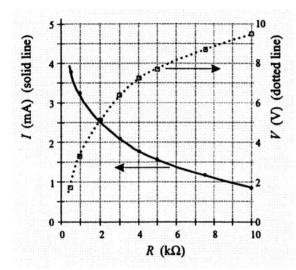

Plot 6-2

Experiment 7: Series Circuits

Procedure:

Table 7-1

Component	Listed Value	Measured Value
R_1	1.0 kΩ	**996 Ω**
R_2	1.5 kΩ	**1.52 kΩ**
R_3	2.2 kΩ	**2.20 kΩ**
R_4	330 Ω	**332 Ω**
$R_T =$	**5.03 kΩ**	**5.05 kΩ**

Table 7-2

	Computed Value	Measured Value
I_T	**2.98 mA**	**3.0 mA**
V_{AB}	**2.98 V**	**2.96 V**
V_{BC}	**4.47 V**	**4.46 V**
V_{CD}	**6.58 V**	**6.54 V**
V_{DE}	**0.98 V**	**0.99 V**

7. $-15.0 + 2.96 + 4.46 + 6.54 + 0.99 = -0.05$ V √

8. Answers vary but should be similar to result from step 7.

9. $-15.0 + 0 + 15.0 + 0 + 0 = 0$ V √   (The +15.0 V reading is across the open).

Evaluation and Review Questions:

1. The numbers used in the summation are the same regardless of the starting point. The commutative property of mathematics applies to Kirchhoff's voltage law.

2. There was no current in the circuit of step 9; yet Kirchhoff's voltage law was found to be valid.

3. The open fuse would have 110 V across it.

4. $V_X = 3$ V.

5. a)   4 V
    b)   0.4 A
    c)   20 Ω

For Further Investigation:

The three currents will all be the same, approximately 1.9 mA. The same current flows throughout a series circuit.

Note: The solutions to Multisim troubleshooting problems are on page 542-544.

Experiment 8: The Voltage Divider

Procedure:

Table 8-1

Resistor	Listed Value	Measured Value	$V_X = V_S \left(\dfrac{R_X}{R_T} \right)$	V_X(measured)
R_1	330 Ω	333 Ω	1.34 V	1.34 V
R_2	470 Ω	473 Ω	1.90 V	1.90 V
R_3	680 Ω	683 Ω	2.75 V	2.75 V
R_4	1000 Ω	998 Ω	4.01 V	4.01 V
Total	2478 Ω	2487 Ω	10.0 V	10.0 V

Circuit for step 5:

+10 V

R_1
330 Ω
R_2
470 Ω
R_3
680 Ω
R_4
1.0 kΩ

V_{out}
6.8 V

Circuit for step 6:

+10 V

R_1
330 Ω
R_3
680 Ω
R_4
1.0 kΩ

V_{out}
5.0 V

Circuit for step 8:

+10 V

R_1
330 Ω
R_4
1.0 kΩ

V_{out}
7.5 V

9.   Computed: $V_{min} = +2.61$ V $V_{max} = +8.17$ V.

10.   Measured: $V_{min} = 2.54$ V $V_{max} = 8.10$ V.

Evaluation and Review Questions:

1.   a)   Output voltage is unchanged.   b)   Power dissipated is a factor of ten less.

2.   a) $V_{out} = 0$ V   b) $V_{out} = 10.0$ V

3.   The range of output voltages increases. $V_{min} = 0.44$ V $V_{max} = 9.7$ V.

4. $V_A = 10$ V $V_B = 1.0$ V $V_C = 0.10$ V $V_D = 0.010$ V

5. V_{min} 0 V $V_{max} = 6.67$ V.

For Further Investigation:

The student should find that a load resistance of ten times the divider resistance it is across will decrease the output voltage by less than 10%.

Experiment 9: Parallel Circuits

Procedure: Measured resistors are: $R_1 = 3.30$ kΩ, $R_2 = 4.71$ kΩ, $R_3 = 6.82$ kΩ, $R_4 = 9.97$ kΩ

Table 9-2

	R_1	$R_1\| R_2$	$R_1\|R_2\|R_3$	$R_1\|R_2\|R_3\|R_4$
R_T (measured)	3.30 kΩ	1.93 kΩ	1.51 kΩ	1.31 kΩ
I_T (measured)				9.15 mA

5.   The voltage across each resistor is the same as the source voltage.

Table 9-3

	$I_1 = \dfrac{V_S}{R_1}$	$I_2 = \dfrac{V_S}{R_2}$	$I_3 = \dfrac{V_S}{R_3}$	$I_4 = \dfrac{V_S}{R_4}$
I (computed)	3.64 mA	2.55 mA	1.76 mA	1.20 mA

Table 9-4

	$I_1 = \left(\dfrac{R_T}{R_1}\right)I_T$	$I_2 = \left(\dfrac{R_T}{R_2}\right)I_T$	$I_3 = \left(\dfrac{R_T}{R_3}\right)I_T$	$I_4 = \left(\dfrac{R_T}{R_4}\right)I_T$
I (computed)	3.63 mA	2.54 mA	1.76 mA	1.20 mA

8.   9.15 mA = 3.64 mA + 2.55 mA + 1.76 mA + 1.20 mA √

9.   The new total current is 7.95 mA.

Evaluation and Review Questions:

1.   Subtract the observed current from the original total current. The difference is the "missing" current due to an open branch. Apply Ohm's law to find the open resistance.

2.   The short is a very low resistance path causing the current to go very high. If the power supply does not have short circuit current limiting, a fuse will blow or damage will result.

3.   a)   Current should be 167 mA.   b)   The 820 Ω resistor is open.

4. I_4 is entering the junction and is equal to 25 mA.

5.   The high current in the short may cause a fuse to open or could cause another open to occur.

For Further Investigation:

The student should be able to confirm Kirchhoff's current law through the measurements.

Experiment 10: Series-Parallel Combination Circuits

Procedure: Measured resistors are: $R_1 = 2.22$ kΩ, $R_2 = 4.69$ kΩ, $R_3 = 5.63$ kΩ, $R_4 = 9.96$ kΩ

2. a) R_1 YES R_2 NO R_3 NO R_4 YES
    b) R_1 NO R_2 YES R_3 YES R_4 NO

3. Equivalent Circuit:

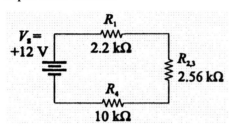

10. Equivalent circuit:

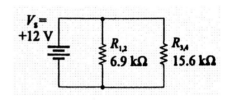

Table 10-2

	Computed		Measured
	Voltage Divider	Ohm's Law	Measured
R_T	14.7 kΩ	14.7 kΩ	14.7 kΩ
I_T		0.82 mA	
V_1	1.81 V	1.82 V	1.81 V
$V_{2,3}$	2.09 V	2.10 V	2.09 V
V_4	8.13 V	8.16 V	8.13 V
I_2		0.45 mA	
I_3		0.37 mA	
V_T	12.0 V	12.0 V	12.0 V

Table 10-3

	Computed	Measured
$R_{1,2}$	6.91 kΩ	6.90 kΩ
$R_{3,4}$	15.59 kΩ	15.6 kΩ
R_T	4.79 kΩ	4.78 kΩ
I_T	2.51 mA	
$I_{1,2}$	1.74 mA	
$I_{3,4}$	0.77 mA	
V_1	3.86 V	3.84 V
V_2	8.16 V	8.16 V
V_3	4.34 V	4.33 V
V_4	7.67 V	7.67 V

Evaluation and Review Questions:

1. a) The voltage divider rule was applied to an equivalent series circuit.

    b) Yes. The voltage divider rule can be applied to any set of series resistor for which the total voltage across the resistors is known. The voltage divider rule can be applied to each series branch in Figure 10-3 independently to find the voltage drops across each resistor.

2. Answers vary. One possible path around the outside loop is:

    -12.0 V $+ 4.33$ V $+ 7.67$ V $= 0$ $\checkmark$

3. The currents entering and leaving the junction are equal. This can be shown as:

    2.51 mA $= 1.74$ mA $+ 0.77$ mA $\checkmark$

4. a) The path through $R_1 - R_2$ is open.

b) Check the resistors to see if a +12 V drop is across one or the other. If not, check for a drop across the connection points.

5. +24 V.

For Further Investigation:

Student should summarize a procedure for solving the problem. The total resistance seen by the voltage source is 1.74 kΩ and the total current is 6.90 mA. The voltage and current for each resistor are as follows:

$V_1 = 12.0$ V	$I_1 = 5.45$ mA
$V_2 = 6.80$ V	$I_2 = 1.45$ mA
$V_3 = 5.20$ V	$I_3 = 0.93$ mA
$V_4 = 5.20$ V	$I_4 = 0.52$ mA

Experiment 11: The Superposition Theorem

Procedure: Measured resistors for this experiment: $R_1 = 4.69$ kΩ, $R_2 = 6.8$ kΩ, $R_3 = 9.90$ kΩ

Table 11-2 Computed and measured resistances.

	Quantity	Computed	Measured
Step 4	R_T (V_{S1} operating alone)	**8.74 kΩ**	**8.73 kΩ**
Step 7	R_T (V_{S2} operating alone)	**9.98 kΩ**	**10.1 kΩ**

Table 11-3 Computed and measured current and voltage.

	Computed Current*			Computed Voltage			Measured Voltage		
	I_1	I_2	I_3	V_1	V_2	V_3	V_1	V_2	V_3
Step 5	**+0.57**	**+0.34**	**+0.23**						
Step 6				**+2.67 V**	**+2.31 V**	**+2.28 V**	**+2.69 V**	**+2.32 V**	**+2.32 V**
Step 8	**−0.68**	**−1.00**	**+0.32**						
Step 9				**−3.19 V**	**−6.80 V**	**+3.18 V**	**−3.18 V**	**−6.80 V**	**+3.18 V**
Step 10 (totals)	**−0.11**	**−0.66**	**+0.55**	**−0.52 V**	**−4.49 V**	**+5.46 V**	**−0.50 V**	**−4.49 V**	**+5.49 V**

*all currents are shown in milliamps

Evaluation and Review Questions:

1. a) −5.0 V + (−0.51 V) + (−4.49 V) + 10 V = 0 √
    b) −1.09 mA = −0.66 mA + 0.55 mA √

2. The actual direction of current is the opposite of the assumed direction.

3. The sign of all results would be reversed. Since the original assumed direction of current is also reversed, the net result is that there is no effect on the circuit.

4. a) Replace all sources except one with their internal resistance.
    b) Compute the current or voltage due to the one source acting alone.
    c) Repeat steps a and b for all sources.
    d) Algebraically sum the results.

5. Current due to V_{S1} is = 54.5 mA. Current due to V_{S2} = −145.5 mA. Net current = −91 mA

For Further Investigation:

The results indicate that the superposition theorem does not apply to power.

Experiment 12: Thevenin's Theorem

Procedure:

Measured resistors: $R_1 = 274\ \Omega$, $R_2 = 556\ \Omega$, $R_3 = 680\ \Omega$, $R_{L1} = 151\ \Omega$, $R_{L2} = 471\ \Omega$, $R_{L3} = 810\ \Omega$

2.   Load voltage calculation (using equivalent circuits and the voltage divider theorem):
- a) $R_{L1} + R_2 = 151\ \Omega + 556\ \Omega = 707\ \Omega$
- b) $(R_{L1} + R_2)\ \|\ R_3 = 707\ \Omega\ \|\ 680\ \Omega = 347\ \Omega$
- c) $V_{L1,2,3} = 10\ \text{V} * (347\ \Omega/594\ \Omega) = 5.62\ \text{V}$
- d) $V_{L1} = 5.62\ \text{V} * (151\ \Omega/707\ \Omega) = 1.20\ \text{V}$

Table 12-2

	Computed	Measured
V_{L1}	1.20 V	1.20 V
V_{L2}	2.76 V	2.76 V
V_{L3}	3.72 V	3.70 V
V_{TH}	7.13 V	7.12 V
R_{TH}	751 Ω	751 Ω

Table 12-3

	Computed	Measured
V_{L1}	1.19 V	1.20 V
V_{L2}	2.74 V	2.76 V
V_{L3}	3.69 V	3.71 V
V_{TH}	7.13 V	7.12 V
R_{TH}	751 Ω	751 Ω

8.   The Thevenin circuit consists of a 7.12 V source in series with a 751 Ω resistor as shown on the right (Measured results are given.)

$R_{TH} = 751\ \Omega$

$V_{TH} = 7.12\ \text{V}$

Thevenin circuit for step 8

Evaluation and Review Questions:

1.   The original circuit and the Thevenin circuit are equivalent as seen by the load resistor.

2.   The load current in a short is 9.5 mA for both circuits.

3.   Calculations are simplified.

4.   The voltage and resistance looking from the output are not affected by R_1, therefore it is not part of the Thevenin circuit.

5.

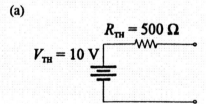

(a) $R_{TH} = 500\ \Omega$ $V_{TH} = 10\ \text{V}$

(b) $R_{TH} = 776\ \Omega$ $V_{TH} = 25.9\ \text{V}$

For Further Investigation:

When the voltage across the load is one-half the unloaded voltage, the internal Thevenin resistance is dropping the same voltage as the load resistor is dropping. Application of the voltage divider theorem shows that the two resistances must be equal.

Experiment 13: The Wheatstone Bridge

Procedure:

Measured resistors: $R_1 = 99\ \Omega$, $R_2 = 151\ \Omega$, $R_3 = 332\ \Omega$, $R_L = 475\ \Omega$, $R_4 = 970\ \Omega$ (max)

Table 13-2

	Computed	Measured
V_A	6.0 V	5.98 V
V_B	7.52 V	7.50 V
R_{TH}	60 Ω	59 Ω
R'_{TH}	248 Ω	246 Ω
V_L	0.92 V	0.91 V

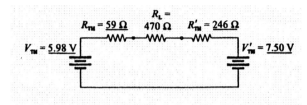

Figure 13-4 (unbalanced bridge)

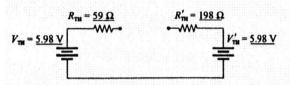 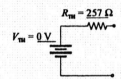

Figure 13-5 (balanced bridge)   Figure 13-6 (balanced bridge)

Evaluation and Review Questions

1. Doubling the load resistance is not doubling the total resistance; therefore, the current is not halved.

2. a) Yes. See the equivalent circuit in Figure 13-4 for example.
   b) No. In a balanced bridge, there is no current in the load.

3. a) The Thevenin resistance would increase causing the total current to decrease.
   b) In a balanced bridge, there is no current in the load. Doubling all bridge resistors keeps the bridge balanced, so has no effect on the current in the load.

4. a) Load current would increase.
   b) Doubling the voltage has no effect on the balance (although is does affect the sensitivity).
   The balanced bridge will remain in balance with no load current.

5. The voltage between point **A** and **B** is zero or no current is sensed in the load.

For Further Investigation:

In 150 feet of wire, the short can be located to within about 1 foot.

Experiment 14: Magnetic Devices

Procedure:

1. Relay diagrams will vary but should show the connections to the coil and contacts, terminal numbers, and measured coil resistance (test relay measured 59 Ω).

3–6. The pull-in and release voltages depend on the specific relay. A typical small 12 V relay that was tested is given as an example:

Table 14-1

		Pull-in Voltage	Release Voltage
Steps 3 and 4	Trial 1	7.4 V	3.4 V
Step 5	Trial 2	7.4 V	3.2 V
	Trial 3	7.5 V	2.9 V
Step 6	Average	7.43 V	3.17 V

7. Red light turns on when S_1 is closed; it stays on when S_1 is open.

8. Relay "buzzes" and both red and green LEDs are rapidly switched on and off. This occurs because when power is applied through the NC contact, the relay coil energizes opening the NC contact and removing power from the coil. With power removed, the NC contact closes, and the process repeats.

Evaluation and Review Questions:

1. Answers depend on the particular relay tested. The relay tested for this experiment had a coil resistance of 59 Ω. The average pull-in current was 126 mA.

2. The tested relay had an average release current of 53.7 mA.

3. The hysteresis of the test relay was 7.43 V − 3.16 V = 4.27 V.

4. a) SPDT means there is one switch with two contacts.
   b) DPST means there are two switches, each with one contact.

5. a) Relay coil could be open, control voltage could be off or too low, or switch S_1 is not making contact.
   b) With switch closed, check voltage on relay coil; if it is correct, the relay is likely bad.

For Further Investigation:

The reversing circuit is shown below.

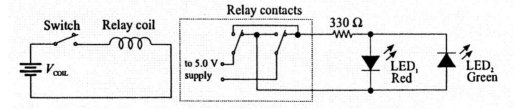

Experiment 15: The Oscilloscope

Procedure:

Table 15-1 (computed values shown)

Power Supply Setting	VOLTS/DIV Setting	Number of Divisions of Deflection	Oscilloscope (measured voltage)	DMM (measured voltage)
1.0 V	0.2 V/DIV	5.0 DIV	1.0 V	1.0 V
2.5 V	0.5 V/DIV	5.0 DIV	2.5 V	2.5 V
4.5 V	1.0 V/DIV	4.5 DIV	4.5 V	4.5 V
8.3 V	2.0 V/DIV	4.15 DIV	8.3 V	8.3 V

Table 15-2 (computed values shown)

Signal Generator Amplitude	VOLTS/DIV Setting	Number of Divisions (peak-to-peak)	Oscilloscope Measured (peak-to-peak)	Oscilloscope Measured (rms)
$1.0 V_{rms}$	0.5 V/DIV	5.6 DIV	$2.8 V_{pp}$	$1.0 V_{rms}$
$2.2 V_{rms}$	1.0 V/DIV	6.2 DIV	$6.2 V_{pp}$	$2.2 V_{rms}$
$3.7 V_{rms}$	2.0 V/DIV	5.25 DIV	$10.5 V_{pp}$	$3.7 V_{rms}$
$4.8 V_{rms}$	2.0 V/DIV	6.8 DIV	$13.6 V_{pp}$	$4.8 V_{rms}$

Evaluation and Review Questions:

1. a) Answers vary.
    b) Answers depend on the specific equipment used but generally favor the DMM. An analog oscilloscope linearity is typically 3% and has less resolution than a DMM. A digital scope depends on the resolution and accuracy of the digitizer.

2. *Vertical controls:* control the vertical axis of the oscilloscope and coupling of the input signal. *Trigger controls:* determine when the horizontal sweep occurs and the source of triggers. *Horizontal controls:* control the horizontal axis (typically the time axis) of the oscilloscope. *Display controls:* control the CRT.

3. Trigger controls.

4. a) $17.0 V_{pp}$ b) $6.01 V_{rms}$

5. The signal is $56.6 V_{pp}$. Use 10.0 volts/div control to spread the signal over 5.7 divisions.

6. When viewing two waveforms on an analog (dual trace) oscilloscope, select ALTernate to view high frequencies, CHOP for low frequencies (below about 1kHz).

For Further Investigation:

Most oscilloscopes will have a 1 kHz square wave output at a small connector labeled Probe Comp. The operator's manual typically will show how to adjust the probe and representative waveforms of a properly compensated probe. Forgetting to check probe compensation and not initializing the control setup of an oscilloscope are the two most common operator errors.

Experiment 16: Sine Wave Measurements

Procedure:

Table 16-1*

Signal Generator Dial Frequency	Computed Period	Oscilloscope SEC/DIV	Number of Divisions	Measured Period
1.25 kHz	0.8 ms	0.1 ms/div	8.0 div	0.8 ms
1.90 kHz	**0.526 ms**	**0.1 ms/div**	**5.26 div**	**0.53 ms**
24.5 kHz	**40.8 µs**	**5.0 µs/div**	**8.16 div**	**40.8 µs**
83.0 kHz	**12.0 µs**	**2.0 µs/div**	**6.0 div**	**12.0 µs**
600.0 kHz	**1.67 µs**	**0.2 µs/div**	**8.35 div**	**1.67 µs**

*computed values shown.

Table 16-2

	Signal Gen. Voltage	Voltage across R_1	Voltage across R_2
Measured	**1.0 V$_{pp}$**	**0.28 V$_{pp}$**	**0.72 V$_{pp}$**
Computed	1.0 V$_{pp}$	0.28 V$_{pp}$	0.72 V$_{pp}$

Evaluation and Review Questions:

1.   a)   Answers vary.
      b)   Signal generator calibration, oscilloscopes time-base error, reading error.

2. $-1.0\ V + 0.28\ V + 0.72\ V = 0$ √

3,   a)   126 ms
      b)   7.9 Hz

4.   10 µs/div

5.   a)   Connect CH 1 to one side of the component and CH 2 to the other side of the component.
      b)   Calibrate both channels and set the VOLTS/DIV to the same setting for each channel.
      c)   Use difference function to measure voltage across the ungrounded component. (For some oscilloscopes, ADD the channels and INVERT CH 2).

Note: You may want to emphasize the danger inherent in attempting to measure voltages that are not referenced to ground. If the scope ground clip is connected to a point in the circuit other than ground, the circuit under test can be destroyed and/or a shock may occur when the ground clip is connected. A shock hazard is also present when measuring "transformerless" ac appliances such as found in certain inexpensive TV sets. These appliances connect one side of the ac line directly to the chassis. If a two-wire plug is connected to the outlet in reverse, or a technician attempts to "hot-wire" the input ac voltage, the entire chassis can become "hot" with respect to ground. Connecting a scope ground to the chassis can lead to a direct short across the ac power. The best solution is to connect the test circuit through an isolation transformer.

For Further Investigation:

It is possible to obtain a stable display at 5 Hz with a small signal, but it is necessary to use NORMAL triggering and care in adjusting the trigger level control.

Experiment 17: Pulse Measurements

Procedure:

Data shown on Tables 17-1, 17-2, 17-3, and 17-4 was taken with an H-P 3311A Function Generator and a Tektronix 2246 oscilloscope (100 MHz bandwidth).

Table 17-1
Oscilloscope.

BW	100 MHz
$t_{(r)}$	3.5 ns

Table 17-2
Signal Generator.
(square wave output)

Rise time, $t_{(r)}$	64 ns
Fall time, $t_{(f)}$	67 ns
Period, T	10.0 μs
Pulse width, t_w	5.0 μs
Percent duty cycle	50%

Table 17-3
Signal Generator.
(with 1000 pF capacitor across output)

Rise time, $t_{(r)}$	1.40 μs
Fall time, $t_{(f)}$	1.27 μs

Table 17-4
Signal Generator.
(pulse output)

Rise time, $t_{(r)}$	11.7 ns
Fall time, $t_{(f)}$	9.1 ns
Period, T	10.0 μs
Pulse width, t_w	1.56 μs
Percent duty cycle	15.6%

Evaluation and Review Questions:

1. Answers depend on equipment used. If the rise time of the scope is at least 4 times faster than the measured rise time, the result is not bandwidth limited, otherwise it is (3% error).

2. The oscilloscope should have a rise time of 2.5 ns which represents a minimum bandwidth of 140 MHz.

3. When the X10 horizontal magnifier is used, the sweep is moving faster to increase the horizontal gain by a factor of ten. The faster sweep means that the time per division across the screen is reduced by a factor of ten.

4. There are 4.0 horizontal divisions between the 10% and 90% levels. The rise time is 8.0 ms.

5. The rise time would be 0.8 ms.

For Further Investigation:

Delayed sweep (also called Horizontal ALT magnification) is described in the Tektronix booklet *The XYZ's of Using a Scope* and an example is given in Exercise 10 of that booklet. The example shows how to use it for a rise time and pulse width measurement.

Experiment 18: Capacitors

Procedure:

1,2.   See Table 18-1 on right.

<table>
<tr><td colspan="4" style="text-align:center">Table 18-1</td></tr>
<tr><td>Capacitor</td><td>Listed Value</td><td>Ohmmeter Test Pass/Fail</td><td>Voltmeter Test Pass/Fail</td></tr>
<tr><td>C_1</td><td>100 µF</td><td>pass</td><td>very slow-fail</td></tr>
<tr><td>C_2</td><td>47 µF</td><td>pass</td><td>very slow-fail</td></tr>
<tr><td>C_3</td><td>1.0 µF</td><td>pass</td><td>pass</td></tr>
<tr><td>C_4</td><td>0.1 µF</td><td>difficult to see</td><td>pass</td></tr>
<tr><td>C_5</td><td>0.01 µF</td><td>cannot see-fail</td><td>pass</td></tr>
</table>

4.   Closing S_1 causes the series LED to flash.

5.   Opening S_1 and closing S_2 causes the parallel LED to flash.

6. $V_1 = \underline{3.4\ V}$ $V_2 = \underline{7.0\ V}$
Observations: The series LED flashes quickly.

7. $Q_1 = \underline{340\ \mu C}$ $Q_2 = \underline{333\ \mu C}$ (computed from measured voltages).
Observations: The parallel LED flashes for a shorter time than in step 5.

8. $V_1 = \underline{10.1\ V}$ $V_2 = \underline{10.1\ V}$
Observations: The series LED flashes for a much longer time than in step 4.

9. $Q_1 = \underline{1010\ \mu C}$ $Q_2 = \underline{475\ \mu C}$ (computed from measured voltages).

10.   The series LED flashes because only the capacitor charging current passes through it. The parallel LED is on nearly steady because of capacitive filtering action.

Evaluation and Review Questions:

1.   The total stored charge was less for the series capacitors.

2.   The charge would be smaller and the LED would flash for an even shorter time.

3.   a) 3.0 µF   b) 0.67 µF   c) The larger voltage is across the 1.0 µF capacitor.

4.   683 = 68,000 pF = 0.068 µF   102 = 1,000 pF = 0.001 µF   224 = 220,000 pF = 0.22 µF

5.   47 pF is coded as 470   10,000 pF is coded as 103   0.033 µF is coded as 333

For Further Investigation:

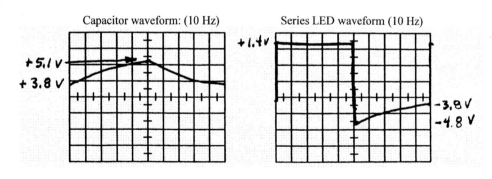

Capacitor waveform: (10 Hz)   +5.1 V   +3.8 V

Series LED waveform (10 Hz)   +1.4 v   -3.8 V   -4.8 V

Plot 18-1   Plot 18-2

Experiment 19: Capacitive Reactance

Procedure:
(computed values shown on tables)

Table 19-2

	Capacitor C_1	Capacitor C_2
Voltage across R_1, V_R	0.532 V	0.283 V
Total current, I	0.532 mA	0.283 mA
Voltage across C, V_C	0.846 V	0.959 V
Capacitive reactance, X_C	1.59 kΩ	3.39 kΩ
Computed capacitance, C	0.10 μF	0.047 μF

Table 19-3

Step		Series Capacitors	Parallel Capacitors
(a)	Voltage across R_1, V_R	0.197 V	0.68 V
	Total current, I	0.197 mA	0.68 mA
(b)	Voltage across capacitors, V_C	0.98 V	0.73 V
(c)	Capacitive reactance, X_{CT}	4.98 kΩ	1.08 kΩ
(d)	Computed capacitance, C_T	0.032 μF	0.147 μF

Evaluation and Review Questions:

1.   The total series reactance is the sum of the capacitive reactances, whereas the parallel reactance is the product-over-sum of the reactances as shown in Table 19-3.

2.   The capacitance of the series capacitors is the product-over-sum of the capacitances, whereas the parallel reactance is the sum of the capacitances as shown in Table 19-3.

3.   The smaller capacitance would have a higher capacitive reactance.

4.   Measure the voltage across the capacitor and determine the current in the capacitor by applying Ohm's law to the resistor. Apply Ohm's law ($X_C = V_C/I$) to these values to find the reactance of the capacitor. Find the capacitance by applying the formula:

$$C = \frac{1}{2\pi f X_C}$$

5.   The capacitive reactance is: 796 Ω.

For Further Investigation:
The circuit was tested with a generator that had a maximum output of 17 V_{pp}. The voltage across the load resistor was 12 Vdc with approximately 0.7 V_{pp} of ripple.

Experiment 20: Series *RC* Circuits

Procedure:

Computed values are shown. Measured values were within 7% of these values.

Table 20-2

Frequency	V_R	V_C	I	X_C	Z
500 Hz	0.63 V	2.93 V	0.092 mA	31.8 kΩ	32.5 kΩ
1000 Hz	1.18 V	2.75 V	0.173 mA	15.9 kΩ	17.3 kΩ
1500 Hz	1.62 V	2.52 V	0.238 mA	10.6 kΩ	12.6 kΩ
2000 Hz	1.95 V	2.28 V	0.287 mA	7.96 kΩ	10.5 kΩ
4000 Hz	2.59 V	1.51 V	0.381 mA	3.98 kΩ	7.88 kΩ
8000 Hz	2.88 V	0.84 V	0.423 mA	1.99 kΩ	7.08 kΩ

8. Impedance and Voltage Phasors for 1000 Hz:

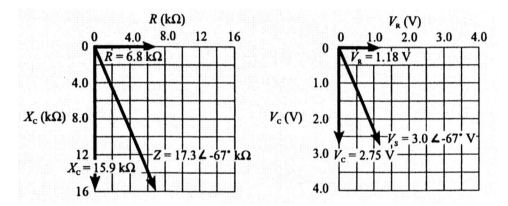

Plot 20-1

9. Impedance and Voltage Phasors for 4000 Hz:

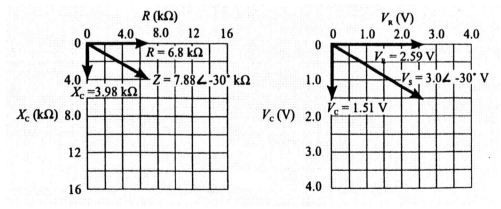

Plot 20-2

10.   Frequency response:

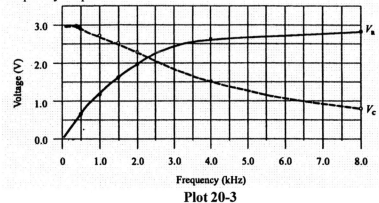

Plot 20-3

Evaluation and Review Questions:

1. $Z = \sqrt{6.8\ k\Omega^2 + 7.96\ k\Omega^2} = 10.5\ k\Omega$ $V_s = \sqrt{1.95\ V^2 + 2.28\ V^2} = 3.0\ V$

2.   Connect the output across the resistor because the maximum voltage at high frequencies is developed across the resistor.

3.   a)   The total impedance decreases as the frequency increases.
       b)   The capacitive reactance decreases but the resistance remains constant; therefore the total impedance becomes more resistive. Hence, the phase angle is smaller.

4. V_C will be smaller at any given frequency and V_R will be larger.

5.   Measure the voltage across each component. The open component will have V_S across it.

For Further Investigation:

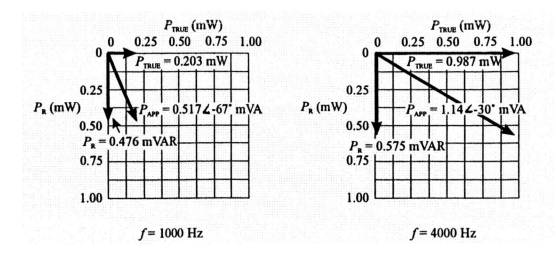

Experiment 21: Parallel *RC* Circuits

Procedure: (computed values shown)

Table 21-1 ($f = 1.0$ kHz)

	Listed Value	Measured Value	Voltage Drop	Computed Current
R_1	100 kΩ	**100 kΩ**	**2.96 V**	**29.6 μA**
R_{S1}	1.0 kΩ	**1.00 kΩ**	**35.2 mV**	**35.2 μA**
R_{S2}	1.0 kΩ	**1.00 kΩ**	**18.7 mV**	**18.7 μA**
C_1	1000 pF	**1000 pF**		

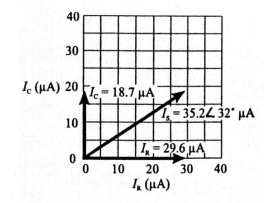

Plot 21-1

6. $X_{C1} = \underline{159 \text{ kΩ}}$ $Z_T = \underline{84.6 \text{ kΩ}}$

7. $I_T = \underline{35.4 \text{ μA}}$

Table 21-2 ($f = 2.0$ kHz)

	Listed Value	Measured Value	Voltage Drop	Computed Current
R_1	100 kΩ	**100 kΩ**	**2.97 V**	**29.7 μA**
R_{S1}	1.0 kΩ	**1.00 kΩ**	**47.7 mV**	**47.7 μA**
R_{S2}	1.0 kΩ	**1.00 kΩ**	**37.7 mV**	**37.7 μA**
C_1	1000 pF	**1000 pF**		

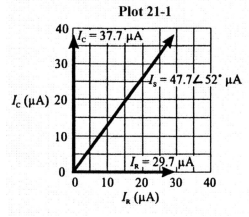

Plot 21-2

Evaluation and Review Questions:

1.   a)   The total impedance is lowered.   b)   The phase angle increases.

2.   a)   Current in R_1 is still approximately 30 μA.
   b)   The capacitor current is approximately 5 times larger than that found in step 4 or 93.5 μA.
   c)   The total current is approximately 98.2 μA.

3.   Current would be smaller in the capacitor but is the same in the resistor. Total current is less.

4.   a)   The cutoff frequency is 265 kHz.
   b)   The branch currents are equal.
   c)   Above this frequency, the capacitor has more current than the resistor.

5.   If the stray capacitance is larger, the cutoff frequency will be lower.

For Further Investigation:
   See plot to the right.

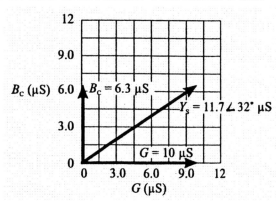

Plot 21-3

Experiment 22: Inductors

Procedure:

1. Observations: Neon bulb fires when switch is opened but not when switch is closed.

2. Observations The bulb will fire with 1 V or less from the power supply.

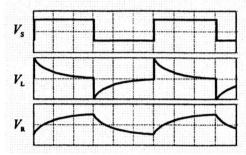

Plot 22-1

Table 22-1

	Computed	Measured
Time constant, τ	0.21 ms	0.22 ms

5. Observations: In parallel, the time constant is shorter. Consequently, the rise of the resistor voltage and fall of the inductor voltage is faster. In series, the time constant is longer, and the waveforms change at a slower rate.

Evaluation and Review Questions:

1. The opening of the switch interrupts the current and causes a very large change in current in the circuit. This large change in current induces a voltage transient across the inductor, according to Lenz's law, which is sufficient to ionize the gas in the neon bulb.

2. The arc is caused by the induced voltage that appears across the coil in response to the large change in current when the switch is opened.

3. The inductance of two 100 mH inductors connected in series is 200 mH. The inductance of two 100 mH inductors connected in parallel is 50 mH.

4. The time constant would be 10 times larger.

5. A higher frequency does not change the time constant. However, at higher frequencies, there is less time for the current to change so the voltage across the resistor approaches a dc level and the inductor voltage approaches a square wave.

For Further Investigation:

The measurement of the time constant, as performed in this experiment, can be used with a known resistor to determine the inductance of an unknown inductor.

Experiment 23: Inductive Reactance

Procedure: (computed values shown on tables)

Table 23-2

	Inductor L_1	Inductor L_2
Voltage across R_1, V_R	0.847 V	0.847 V
Total current, I	0.847 mA	0.847 mA
Voltage across L, V_L	0.532 V	0.532 V
Inductive reactance, X_L	628 Ω	628 Ω
Computed inductance, L	100 mH	100 mH

Table 23-2

Step		Series Inductor	Parallel Inductor
(a)	Voltage across R_1, V_R	0.622 V	0.954 V
	Total current, I	0.622 mA	0.954 mA
(b)	Voltage across inductors V_L	0.782 V	0.300 V
(c)	Inductive reactance, X_L	1.26 kΩ	314 Ω
(d)	Computed inductance, L	200 mH	50 mH

Evaluation and Review Questions:

1.   a)   The computed sum is 1.256 kΩ.
   b)   The computed product-over-sum is 314 Ω.
   c)   The inductive reactance of series inductors is additive. The inductive reactance of parallel inductors uses the product-over-sum rule.

2. Ignoring mutual inductance, the inductance of series inductors is additive. The inductance of parallel inductors uses the product-over-sum rule.

3. If the actual frequency is higher than the measured frequency, the inductive reactance will appear higher than its actual value and, in turn, will cause the measured inductance to appear high. If the actual frequency is lower than the measured frequency, the reverse is true.

4. Determine the current in the resistor by applying Ohm's law. Apply Ohm's law ($X_L = V_L/I$) to find the reactance of the inductor. Find the inductance by: $L = \dfrac{X_L}{2\pi f}$

5. 15.7 kΩ

For Further Investigation:

A small power transformer was tested using a 330 Ω series resistor at a frequency of 20 kHz (to increase the voltage across the windings). Results indicated an inductive reactance from center tap to either side of 220 Ω but an inductive reactance of both sides taken together of 1000 Ω. The computed inductance of each side alone was 1.7 mH but together was 8 mH! Results were checked and verified as mutual inductance was higher than expected.

Experiment 24: Series *RL* Circuits

Procedure:

<table>
<tr><td colspan="3" align="center">Table 24-1</td></tr>
<tr><td>Component</td><td>Listed Value</td><td>Measured Value</td></tr>
<tr><td>L_1</td><td>100 mH</td><td>**98 mH**</td></tr>
<tr><td>R_1</td><td>10 kΩ</td><td>**9.94 kΩ**</td></tr>
</table>

Table 24-2 (f = 25 kHz)

V_R	V_L	I	X_L	Z_T
1.6 V$_{pp}$	**2.5 V$_{pp}$**	**0.16 mA$_{pp}$**	**15.6 kΩ**	**18.6 kΩ**

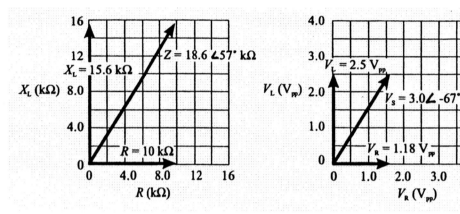

Plot 24-1

Table 24-3

Computed Phase Angle θ	Measured Period T	Time Difference Δt	Phase Angle Method 1 θ	Method 2 θ
57.5°	**40.0 μs**	**6.5 μs**	**58.5°**	**60°**

Evaluation and Review Questions:

1.   a)   The impedance increases.
     b)   The impedance increases.

2.   a)   The phase angle (seen by the generator) will increase.
     b)   The phase angle (seen by the generator) will increase.

3.   Answers will vary. A 1.7% error was observed in the test circuit.

4.   The computed critical frequency is <u>15.9 kHz</u> and the phase shift at this frequency is <u>45°</u>.

5.   a)   The current in the inductor is the same as in the resistor: <u>30 mA</u>.
     b)   The inductive reactance is <u>377 Ω</u>.
     c)   The voltage across the inductor is <u>11.3 V</u>.
     d)   The source voltage is <u>11.7 V</u>.
     e)   The phase angle is <u>75°</u>.

For Further Investigation:

     The Lissajous figure method should give a result consistent with Table 24-3.

Experiment 25: Parallel *RL* Circuits

Procedure:

Table 25-1

	Listed Value	Measured Value	Voltage Drop	Computed Current
R_1	3.3 kΩ	**3.30 kΩ**	**5.88 V$_{pp}$**	**1.78 mA$_{pp}$**
R_{S1}	47 Ω	**47 Ω**	**123 mV$_{pp}$**	**2.62 mA$_{pp}$**
R_{S2}	47 Ω	**47 Ω**	**87 mV$_{pp}$**	**1.85 mA$_{pp}$**
L_1	100 mH	**100 mH**		**1.85 mA$_{pp}$**
R_W (L_1 resistance)		**155 Ω**		

Table 25-2

Phase Angle Between:	Computed	Measured
I_T and I_R	**46.1°**	**45°**
I_R and I_L	90°	**88°**
I_T and I_L	**43.9°**	**43°**

Evaluation and Review Questions:

1.   a) $I_T = \sqrt{1.85\,\text{mA}^2 + 1.78\,\text{mA}^2} = 2.57\,\text{mA}$ √
   b)   The inductor's resistance and measurement error contribute to the differences read.

2.   The coil resistance makes the inductor look more resistive; hence reduces the phase angle.

3.   The sense resistors should be small compared to the impedance in the branch they are used.

4.   a)   The total current would equal the resistor current.
   b)   The phase angle would be 0°.
   c)   The generator voltage rises due to the reduced drop across its Thevenin resistance.

5.   a)   The total current would decrease.
   b)   The phase angle would decrease.
   c)   The generator voltage rises due to the reduced drop across its Thevenin resistance.

For Further Investigation:

The loading effects depend on the Thevenin impedance of the generator. The total impedance of the circuit is 2.3 kΩ; a 600 Ω generator represents about 26% of this impedance.

Experiment 26: Series Resonance

Procedure:

Table 26-1

	Listed Value	Measured Value
L_1	100 mH	**101 mH**
C_1	0.01 µF	**0.010 µF**
R_1	100 Ω	**101 Ω**
R_{S1}	47 Ω	**47 Ω**
R_W (L_1 resistance)		**292 Ω**

Table 26-2

	Computed	Measured
R_T	**425 Ω**	
f_r	**5003 Hz**	**5072 Hz**
Q	**7.48**	
V_{RS1}		**124 mV$_{pp}$**
f_2		**5409 Hz**
f_1		**4645 Hz**
BW	**669 Hz**	**764 Hz**

12. The voltage across the inductor and capacitor are equal; approximately Q times V_S. (7.5 V$_{pp}$)

Evaluation and Review Questions:

1. a) Answers will vary. For the test circuit, the difference was 1.4%.
   b) Measurement of components, voltage, frequency, and non-ideal components.

2. a) The total impedance at resonance is the equivalent resistance found in step 3; for the test circuit, this was 425 Ω. (Note that coil resistance in test circuit was relatively high).
   b) At resonance, the circuit appears resistive, and the phase shift is zero.

3. a) The voltages are out of phase and their sum is not greater than the source voltage; Kirchhoff's voltage law is still satisfied at each instant in time.
   b) Yes.

4. a) The resonant frequency is the same.
   b) The Q is doubled so the bandwidth is halved.

5. a) 712 kHz.
   b) $Q = 22.4$ and $BW = 31.8$ kHz.

For Further Investigation:

Data taken for test circuit:

f (Hz)	I (mA)
4000	0.74
4250	1.00
4500	1.34
4750	2.04
5000	2.46
5250	2.06
5500	1.49
5750	1.15
6000	0.69

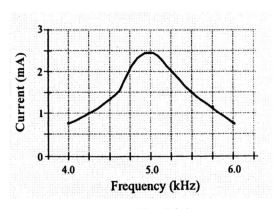

Plot 26-1

Experiment 27: Parallel Resonance

Procedure:

Table 27-1

	Listed Value	Measured Value
L_1	100 mH	**101 mH**
C_1	0.047 μF	**0.0505 μF**
R_{S1}	1.0 kΩ	**1.03 kΩ**
R_W (L_1 resistance)		**292 Ω**

Table 27-2

	Computed	Measured
f_r	**2228* Hz**	**2170 Hz**
Q	**4.84**	
BW	**460 Hz**	**506 Hz**
$f_i = \dfrac{BW}{4}$	**115 Hz**	

*listed values of components give 2251 Hz

Table 27-3

Computed Frequency	V_{RS1}	I	Z
$f_r - 5f_i$ = **1652 Hz**	**350 mV**	**340 μA**	**2.94 kΩ**
$f_r - 4f_i$ = **1768 Hz**	**285 mV**	**275 μA**	**3.64 kΩ**
$f_r - 3f_i$ = **1883 Hz**	**230 mV**	**222 μA**	**4.50 kΩ**
$f_r - 2f_i$ = **1998 Hz**	**175 mV**	**169 μA**	**5.92 kΩ**
$f_r - 1f_i$ = **2113 Hz**	**148 mV**	**143 μA**	**6.99 kΩ**
f_r = **2228 Hz**	**134 mV**	**130 μA**	**7.69 kΩ**
$f_r + 1f_i$ = **2343 Hz**	**144 mV**	**139 μA**	**7.19 kΩ**
$f_r + 2f_i$ = **2458 Hz**	**185 mV**	**179 μA**	**5.59 kΩ**
$f_r + 3f_i$ = **2573 Hz**	**235 mV**	**227 μA**	**4.40 kΩ**
$f_r + 4f_i$ = **2688 Hz**	**275 mV**	**269 μA**	**3.72 kΩ**
$f_r + 5f_i$ = **2803 Hz**	**325 mV**	**314 μA**	**3.18 kΩ**

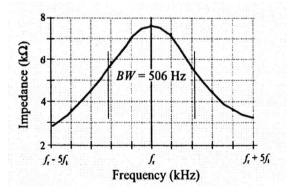

Plot 27-1

Evaluation and Review Questions:

1. a) In a series resonant circuit, the impedance is minimum at the resonant frequency; in a parallel resonant circuit, the impedance is maximum at the resonant frequency.
    b) In a series resonant circuit, the current is maximum at the resonant frequency; in a parallel resonant circuit, the current is minimum at the resonant frequency.

2. At resonance, current and voltage are in phase.

3. Ignoring the inductor's resistance, the current in the inductor is the source voltage divided by the inductive reactance; current in the capacitor is the source voltage divided by the capacitive reactance.

4. The Q depends on X_L and R_W for the coil. The circuit Q will be different than that of the inductor if there is additional resistance in the circuit.

5. a) $f_r = 5033$ Hz
    b) $X_L = 3.16$ kΩ
    c) $Q = 26.4$
    d) $BW = 191$ Hz.

For Further Investigation:

One way to calibrate the frequency is to note the amplitude of the frequency response at two points, then take the scope out of X-Y mode and change the sweep generator to a constant output frequency. Tune the generator until the same amplitude is found and the frequency is measured.

Procedure:

Measured values of components used in this experiment are: $L_1 = 101$ mH, $C_1 = 0.100$ μF, $C_2 = 0.099$ μF, $C_3 = 0.033$ μF, $R_{L1} = 681$ Ω, $R_{L2} = 1.61$ kΩ.

Measured results are shown on all tables and plots.

Table 28-2

Frequency	V_{RL1}
500 Hz	2.06 V
1000 Hz	1.94 V
1500 Hz	1.65 V
2000 Hz	1.29 V
3000 Hz	0.74 V
4000 Hz	0.44 V
8000 Hz	0.12 V

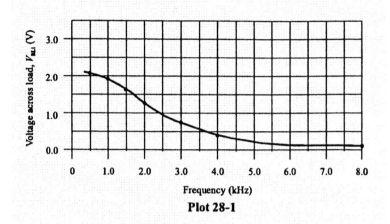

Plot 28-1

Table 28-3

Frequency	V_{RL2}
500 Hz	0.07 V
1000 Hz	0.39 V
1500 Hz	1.01 V
2000 Hz	1.70 V
3000 Hz	2.51 V
4000 Hz	2.77 V
8000 Hz	2.92 V

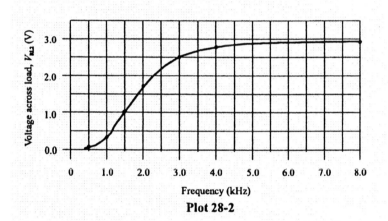

Plot 28-2

Table 28-4

Frequency	V_{RL1}
500 Hz	0.69 V
1000 Hz	1.50 V
1500 Hz	2.06 V
2000 Hz	1.81 V
3000 Hz	1.18 V
4000 Hz	0.85 V
8000 Hz	0.40 V

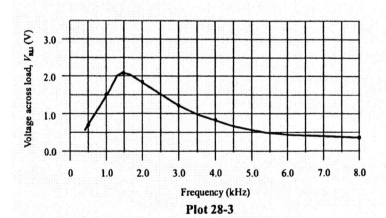

Plot 28-3

Evaluation and Review Questions:
1. Pi filter cutoff frequency = <u>1800 Hz</u> (approximate)
    T filter cutoff frequency = <u>2400 Hz</u> (approximate)

2. The cutoff frequency for the filter in Experiment 20 was nearly the same as the T filter but the frequency response of both the pi and T filters is steeper, indicating better filtering action.

3. a) Plot 28-1 (pi filter): <u>low pass</u>
    b) Plot 28-2 (T filter): <u>high pass</u>
    c) Plot 28-3 (resonant filter): <u>band pass</u>

4. The voltage across the two components (inductor and capacitor) is the difference between the source voltage and the voltage measured across the load resistor. Thus the response curve is that of a notch filter instead of a bandpass filter.

5. (a)   (b)

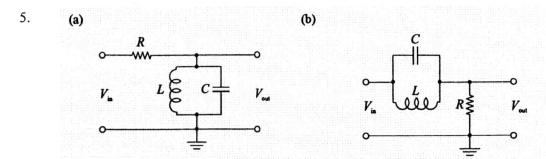

For Further Investigation:

Student results vary. A 100 mH inductor and a 0.1 µF capacitor were tested in parallel and then connected to a series 680 Ω resistor. The signal generator was kept at a constant 3.0 V. Data taken across the resistor is tabulated below:

Frequency	$V_{resistor}$
500 Hz	2.68 V
1000 Hz	2.04 V
1500 Hz	0.51 V
1640 Hz	0.40 V
2000 Hz	0.44 V
3000 Hz	0.64 V
4000 Hz	1.34 V
6000 Hz	1.86 V
8000 Hz	2.14 V

Plot 28-4

514

Experiment 29: Transformers

Procedure:

Results for a Triad F-26-X transformer (115 V_{rms} primary to 12.6 V_{rms} center-tapped secondary) are shown in Table 29-1.

Table 29-1

Primary winding resistance, R_P	**18 Ω**
Secondary winding resistance, R_S	**1 Ω***
Turns ratio, n (computed)	**0.11**
Turns ratio, n (measured)	**0.126**
% difference	**13%**

*limit of meter

5. Observations: Primary and secondary voltages are in phase.
$V_p = 14$ V_{pp}; $V_S = 1.75$ V_{pp}

6. Observations: Secondary voltages are 180° out of phase with each other.
$V_p = 14$ V_{pp}; V_S (measured from each side of the line to the center-tap) = 0.83 V_{pp}

7. Test speaker (8 Ω), $V_{SPKR} = \underline{100\ mV}$

8. Answers depend on the particular Thevenin impedance and the speaker impedance. For a 600 Ω Thevenin impedance and an 8 Ω speaker, the computed optimum turns ratio is $\underline{0.115}$.

9. Using the Triad TY30X impedance-matching transformer and same speaker, $V_{SPKR} = \underline{355\ mV}$.

Evaluation and Review Questions:

1. a) Anwers vary. For the Triad F-26-X transformer tested, the resistance ratio was $\underline{0.056}$.
   b) The wire size could be different and measurement error is present, especially for the very small secondary winding resistance.

2. The computed turns ratio assumes an ideal transformer which implies that all of the flux generated in the primary winding passes through the secondary winding. The Summary of Theory cites several other factors that contribute to the difference between the ideal and the actual transformer. These include losses due to magnetizing current, eddy current, and coil resistance.

3. The voltage across the speaker increased because the impedance-matching transformer causes the load to appear larger to the source. This means that more power can be delivered to the load.

4. The power delivered to an ideal transformer is equal to the power delivered to the load; hence if there is no load, there is (ideally) no power delivered to the primary.

5. a) The power delivered to the primary is $\underline{23\ watts}$; ideally, this is all delivered to the load.
   b) The secondary current is $\underline{0.958\ mA}$.
   c) The turns ratio is $\underline{0.209}$.

For Further Investigation:

Magnetizing current decreases as frequency is raised. Data for a Triad TY-30X impedance-matching transformer indicate a current of 1.3 mA at 1 kHz and 0.53 mA at 10 kHz.

Experiment 30: Integrating and Differentiating Circuits

Procedure:

Table 30-1

	Listed Value	Measured Value
L_1	100 mH	**101 mH**
C_1	0.01 μF	**0.010 μF**
C_2	1000 pF	**1040 pF**
R_1	10 kΩ	**9.98 kΩ**

Table 30-2

	Computed	Measured
RC time constant	**0.106 ms***	**0.10 ms**

* includes R_{TH} of 600 Ω

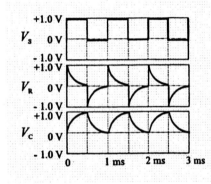

Plot 30-1

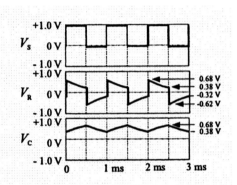

Plot 30-2

Step 6 - Triangle waveform results:
<u>Capacitor waveform looks sinusoidal, centered about 0.5 V (170 V_{pp}).</u>

Step 7 - Square wave with 1000 pF capacitor:
<u>Resistor waveform is similar to Plot 30-1, except frequency is 10× higher.</u>

Step 8 - Square wave with 100 mH inductor:

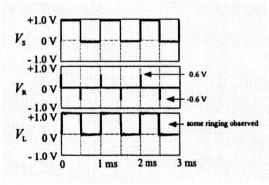

Plot 30-3

Evaluation and Review Questions:

1.   a)   The total resistance in the charging circuit includes the Thevenin resistance. By setting the output square wave with the generator disconnected, the Thevenin resistance affects only the *RC* time constant, not the final charging voltage.

        b)   Measure the resistance and the time constant for the circuit; solve for *C*.

2.   a)   Answers will vary.

        b)   Component measurements, oscilloscope calibration, instrument reading error.

3.   The capacitor does not have time to fully charge and discharge.

4.

(a) An *RC* integrating circuit:

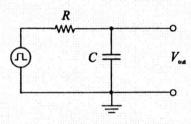

An *RC* differentiating circuit:

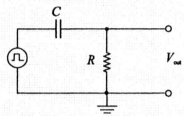

(b) An *RL* integrating circuit:

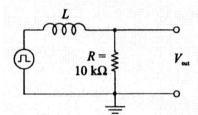

An *RL* differentiating circuit:

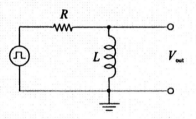

5.   The signal path could be open, causing a capacitively coupled path to the scope. At low frequencies, the input signal is differentiated.
Note: This can be demonstrated by setting up a signal generator for a large amplitude 100 Hz square wave. Attach a test lead from the generator and use an alligator clip to connect the generator to the insulated tip of an oscilloscope probe. Another way of showing a differentiated pulse is to connect the generator to a protoboard and probe on an adjacent row.

For Further Investigation:

     $R_{TH} = 5.0$ kΩ. $V_{TH} = 1.0$ V$_{pp}$. V_C will charge toward 1.0 V with a time constant of 50 µs.

Experiment 31: Diode Characteristics

Procedure:

Table 31-1

Component	Listed Value	Measured Value
R_1	330 Ω	331 Ω
R_2	1.0 MΩ	1.05 MΩ
D_1 forward resistance		500 Ω*
D_1 reverse resistance		no reading

*depends on meter

Table 31-2

V_F (measured)	V_{R1} (measured)	I_F (measured)
0.45 V	3.8 mV	11 μA
0.50 V	16.3 mV	49 μA
0.55 V	83 mV	250 μA
0.60 V	230 mV	695 μA
0.65 V	690 mV	2.08 mA
0.70 V	1.85 mV	5.59 mA
0.75 V	4.58 mV	13.8 mA

Table 31-3

V_R (measured)	V_{R2} (measured)	I_R (computed)
5.0 V	454 mV	0.43 μA
10.0 V	890 mV	0.85 μA
15.0 V	1.3 V	1.24 μA

6.   The addition of heat causes the voltage across the diode to drop resulting in an increase in diode current. Cooling the diode does the opposite.

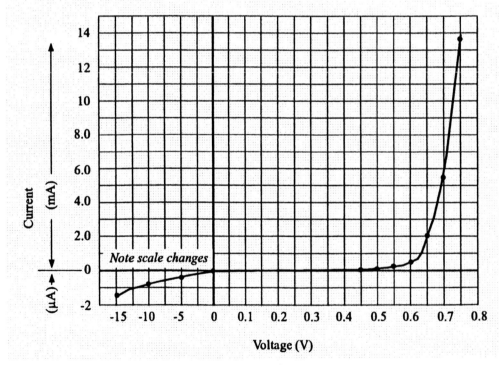

9.   Heat again causes an increase in diode current; cooling the diode does the opposite.

Evaluation and Review Questions:

1. $r_{ac}(0.5\ V) = \underline{418\ \Omega}$ $r_{ac}(0.6\ V) = \underline{55\ \Omega}$ $r_{ac}(0.7\ V) = \underline{8.5\ \Omega}$

2.   The diodes reverse resistance is constant. The change in voltage divided by the change in current is approximately the same for each data point taken.

3.   Answers vary. For the diode tested, the maximum power dissipated in the diode was 10.4 mW.

4.   The barrier potential is decreased with the addition of heat.

5.   The meter leads must be identified for the polarity of the voltage present on the ohms function. (The normal positive lead can have a negative potential). The diode resistance is measured in both directions. The cathode is connected to the most negative lead when the resistance is lowest.

6.   The anode of the diode is lead 1.

For Further Investigation:

A straight line plot will be observed on the semilog plot paper.

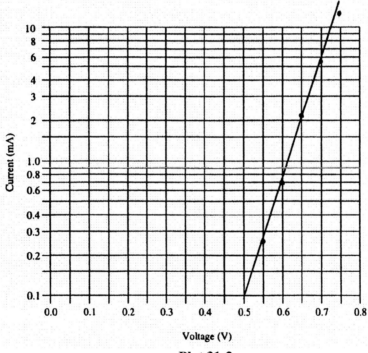

Plot 31-2

Experiment 32: Rectifier Circuits

Procedure:

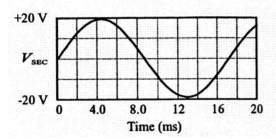
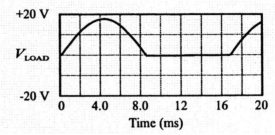

Plot 32-1

Table 32-1 Half-wave rectifier circuit.

Without Filter Capacitor				With Filter Capacitor		
Computed	Measured	Computed	Measured	Measured		Ripple Frequency
V_{IN}(rms)	V_{SEC}(rms)	V_{LOAD}(peak)	V_{LOAD} (peak)	V_{LOAD} (dc)	V_{RIPPLE}	
12.6 V ac	14.4 V_{rms}	20.3 V_p	20.0 V_p	19.1 V_{dc}	1.4 V_{pp}	60 Hz

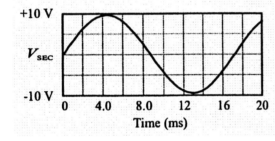
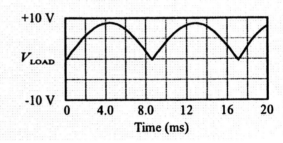

Plot 32-2

Table 32-2 Full-wave rectifier circuit.

Without Filter Capacitor				With Filter Capacitor		
Computed	Measured	Computed	Measured	Measured		Ripple Frequency
V_{SEC} (rms)	V_{SEC} (rms)	V_{LOAD} (peak)	V_{LOAD} (peak)	V_{LOAD} (dc)	V_{RIPPLE}	
6.3 V ac	7.3 V_{rms}	10.2 V_p	9.8 V_p	9.5 V_{dc}	0.35 V_{pp}	120 Hz

5.   A second parallel load resistor increases the load current and the ripple voltage.

Table 32-3 Bridge rectifier circuit.

Without Filter Capacitor				With Filter Capacitor		
Computed	Measured	Computed	Measured	Measured		Ripple Frequency
V_{SEC} (rms)	V_{SEC} (rms)	V_{LOAD} (peak)	V_{LOAD} (peak)	V_{LOAD} (dc)	V_{RIPPLE}	
12.6 V ac	14.5 V_{rms}	20.5 V_p	19.5 V_p	19.0 V_{dc}	0.65 V_{pp}	120 Hz

8.   The output voltage drops. The ripple voltage is doubled; ripple frequency is 60 Hz.

Evaluation and Review Questions:

1.   The full-wave circuit is more efficient and has less ripple than the half-wave circuit.

2.   Given a specific transformer and load, the bridge circuit has a higher output voltage and current (nearly double). For both configurations, the diode current is approximately one-half the dc load current, but because of the bridge's higher output voltage, the diode currents will be greater.

3.   If a diode is open in a bridge circuit, the ripple frequency will be halved.

4.   If the scope ground is the same as the center-tap of the transformer, the probes need to be connected as shown to avoid placing a direct short across the secondary.

5.   a)   The bridge output voltage is the peak voltage minus two diode drops = 24 Vdc.
        b)   The full-wave output voltage is one-half peak voltage minus one diode drop = 12 Vdc.

For Further Investigation:

The test circuit output had approximately 1 mV of ripple. The ripple waveform showed only the tip of the positive waveform. Noise level was less than 1 mV.

Experiment 33: Bipolar Junction Transistors

Procedure:

Table 33-1

	Listed Value	Measured Value
R_1	33 kΩ	**32.8 kΩ**
R_2	100 Ω	**104 Ω**

Values shown are for a 2N3904 transistor.

Table 33-2

V_{CE} (measured)	Base Current = 50 μA		Base Current = 100 μA		Base Current = 150 μA	
	V_{R2} (measured)	I_C (computed)	V_{R2} (measured)	I_C (computed)	V_{R2} (measured)	I_C (computed)
2.0 V	**0.900 V**	**8.65 mA**	**1.91 V**	**18.4 mA**	**2.93 V**	**28.2 mA**
4.0 V	**0.931 V**	**8.95 mA**	**2.01 V**	**19.3 mA**	**3.14 V**	**30.2 mA**
6.0 V	**0.955 V**	**9.18 mA**	**2.13 V**	**20.5 mA**	**3.38 V**	**32.5 mA**
8.0 V	**0.992 V**	**9.54 mA**	**2.23 V**	**21.4 mA**	**3.58 V**	**34.4 mA**

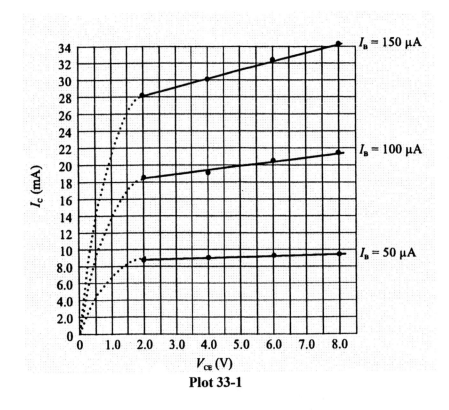

Plot 33-1

Table 33-3

V_{CE}	Current Gain, β_{dc}		
	$I_B = 50\ \mu A$	$I_B = 100\ \mu A$	$I_B = 150\ \mu A$
3.0 V	176	189	193
5.0 V	192	200	209

Evaluation and Review Questions:

1. For the test transistor, the β_{dc} was not constant at all points (see Plot 33-1). This has an effect on linearity as the gain will change as the operating point changes.

2. It would raise all of the curves.

3. Answers vary. For the test transistor, maximum power dissipated was 8 V × 34 mA = 272 mW.

4. a) $\beta_{dc} = \dfrac{I_C}{I_B}$

    $\alpha = \dfrac{I_C}{I_E} = \dfrac{I_C}{I_C + I_B} = \dfrac{I_C / I_B}{I_C / I_B + I_B / I_B} = \dfrac{\beta_{dc}}{\beta_{dc} + 1}$

    b) Answers vary. The alpha for the test transistor was approximately 0.995.

5. V_{CE} would equal V_{CE}. Without base current, there would be no collector current and the supply voltage would appear across the transistor.

For Further Investigation:

The transistor curve tracer confirms the result plotted in Plot 33-1. Heating the transistor causes the beta to rise.

Experiment 34: The Common-Emitter Amplifier

Procedure:

Table 34-1

Resistor	Listed Value	Measured Value
R_1	47 kΩ	**47.3 kΩ**
R_2	10 kΩ	**10.1 kΩ**
R_3	10 kΩ	**10.1 kΩ**
R_4	100 Ω	**99 Ω**
R_E	2.2 kΩ	**2.20 kΩ**
R_C	6.8 kΩ	**6.92 kΩ**
R_L	10 kΩ	**10.1 kΩ**

Table 34-2

DC Parameter	Computed Value	Measured Value
V_B	**1.76 V**	**1.74 V**
V_E	**1.06 V**	**1.10 V**
I_E	**0.48 mA**	
V_C	**6.66 V**	**6.56 V**
V_{CE}	**5.60 V**	**5.46 V**

Table 34-3

AC Parameter	Computed Value	Measured Value
$V_b = V_{in}$	**10 mV$_{pp}$**	**10 mV*$_{pp}$**
r_e	**52 Ω**	
A_v	**78.8**	**75**
$V_c = V_{out}$	**788 mV$_{pp}$**	**750 mV$_{pp}$**
$R_{in(T)}$	**3.19 kΩ**	**3.0 kΩ**

*Based on setting V_S to 1.0 V$_{pp}$

7. V_{in} and V_{out} are 180 degrees out of phase.

8. The gain drops when C_2 is opened.

9. The gain rises with R_L removed.

10. Transistor is cutoff since there is no path for base current. (Note that a measurement of V_{CE} could mislead student to thinking transistor is near saturation; however, the power supply voltage is across the reverse biased base-collector junction, not across RC).

11. Transistor is saturated. V_C and V_E are nearly the same and current is limited only by R_C and R_E. Maximum current is in the collector circuit.

Evaluation and Review Questions:

1. When C_2 is open, the ac resistance of the emitter circuit is increased. Since voltage gain is the ratio of the ac collector resistance divided by the ac emitter resistance, the gain is reduced.

2. Monitoring the output voltage ensures that the amplifier is performing normally during the test. If the output is clipped or distorted, the measurement is invalid.

3. The collector resistance is too high causing saturation to occur at approximately 0.5 mA. (Approximately 20 kΩ in the collector circuit will give these conditions).

4. a) dc base voltage $= + 0.7$ V
    b) dc collector voltage $= + 0.1$ V

5. Measure V_{CE}. If V_{CE} is near zero, the transistor is saturated; if V_{CE} is equal to V_{CC} the transistor is cutoff.

6. A "stiff" voltage divider implies that the load current is small compared to the current in the divider (normally I_L is <0.1 of $I_{divider}$). For voltage divider bias, this means that a change in conditions (variations in transistors or other circuits parameters) will have little effect on the base voltage.

For Further Investigation:

The lower cutoff frequency is approximately 80 Hz. The capacitors affect only the lower cutoff frequency. If C_1 and C_2 are switched, the new lower cutoff frequency is approximately 3.1 kHz (due to C_1).

Procedure:

Table 35-1

	Listed Value	Measured Value
R_1	33 kΩ	**32.8 kΩ**
R_2	100 Ω	**100 Ω**

Values shown are for a 2N5458 transistor: **Table 35-2**

V_{DS} (measured)	Gate Voltage = 0 V		Gate Voltage = –1.0 V		Gate Voltage = –2 V	
	V_{R2} (measured)	I_D (computed)	V_{R2} (measured)	I_D (computed)	V_{R2} (measured)	I_D (computed)
1.0 V	**0.320 V**	**3.2 mA**	**0.208 V**	**2.1 mA**	**0.109 V**	**1.1 mA**
2.0 V	**0.510 V**	**5.1 mA**	**0.310 V**	**3.1 mA**	**0.133 V**	**1.3 mA**
3.0 V	**0.604 V**	**6.0 mA**	**0.345 V**	**3.5 mA**	**0.140 V**	**1.4 mA**
4.0 V	**0.639 V**	**6.4 mA**	**0.357 V**	**3.6 mA**	**0.142 V**	**1.4 mA**
6.0 V	**0.640 V**	**6.4 mA**	**0.364 V**	**3.6 mA**	**0.145 V**	**1.5 mA**
8.0 V	**0.645 V**	**6.5 mA**	**0.367 V**	**3.7 mA**	**0.147 V**	**1.5 mA**

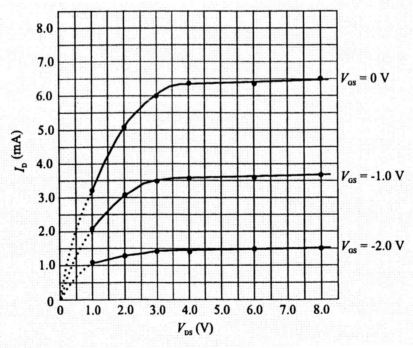

Plot 35-1

10.   Between V_{GS} and 0 V and –1 V, the test transistor had a transconductance of 2760 μS.

Evaluation and Review Questions:

1. a) Measure the drain current in the flat portion of the $V_{GS} = 0$ V curve.
    b) Answers vary. I_{DSS} for the test transistor was found to be 6.5 mA.

2. Tie gate and source leads together.

3. a) The transconductance is not constant. This can be seen by measuring it using two different changes of V_{GS}.
    b) The V_{GS} curves are not equally far apart.

4. Answers vary. $V_{GS(off)}$ for the test transistor was found to be -3.5 V.

5. The gate-source junction of a JFET forms a *PN* diode. If a positive gate voltage is applied to this junction, it would be forward-biased, causing diode conduction and lowering the input impedance.

For Further Investigation:

Data for a 2N5458 transistor is shown. The plot of $\sqrt{I_D}$ versus V_{GS} is linear as shown below as the dashed line. I_D versus V_{GS} is the solid line.

Table 35-3

V_{GS} (measured)	I_D (measured)	$\sqrt{I_D}$ (computed)
0.0 V	6.5 mA	2.55 $\sqrt{mA}$
−0.5 V	4.9 mA	2.21 $\sqrt{mA}$
−1.0 V	3.7 mA	1.92 $\sqrt{mA}$
−1.5 V	2.5 mA	1.58 $\sqrt{mA}$
−2.0 V	1.5 mA	1.22 $\sqrt{mA}$
−2.5 V	0.71 mA	0.84 $\sqrt{mA}$
−3.0 V	0.16 mA	0.40 $\sqrt{mA}$
−3.5 V	0.02 mA	0.14 $\sqrt{mA}$
−4.0 V	(pinchoff) 0	0
−4.5 V	0	0
−5.0 V	0	0

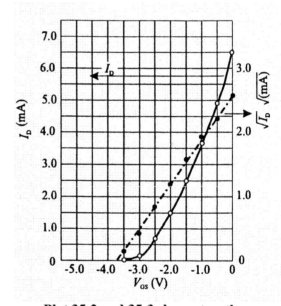

Plot 35-2 and 35-3 shown together

Procedure:

Resistors: $R_1 = 9.98$ kΩ, $R_2 = 3.31$ kΩ, $R_{E1} = 50$ Ω*, $R_{E2} = 1.01$ kΩ, $R_C = 2.69$ kΩ

*Potentiometer set to 50 Ω

Table 36-2

DC Parameter	Computed Value	Measured Value
V_B	3.01 V	2.97 V
V_E	2.31 V	2.32 V
I_E	2.18 mA	
V_C	6.11 V	6.07 V

Table 36-3

AC Parameter	Computed Value	Measured Value
V_b	100 mV$_{pp}$	100 mV$_{pp}$
r_e	61.5 Ω	
A_v	43.9	39.0
V_c	4.39 V$_{pp}$	3.90 V$_{pp}$

5. The measured frequency decreased to 781 kHz. (Slight distortion noted on bottom of waveform before and after this change).

6. Both the amplitude and the frequency of the oscillator decreased.

Table 36-4

Colpitts Oscillator	Computed Value	Measured Value
Frequency	1.06 MHz	1.04 MHz
V_{pp}		7.4 V$_{pp}$

Table 36-5

Hartley Oscillator	Computed Value	Measured Value
Frequency	969 kHz	961 kHz
V_{pp}		5.5 V$_{pp}$

Evaluation and Review Questions:

1. The amount of feedback decreased.

2. The two conditions are positive feedback and a loop gain equal to or greater than 1.

3. Temperature change can cause a frequency drift in an oscillator.

4. In the Hartley oscillator, an inductor is used to provide positive feedback from the tank circuit; in a Colpitts oscillator, a capacitor is used to supply positive feedback.

5. a) Gain will increase, so the output will increase and clip.
    b) Feedback voltage will increase, output will increase and clip.
    c) Gain will decrease, so oscillation may cease.
    d) Output will decrease.

For Further Investigation:

The oscillator frequency measured for the test circuit was 990 kHz, with a varying amplitude (probably due to thermal effects.) Freeze spray caused oscillations to cease. As the temperature rose, the circuit resumed oscillating.

Experiment 37: The Differential Amplifier

Procedure:

Resistors: $R_{B1} = 47.2$ kΩ, $R_{B2} = 47.0$ kΩ, $R_{E1} = 47.6$ Ω, $R_{E2} = 48.1$ Ω, $R_T = 9.92$ kΩ, $R_C = 9.90$ kΩ.

Table 37-2

DC Parameter	Computed Value	Measured Values	
		Q_1	Q_2
I_E	557 μA		
I_B	2.78 μA*		
V_B	–0.13 V	–0.162 V	–0.149 V
V_E	–0.83 V	–0.77 V	–0.76 V
V_A	–0.86 V	–0.79 V	
$V_{C(Q2)}$	6.43 V		5.84 V

*using measured $\beta_{dc} = 200$)

Table 37-3

AC Parameter	Computed Value	Measured Value
r_e	44.9 Ω	
$V_{b(Q1)}$	100 mV$_{pp}$	100 mV$_{pp}$
$V_{A(ac)}$	50 mV$_{pp}$	50 mV$_{pp}$
$V_{v(d)}$	54.4	48
$V_{c(Q2)}$	5.4 V$_{pp}$	4.8 V$_{pp}$
A_{cm}	–0.50	–0.52

Evaluation and Review Questions:

1.   Computed = 40.6 dB. Measured 39.3 dB.

2.   The current in the tail resistor has emitter currents from both transistors.

3.   Ignoring the tail resistor, the signal at point **A** is between $R_{E2} + r_{e(Q2)}$ and ground. The input signal is applied to the base of Q_1 and is between $r_{e(Q1)} + R_{E1} + R_{E2}, + r_{e(Q2)}$ and ground. The voltage at point **A** is found by applying the voltage divider rule. The gain is 0.5.

4.   By applying Kirchhoff's voltage law, $V_A = -1.26$ V.

5. R_C shorted, Q_2 open, R_{E2} open.

For Further Investigation:

The addition of the current source will significantly improve the common-mode rejection ratio. The test circuit measured 66 dB for CMRR.

Experiment 38: Op-Amp Characteristics

Procedure:

Resistors: $R_f = 1.01$ MΩ, $R_i = 10.2$ kΩ, $R_C = 10.2$ kΩ, $R_1 = 102$ kΩ, $R_2 = 102$ kΩ, $R_A = 102$ Ω, $R_B = 101$ Ω, $R_C = 102$ kΩ, $R_D = 102$ kΩ.

Table 38-1

Step	Parameter	Specified Value			Measured Value
		Minimum	Typical	Maximum	
2d	Input offset voltage, V_{IO}		2.0 mV	6.0 mV	0.66 mV
3d	Input bias current, I_{BIAS}		80 nA	500 nA	98 nA
3e	Input offset current, I_{OS}		20 nA	200 nA	1 nA
4b	Differential gain, $A_{v(d)}$				1000
4c	Common-mode gain, A_{cm}				0.032
4d	CMRR	70 dB	90 dB		89.9 dB

Evaluation and Review Questions:

1. (+) means non-inverting input.
   (−) means inverting input.

2. The dc voltage that must be applied between the op-amp's inputs to produce zero volts output.

3. The input bias current is the average of the input currents; the input offset current is the difference between the input currents when the output voltage is 0 V.

4. Differential gain is the amplification of the voltage between the inputs of the op-amp; common mode gain is the amplification of the voltage present at both inputs of the op-amp.

5. A common-mode signal was placed on both inputs of the op-amp and the gain was measured. The differential gain was computed. The ratio of the differential gain to the common-mode gain was calculated and then converted to dB. A high CMRR means that less common-mode noise will appear at the output.

For Further Investigation:

The measured slew rate was 800 mV/μs. (min. specified = 300 mV/μs. typical = 700 mV/μs.)

Experiment 39: Linear Op-Amp Circuits

Procedure:

Table 39-1

R_f Measured Value	R_i Measured Value	V_{in} Measured	$A_{cl(NI)}$ Computed	V_{out} Computed	V_{out} Measured (pin 6)	$V_{(-)}$ Measured (pin 2)	R_{in} Measured
10.2 kΩ	1.02 kΩ	500 mV$_{pp}$	11	5.5 V$_{pp}$	5.5 V$_{pp}$	500 mV$_{pp}$	5 MΩ

Table 39-2

R_f Measured Value	R_i Measured Value	V_{in} Measured	$A_{cl(NI)}$ Computed	V_{out} Computed	V_{out} Measured (pin 6)	$V_{(-)}$ Measured (pin 2)	R_{in} Measured
10.2 kΩ	1.02 kΩ	500 mV$_{pp}$	−10	−5.0 V$_{pp}$	−4.95 V$_{pp}$	0 V	1.0 kΩ

3. The circuit is shown to the right. The closed-loop gain was −47 with a 100 mV$_{pp}$ input. The output becomes slew-rate limited when the input frequency is above 10 kHz. With 100 mV$_{pp}$ input, f_{MAX} was approximately 40 kHz. With 500 mV$_{pp}$ input, f_{MAX} was approximately 10 kHz. For a slew rate, S, at a frequency, f, the output is limited to $V_{out(pp)} < S/\pi f$.

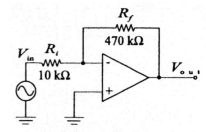

Evaluation and Review Questions:

1. Amplifier 1 gain = 20 log (11) = 20.8 dB.
    Amplifier 2 gain = 20 log (10) = 20.0 dB.

2. Operational amplifiers are dc amplifiers using positive and negative power supplies to enable the input to go above and below ground reference.

3. a) $A_{cl(NI)} = 2$.
    b) $A_{cl(I)} = -1$.

4. a) Unity gain.
    b) Voltage-follower.

5. A square wave due to the amplifier operating with open-loop gain.

For Further Investigation:

The ohmmeter accuracy depends on the standard resistor, meter used and the op-amp. The test circuit readings were within 3% of a lab DMM.

Experiment 40: Nonlinear Op-Amp Circuits

Procedure:

Table 40-1

V_{OUT}		V_{ref} Threshold
Red On	Green On	
+2.1 V	–2.0 V	0.001 V

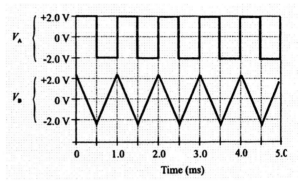

Plot 40-1

3. Duty cycle changes as R_3 is varied. Output **B** slope changes to follow.

Table 40-2

Trouble	Symptoms
No negative power supply	**Red LED on, B goes to positive saturation**
Red LED open	**A = –2 V to positive sat.**
	B = negative sat. + small deviations
C_1 open	**B goes to a square wave (saturation).**
R_4 open	**no change in A; B goes toward negative sat.**

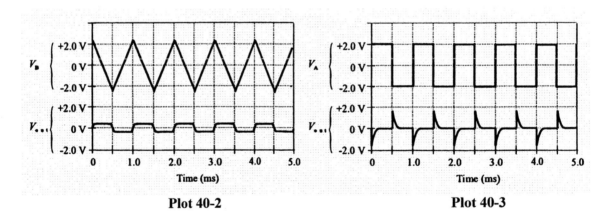

Plot 40-2   **Plot 40-3**

Evaluation and Review Questions:

1. $V_{ref(min)} = \underline{-714\ mV}$ $V_{ref(max)} = \underline{+714\ mV}$

2.   The LEDs drop a maximum of about 2.0 V at the op-amp's current limit.

3.   a) R_4 establishes a virtual ground at the inverting input through negative feedback and stabilizes the operating point. Without it, the output will saturate.
      b)   The output went to a negative saturation.

4.   Differentiator circuit.

5.   Higher amplitude due to longer charging of the capacitor until clipping occurs on both the positive and negative peaks.

For Further Investigation:
The output switches between positive and negative saturation. The positive trip point was +0.61 V and the negative trip point was −0.61 V. This can be observed by comparing input and output waveforms on a two-channel oscilloscope.

Experiment 41: The Wien Bridge Oscillator

Procedure:

2.   The output saturates on both positive and negative peaks. Freeze spray causes circuit to change; some components cause oscillations to cease, others cause changes in the saturation level.

Table 41-2

f_r	
Computed	Measured (pin 6)
1.59 kHz	**1.46 kHz**

Table 41-3

Measured Voltages			
$V_{out(pp)}$ (pin 6)	$V_{(+)(pp)}$ (pin 3)	$V_{(-)(pp)}$ (pin 2)	V_{GATE}
4.0 V$_{pp}$	**1.5 V$_{pp}$**	**1.5 V$_{pp}$**	**−1.0 V$_{pp}$**

5.   The phase shift between the output and the feedback voltage is 0 degrees (positive feedback).

6.   Very little effect with freeze spray. The output is much more stable.

Table 41-4

Measured Voltages—Extra Diode			
$V_{out(pp)}$ (pin 6)	$V_{(+)(pp)}$ (pin 3)	$V_{(-)(pp)}$ (pin 2)	V_{GATE}
4.6 V$_{pp}$	**1.56 V$_{pp}$**	**1.56 V$_{pp}$**	**−1.29 V$_{dc}$**

Evaluation and Review Questions:

1.   Feedback fraction is very close to 1/3. The measured result agrees with theory.

2.   The extra diode causes C_3 to charge for a smaller part of the cycle decreasing V_G. This causes the FET resistance to drop and (temporarily) increases the op-amp's gain. The op-amp's output increases until the charge on C_3 is returned to the proper level for a stable output.

3.   The diode causes the negative half-cycle of the output to charge the capacitor and bias the FET with a negative bias voltage.

4.   The frequency is halved to 790 Hz.

5.   Use a ganged resistor for R_1 and R_2 or a ganged capacitor for C_1 and C_2.

For Further Investigation:

The bulb will help stabilize the output. Some instability remains as can be demonstrated by touching the non-inverting input.

Experiment 42: Active Filters

Procedure:

Table 42-2

Component	Listed Values	Measured Values			
		1	2	3	4
R_1 to R_4	8.2 kΩ	**8.17 kΩ**	**8.37 kΩ**	**8.00 kΩ**	**8.22 kΩ**
C_1 to C_4	0.01 μF	**0.010 μF**	**0.010 μF**	**0.010 μF**	**0.010 μF**
R_{i1}	10 kΩ	**10.1 kΩ**			
R_{f1}	1.5 kΩ	**1.50 kΩ**			
R_{i2}	22 kΩ	**21.9 kΩ**			
R_{f2}	27 kΩ	**26.8 kΩ**			

Table 42-3

Frequency	V_{RL}
500 Hz	**2.55 V**
1000 Hz	**2.52 V**
1500 Hz	**2.45 V**
2000 Hz	**1.72 V**
3000 Hz	**0.45 V**
4000 Hz	**0.14 V**
8000 Hz	**0.009 V**

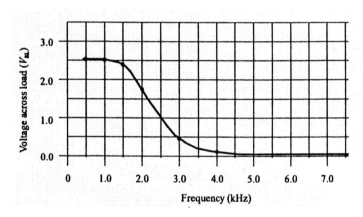

Plot 42-1

Note: Data from Table 42-3 is also plotted on Plot 42-2 shown on the next page.

Evaluation and Review Questions:

1. a) The cutoff frequency is approximately 2 kHz.
    b) Answers vary.

2. The transition region is much steeper.

3. The output voltage is reduced by a factor of 104 (80 dB) which is approximately 250 μV.

4. Actual filter is very close to theoretical roll-off rate.

5. a) Answers vary. Required gain for first section is 1.152.
    b) Required gain for second section is 2.235.

For Further Investigation:

The 6-pole filter will have a theoretical roll-off of −120 dB. Gains for each section are listed in Table 42-1. The frequency determining resistors and capacitors will depend on the student design.

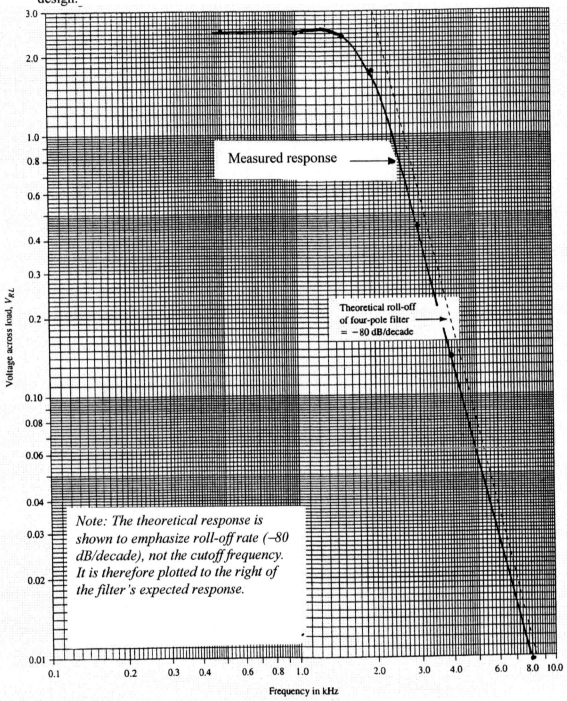

Note: The theoretical response is shown to emphasize roll-off rate (−80 dB/decade), not the cutoff frequency. It is therefore plotted to the right of the filter's expected response.

Measured response ⟶

Theoretical roll-off of four-pole filter ⟶ = −80 dB/decade

Frequency in kHz

Voltage across load, V_{RL}

Plot 42-2 (Data from Table 42-3)

Experiment 43: The Instrumentation Amplifier

Procedure:

Table 43-1

Resistor	Listed Value	Measured Value
R_1	10 kΩ	**9.87 kΩ**
R_2	10 kΩ	**9.87 kΩ**
R_G	470 Ω	**463 Ω**
R_3	10 kΩ	**9.91 kΩ**
R_4	10 kΩ	**9.87 kΩ**
R_5	10 kΩ	**9.88 kΩ**
R_6	8.2 kΩ	**8.10 kΩ**
R_8	100 kΩ	**101 kΩ**
R_9	100 kΩ	**100 kΩ**

Table 43-2

Step	Parameter	Computed Value	Measured Value
3	Differential Input Voltage, $V_{in(d)}$	300 mV$_{pp}$	**300 mV$_{pp}$**
	Differential Gain, $A_{v(d)}$	**43.5**	**43.0**
	Differential Output Voltage, $V_{out(d)}$	**13.1 V$_{pp}$**	**13.0 V$_{pp}$**
4	Common-mode Input Voltage, $V_{in(cm)}$	10 V$_{pp}$	**10.0 V$_{pp}$**
	Common-mode Gain, $A_{v(cm)}$		**0.008**
	Common-mode Output Voltage, $V_{out(cm)}$		**80 mV$_{pp}$**
5	CMRR′		**74.6 dB**

8. The differential signal, provided by the 555 timer, was a 682 Hz (measured) square wave with amplitude of approximately 200 mV. The differential-mode signal was amplified by the IA but the 10 V$_{pp}$ common-mode signal, provided by the signal generator, was almost completely eliminated from the output as viewed on an oscilloscope.

Evaluation and Review Questions:

1. Any noise that comes into the IA in differential-mode form cannot be eliminated from the output. This includes thermal noise, shot noise, or other noise from the source. It can also include any common-mode signal that has been converted to a differential signal.

2. A CMRR′ of 130 dB means the ratio of the differential- to common-mode gain is 3.16×10^6. This implies that the common-mode gain for the experiment is $43/3.16 \times 10^6 = 13.6 \times 10^{-6}$. The expected output signal is $10 \text{ V}_{pp} \times 13.6 \times 10^{-6} = 136 \text{ μV}_{pp}$.

3. The oscillator signal was a differential mode signal but the signal generator was a common-mode signal.

4. The reference ground for the 555 timer needs to be isolated from the reference ground for the IA. The simplest way to do this is power it from an independent source.

5.   Both inputs to the IA are balanced and have relatively high input impedance. (In the experiment, the input impedance was 100 kΩ, but it can be much higher).

For Further Investigation:
When R_B was replaced with a CdS cell, the frequency varied from 520 Hz (dark) to 7.9 kHz (bright room light). An application is a digital light meter (or any other case where the intensity of light needs to be assigned a numeric value).

Experiment 44: Active Diode Circuits

Procedure:

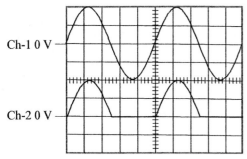

Ch-1 0 V

Ch-2 0 V

Vertical = 1 V/div Horizontal = 1 ms/div

Plot 44-1

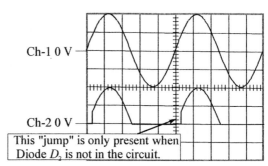

Ch-1 0 V

Ch-2 0 V

This "jump" is only present when Diode D_2 is not in the circuit.

Vertical = 1 V/div Horizontal = 100 μs/div

Plot 44-2

4.   With the extra diode, the output of the op-amp is pulled to one diode drop below ground during the negative half cycle. As a result, it does not have a large change in voltage, and the slew rate limiting, shown in Plot 44-2, is eliminated.

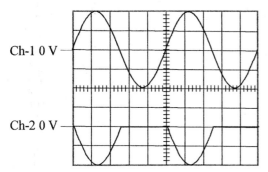

Ch-1 0 V

Ch-2 0 V

Vertical = 1 V/div Horizontal = 1 ms/div

Plot 44-3

6.   Any portion of the negative portion of the input sine wave can be removed by adjusting R_3. When the dc voltage is less than –2 V, the entire sine wave appears at the output; when it is above +2 V, only a positive dc level is observed.

7.   Reversing the diode causes a portion of the positive signal to be removed. When the dc voltage is greater than +2 V, the entire sine wave appears at the output; when it is less than -2 V, only a negative dc level is observed.

8.   When the reference level on pin 3 is set for zero volts, an active positive clamping circuit is observed at the output. With a 4 Vpp input signal, the dc level on the output can be adjusted from about -2.3 V (measured) to about +5.0 V (measured).

9.   When the reference level on pin 3 is set for zero volts, an active negative clamping circuit is observed at the output. With a 4 Vpp input signal, the dc level on the output can be adjusted from about –5.0 V (measured) to about +2.0 V (measured).

10.   The output is a dc level that follows the peak. There is about 100 mV of "droop" at 200 Hz with a 4 V_{pp} input signal.

Evaluation and Review Questions:

1. a) Pin 6 will be about $+1.7$ V (one diode drop higher than the input).
    b) Pin 2 will be $+1.0$ V.

2. a) Pin 6 will be approximately -13 V (negative saturation) because the feedback path is open.
    b) Pin 2 will be 0 V.

3. The current limit of the op-amp (about 25 mA).

4. Approximately ± 5 V.

5. The load resistor forms an unwanted voltage divider with the input signal and must be much larger than the input resistance of 10 kΩ to avoid loading effects.

For Further Investigation:

The circuit is a full-wave negative rectifier. Reversing the diode creates a positive full-wave rectifier. It is common for every other cycle to have higher amplitude. This is caused by a gain difference in the two paths – it can be balanced by changing the gain in one of the paths using a variable resistor.

Experiment 45: The SCR

Procedure:

Table 45-1

Resistor	Listed Value	Measured Value
R_1	1.0 kΩ	**993 Ω**
R_3	160 Ω	**161 Ω**
R_4	1.0 kΩ	**1.001 kΩ**
R_5	10 kΩ	**9.94 kΩ**

Table 45-2

	Transistor Latch	SCR
V_{AK} (off state)	**13.5 V**	**13.5 V**
V_{AK} (on state)	**0.803 V**	**0.769 V**
$V_{Gate\ Trigger}$	**0.768 V**	**0.736 V**
V_{R4}	**3.42 V**	**3.83 V**
$I_{Holding\ (min)}$	**3.42 mA**	**3.83 mA**

7. S_1 turns on the SCR. S_2 turns it off.

8.

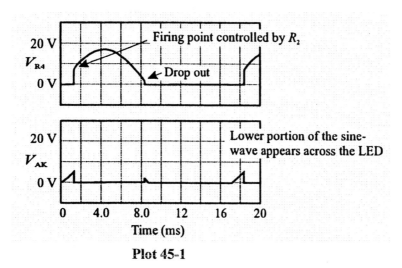

Plot 45-1

Evaluation and Review Questions:

1.   Lower anode voltage so that the current drops below the holding current.

2.   Commutation refers to the process of interrupting anode current or "opening" a solid-state switch.

3.   A short to the anode removes the load resistance for the power supply. The power supply's short circuit current may be higher than the SCR's peak current.

4.   The LED is on all the time and S_2 would not be able to turn it off.

5.   The voltage across R_4 is proportional to the conduction current. The SCR is on for a shorter time and the back of the SCR waveform will drop earlier.

For Further Investigation:

Waveforms are similar to those in Plot 45-1 but the photocell will cause the SCR trigger point to vary according to the light level. Applications include alarms, automatic night lighting control, or light control of a process.

Multisim Troubleshooting Solutions
The following are the file names and simulated troubles for the circuits. The password for the Global Restrictions is testbench. Circuits can be read on the website by choosing "Files of type: msm" in the Open window.

Folder Name: Lab-07

File Name	Fault
EXP7-4-nf	none
EXP7-4-f1	R2 is open
EXP7-4-f2	VS = 12 V but should be 15 V
EXP7-4-f3	R3 is shorted

Folder Name: Lab-08

File Name	Fault
EXP8-3-nf	none
EXP8-3-f1	potentiometer has open pin 3
EXP8-3-f2	R1 is shorted
EXP8-3-f3	source voltage is 8 V but should be 10 V

Folder Name: Lab-10

File Name	Fault
EXP10-2-nf	none
EXP10-2-f1	R3 is open
EXP10-2-f2	R1 is shorted
EXP10-2-f3	R4 is open

Folder Name: Lab-11

File Name	Fault
EXP11-1-nf	none
EXP11-1-f1	VS1 open
EXP11-1-f2	R3 open
EXP11-1-f3	VS1 is reversed

Folder Name: Lab-12

File Name	Fault
EXP12-3-nf	none
EXP12-3-f1	R2 is shorted
EXP12-3-f2	R3 is open
EXP12-3-f3	RL is 60 ohms but should be 150 ohms due to leakage.

Folder Name: Lab-13

File Name	Fault
EXP13-7-nf	none
EXP13-7-f1	RL is shorted
EXP13-7-f2	R1 shorted
EXP13-7-f3	R2 is actually only 220 ohms (by adding "leakage")

Folder Name: Lab-19

File Name	Fault
EXP19-2-nf	none
EXP19-2-f1	R1 open
EXP19-2-f2	C1 open
EXP19-2-f3	C3 has leakage resistance

Folder Name: Lab-20

File Name	Fault
EXP20-2nf	none
EXP20-2f1	R1 shorted
EXP20-2f2	C1 shorted
EXP20-2f3	C1 has leakage resistance

Folder Name: Lab-21

File Name	Fault
EXP21-2-nf	none
EXP21-2-f1	RS2 shorted
EXP21-2-f2	R1 open
EXP21-2-f3	C1 shorted

Folder Name: Lab-23

File Name	Fault
EXP23-2-nf	none
EXP23-2-f1	R1 has leakage of 0 ohms
EXP23-2-f2	L1 shorted
EXP23-2-f3	Ammeter open

Folder Name: Lab-26

File Name	Fault
EXP26-3-nf	none
EXP26-3-f1	L1 is open
EXP26-3-f2	Bode plotter input connected to wrong side of inductor
EXP26-3-f3	C1 has 50 ohms leakage

Folder Name: Lab-27

File Name	Fault
EXP27-3-nf	none
EXP27-3-f1	L1 open
EXP27-3-f2	leads to Bode plotter are reversed (no circuit fault)
EXP27-3-f3	C1 has leakage resistance

Folder Name: Lab-28

File Name	Fault
EXP28-3-nf	none
EXP28-3-f1	C2 open
EXP28-3-f2	RL open
EXP28-3-f3	function generator has -800 mV dc offset

Folder Name: Lab-30

File Name	Fault
EXP30-3nf	none
EXP30-3f1	L1 has leakage resistance
EXP30-3f2	C1 open
EXP30-3f3	R1 has leakage resistance

Folder Name: Lab-32

File Name	Fault
EXP32-3-nf	none
EXP32-3-f1	D1 has leakage resistance
EXP32-3-f2	R1 is shorted
EXP32-3-f3	T1 pins 1 and 3 shorted

Folder Name: Lab-34

File Name	Fault
EXP34-3-nf	none
EXP34-3-f1	RE open
EXP34-3-f2	C2 open
EXP34-3-f3	R2 open

Folder Name: Lab-37

File Name	Fault
EXP37-2-nf	none
EXP37-2-f1	RC Shorted
EXP37-2-f2	C2 open
EXP37-2-f3	-12 Volt DC open

Folder Name: Lab-39

File Name	Fault
EXP39-3-nf	none
EXP39-3-f1	Switch J1 shorted
EXP39-3-f2	Rf open
EXP39-3-f3	Ri1 shorted

Folder Name: Lab-40

File Name	Fault
EXP40-3-nf	none
EXP40-3-f1	Generator set to 100 Hz instead of 1 kHz
EXP40-3-f2	Green LED is open
EXP40-3-f3	R4 open

Folder Name: Lab-41

File Name	Fault
EXP41-3-nf	none
EXP41-3-f1	C2 is incorrect value (0.0047 micro); can be found by inspection.
EXP41-3-f2	C3 shorted. May look like R4 or FET is the problem; needs to be removed for confirmation.
EXP41-3-f3	Q1 is shorted from drain to source

Folder Name: Lab-43

File Name	Fault
EXP43-2-nf	none
EXP43-2-f1	R4 shorted
EXP43-2-f2	R5 open
EXP43-2-f3	RG open

Folder Name: Lab-44

File Name	Fault
EXP44-4-nf	none
EXP44-4-f1	VS+ and VS- reversed
EXP44-4-f2	R1 shorted
EXP44-4-f3	D1 Shorted

PART SEVEN

Partial List of CEMA Skills

PARTIAL SKILLS LIST

EIA CONSUMER ELECTRONICS MANUFACTURER'S ASSOCIATION (CEMA)

BEHAVIOR SKILLS AND WORK HABITS

- Implement responsibilities of job position including exhibiting dependability and meeting organizationally defined expectations.
- Follow rules, regulations, and policies as established, including interpreting employer/employee handbook and procedures.
- Understand and practice cost effectiveness.
- Practice time management and follow work schedule.
- Assume responsibility for own decisions and actions.
- Exhibit pride.
- Display initiative in undertaking new tasks.
- Show assertiveness appropriate to the situation.
- Seek work challenges.
- Understand and apply ethical principles to decision making.
- Comply with company standards including dress, personal hygiene, and cleanliness.
- Understand the importance of providing good customer service (internal and external).
- Respond constructively to suggestions for improvement.
- Provide praise and suggestions for improvement.
- Channel/control emotional reactions constructively.
- Recognize problems and work toward their solution.
- Exhibit positive behavior.
- Exhibit sensitivity to internal and external customer needs.
- Treat people with respect.
- Recognize nonverbal communication.
- Understand interactive relationships required for effective teamwork.
- Understand team's operating procedures.
- Adapt as necessary to complete the team task.
- Evaluate outcome

GENERAL

- Demonstrate an understanding of proper safety techniques for all types of circuits.
- Demonstrate an understanding of and comply with relevant OSHA safety standards.
- Demonstrate an understanding of proper troubleshooting techniques.
- Demonstrate an understanding of basic assembly skills using hand and power tools.
- Demonstrate an understanding of acceptable soldering/desoldering techniques.
- Demonstrate an understanding of proper solderless connections.
- Demonstrate an understanding of use of data books and cross references/technical manuals and requisition of electronic components.
- Demonstrate an understanding of the interpretation and creation of electronic schematics, drawings, and flow diagrams.

- Demonstrate an understanding of design curves, tables, graphs, and recording of data.
- Demonstrate an understanding of color codes and other component descriptors.
- Demonstrate an understanding of site electrical and environmental survey.
- Demonstrate the use of listening skills or assistive devices to assess signs and symptoms.

DC CIRCUITS

- Demonstrate an understanding of sources of electricity in dc circuits.
- Demonstrate an understanding of principles and operation of batteries.
- Demonstrate an understanding of the meaning of and relationships among and between voltage, current, resistance, and power in dc circuits.
- Demonstrate an understanding of measurement of resistance of conductors and insulators.
- Demonstrate an understanding of application of Ohm's law to series, parallel, and series-parallel circuits.
- Demonstrate an understanding of magnetic properties of circuits and devices.
- Demonstrate an understanding of the physical, electrical characteristics of capacitors and inductors.
- Understand principles and operations of dc series circuits.
- Fabricate and demonstrate dc series circuits.
- Troubleshoot and repair dc series circuits.
- Understand principles and operations of dc parallel circuits.
- Fabricate and demonstrate dc parallel circuits.
- Troubleshoot and repair dc parallel circuits.
- Understand the principles and operations of dc series-parallel and bridge circuits.
- Fabricate and demonstrate dc series-parallel and bridge circuits.
- Troubleshoot and repair dc series-parallel and bridge circuits.
- Understand principles and operations of the Wheatstone bridge.
- Understand principles and operations of dc voltage divider circuits (loaded and unloaded).
- Fabricate and demonstrate dc voltage divider circuits (loaded and unloaded).
- Troubleshoot and repair dc voltage divider circuits (loaded and unloaded).
- Understand principles and operations of dc RC and RL circuits.
- Fabricate and demonstrate dc RC and RL circuits.
- Troubleshoot and repair dc RC and RL circuits.
- Demonstrate an understanding of measurement of power in dc circuits.

AC CIRCUITS

- Demonstrate an understanding of sources of electricity in ac circuits.
- Demonstrate an understanding of the properties of an ac signal.
- Demonstrate an understanding of the principles of operation and characteristics of sinusoidal and nonsinusoidal waveforms.
- Demonstrate an understanding of basic motor/generator theory and operation.
- Demonstrate an understanding of measurement of power in ac circuits.
- Demonstrate an understanding of the principle of operation of various power conditioning devices (transformers, surge suppressers, uninterruptable power systems).
- Demonstrate an understanding of the principle and operation of safety grounding systems (arresters, ground fault interrupters, etc.).
- Understand principles and operation of ac capacitive circuits.
- Fabricate and demonstrate ac capacitive circuits.

- Troubleshoot and repair ac capacitive circuits.
- Understand principles and operation of ac inductive circuits.
- Fabricate and demonstrate ac inductive circuits.
- Troubleshoot and repair ac inductive circuits.
- Understand principles and operations of ac circuits using transformers.
- Demonstrate an understanding of impedance matching theory.
- Fabricate and demonstrate ac circuits using transformers.
- Troubleshoot and repair ac circuits using transformers.
- Understand principles and operations of ac differentiator and integrator circuits (determine RC and RL time constants).
- Fabricate and demonstrate ac differentiator and integrator circuits.
- Troubleshoot and repair ac differentiator and integrator circuits.
- Understand principles and operations of ac series and parallel resonant circuits.
- Fabricate and demonstrate ac series and parallel resonant circuits.
- Troubleshoot and repair ac series and parallel resonant circuits.
- Understand principles and operations of ac RC, RL and RLC circuits.
- Fabricate and demonstrate ac RC, RL, and RLC circuits.
- Troubleshoot and repair ac RC, RL, and RLC circuits.
- Understand principles and operations of ac frequency selective filter circuits.
- Fabricate and demonstrate ac frequency selective filter circuits.
- Troubleshoot and repair ac frequency selective filter circuits.

DISCREET SOLID STATE

- Demonstrate an understanding of the properties of semiconductor materials.
- Demonstrate an understanding of pn junctions.
- Demonstrate an understanding of bipolar junction transistors.
- Demonstrate an understanding of field effect transistors (FETs/MOSFETs).
- Demonstrate and understanding of special diodes and transistors.
- Understand principles and operations of diode circuits.
- Fabricate and demonstrate diode circuits.
- Troubleshoot and repair diode circuits.
- Understand principles and operations of optoelectronic circuits.
- Fabricate and demonstrate optoelectronic circuits.
- Troubleshoot and repair optoelectronic circuits.
- Understand principles and operations of single stage amplifiers.
- Fabricate and demonstrate single stage amplifiers.
- Troubleshoot and repair single stage amplifiers.
- Understand principles and operations of thyristor circuits (SCR, TRIAC, DIAC, etc.).
- Fabricate and demonstrate thyristor circuits (SCR, TRIAC, DIAC, etc.).
- Troubleshoot and repair thyristor circuits (SCR, TRIAC, DIAC, etc.).

ANALOG CIRCUITS

- Understand principles and operations of multistage amplifiers.
- Fabricate and demonstrate multistage amplifiers.
- Troubleshoot and repair multistage amplifiers.
- Understand principles and operations of linear power supplies and filters.
- Fabricate and demonstrate linear power supplies and filters.

- Troubleshoot and repair linear power supplies and filters.
- Understand principles and operations of operational amplifier circuits.
- Fabricate and demonstrate operational amplifier circuits.
- Troubleshoot and repair operational amplifier circuits.
- Understand principles and operations of audio power amplifiers.
- Fabricate and demonstrate audio power amplifiers.
- Troubleshoot and repair audio power amplifiers.
- Understand principles and operations of active filter circuits.
- Fabricate and demonstrate active filter circuits.
- Troubleshoot and repair active filter circuits.
- Understand principles and operations of sinusoidal and nonsinusoidal oscillator circuits.
- Fabricate and demonstrate sinusoidal and nonsinusoidal oscillator circuits.
- Troubleshoot and repair sinusoidal and nonsinusoidal oscillator circuits.

BASIC AND PRACTICAL SKILLS PART 1

- Read and apply various sources of technical information.
- Determine if a solution is reasonable.
- Demonstrate ability to use a simple electronic calculator.
- Round and/or truncate numbers to designated place value.
- Compare order and determine equivalencies of real numbers (e.g. fractions, decimals, percentages).
- Solve problems and make applications involving integers, fractions, decimals, percentages.
- Translate written and/or verbal statements into mathematical expressions.
- Convert, compare, and compute with common units of measurement within and across measurement systems.
- Read scales on measurement devices and make interpolations where appropriate.
- Collect and organize data into tables, charts, and/or graphs.
- Identify patterns, note trends, and/or draw conclusions from tables, charts, maps, and/or graphs.
- Compute and interpret mean, median, and/or mode.
- Simplify and solve algebraic expressions and formulas.
- Select and use formulas properly.
- Understand and use scientific notation.
- Use properties of exponents and logarithms.
- Determine slope, midpoint, and distance.
- Graph functions.
- Recognize, classify, and use properties of lines and angles.
- Apply Pythagorean theorem.
- Identify basic functions of sine, cosine, and tangent.
- Compute and solve problems using basic trigonometric functions.
- Understand principles of electricity including its relationship to the nature of matter.

BASIC AND PRACTICAL SKILLS PART 2

- Demonstrate basic keyboard skills.
- Maintain state-of-the art skills through participation in in-service or other training.
- Participate in continuing education.
- Understand and apply continuous improvement principles.
- Demonstrate knowledge of the business products/services.

- Use effective written and other communication skills.
- Use telephone etiquette including relaying messages accurately.
- Employ appropriate skills for gathering and relating information.
- Interpret written, graphic, and oral instructions.
- Interact with co-workers and customers in a logical, clear, and understandable manner.
- Use language appropriate to the situation.
- Participate in meetings in a positive and constructive manner.
- Use job-relating terminology.
- Write technical reports, letters, and memoranda as appropriate to the audience.
- Document work projects, procedures, test, and equipment failures.
- Identify the problem.
- Clarify purposes and goals.
- Identify available solutions and their impact, including evaluating credibility of information.
- Evaluate options.
- Set priorities.
- Select/implement options/decisions including predicting results of proposed action.
- Organize personal workloads.
- Participate in brainstorming sessions to generate new ideas and solve problems.